£14.95

CIRCUITS, SIGNALS AND DEVICES

CIRCUITS, SIGNALS AND DEVICES

MICHAEL JULIAN

Copublished in the United States with
John Wiley & Sons, Inc., New York

Longman Scientific & Technical
Longman Group UK Limited
Longman House, Burnt Mill, Harlow
Essex CM20 2JE, England
and Associated Companies throughout the world

Copublished in the United States with
John Wiley & Sons, Inc., 605 Third Avenue, New York, NY 10158

First Published 1988

British Library Cataloguing in Publication Data
Julian, Michael
  Circuits, signals and devices.
  1. Electronics
  I. Title
  621.381   TK7815
  ISBN 0-582-99467-5

Library of Congress Cataloging in Publication Data
Julian, Michael, 1935–
  Circuits, signals, and devices.
  Bibliography: p.
  Includes index.
  1. Electronics. 2. Electric engineering. I. Title.
TK816.J84   1987   621.381   86-24552
ISBN 0-470-20732-9 (Wiley, USA only)

Set in 10/11pt Monophoto Times Roman
Produced by Longman Group (FE) Limited
Printed in Hong Kong

Contents

Preface

This book is not intended to match the precise details of any particular course of study but to present a body of information which should be of value in a range of courses. These might include the electronic content of mechanical, manufacturing and information-engineering courses as well as that within the electrical/electronic discipline.

The level is broadly suited to first- and second-year undergraduates and diploma students having 'A' level qualifications in mathematics, physics and related areas or a technology biased Ordinary National Diploma/Certificate. The mathematical content is broadly consistent with the intended readership, although there is some variation within the text; microprocessors can be introduced with rather less mathematical support than can, for example, the Fourier transform.

The style is primarily descriptive with supporting mathematical statements, designed for the student meeting a topic for the first time. Consistent with this approach, and to ease the task of the first-time reader, back referencing through equation numbers is avoided: there are, however, cross-references between chapters and between sections within a given chapter. The aim throughout is to provide the aware reader with, at least, an appreciation of the basic concepts of any indexed topic. It is of course not possible in a broad-based text of this nature to include the depth of rigorous discussion which may be found in more specialised works.

Study topics are listed in the form of learning objectives; these refer to sections within the chapter and to student exercises at the end of the chapter. The exercises are primarily intended to consolidate the study material but, on occasions, they extend the treatment into an area not covered in the body of the text. The more important concepts are summarised at the end of each chapter together with references to further reading.

Acknowledgements

The breadth of the text has led me to impose on many colleagues for their valued assistance and opinions. Principally, I must thank Steve Hoddell and Ashley Longden who actually contributed material. Amongst those who read chapters and provided helpful comments are Peter Calvert, Jim Crawley, Graham Currell, Bob Cutts, Terry Evans, Jackie Glover, Mike Harris, John Hill, Colin Jefferson, Derek Kidson, Terry Pick, Stephen Ryrie, Mike Tyler and David Williams. For additional typing, collating and checking, my wife's help has been invaluable.

Wotton-under-Edge, Gloucestershire   MICHAEL JULIAN
1987

Section A Circuits

1 Basic principles

The principal learning objectives of this chapter are to:

	Section	Exercise
• appreciate the concepts of electric field and flux and their relationship to electric charge and forces;	1.1–1.3	1.1
• define electric potential and relate it to electric field strength;	2.1, 2.2	1.2
• describe the component parts and the basic mechanisms in an elementary electric circuit;	2.3	
• relate charge movement and current;	3.1	1.3
• understand the concepts of magnetic field and flux and their relationship to electric current and forces;	4.1, 4.2	1.4
• use reluctance to determine the behaviour of simple magnetic circuits;	4.3	1.5
• recognise common usage and terminology associated with voltages and current;	5.1–5.3	
• interpret the basic relationships between power, energy, voltage and current;	6	1.6, 1.7
• apply the two fundamental electric-circuit relationships known as the Kirchhoff laws;	7	1.8, 1.9
• determine how the properties known as resistance, capacitance and inductance are related to simple conductor/medium configurations, and deduce their energy-storage capability;	8.1–8.4	1.10–1.12
• state the Faraday law relating to the determination of the voltage induced in a circuit whose flux is changing with respect to time;	8.4	1.13
• appreciate that analogues and duals exist between physical systems.	9	

1.1 Electric charge, field and flux

1.1.1 Electric charge

As the study of a mechanical system may start with the fundamental property of matter known as mass, it is appropriate to commence the study of electrical and electronic systems with the property known as **electric charge**. Like mass, charge cannot be created or destroyed. The unit of charge is the coulomb, unit symbol C, and the quantity symbol is Q with lower-case q used for time-varying charge. The smallest quantity of charge is that carried by an electron, whose charge is considered to be negative with a magnitude of 1.602×10^{-19} C. With a mass of 9.11×10^{-31} kg at rest, the charge/mass ratio of an electron is 1.759×10^{11} C/kg. Removal of an electron from an initially neutral material leaves an effective positive charge of the same magnitude as that of the electron.

Experimental work by Coulomb in the eighteenth century indicated that there was a force between charged particles whose magnitude was inversely proportional to the square of the distance between them. If the particles held charges of the same polarity, the force was one of repulsion but if they were of the opposite polarity, the force was an attraction. In its present-day form (in the S.I. system of units summarised in Appendix 1A) the Coulomb law is stated as

$$\text{force} = \frac{q_1 q_2}{4\pi r^2 \varepsilon},$$

where q_1 and q_2 are the magnitudes of the two charges, r is the distance between them and ε is a constant for the material. In free space, ε is the **electric space constant** ε_0. In a material medium ε is given by the product of ε_0 and the **relative permittivity** of the material, ε_r, i.e. $\varepsilon = \varepsilon_r \varepsilon_0$. The value of ε_0 to four significant figures is 8.854×10^{-12} and its unit is the farad/metre (F/m). This expression gives the magnitude of the force; its direction is along a line joining the positions of the two particles.

1.1.2 The electric field

It is natural that the force between charged particles should be compared with the gravitational force between two masses, even though the gravitational force is always attractive. Both obey the inverse-square law relationship and both share the use of the term **field**, a concept by which the force between two charges or between two masses is described in terms of a 'map' in space showing the magnitude and direction of the force exerted on unit positive charge (or unit mass) by another charge or charges (masses). Thus the strength of the Earth's gravitational field at a point is given by the magnitude and direction of the force on a 1 kg mass at that point. Similarly, the electric field due to charge q_1 (for example) is obtained by setting q_2 to $+1$ in the force expression giving

electric field, $\quad E = \dfrac{q_1}{4\pi r^2 \varepsilon}$,†

directed radially away from q_1 when q_1 is positive. The unit of electric field strength is newton/coulomb or, as explained in Section 1.2 below, volt/metre. The expression defines the electric field at a point in space distance r from the originating charge: as r varies, so the strength of the electric field may be determined at any point in the medium surrounding the charge.

The whole field concept is based on the principle of being able to define a force without requiring the presence of the body or particle on which the force acts. However, if such a body or particle is present, then the force on it is given by the product of the field strength and its charge, i.e. for the example above, the force on charge q_2 in field E would be $q_2 E$ in the same way as the gravitational force on mass m in gravitational field g is mg.

1.1.3 Electric flux

Although not used in the gravitational case, the **flux** concept is widely employed: a single charge or charge configuration may be thought of as setting up a flux which 'flows' away from positive charge or towards negative charge. A single point charge is the easiest to visualise; the flux leaves (or enters) radially in all directions, as illustrated in Fig. 1.1. Flux is measured in the same unit as charge (coulomb) and the quantity symbol is the same as for charge.

Electric flux and charge are related through the **Gauss law** which states that if a closed surface completely surrounds a charge or system of charges, the total flux crossing this surface is equal to the magnitude of the charge enclosed. In Fig. 1.1, for example, a closed spherical surface would be suitable and in this context is known as a Gaussian surface.

While the total flux is equal to the total enclosed charge, it is the density of the flux (which may be defined as flux per unit normal area at a point in space) which determines the system behaviour. In Fig. 1.1, the flux distribution is uniform over the surface of the sphere and the flux density (quantity symbol D and unit symbol C/m^2) at a point is given by the total flux q divided by the surface area $4\pi r^2$, i.e. $q/4\pi r^2$. Flux density has magnitude and direction in the same way as does electric field and, indeed, if the expression for flux density and electric field are compared they will be seen to be related by $D = \varepsilon E$, an expression which is valid at any point in a homogeneous medium of permittivity ε whatever the source of the flux.

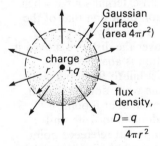

Fig. 1.1 A spherical Gaussian surface surrounding a point charge

Gaussian surface (area $4\pi r^2$)

charge r $+q$

flux density, $D = \dfrac{q}{4\pi r^2}$

---

† Electric and magnetic field strength and flux densities are all vector quantities, in the sense that they have both magnitude and direction. However, in this book the expressions involve only the magnitude of the quantity (information on direction, where necessary, being stated separately), and thus no special notation is used. (In more specialised texts it is common practice to use boldface type to indicate a vector quantity.)

The relationships between flux, flux density and electric field may be summarised as follows: the flux originates at the charge and its magnitude is independent of the medium; at any point in the medium, the flux density is defined as the flux per unit normal area and the electric field, whose magnitude is dependent on the medium, is given by $E = D/\varepsilon$. The directions of the flux density and of the field are the same.

Example 1.1

Determine the electric flux density distance r from an infinite line charge of q per unit length. Use this result to calculate the electric field strength in air 5 mm from a line charge of 16 pC/m. Take $\varepsilon_0 = 8.85 \times 10^{-12}$ F/m.

A suitable Gaussian surface is a unit-length cylinder of radius r surrounding the line charge as shown in Fig. 1.2. Using Gauss' law, the flux crossing the surface $= q$ per unit length. Area of surface $= 2\pi r$ per unit length and therefore the flux density, $D = q/2\pi r$. Electric field strength $E = D/\varepsilon = q/2\pi r\varepsilon$. Substituting values, $E = 16 \times 10^{-12}/2\pi 5 \times 10^{-3} \times 8.85 \times 10^{-12} = 57.6$ N/C.

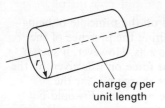

charge q per unit length

Fig. 1.2 A cylindrical Gaussian surface surrounding a line charge

1.2 Electric potential

1.2.1 Work required to move charge: potential

Because there is a force on a charge situated in an electric field, energy must be supplied from an external source when positive charge is moved in a direction opposing that of the field. The work done on the charge is given by integrating the force acting against the charge over the distance moved in the direction of the force. The situation is analogous to carrying a mass from the bottom of a hill to the top against the force of gravity: in either case, the work done is turned into potential energy. The **electric potential** at a point is defined as the work which must be done in moving unit positive charge to that point from an initial reference point. The unit of potential is the **volt** (unit symbol V), a potential of 1 V being the work done in moving 1 C of charge through 1 m in a uniform electric field of 1 N/C. If the initial potential is zero the final potential is the **absolute potential** of the finishing point; if the initial potential is not zero, the change in potential energy is the **potential difference** between the two points. Because potential differences are also known as **voltages** the quantity symbol is also V (or v for time-varying quantities). The volt will be seen to be equivalent to N-m/C from which the unit of electric field (previously given as N/C) may be expressed alternatively as V/m, this being the more usual form.

1.2.2 Relationship between potential and electric field

Because the force on unit positive charge is the electric field strength E and potential is the work done on unit positive charge, the potential of point B with respect to point A in Fig. 1.3 is given by,

$$V_{BA} = -\int_A^B E_T \, dx,$$

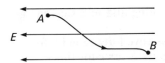

Fig. 1.3 An integration path within an electric field

where E_T is the tangential component of the electric field in the direction of the path of integration. The negative sign is necessary to make the potential positive when moving against the direction of the field just as when a mass is moved up a hill in the direction opposite to the gravitational force its potential energy increases. In many cases, the direction of movement will be in line with the direction of the field and the suffix T is unnecessary. Provided that movement and field direction are in line, the differential form of the relationship $E = -dV/dx$ may be used if it is required to determine the strength of the field at a point and the potential distribution is known: dV/dx is called the **potential gradient**.

The potential difference between two points in a given field is dependent only on the positions of those points. The path taken between them is unimportant, just as, neglecting frictional effects, the work done in walking up a hill is the same whether walking directly upward or whether taking a zig–zag path. The power required (i.e. the rate of doing work) will be less on the zig–zag path but the journey will take longer. Energy and power are again discussed in Section 1.6.

Example 1.2   *Calculate the potential difference between two points $r_1 = 2$ mm and $r_2 = 4$ mm from a line charge of 16 pC/m in a material of relative permittivity $\varepsilon_r = 3$.*

Using the result of Example 1.1 the field strength distance r from a line charge is $q/2\pi r\varepsilon$. The potential difference between two points is therefore

$$-\int_{r_2}^{r_1} \frac{q\,dr}{2\pi r\varepsilon} = \frac{q}{2\pi\varepsilon} \ln\left(\frac{r_2}{r_1}\right).$$

Substituting values, potential difference is

$$\frac{16 \times 10^{-12}}{2\pi 8.85 \times 10^{-12} \times 3} \ln\left(\frac{4}{2}\right) = 66\,\text{mV}.$$

Note: The practice of simply multiplying the potential gradient (i.e. the field strength) by distance does not give the correct result in this case because the gradient is a function of distance. Where it is constant, near a large sheet charge for example, a simple product can be used.

1.2.3 Electromotive force (e.m.f.) and potential difference (p.d.)

The simplest electric circuit comprises a device which raises the potential energy of charge, known as a **source**, and a device which lowers the energy level, known as a **sink**. The concept is shown in Fig. 1.4. The source generates electrical energy by conversion from another form (e.g. chemical energy, in the case of the battery) whereas the sink absorbs energy either through storage or by conversion into another form such as heat, light or mechanical energy. A simple example is a battery which is connected to an electric lamp, thereby converting the chemical energy stored in the battery into electrical energy and thence to light (and heat) energy. But it is important to appreciate that many electrical components do not behave as clearly identifiable sources or sinks in this way. For example, the capacitor described in Section 1.8 is capable of storing electrical energy and its

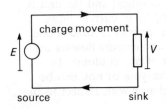

Fig. 1.4 Charge movement from source to sink

normal operating mode is one of storing and releasing energy in a cyclical way.

The source is a source of **electromotive force** (e.m.f.), for which the quantity symbol is normally E (or e for time-varying quantities). The unit symbol is V, consistent with the fact that it is a voltage; because voltage is energy per unit charge, the term 'force' is unfortunate, but the terminology is now well established. The sink, which causes a fall in potential, is said to result in a **potential drop**, which is abbreviated to p.d. The fact that p.d. is also the abbreviation for potential difference is a mixed blessing. As Fig. 1.4 shows, the magnitude of the source e.m.f. E must, in this elementary circuit, be equal to the magnitude of the p.d. (potential drop) V across the sink. Furthermore, both may be correctly termed a potential difference, and, indeed, only one potential difference exists across the circuit, namely, that between the upper and the lower connections between source and sink.

Where the distinction between electromotive force and potential drop becomes important is in relation to the direction of the charge movement which occurs when source and sink are connected together. Conventionally, the direction of movement is assumed to be out of the more-positive terminal of the source and into the positive terminal of the sink. Thus, the charge movement is in the same direction as the arrow used to indicate the polarity of the source e.m.f., but in the opposite direction to the arrow indicating the polarity of the p.d. across the sink, the head of the arrow in each case pointing to the positive terminal of the device. It follows from the definition of potential that use of this convention effectively assumes that the moving charge is positive. However, in circuits such as these the charge carriers are electrons (which have negative charge) so that the actual direction of charge movement is opposite to that assumed; nevertheless, the positive charge-carrier convention is almost universally adopted and does accord with reality in devices in which the charge carriers are positive.

1.3 Electric current

1.3.1 The movement of charge

In the previous section it was implicit that the charge moved from the source to the sink and it is this movement of charge which constitutes an **electric current**. The quantity symbol for current is I (or i for time-varying quantities) and the unit is the **ampere,** unit symbol A. One ampere of current flows when the rate of flow of charge with respect to time is one coulomb per second; alternatively, one ampere flowing for one second means a charge transfer of one coulomb. In general, any current, whether time-varying or not, can be expressed as the rate of change of charge with respect to time,

$$i = \frac{\mathrm{d}q}{\mathrm{d}t}.$$

When it is required to relate the variation of charge with respect to time to its displacement in a material, the relationship $i = dq/dt = (dq/dx)(dx/dt)$ may be used. In this expression, x represents displacement, and therefore dq/dx is the rate of change of charge with respect to position within a material and dx/dt is its velocity: this is analogous to calculating traffic flow in vehicles per hour by multiplying the number of vehicles in a one-mile length of road by their speed in miles per hour. For the assumed uniform charge flow in Fig. 1.5 the charge contained in unit length is nqA, where n is the number of charge carriers in unit volume, q is the charge on each carrier and A is the cross-sectional area. With the magnitude of the velocity u the magnitude of the current is given by

$$i = nqAu.$$

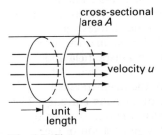

Fig. 1.5 Charge movement in a conductor

In the battery-lamp situation the charge movement takes place through **conductors**; typically, these are copper wires containing a large number of electrons (negative-charge carriers) which are free to move about within the material. The magnitude of the current flow may be related to the free-electron density and the electron velocity by means of the expression derived above.

Example 1.3 *Calculate the velocity of the electrons in a conductor having 10^{29} free electrons per cubic metre and a cross-sectional area of $2\,mm^2$ when the current flow is $23\,mA$.*

Substituting values into the expression for the current:

$$23 \times 10^{-3} = 10^{29} \times 1.603 \times 10^{-19} \times 2 \times 10^{-6}u,$$

from which

$$u = 7.2 \times 10^{-7}\,\text{m/s}.$$

It will be seen that the mean velocity of the electrons is very small and is analogous to the average speed of vehicles along a road. The much higher velocity associated with electrical phenomena is that with which a disturbance or current-magnitude change travels along the conductor. For example, if in a queue of 100 cars, travelling relatively slowly, the first car were to stop suddenly, an average driver-reaction time of 0.5 second would mean that the last car would stop 50 seconds later. Assuming an average spacing between cars of, perhaps, 8 m, the disturbance would have travelled 800 m in 50 seconds, or 16 m/s. It will be seen that the disturbance has travelled with a relatively high speed in comparison with the car speeds, which may be as low as 2 m/s or less. It may also be noted that it is possible for the disturbance to travel in the opposite direction from that in which the individual particles (cars!) are moving. Travelling waves are discussed in Chapter 5.

1.4 Magnetic field

1.4.1 Magnetic field and flux

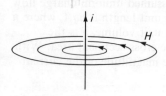

Fig. 1.6 Direction of magnetic field surrounding a long straight conductor

Not only is there a force between static charges but an additional force is set up when there is a movement of charge, i.e. a current. As the force between static charges was associated with an electric field and electric flux, the force between currents is associated with a **magnetic field** and **magnetic flux**.

Fig. 1.6 illustrates the direction of the magnetic field surrounding a long straight conductor carrying current i. The current is the source of the field whose strength is given by the **Ampere law**, which states that the summation of the magnetic field strength (quantity symbol H) around a closed path is equal to the magnitude of the current enclosed within that path. For a circular path of radius r in a uniform field H (Fig. 1.6) the summation is $2\pi rH$ which is equal to i. Thus, the magnetic-field strength distance r from a long straight conductor is given by $H = i/2\pi r$. The unit is the ampere/metre, unit symbol A/m.

Associated with the magnetic field is a magnetic flux whose quantity symbol is Φ and unit is the weber (unit symbol Wb). The density of this flux, quantity symbol B, is related to the field strength through $B = \mu H$ where μ is the **permeability** of the medium. In free space, μ is the **magnetic space constant** μ_0 whose value is $4\pi \times 10^{-7}$ and whose unit is the henry/metre (H/m). In a material medium, $\mu = \mu_0\mu_r$ where μ_r is the **relative permeability** of the medium. The unit of magnetic flux density is the tesla, unit symbol T. One tesla is equivalent to one weber per square metre.

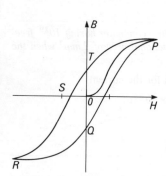

Fig. 1.7 Relationship between magnetic field strength and magnetic flux density

Values of μ_r for materials such as iron or ferrite are of the order of hundreds so that, in a magnetic field of given strength, the flux density will be much higher within the material than in the surrounding space. This is an important property of magnetic systems. Not only is the value of μ_r typically high for certain materials but it is non-linear. Path OP in Fig. 1.7 shows a typical relationship between B and H, sometimes called a **BH curve**. As H is increased for the first time in a previously unmagnetised material, the relationship follows the non-linear path OP; furthermore if H is now reduced to zero, the same path is not followed, path PT being taken. The effect of successive variations in H between the positive and negative limits shown then traces out the loop shown. The material exhibits **hysteresis** meaning that the path traced is direction dependent.

1.4.2 Force between electric currents

electric field E

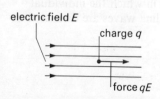

charge q

force qE

In the electric case force on charge q in electric field strength E is qE. In the magnetic case, force on current, i, flowing in conductor length l in a normal flux of density B is Bil. Directions are illustrated in Fig. 1.8. Furthermore, as electric field was defined as force on unit charge so magnetic flux density is defined as force on unit current in unit-length conductor, i.e. a magnetic flux density of 1 T is that which will produce a force of 1 N on a 1 m conductor carrying a current of 1 A.

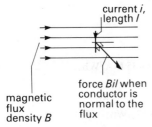

current i,
length l

force Bil when
conductor is
normal to the
flux

magnetic
flux
density B

Fig. 1.8 Direction of forces
in electric and magnetic
fields

The force between long straight parallel current-carrying conductors is used in the definition of the unit of current, one of the base units in the S.I. system (Appendix 1A). Given that the field strength set up at a point 1 m away from one of the conductors carrying a current of 1 A is $1/2\pi$ (putting i and $r = 1$ in the ampere-law expression), the flux density in vacuum will be $\mu H = (4\pi \times 10^{-7})/2\pi = 2 \times 10^{-7}$ T. The force on a second conductor also carrying 1 A will then be 2×10^{-7} newton per metre length. This figure defines the ampere.

1.4.3 The magnetic circuit

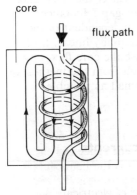

core

flux path

Fig. 1.9 A coil and core
assembly

The high-permeability core used in the construction of electromagnetic components has the effect of confining the flux to the core. A typical arrangement is shown in Fig. 1.9 with a flux direction consistent with that shown in Fig. 1.6. In such cases, it is convenient to treat the arrangement as a **magnetic circuit** in which the flux set up by the current flowing in the coiled conductor is calculated in a similar way to that used to determine the current flowing in a resistive circuit when an e.m.f. is applied (Section 1.8.2). Indeed, the product of the current and the number of turns of the conductor is known as the **magnetomotive force** (m.m.f.) and the 'resistance' of the magnetic path is known as the **reluctance**. The quantity symbol for m.m.f. is F and the unit is the ampere. The quantity symbol for reluctance is R_m and the unit is ampere per weber (A/Wb). Thus, as current in a resistive circuit is given by,

$$\text{current} = \frac{\text{e.m.f.}}{\text{resistance}},$$

the flux in a magnetic circuit is given by,

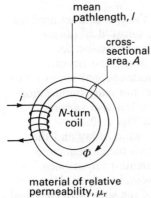

mean
pathlength, l

cross-
sectional
area, A

N-turn
coil

i

Φ

material of relative
permeability, μ_r

Fig. 1.10 A circular core and
coil assembly

$$\text{flux} = \frac{\text{m.m.f.}}{\text{reluctance}} \quad \text{or} \quad \Phi = \frac{F}{R_m}.$$

In accordance with the Ampere law, the product of the constant field H and the path length l gives the magnitude of the current enclosed, i.e., for Fig. 1.10, $Ni = Hl$ where N is the number of turns. But H is also equal to B/μ and hence to $\Phi/A\mu$, where Φ, μ and A are shown in Fig. 1.10. Thus

$$Ni = Hl = \frac{\Phi l}{\mu A},$$

and, since Ni is the m.m.f., the flux may be expressed as m.m.f./reluctance where the reluctance is $l/\mu A$.

Example 1.4 *Determine the magnetic flux density in the core of the magnetic circuit shown in Fig. 1.11. Assume that the relative permeability of the core is 1000 under operational conditions and neglect any fringing of the flux at the air gap.*

Using the relationship derived above, the reluctance of the core is

$$\frac{3 \times 10^{-2}}{4\pi \times 10^{-7} \times 1000 \times 0.5 \times 10^{-4}} = 0.477 \text{ MA/Wb}.$$

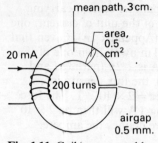

Fig. 1.11 Coil/core assembly for Example 1.4

and reluctance of air gap is

$$\frac{0.5 \times 10^{-3}}{4\pi \times 10^{-7} \times 0.5 \times 10^{-4}} = 7.958 \text{ MA/Wb}.$$

$\therefore$ Total reluctance $= 0.477 + 7.958 = 8.435 \text{ MA/Wb}$.

But m.m.f. $= Ni = 4$ A.

$$\therefore \quad \text{Flux} = \frac{\text{m.m.f.}}{\text{reluctance}} = \frac{4}{8.435 \times 10^6} = 0.47 \ \mu\text{Wb}.$$

Although the air gap in Example 1.4 is very small its reluctance forms a substantial proportion of the total. In cases such as this and where only an approximate result is required it may be possible actually to neglect the reluctance of core. It also follows that where the air-gap reluctance predominates operation is substantially independent of the core permeability and is therefore substantially linear. If on the other hand it is required to maximise the core flux, any air gaps (which might, for example, result from the method of construction of the core) should be as small as possible.

1.5 Time-varying voltages and currents

1.5.1 Direct and alternating currents

In early days the study of the behaviour of electrical components and circuits at an introductory level was largely based on the effects of either constant or sinusoidally varying source voltages.

Arising from the predominance of the two distinct analysis techniques is the adjectival use of the terms 'd.c.' (**direct current**) and 'a.c.' (**alternating current**) to describe, for example, circuit models. In common usage, the adjective d.c. is normally used to mean not only unidirectional but constant with respect to time, and the term a.c. normally implies not just alternating in polarity or direction but also varying sinusoidally with time as illustrated in Fig. 1.12.

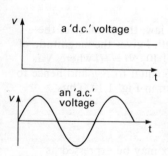

Fig. 1.12 Direct and alternating voltages

These analysis methods are equally valid today and the analysis of circuits and systems in which the currents and voltages are sinusoidal is still of the greatest importance. Indeed, Chapter 4 is devoted to sinusoidal analysis. However, in more recent times, broader views of the subject of electrical engineering have developed, and it is desirable to take a more fundamental approach to introductory circuit analysis. Accordingly, the voltages and currents are, in the general case, regarded as **time-varying quantities**, meaning simply that their magnitudes vary with respect to time; they need not necessarily be alternating in the sense that their polarity or direction changes with time, nor is a sinusoidal variation necessarily implied. This permits a wider variety of functions to be considered including, as a special case, the non-time-varying 'd.c.' (i.e. constant) condition. In this book such quantities are normally referred to as **direct quantities**.

1.5.2 Notation

It is common practice to use upper-case symbols to stand for direct quantities and lower-case symbols to signify time-varying quantities. For example, a direct voltage is given by $V = +5$ V, but an alternating voltage is given by $v = 5 \sin \omega t$ V. Complications arise when time-varying quantities are represented by expressions which are not themselves functions of time; for example, in Chapter 4 sinusoids are represented by complex numbers. In this book upper-case symbols will be used in such cases.

When expressed as a function of time (e.g. $v = 5 \sin \omega t$), voltages and currents are often referred to as **instantaneous** voltages and currents, the implication being that, if a particular value of t is substituted into the expression, the value of the voltage or current at that particular instant in time will result. This term is used because it is frequently the average effect of, for example, a current flowing for a relatively long period which is more important than its time-varying effect. In these circumstances, it is common practice to work in terms of its effective (r.m.s.) value (see Chapter 4), rather than its instantaneous value, and to quantify the current accordingly. For example, when the current flowing in an electric-heater circuit connected to the mains supply is quoted as 4 A, the value implied is the effective value. Similar arguments apply to the power ratings of electrical equipment, as discussed in Section 1.6.6.

A variation on the lower-case notation is the use of $v(t)$ and $i(t)$ to indicate time-varying voltages and currents following the mathematical practice of using $f(t)$ for functions of time. This strengthens the lower-case form by clearly identifying the quantity as a function of time and will be used in this book where it is required to emphasise that this is the case.

1.5.3 Time-varying voltages and currents

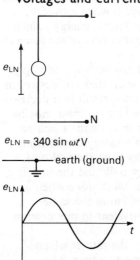

$e_{LN} = 340 \sin \omega t$ V

Fig. 1.13 Line-to-neutral voltage

A typical example of a time-varying voltage is the sinusoidal voltage, which appears between the line and neutral terminals of a domestic mains-supply system. The nature of the voltage may be appreciated by 'standing' on the neutral line and observing the relative potential of the line. In this example, the voltage is alternating in the sense that it changes polarity and it is periodic, repeating itself 50 times per second. Fig. 1.13 shows the potential of the line with respect to the neutral, the suffixed notation e_{LN} being used to signify this. In principle, either line or neutral could be taken as reference but taking the neutral as reference is convenient because its potential is at or near the more substantial reference provided by the **earth** or **ground** whose symbol is also shown.

Accepting that the polarity arrows (first used in Section 1.2.3), or another suitable notation such as small + and − signs, are necessary to indicate the polarity of direct voltages, it may be wondered what interpretation should be placed on polarity arrows when the voltage is alternating, or, indeed, whether arrows are necessary at all. In fact, they are necessary and they must be interpreted as indicating the **reference polarity** of the voltage. For example, in Fig. 1.13 the combination of the polarity arrow and the mathematical description of the source voltage states that, when e_{LN} is instantaneously positive (i.e. when $340 \sin \omega t$ is positive), terminal L is positive with respect to terminal N. When e_{LN} is instantaneously negative, terminal L is negative with respect to N. If the arrow were reversed, but the mathematical description remained the same, terminal N would be positive with respect to L when e_{LN} is positive, and vice-versa. Thus, both arrow and mathematical description are essential in order to completely define the potential of L with respect to N, the arrow signifying the true polarity when the voltage is instantaneously positive and the reverse polarity when the voltage is instantaneously negative. If a source generating a time-varying e.m.f., such as that shown in Fig. 1.13, is connected to a sink, it would seem reasonable to assume that the current flow in the conductors would also be time varying. The nature of varying current will in fact depend on the nature of the sink but, assuming that the current variation is in direct proportion to the e.m.f., it would also vary sinusoidally, reversing its direction twice in each cycle. Thus, the arrows indicating the direction of current flow in a circuit have the same significance as the voltage–polarity arrows; they indicate a reference direction for the current and must be related to a mathematical description of the current.

1.6 Energy and power

In Section 1.2.3 the sink was introduced as a device which absorbs energy from a source. Depending on the nature of the sink, this energy is either converted into another form or stored within the sink.

Energy is a measure of the amount of work done on a system or its ability to do work. Everyday examples of energy are the potential energy gained by a mass when moved up a hill against the force of gravity, or the kinetic energy gained by a mass falling from a height in the direction of the force of gravity.

Reference to gaining energy should not be taken to imply that energy is created; it can neither be created nor destroyed and any energy increase in one form must result in a decrease in another. The potential energy gained by the mass moving up the hill would have come from the man or the machine which did the lifting; in turn, the man's energy comes from the food he eats – the machine's energy from the fuel oil it burns. The quantity symbol for energy is W and the unit is the joule, unit symbol J, defined as the work done when a force of 1 N acts through a distance of 1 m in the same direction as the force. The joule is equivalent to one newton metre.

Power is the rate of doing work, i.e. the rate at which energy increases or decreases with respect to time. The quantity symbol is P, the unit is the watt and the unit symbol is W; one watt is a work rate of one joule per second. Using the lower-case quantity symbols for power and energy to indicate time-varying (or instantaneous) values,

$$p = \frac{dw}{dt} \quad \text{or} \quad w = \int_0^t p \, dt.$$

To relate energy and power to voltage and current the power–energy relationship can be expressed in the form, $p = (dw/dq)(dq/dt)$, where q is charge. Now dw/dq is work done per unit charge, i.e. potential, and dq/dt is rate of flow of charge, i.e. current. Thus, power is also the product of voltage and current, i.e. $p = vi$. It follows that if a current of 1 A flows into a sink across which the potential drop is 1 V, the rate of loss of electrical energy is 1 W. If 1 A flows from a source whose e.m.f. is 1 V the rate of generation of electrical energy is 1 W.

It is important to establish whether, in a given device, electrical energy is increasing or decreasing, and this information should be related to the voltage polarities and current directions associated with the device.

It has already been established that current leaves the more-positive terminal of a source and enters that of a sink, as shown in Fig. 1.14. Thus, for the reference directions shown, a positive value for $p_{\text{source}}(= ei)$ will indicate energy generated by the source and a positive value for $p_{\text{sink}}(= vi)$ will indicate energy absorbed by the sink. In general, if the product of voltage and current is positive, current leaving the positive terminal of a device indicates energy generated and current entering the positive terminal indicates energy absorbed.

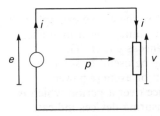

Fig. 1.14 Power flow from source to sink

Example 1.5 *Determine the power flowing into an electrical sink for which the voltages and currents (with reference directions as shown in Fig. 1.14) are as follows:*

    (i) $v = 5$ V; $i = 50$ mA;
    (ii) $v = 6$ V; $i = 20 - 3t$ A;
    (iii) $v = 340 \sin \omega t$ V; $i = 5.6 \sin \omega t$ A where $\omega = 0.2\pi$ rad/s.

Also determine the energy absorbed (or generated) in each case during a 10 s period starting at time, $t = 0$.

(i) $p = vi = 5 \times 50 \times 10^{-3} = 0.25$ W;

$$W = \int_0^{10} vi \, dt = 0.25 \times 10$$

                        (since p is constant with respect to time)

$$= 2.5 \text{ J};$$

(ii) $p = vi = 6(20 - 3t)$

$$= 120 - 18t \text{ W}.$$

Sketching p against t over the period (Fig. 1.15) shows p to be positive during the period 0–6.67 s and negative for the remainder of the period. Thus, energy is absorbed during the first part of the period and returned in the second. The net energy lost or gained during the whole period is given by,

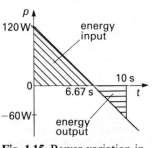

Fig. 1.15 Power variation in Example 1.5(ii)

$$W = \int_0^{10} (120 - 18t) \, dt$$

$$= 300 \text{ J}.$$

The positive result indicates net energy absorbed by the sink over the 10 s period; integration of the function over the period, 0–6.67 s, gives $+400$ J and integration over the period, 6.67–10 s, gives -100 J, indicating 400 J input during the first period and 100 J output during the second.

(iii) $p = vi = 340 \sin \omega t \times 5.6 \sin \omega t$

$$= 1904 \sin^2 \omega t \text{ W}.$$

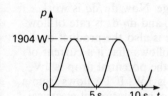

Fig. 1.16 Power variation in Example 1.5(iii)

Sketching p against t in this case (Fig. 1.16) shows p to be positive at all times, indicating that a sink having this voltage–current relationship is purely dissipative. The energy absorbed in the 10 s period is,

$$W = \int_0^{10} 1904 \sin^2 \omega t \, dt$$

$$= \int_0^{10} 1904 \left(\frac{1}{2} - \frac{\cos 2\omega t}{2} \right) dt.$$

But, $\int_0^{10} (\cos 2\omega t / 2) \, dt = 0$ when $\omega = 0.2\pi$, and, hence, $W = 9520$ J.

The power expressions calculated in the above example will be seen, in general, to be functions of time; power expressed in this way is known as the **instantaneous power**. The instantaneous-power expression may be useful in some applications, but often it is the **mean** or **average power** delivered to or received from a device over a period which is of greater interest. Most power measuring devices indicate mean power and the power rating of a device (i.e. the power delivered to or received from a device in specified operating conditions) is normally the mean-power rating. To determine the mean power, it is necessary to integrate the instantaneous power over the relevant period. For periodic functions, such as the sinusoidal voltage and current illustrated above, it is sufficient to perform the integration over one period of the waveform. In general, the mean power is given by

$$P = \frac{1}{T} \int_0^T vi \, dt = \frac{W}{T},$$

where T is the relevant period.

Example 1.6   *Calculate the mean powers over the 10 s period using the results obtained in Example 1.5.*

(i) $P = \dfrac{W}{T} = \dfrac{2.5}{10} = 0.25$ W.

In this case, the mean and 'instantaneous' power are the same because the voltage and current are direct quantities.

(ii) $P = \dfrac{W}{T} = \dfrac{300}{10} = 30$ W.

(iii) $P = \dfrac{W}{T} = \dfrac{9520}{10} = 952$ W.

In this case, because the waveform of both voltage and current is periodic, the same result will be obtained for any value of T which is an exact multiple of the waveform period.

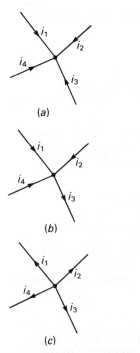

(a)

(b)

(c)

Fig. 1.17 Currents at a node sum to zero

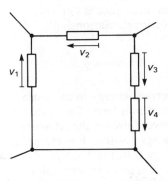

Fig. 1.18 Voltages around a mesh sum to zero

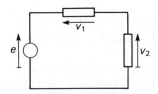

Fig. 1.19 Illustrating the Kirchhoff voltage law

1.7 The Kirchhoff laws

The first law is known as the **Kirchhoff current law** and states that at a joining point or **node** (Fig. 1.17(a)) in an electric circuit, the algebraic sum of the currents flowing into it is zero. Thus, for Fig. 1.17(a),

$$i_1 + i_2 + i_3 + i_4 = 0.$$

For example, if the currents have the direct values, $I_1 = +5$ A, $I_2 = -2$ A and $I_3 = +0.5$ A then I_4 would be -3.5 A in order that the sum is zero. The law applies equally for time-varying currents. For example, if $i_1 = 5$ A, $i_2 = -2 \sin \omega t$ A, $i_3 = 0$ and $i_4 = -5 + 2 \sin \omega t$ A then the law is satisfied. Account must be taken of the reference directions so that, for Fig. 1.17(b), in which the direction of i_3 has been reversed, $i_1 + i_2 - i_3 + i_4 = 0$. In such cases an alternative form of the law, stating that the algebraic sum of the currents entering a node is equal to the sum of those leaving, is sometimes used. Yet another form, applicable to the situation shown in Fig. 1.17(c), is that the sum of the currents leaving a node is zero. All statements have the same meaning provided that reference directions are correctly observed.

The law is a direct consequence of the relationship between charge and current and the principle of conservation of charge; if cars arrive at a roundabout on one road at a rate of 100 per hour and on another at 50 per hour then the total number leaving must be 150 per hour.

As the first law is a consequence of conservation of charge the **voltage law** arises from the principle of conservation of energy and the definition of electric potential. The law states that the algebraic sum of the voltages around a closed loop or **mesh** in an electric circuit is zero. Fig. 1.18 shows four circuit branches forming a mesh with arbitrary reference polarities. Working around the mesh in a clockwise direction, gives,

$$v_1 - v_2 + v_3 + v_4 = 0.$$

The law applies for both direct and time-varying quantities. For example, if $v_1 = 5$ V, $v_2 = 2 \sin \omega t$, and $v_3 = 1.5 \sin \omega t$ then

$$v_4 = -v_1 + v_2 - v_3$$
$$= -5 + 2 \sin \omega t - 1.5 \sin \omega t$$
$$= -5 + 0.5 \sin \omega t \text{ V}.$$

As for the currents in the first law, it is essential to observe the reference polarities; provided that this is done, it is not important whether the voltages are summed in a clockwise or in an anticlockwise direction.

The preceding statement is always applicable, but, in cases where the circuit elements can be clearly identified as sources or sinks, the alternative form of the law, namely that the algebraic sum of the e.m.f.'s around a mesh is equal to the p.d.'s, may be used. In Fig. 1.19, for example, $e = v_1 + v_2$. It will be seen that application of the 'rule' established for

Fig. 1.18 gives $e - v_1 - v_2 = 0$, which is precisely the same result.

1.8 Resistance, capacitance and inductance

1.8.1 Introduction

The way in which charge, potential, current and flux linkage are related in real systems depends on certain properties of those systems. The three properties described in this section are

(i) resistance, relating potential and current;
(ii) capacitance, relating charge and potential; and
(iii) inductance, relating current and flux linkage.

These properties may be used to model physical systems or describe the behaviour of especially manufactured electric-circuit components and will serve as the basis for the work on voltage–current relationships in Chapter 2.

1.8.2 Resistance

The circuit symbol for resistance or for a resistor is shown in Fig. 1.20(*a*). The ideal **resistor** has the property that the current flowing through it is directly proportional to the potential difference across it, the constant of proportionality being the **resistance** whose unit is the ohm (unit symbol Ω) and whose quantity symbol is R or r. One ohm is that resistance across which the potential difference is one volt when one ampere flows. The proportional relationship

$$v = Ri \quad \text{or} \quad i = \frac{v}{R}$$

is known as **Ohm's law**.

The resistor is a true sink of electrical energy in the sense that the absorbed energy is converted into heat. The device is said to dissipate the energy; the power flow for the reference directions shown in Fig. 1.20 is always positive. For example, the voltage and current specified in part (iii) of Example 1.5 could be the voltage and current in a resistor (whose value would be $340/5.6 = 60.7 \, \Omega$). Materials having the property of resistance have a large number of charge carriers (normally electrons) which are free to move within the material under the influence of an applied electric field. This was the condition assumed for the conductors discussed in Section 1.3.1, where it was shown that the magnitude of the current flow was given by $i = nqAu$. For the uniform block of resistive material shown in Fig. 1.20(*b*) the current must be the same throughout the material and, since A is constant and q is fixed for a given type of charge carrier, the product of the carrier density n and the carrier velocity u must be constant.

The electric field associated with the potential difference across the ends of the material might be expected to cause the carriers to accelerate through the material. However, as a result of collisions with fixed ions, they acquire a nominally

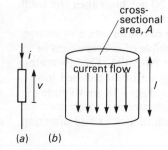

cross-sectional area, A

current flow

(*a*)   (*b*)

Fig. 1.20 Representation of a resistor

constant velocity when viewed on a macroscopic scale. This is known as the **drift velocity** and is the velocity u referred to above. Drift velocity is linearly related to the field strength through the relationship $u = \mu E$, where μ is the **mobility** of the charge carriers. Because the carrier velocity is constant, the carrier density throughout the material is also constant.

An expression for the resistance of the block of material shown in Fig. 1.20 may be derived as follows: if the potential difference across the material is v, the field strength will be v/l and the drift velocity, $u = \mu v/l$. Substituting into the current expression gives $i = nqA\mu v/l = \sigma Av/l$, where σ is $nq\mu$ and is a constant for the material, known as the **conductivity**. The ratio, $i/v(= \sigma A/l)$, is known as the **conductance** of the block of material and is measured in **siemens** (unit symbol S) with a quantity symbol G or g. The conductance is the reciprocal of the resistance, i.e. $G = 1/R$, and the resistance is therefore given by $R = l/\sigma A$, or by the alternative form, $R = \rho l/A$ where ρ is the **resistivity** of the material and is equal to the reciprocal of the conductivity.

Whilst linearity is implicit in most of the discussion in this text, non-linear devices exist which do not obey the Ohm law but do nevertheless still have a resistive property.

1.8.3 Capacitance

Consider two conducting plates (Fig. 1.21) with positive charge $+q$ moved from the lower to the upper plate, resulting in a net positive charge on the upper plate and an equal net negative charge on the lower. It is assumed that the plates are suspended in a **dielectric** material (or free space) which will not provide a return path for the charge.

In accordance with Gauss' law flux leaves the upper plate and enters the lower plate and, assuming that it is always normal to the face of the plates, as shown in Fig. 1.21, the total flux between the plates is q, $\frac{1}{2}q$ being contributed by the upper plate and $\frac{1}{2}q$ by the lower. The flux density is then q/A where A is the area of the plates (viewed from above or below) and the electric field strength is $q/\varepsilon A$, in the same direction as the flux. The existence of an electric field means that there is a potential difference between the plates whose magnitude is given by integrating the field along the path between the plates; because the field strength is constant, the potential difference v is simply El, where l is the path length. Also, because positive charge is moved against the field direction toward the upper plate, this has the higher potential.

Substituting the expression for the field strength into the potential expression gives $v = El = ql/\varepsilon A$. The potential (work per unit charge) is proportional to charge and the ratio of potential difference v to charge q is the **capacitance** C. Thus,

$$q = Cv \quad \text{or} \quad C = \frac{q}{v}.$$

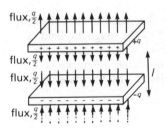

flux,$\frac{q}{2}$

flux,$\frac{q}{2}$

flux,$\frac{q}{2}$

flux,$\frac{q}{2}$

Fig. 1.21 Charge and electric flux distribution on a parallel-plate capacitor

For the plates in Fig. 1.21, $C = \varepsilon A/l$. As indicated, the quantity symbol for capacitance is C and the unit is the **farad**, unit symbol F. The farad (the capacitance resulting in a p.d. of 1 V per 1 C of charge) is a very large unit and typical capacitors have capacitances in the range of a few picofarads to a few thousand microfarads.

Because work is done in transferring charge, energy is stored in the capacitor. An expression for this energy may be obtained by integrating the power flow as the charge is being transferred. During the period $t = 0$ to $t = t'$, the energy stored will be

$$\int_0^{t'} vi \, \mathrm{d}t = \int_0^{t'} \frac{q}{C} \frac{\mathrm{d}q}{\mathrm{d}t} \, \mathrm{d}t = \tfrac{1}{2} Q^2 / C,$$

assuming that charge Q is transferred during the period. Alternatively, using $q = Cv$, energy is $\tfrac{1}{2} CV^2$, where V is the final voltage reached in the charging period.

1.8.4 Inductance

In Fig. 1.10, the magnetic flux set up by the current links the current itself, and a quantity known as the magnetic **flux linkage** can be defined as the product of the number of turns and the flux. Flux linkage has the same unit as flux (weber) and the quantity symbol is ψ. Now, the flux is dependent on the current (and is given by $\mu N A i / l$ for the arrangement shown in Fig. 1.10) and the flux linkage is therefore $\mu A N^2 i / l$. The ratio of the flux linkage to the current is then given by $\psi / i = \mu A N^2 / l$ and is known as the **inductance** of the coil and core arrangement. The unit of inductance is the **henry** (symbol H) and the quantity symbol is L. From the argument above, it will be seen that, in general,

$$\psi = Li \quad \text{or} \quad L = \frac{\psi}{i}.$$

In the context of the topics to be discussed in the following chapters, the most important aspect of the magnetic field is the generation of a potential difference within a conductor linked by a time-varying flux. The potential difference is known as an **induced e.m.f.** and is defined by the statement,

$$e = \frac{\mathrm{d}\psi}{\mathrm{d}t},$$

where ψ is the time-varying flux linkage. This is the **Faraday law**. A minus sign is sometimes written in front of $\mathrm{d}\psi/\mathrm{d}t$ but, without circuit reference polarities, this has no significance. The reason for doing it, however, is to draw attention to what is generally known as the Lenz law, which states that, in general, the direction of the induced e.m.f. is such as to oppose the change in the flux linkage. In the case under consideration here, where a change in flux linkage can only be associated with a change in current, the induced e.m.f. acts to oppose the change in current which sets up the flux change: this is discussed in Chapter 2 where suitable reference polarities are shown.

Energy is stored within a coil-core arrangement when a current flows in the coil. The value of the energy may be determined by integrating the power flow into the inductance whilst the current flow is established. Thus, energy stored is

$$\int_0^{t'} ei \, dt = \int_0^{t'} \frac{d\psi}{dt} \frac{\psi}{L} \, dt = \tfrac{1}{2}\Psi^2/L,$$

assuming that flux linkage Ψ is established in the time period $t = 0$ to $t = t'$. Alternatively, using $\psi = Li$, the energy stored is $\tfrac{1}{2}LI^2$ where I is the final value of the current.

1.9 Duality

It is possible to develop a set of **dual** relationships between charge and flux linkage, current and voltage, capacitance and inductance, etc., by which a valid relationship in one set of variables translates directly into a valid relationship in the other. This is known as **duality**.

By reference to the dual sets of quantities shown in Table 1.1, it is possible to see that, for example, having developed the relationship $q = Cv$ for the capacitor, the relationship $\psi = Li$ for the inductor may be predicted. Even more fundamental is the possibility of predicting the Faraday law $e = d\psi/dt$ from the relationship between charge and current, $i = dq/dt$. A set of analogous mechanical quantities is also shown in the table. Using this set, it is possible to infer corresponding mechanical relationships (or vice-versa). For example, energy stored $\tfrac{1}{2}Cv^2$ or $\tfrac{1}{2}Li^2$ for the electrical systems corresponds to $\tfrac{1}{2}mu^2$ for the mechanical system.

Table 1.1 *Dual quantities*

Dual electrical				*Mechanical*	
charge	(q)	flux linkage	(ψ)	displacement	(s)
inductance	(L)	capacitance	(C)	mass	(m)
time	(t)	time	(t)	time	(t)
current	$\left(i = \dfrac{dq}{dt}\right)$	voltage	$\left(v = \dfrac{d\psi}{dt}\right)$	velocity	$\left(u = \dfrac{ds}{dt}\right)$
voltage	$\left(v = L\dfrac{di}{dt}\right)$	current	$\left(i = C\dfrac{dv}{dt}\right)$	force	$\left(f = m\dfrac{du}{dt}\right)$
resistance	$\left(R = \dfrac{v}{i}\right)$	conductance	$\left(G = \dfrac{i}{v}\right)$	damping coefficient	$\left(D = \dfrac{f}{u}\right)$
capacitance	$\left(C = \dfrac{q}{v}\right)$	inductance	$\left(L = \dfrac{\psi}{i}\right)$	compliance	$\left(\lambda = \dfrac{s}{f}\right)$
energy	$\left(w = \displaystyle\int v \, dq\right)$	energy	$\left(w = \displaystyle\int i \, d\psi\right)$	energy	$\left(w = \displaystyle\int f \, ds\right)$
power	$\left(p = \dfrac{dw}{dt} = v \cdot i\right)$	power	$\left(p = \dfrac{dw}{dt} = i \cdot v\right)$	power	$\left(p = \dfrac{dw}{dt} = f \cdot u\right)$

Key points to remember

- electric charge sets up an electric flux and the electric-field strength is related to flux density through $D = \varepsilon E$;
- electric potential is work done in moving unit charge against the electric field;
- electric current is rate of change of charge with respect to time;
- electric current sets up a magnetic field and the magnetic flux density is related to field strength through $B = \mu H$;
- magnetic flux density is force on unit current in a unit-length conductor;
- instantaneous power is the product of voltage and current;
- the Kirchhoff voltage law states that $\sum V = 0$ and the current law that $\sum I = 0$;
- the Ohm law relates voltage current and resistance by $v = Ri$;
- capacitance relates charge and voltage through $q = Cv$; energy stored is $\frac{1}{2}CV^2$;
- inductance relates flux linkage and current through $\psi = Li$; energy stored is $\frac{1}{2}LI^2$;
- induced e.m.f. is rate of change of flux linkage with time (the Faraday law).

Further reading

Bobrow, L. S., *Elementary Linear Circuit Analysis.* Holt, Rinehart and Winston (1981).

Hammond, P., *Electromagnetics for Engineers* (3rd edn). Pergamon Press (1986).

McKenzie Smith, I. and Hosie, K. T., *Basic Electrical Engineering Science.* Longman (1972).

Appendix 1A Summary of S.I. units

	Quantity	Unit	Unit symbol
(a) The seven base units are:	Length	metre	m
	Mass	kilogram	kg
	Time	second	s
	Current	ampere	A
	Luminous intensity	candela	cd
	Quantity of substance	mole	mol
	Temperature	kelvin	K

(b) The two supplementary units are:

| Plane angle | radian | rad |
| Solid angle | steradian | sr |

Note: the degree (symbol °) equal to $\pi/180$ rad is widely used but is not an S.I. unit.

(c) The principal derived units used in this book are:

Force	newton	N
Energy	joule	J
Power	watt	W
Electric potential	volt	V
Electric charge (flux)	coulomb	C
Electric-flux density	coulomb/ sq. metre	C/m^2
Electric-field strength	volt/metre	V/m
Magnetic flux	weber	Wb
Magnetic-flux density	tesla	T
Magnetic-field strength	ampere/metre	A/m
Resistance	ohm	Ω
Capacitance	farad	F
Inductance	henry	H
Frequency	hertz	Hz

Multiple and submultiple prefixes

The following symbols are used to prefix the unit symbols for quantities larger or smaller than the standard unit.

10^3	kilo	k	10^{-3}	milli	m
10^6	mega	M	10^{-6}	micro	μ
10^9	giga	G	10^{-9}	nano	n
10^{12}	tera	T	10^{-12}	pico	p
10^{15}	peta	P	10^{-15}	femto	f
10^{18}	exa	E	10^{-18}	atto	a

These prefixes (with powers in steps of 3) are normally used. However, the following may be found in literature.

10^{-2}	centi	c
10^{-1}	deci	d
10^1	deca	da
10^2	hecto	h

EXERCISES I

1.1 A square sheet of charge with 1 cm sides has charge density $2\,nC/m^2$. Determine the electric field strength and flux density in free space at a point very close to the sheet. Making a reasonable assumption, what would be the new field strength and flux density at a distance of 1 m from the sheet?

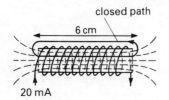

closed path

6 cm

20 mA

Fig. E1.1

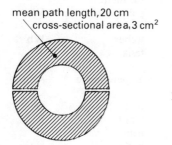

mean path length, 20 cm
cross-sectional area, 3 cm²

Fig. E1.2

1.2 Using the results of Exercise 1, what would be the potential difference between two points (stating any assumptions).

(i) 1 mm and 2 mm from the sheet; and
(ii) 1 m and 2 m from the sheet?

1.3 A certain material has 10^{27} free electrons per cubic metre: what would be the velocity of the electrons in a conducting wire of radius 0.16 mm carrying a direct current of 300 mA? what would be the acceleration of the electrons (as a function of time) when carrying a current of $300 \sin 10^4 t$ mA?

1.4 Use Ampere's law to estimate the magnetic field strength inside a coil by following a closed path looping through it as shown in Fig. E1.1 assuming that the field strength inside the coil is uniform and that in the path outside the coil is negligible. Subject to a reasonable approximation, would the field strength be affected if the core were closed upon itself in the form of a ring?

1.5 A magnetic device has its core manufactured in two halves as shown in Fig. E1.2. Estimate the reluctance of the core assuming that the air gaps are negligibly small and the relative permeability of the core material is 2000 at the operating current.
Also determine reluctance if, as a result of faulty assembly, the air gaps are 1 mm and 2 mm.
If the core permeability reduces by 10% when the operating current increases by 40% determine the percentage increase in flux resulting from such a current increase in the correctly and the incorrectly assembled cases.

1.6 An electron accelerates in a vacuum from a point of zero potential towards a large plate 2 mm away held at a relative potential of 25 V. Determine the velocity with which it will strike the plate by

(i) writing down an equation of motion for the electron and substituting relevant values; and
(ii) equating the initial potential energy to the final kinetic energy.

1.7 A sink (Fig. 1.14) has an alternating voltage $v = V_m \sin \omega t$ maintained across it whilst a current $i = I_m \sin(\omega t + \phi)$ flows in it. Determine an expression for the instantaneous power flow into the sink and sketch this flow as a function of time when $\phi \simeq 60°$. Determine whether the sink is a net absorber of energy and, if so, the mean power flow into the device in a period $2\pi/\omega$ in terms of V_m, I_m and ϕ.

1.8 In the arrangement shown in Fig. E1.3 determine v_1 and v_2 if

$$v_A = 10 \text{ V},$$

$$v_B = 10 \cos \omega t \text{ V},$$

and

$$v_3 = (5 - 6 \cos \omega t) \text{ V}.$$

What would v_1 and v_2 become if the quoted values for v_A and v_B were with respect to a point 5 V below earth potential.

1.9 If in Fig. E1.3 the two sinks A and B are devices which exhibit a linear unit-slope relationship between their respective voltages and currents, determine i_3.

1.10 A resistor is manufactured in cylindrical form from a material having a conductivity of 0.6 S/m. Determine its resistance and conductance if it has a cross-sectional area of 0.1 cm² and length 1.32 cm.

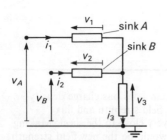

V_1 sink A

i_1 sink B

V_2

V_A i_2

V_B V_3

i_3

Fig. E1.3

1.11 An air-dielectric capacitor with parallel plates of area $2.6\,\text{cm}^2$ and 1 mm spacing is charged to 25 V. Calculate the energy stored. Also calculate the new potential difference across the plates and new energy if a lossless dielectric of relative permittivity 5 is introduced into the already charged capacitor.

1.12 Use the Ampere law to determine an expression for the magnetic field strength between the two conductors of a coaxial cable and hence determine the cable inductance if inner and outer conductor radii are a and b respectively.

1.13 A current, comprising a direct component on which is superimposed a small alternating component $2\sin 10^3 t\,\text{mA}$, is passed through a coil like that in Exercise 1.4 but with $N = 50$, $l = 1\,\text{cm}$ and cross-sectional area $1.5\,\text{cm}^2$. Determine the magnitude of the a.c. component of the voltage appearing at the coil terminals given that the slope of the *B–H* curve at the operating point is $1.2 \times 10^{-3}\,\text{H/m}$.

2 Voltage, current and power relationships in resistors, capacitors and inductors

The principal learning objectives of this chapter are to:

	Section	Exercise
• apply the Ohm law relating voltage and current in the resistor;	2.1	2.1
• calculate associated power and energy values;	2.1	2.1, 2.3
• explain and apply the voltage–current relationship for the capacitor;	2.2	2.2, 2.4
• explain and apply the inductor voltage–current relationship;	2.3	2.5
• apply the general power relationship to the capacitor and inductor;	2.2, 2.3	2.6
• show that coils may be coupled through mutually linking magnetic flux;	3.1	
• apply coupled-circuit principles to explain the operation of a transformer;	3.2	2.7
• deduce continuity conditions for capacitor voltage and inductor current;	4.1	2.8
• explain how near-impulsive conditions can arise in practical circuits.	4.2	2.9

2.1 Introduction

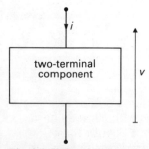

Fig. 2.1 Voltage and current convention for a two-terminal device

The terms resistor, capacitor and inductor are the names used to describe the devices manufactured to provide, respectively, those properties of conductor systems known as resistance, capacitance and inductance which were discussed in Chapter 1. Practical components are not ideal and, for example, the inductor may have a significant resistive property. However, in this initial treatment, idealised circuit elements will be assumed and, particularly for the capacitor and the resistor, this should provide a sufficiently accurate representation of the practical device for most purposes. Later chapters will show how non-ideal components can be represented by combinations of ideal components.

The components will be represented as **two-terminal** devices, using the energy-sink model shown in Fig. 2.1. Thus, whilst the component may be manufactured using a variety of materials and configurations, only the terminal voltage v and the terminal current i will be considered and there is no further discussion of the internal behaviour beyond that described in Chapter 1. Nevertheless, the physical arrangements described there do provide a basis for the manufacture of the components and also for the circuit symbols. Fig. 2.2 shows these symbols together with the relevant expression for the resistance, capacitance and inductance of the idealised component of cross-sectional area A and length l.

Fig. 2.2 The three idealised circuit elements

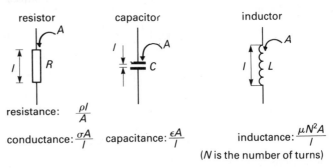

resistor   capacitor   inductor

resistance: $\dfrac{\rho l}{A}$

conductance: $\dfrac{\sigma A}{l}$ capacitance: $\dfrac{\epsilon A}{l}$ inductance: $\dfrac{\mu N^2 A}{l}$

(N is the number of turns)

2.2 The voltage–current relationships

2.2.1 The resistor

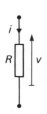

Fig. 2.3 Reference directions in a resistor

From Section 8 of Chapter 1 the Ohm law may be stated in the form $v = Ri$, where R is the resistance or, in the dual form, $i = Gv$, where G is the conductance. Fig. 2.3 shows the circuit symbol with reference-direction and polarity arrows attached. The energy-sink representation is consistent with the physical behaviour of the device in which the positive-charge flow indicated by the current-direction arrow into the upper terminal causes its potential to become more positive than that of the lower terminal; as the charge moves through the device electrical energy is converted into heat energy. As discussed in Chapter 1, the arrows must be associated with mathematical descriptions of the voltage and current, even if these are only in a simple form, such as $i = +3$ mA and $v = +5$ V, for example.

The Ohm law may be applied either in the $v = Ri$ or the $i = Gv$ forms. For example, if a direct current of 4 mA flows in a 2.7 kΩ resistor, the p.d. across it will be $(2.7 \times 10^3) \times (4 \times 10^{-3}) = 10.8$ V. Again, a p.d. of 5 V across a 6.8 kΩ resistor (whose conductance is 0.147 mS) results in a current of $5 \times 0.147 \times 10^{-3} = 0.74$ mA. Fig. 2.4 illustrates these results.

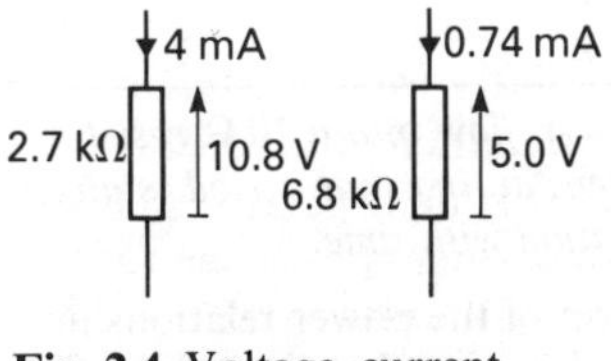

Ohm's law applies for direct and time-varying quantities and the following example illustrates the application of the law when the current flowing through a resistor has a triangular waveshape. It illustrates the interpretation of voltage and current reference directions which, due to other constraints, may not be in accordance with Fig. 2.1. The

4 mA   0.74 mA

2.7 kΩ   10.8 V   5.0 V
      6.8 kΩ

Fig. 2.4 Voltage–current relationships in a resistor

voltage v_{CB} is drawn with its polarity reversed in order to illustrate the point. Thus, when Ohm's law is applied, the form used will be $v_{CB} = -R_2i$, the minus sign being included to take account of the reversed polarity. Also illustrated is the use of subscript letters to indicate reference polarity: v_{CB} means the potential of point C with respect to point B.

Example 2.1 *Sketch the waveforms for the voltages v_{AB} and v_{CB} in the circuit shown in Fig. 2.5(a) when the current flowing has the waveform shown in Fig. 2.5(b).*

Fig. 2.5 Circuit and waveform for Example 2.1

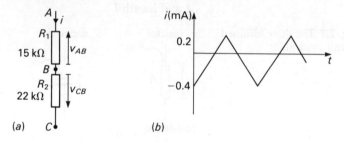

(a)   (b)

The waveforms are shown in Fig. 2.6(a) and (b).

Fig. 2.6 Solution to Example 2.1

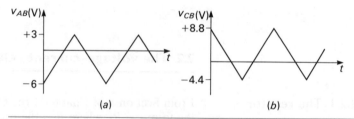

(a)   (b)

The instantaneous power absorbed by resistor R is given by the general form $p = vi$, derived in Section 1.6 (Chapter 1). Substituting the relationship $v = Ri$ gives

$$p = Ri^2 \quad \text{or} \quad p = \frac{v^2}{R}.$$

Because i^2 and v^2 are always positive, the power must always be positive, whatever the sign of i or v. This is consistent with the component behaving as a sink of electrical energy at all times.

The following example uses the same current value as Example 1.5 in Chapter 1, namely $i = (20 - 3t)$ A, but whereas in that case the voltage was simply 6 V, it is now proportionately related to the current; i.e. for the $10\,\Omega$ resistor, the voltage is $10(20 - 3t)$ V. Fig. 2.7, showing the power–time relationship, may be compared with that shown in Fig. 1.15.

Example 2.2 *Calculate the instantaneous and mean power flow into a $10\,\Omega$ resistor during the time period 0–10 s, if the current during that period is given by $i = (20 - 3t)$ A. Sketch the power variation with time.*

Since the current is given, the easiest form of the power relationship to use is $p = Ri^2$. However, it will be readily seen that the voltage is $10(20 - 3t)$ and the use of $p = vi$ is almost equally convenient.

Instantaneous power, $p = Ri^2$

$$= 10(20 - 3t)^2$$

$$= 4000 - 1200t + 90t^2 \text{ W}.$$

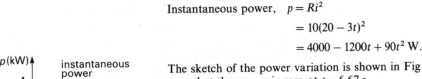

p(kW)

instantaneous power

mean power

4

2

0

5 6.67 10

t(s)

Fig. 2.7 Resistor-power variation in Example 2.2

The sketch of the power variation is shown in Fig. 2.7. It will be seen that the power is zero at $t = 6.67$ s.

It is significant that, although the power is instantaneously zero in this example, it is not, and never can be, negative. A negative value would imply that the resistor were behaving as a source of energy.

Mean power, $P = \dfrac{1}{T} \displaystyle\int_0^T Ri^2 \, dt$,   where T is the time period.

Substituting values,

$$P = \frac{1}{10} \int_0^{10} 10(20 - 3t)^2 \, dt$$

$$= \frac{10}{10} (4000t - 600t^2 + 30t^3) = 1000 \text{ W} = 1.0 \text{ kW}.$$

The energy dissipated during the 10 s period is $10 \times 1 = 10$ kJ.

2.2.2 The capacitor

The discussion in Section 1.8.3 in Chapter 1 defined capacitance as the ratio of charge and voltage, giving $C = q/v$ or $q = Cv$. Combining this statement with the current–charge relationship $i = dq/dt$ results in the voltage–current relationship for the capacitor,

$$i = C \frac{dv}{dt}.$$

The relationship assumes that C is independent of v and t, a condition known as the **linear**, **time-invariant** (l.t.i.) condition. Essentially, the relationship states that the current flowing into a capacitor is proportional to the rate of change of voltage with respect to time; the constant of proportionality is the capacitance.

In considering the problem of a current flowing into a device having two conducting plates between which there may be free space, it should be remembered that any change in the potential difference between the plates must be associated with charge movement in the connecting lead and that charge movement constitutes a current flow. If the voltage is constant there is no current flow and the capacitor is said to behave as an **open circuit**.

Although the capacitor is an energy-storage element, it is treated as if it were an energy sink with the voltage and current reference directions shown in Fig. 2.8. These directions are consistent with the principles discussed in Chapter 1, where an increase in positive-charge accumulation on the upper plate (i.e. i positive) resulted in an increase in the potential of that plate with respect to the lower plate. It should be noted, however, that the absolute value of v could be positive or negative; a positive current simply means that the value of the voltage becomes more positive as time proceeds. This is analogous to water flowing

C i v

Fig. 2.8 Reference directions in a capacitor

into a tank. The flow of water represents the current, the height of water represents the voltage, the cross-sectional area represents the capacitance and the volume of water represents the charge. When a stream of water is flowing into the tank, the water level will rise even though its initial height may be below a datum mark on the tank which, for this purpose, could be considered to represent zero voltage. If water is now drawn from the tank, corresponding to a negative-current flow from the capacitor, the water level will decrease with respect to time, corresponding to a decreasing voltage. The primary function of the water tank is, alternately, to store and release water and the same is true of the charge on the capacitor. Thus, unlike the resistor, energy is stored in the capacitor for later use. When releasing energy the sign of the current will reverse, the expression for the power absorbed becomes negative and, although the device is behaving as a source in these circumstances, the energy-sink representation remains valid throughout. An example of this behaviour, when the voltage is sinusoidal, is given at the end of this section.

Reference to sources and sinks should not overshadow the fact that the current is simply proportional to the rate of change of voltage with time and two examples illustrate this point.

Example 2.3

The potential difference across a capacitor C has the waveform shown in Fig. 2.9(a). Sketch the current waveform.

During the time period $0-T/4$, the slope of the voltage waveform is $+(4/T)$ V and, hence, i is constant at $(4C/T) V$. In the period, $T/4-(3T/4)$, the voltage waveform has a constant slope of $-(4/T)V$ and the resulting current is therefore a squarewave varying between the limits, $\pm(4C/T)V$. The waveform is shown in Fig. 2.9(b).

Fig. 2.9 A triangular voltage waveform results in a square current waveform in an ideal capacitor

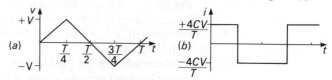

Example 2.4

Sketch the waveform of the current flowing in a capacitor across which a voltage $v = V_m \sin \omega t$ is maintained (Fig. 2.10(a)).

The current waveform is given by $i = C\, dv/dt = \omega C V_m \cos \omega t$. The cosine waveform, having a peak value $\omega C V_m$, is shown in Fig. 2.10(b).

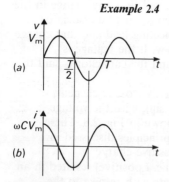

Fig. 2.10 A sinusoidal voltage waveform results in a cosinusoidal current waveform in an ideal capacitor

It is possible, of course, that the current flowing in a capacitor is known but the voltage is not. If this is the case, the integral form of the voltage–current relationship must be used. This may be expressed in the form,

$$v = \frac{1}{C} \int_{-\infty}^{t_1} i\, dt.$$

This form of the relationship gives the voltage at a particular time t_1 assuming that the voltage value at time $t = -\infty$ is zero. Unlike the current, which is uniquely defined by the rate of change of voltage at a particular instant (i.e. $i = C \, dv/dt$), the voltage is dependent on the whole history of the current since $t = -\infty$; this is characteristic of a device having an energy-storage property.

Because conditions are normally specified such that the current is a known function of time from $t = 0$ onward, and the nature of the function before this time is not known, it is convenient to split the integral into two parts:

$$v = \frac{1}{C} \int_{-\infty}^{0} i \, dt + \frac{1}{C} \int_{0}^{t_1} i \, dt.$$

Expressing the first part as $v(0)$, the value of v at $t = 0$, the complete expression for v may be written as,

$$v = \frac{1}{C} \int_{0}^{t_1} i \, dt + v(0).$$

$v(0)$ is known as the **initial value** of v. In situations where a number of initial values are specified, they are collectively known as **initial conditions**. In the water-tank analogy, the height of the water may be determined from the flow rate and from the period during which the water has been running but this result would then have to be added to the height of the water in the tank when the timing period started.

The following example illustrates the use of the integral form when the initial voltage is not zero.

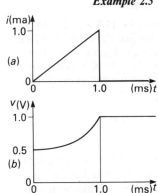

i(ma) ... (a) ... 1.0 ... 0 ... 1.0 (ms)*t*

v(V) ... (b) ... 1.0 ... 0.5 ... 0 ... 1.0 (ms)*t*

Fig. 2.11 A linear-ramp current results in a square-law voltage

Example 2.5 *Determine the voltage waveform across a 1 µF capacitor through which a current, having the waveform shown in Fig. 2.11(a), is flowing. The capacitor voltage is initially 0.5 V.*

During the period 0–1 ms, the current may be described by $i = t$. Thus, taking the initial voltage, $v(0)$, into account, the total voltage is,

$$\frac{1}{C} \cdot \frac{t^2}{2} + v(0).$$

Substituting $v(0) = 0.5$ V and plotting v during the period, $t = 0$ to $t = 1$ ms, gives the result shown in Fig. 2.11(b). For t greater than 1 ms, $i = 0$ and therefore v remains constant.

It was established in Chapter 1 that a positive value for the instantaneous power, p, indicates that the capacitor is absorbing energy from the rest of the circuit and that a negative value indicates a return of the energy. To investigate the significance of this statement in a particular case, a sinusoidal voltage, $v = V_m \sin \omega t$, is assumed to exist across the capacitor. The current is then given by $C(dv/dt)$, which becomes $\omega C V_m \cos \omega t$, and the instantaneous power,

$$p = vi = \omega C V_m^2 \sin \omega t \cos \omega t = \frac{\omega C V_m^2}{2} \sin 2\omega t.$$

Plotting v, i and p against t (Fig. 2.12) shows that, when v and i have the same sign, the power is positive (energy absorbed) and when v and i have opposite signs, the power is

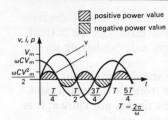

Fig. 2.12 Cyclical power flow into and out of a capacitor

negative (energy returned). For this (sinusoidal) condition there is a periodic transfer of energy between the circuit and the capacitor. The graph clearly shows that the mean power is zero, consistent with the ideal capacitor containing no material capable of dissipating electrical energy.

Also of interest is the maximum energy stored; inspection of the graph will show that this is given by $\int_0^{T/4} (\omega C V_m^2/2) \sin 2\omega t \, dt$ which may be evaluated as $\frac{1}{2}C V_m^2$. In general, the energy stored (or returned) is dependent only on the initial and the final values of the voltage and is independent of the waveform. It was shown in Section 1.8.3 in Chapter 1 that when a capacitor voltage is raised from zero to V, the energy stored is $\frac{1}{2}CV^2$; substituting $V = V_m$ for this case gives the same result as that obtained above.

Example 2.6

Determine the energy stored in a 0.22 μF capacitor over the period $t = 1$ s to $t = 2$ s if a potential difference $(2 + 3t)$ V is maintained across it.

(To avoid awkward numbers, and to clarify the working, the capacitance value is represented by C until the final line is reached.)
In general, energy stored during the period, T_1 to T_2 is $\int vi \, dt = \int_{T_1}^{T_2} vC(dv/dt) \, dt$. In this example, $dv/dt = d/dt(2 + 3t) = 3$, and therefore

$$\text{the energy stored} = \int_1^2 C(2 + 3t) \cdot 3 \, dt$$

$$= 3C[2t + 1.5t^2]_1^2$$

$$= 19.5C \, \text{J} \quad \text{(with } C \text{ in farads).}$$

Substituting $C = 0.22 \, \mu\text{F}$, gives energy stored $= 19.5 \times 0.22 \times 10^{-6}$ J or 4.3 μJ. This result may be checked using just the initial and final values of the voltage: thus, when $t = 1$, $v = 2 + 3 = 5$ V, and when $t = 2$, $v = 2 + 6 = 8$ V. Energy stored when $t = 1$ is $\frac{1}{2}C5^2$ and energy stored when $t = 2$ is $\frac{1}{2}C8^2$. The increase in stored energy is, therefore,

$$\frac{1}{2}C(8^2 - 5^2) = 19.5C \, \text{J} \quad \text{(with } C \text{ in farads).}$$

Substituting the capacitance value gives 4.3 μJ, as before.

2.2.3 The inductor

Following the same approach as that used for the capacitor in the previous section, the voltage–current relationship for the inductor is obtained by combining the expression for the magnitude of the induced e.m.f., $e = d\psi/dt$, from Section 1.8.4 in Chapter 1 and the inductance relationship $\psi = Li$. Together, these result in the relationship $e = d\psi/dt = d(Li)/dt$, from which

$$e = L\frac{di}{dt}.$$

It is implicit in this relationship that the inductance is independent of time and current. The latter is often not the case because of the non-linear nature of the B–H curve. In such cases it is necessary to use $e = (d\psi/di)(di/dt)$. Dependence of L upon time requires the form $e = (L \, di/dt) + (i \, dL/dt)$. It is convenient and helpful to regard the voltage–current relationship for the inductor as the dual

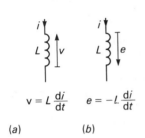

$$v = L\frac{di}{dt} \qquad e = -L\frac{di}{dt}$$

(a)   (b)

Fig. 2.13 Alternative reference directions in an inductor

of that for the capacitor. Thus, whereas the capacitor current was proportional to the rate of change of voltage with time, the inductor voltage is proportional to the rate of change of current with respect to time and the constant of proportionality is the inductance. As the capacitor behaved as an open circuit when the voltage was constant, so the inductor has zero voltage across it when the current is constant and it behaves as a **short circuit**.

As well as discussing the magnitude of the induced e.m.f., Section 1.8.3 (Chapter 1) referred to its polarity, observing that this was such as to oppose the change in flux linkage and, hence, in this case, the change in current. Thus, with a reference current direction into the upper terminal of the device, a positive rate of increase in the current will cause the potential of this terminal to become positive with respect to that of the lower terminal. Fig. 2.13(a) relates this statement to the circuit symbol where, to be consistent with the notation used for the capacitor and the resistor, the difference in the potential is labelled v. It follows that the relationship should be expressed as,

$$v = L\frac{di}{dt},$$

consistent with the fact that, when di/dt is positive, v is positive. The voltage will now be referred to as a p.d. rather than an e.m.f. and, in effect, the inductor is treated as a sink of electrical energy although, like the capacitor, it does in fact store and release energy. If for any reason it is required to use the e.m.f. notation, then, to be consistent with the previously established principles, the reference–polarity arrow must be as shown in Fig. 2.13(b) and the relationship stated in the form

$$e = -L\frac{di}{dt}.$$

The expression $v = L\,di/dt$ is the exact dual of the corresponding capacitor expression $i = C\,dv/dt$ (with i replacing v and L replacing C as listed in Table 1.1) and, for this reason, coupled with the consistency of the energy-sink representation for all three circuit elements, it is the form preferred in circuit analysis.

The following examples illustrate the voltage–current relationship for the inductor using the differential relationship derived above and the corresponding integral relationship,

$$i = \frac{1}{L}\int_0^{t_1} v\,dt + i(0),$$

where $i(0)$ is the initial current. To illustrate the duality principle, the first example is chosen so as to have the same form as Example 2.3 but with the voltage and the current interchanged.

Example 2.7   *The current flowing in an ideal inductor L has the waveform shown in Fig. 2.14(a). Sketch the voltage waveform.*

During the time period $0–T/4$ the slope of the current waveform is $+(4/T)I$ and, hence, v is constant at $(4L/T)I$. In the period $T/4–3T/4$ the current waveform has a constant slope of $-(4/T)V$ and the resulting voltage is therefore a squarewave varying between the limits $\pm(4L/T)I$. The waveform is shown in Fig. 2.14(b).

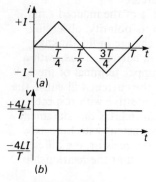

Fig. 2.14 A triangular current waveform results in a square voltage waveform in an ideal inductor

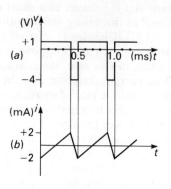

Fig. 2.15 Waveforms for Example 2.8

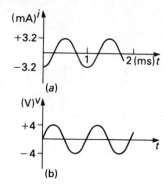

Fig. 2.16 A negative cosinusoidal current waveform results in a sinusoidal voltage waveform in an ideal inductor

Example 2.8   *Determine the waveform of the current flowing in an ideal 0.1 H inductor if the voltage waveform is as shown in Fig. 2.15(a) and the initial current (at $t = 0$) is $-2\,mA$.*

Since the voltage amplitude is constant between transitions, the current will form a linear ramp whose slope is equal to the product of $1/L$ and the voltage amplitude. Following this rule, and inserting an initial current of $-2\,\text{mA}$, gives the result shown in Fig. 2.15(b).

Example 2.9   *Sketch the voltage waveform across an ideal 200 mH inductor through which the sinusoidal current shown in Fig. 2.16(a) is flowing.*

The current waveform is a negative cosine wave of amplitude, 3.2 mA and period, 1 ms. Expressing this as $i = -3.2\cos \omega t$ mA, the voltage is $0.2 \times 3.2 \times 10^{-3}\omega \sin \omega t$ V. Substituting $\omega = 2\pi \times 10^3$ rad/s, $v = 4.0 \sin \omega t$ V, as shown in Fig. 2.16(b).

The qualifying adjective 'ideal' has been used in the examples involving the inductor to emphasise that the practical inductor often has a significant resistive component, unlike the capacitor whose behaviour is much nearer that of the ideal. The resistive component in the inductor is due to the coil resistance and to resistive losses in the core material (when a core is used). The latter are known as **iron losses**. The effect of the resistive component in the inductor is discussed in later chapters.

The various expressions relating to power and energy in the inductor may be derived from the duality principle. All the results previously obtained for the capacitor may therefore be used by exchanging v for i, i for v and C for L.

Alternatively, basic principles may be applied, starting with the fundamental relationship, $p = vi$. The following example illustrates this approach by the use of the relationship

$$p = vi$$

$$= Li\frac{di}{dt}.$$

Example 2.10   *The current in a 50 mH inductor decreases linearly from 0.5 A to 0.1 A in 4 ms. Determine an expression for the rate at which energy is transferred from the inductor as a function of time and then integrate this expression to find the total energy transferred. Check the result using only the initial and final values of the current.*

From Fig. 2.17, $i = 0.5 - 100t$ A. The rate of transfer of energy,

the power $= vi = Li\dfrac{di}{dt}$.

Substituting values

$$p = 50 \times 10^{-3}(0.5 - 100t)(-100)$$

$$= 500t - 2.5 \,\text{W}.$$

Total energy transferred $= \displaystyle\int_0^{4\times 10^{-3}} (500t - 2.5)\,dt$

$$= [250t^2 - 2.5t]_0^{4\times 10^{-3}}$$

$$= -6 \,\text{mJ}$$

Fig. 2.17 Current flow in Example 2.10

(the minus sign indicates energy transfer *from* the inductor). Using initial and final values (and subtracting the initial energy from the final energy):

Total energy transferred $= \tfrac{1}{2}50 \times 10^{-3}(0.1^2 - 0.5^2)$

$$= -6 \,\text{mJ}.$$

2.3 Mutual inductance and the transformer

2.3.1 Mutual inductance   The inductance referred to in the previous sections of this chapter and in Chapter 1 is, strictly, the **self-inductance** of the coil–core arrangement. The flux linking the current-carrying coil is that set up by the current itself. However, many electronic devices depend on the e.m.f. induced in one coil by the flux set up by another, a situation in which there is said to be **mutual inductance** between the two coils. Mutual inductance M may therefore be defined by the statement,

$$\psi_m = Mi,$$

where ψ_m is the mutual flux linkage of one coil arising from a current i flowing in another. For a given pair of coils in a given disposition, the same value of M results from flux linkage of the first coil arising from current in the second. The unit of mutual inductance is the henry, the same as for self-inductance.

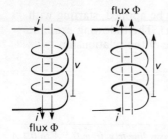

Fig. 2.18 Voltage polarity in an isolated coil is unaffected by the sense of winding

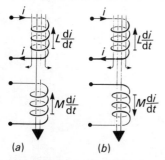

Fig. 2.19 Mutually-induced e.m.f. polarities depend on the relative senses of the two windings

Before investigating the behaviour of the two coils, it is necessary to consider a factor not previously mentioned when discussing the single coil; this is the sense of the winding. Fig. 2.18 shows two coils wound in different senses. Now, following the flux-direction rule established in Fig. 1.6, the flux will act in different directions as shown. However, the flux linkage is still in the same sense in each case (i.e. the current is still linked in the same sense) and the induced e.m.f. will have the same polarity. In effect, the winding sense has no effect on the polarity of the e.m.f.

Although the sense of the winding has no effect on the polarity of the self-induced e.m.f. the same is not true of the **mutually induced e.m.f.** resulting from a flux set up by an independent source. Fig. 2.19(*a*) and (*b*) shows two pairs of coils between which there is a mutual flux but whose relative winding senses are different. The magnitude of the mutually induced e.m.f. is the same in each case, being $M \, di/dt$, but the polarities are different. As the self-induced e.m.f. in a coil is $d\psi/dt$ (or $L \, di/dt$) so the mutually induced e.m.f. in the lower coil is $M \, di/dt$ and, as shown in Fig. 2.19, has a polarity dependent upon the sense of the windings.

Finally, the effect of joining two coils of self-inductance, L_1 and L_2, in series is considered. The arrangement is shown in Fig. 2.20. Both coils now have the same current flowing in them and both have self- and mutually-induced e.m.f.'s set up across their terminals. However, the directions of these e.m.f.'s are such that the effective total inductance of the two coils whose windings are in the same sense (Fig. 2.20(*a*)) is $L_1 + L_2 + 2M$ and that of the two coils whose windings are in the opposite sense (Fig. 2.20(*b*)) is $L_1 + L_2 - 2M$. Thus, the effective inductance is either increased or decreased by the mutual effect between them, according to whether the sense of the windings of the two component coils is, respectively, the same or opposite. The degree of coupling is quantified by the **coefficient of coupling**, k, given by $M = k\sqrt{(L_1 L_2)}$. The maximum value of k (i.e. no leakage flux) is unity.

2.3.2 The transformer

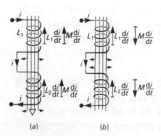

Fig. 2.20 Effect of winding sense with coils in series

Mutual coupling is the essence of the action of the **transformer** (Fig. 2.21) in which **primary** and **secondary windings** are linked by a low-reluctance core. A number of approximate but useful relationships may be deduced on the assumption of zero losses and perfect coupling, the latter signifying that there is no 'leakage' flux, i.e. that all the flux from one coil links the other. Because the flux is the same, applying a time-varying voltage, such as a sinusoidal voltage, to one winding will result in a voltage of the same wave shape at the other winding with an amplitude ratio equal to the ratio of the number of turns, i.e. $v_2/v_1 = N_2/N_1$. Thus the transformer may be used to change the amplitudes of time-varying voltages. An interesting situation arises when v_1 is fixed by an external source connected to the primary winding and the load resistance R_L is varied. From the argument above, the secondary voltage v_2 is fixed by v_1 (and the turns

Fig. 2.21 Representation of a transformer

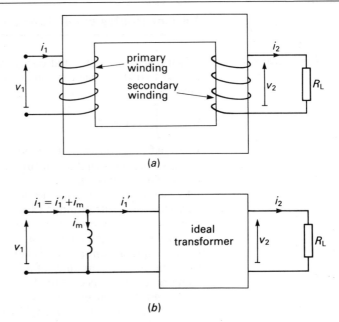

(a)

(b)

ratio) and therefore (in accordance with Ohm's law) i_2 will vary inversely with R_L. Variation in the magnitude of i_2 might be expected to change the magnetic-circuit m.m.f., thus changing the flux and hence v_1. But, because v_1 is fixed by the source an additional current flows in the primary circuit which sets up an m.m.f. which just cancels the m.m.f. set up by i_2 and there is said to be an **ampere-turn balance**. In effect, the primary current of the transformer has two components, the **magnetising current** needed to set up the flux and the additional current i_1' needed to maintain the ampere-turn balance. The additional current is given by $i_1'N_1 = i_2N_2$.

Fig. 2.21(b) is a representation of the transformer (neglecting core and winding losses) showing magnetising and additional primary currents. The ideal transformer shown here is a perfect voltage or current magnitude-converter. It is also an impedance converter in the sense that, neglecting the magnetising current,

$$\frac{v_1}{i_1} = \left(\frac{N_1}{N_2}v_2\right)\bigg/\left(\frac{N_2}{N_1}i_2\right) = \left(\frac{N_1}{N_2}\right)^2 R_L,$$

giving an input resistance (i.e. effective resistance across the primary terminals) equal to the load resistance multiplied by the turns ratio squared. Further development of the model in Fig. 2.21(b), with due allowance for core and winding losses, leads to a representation suited to the closely-coupled power transformer. An alternative approach retains mutual inductance as a circuit parameter and thereby applies for any degree of coupling.

2.4 Continuity conditions and impulses

2.4.1 Continuity

When discussing the initial conditions in Section 2.2 it was argued that the capacitor voltage was, for practical purposes, given by

$$v_C = \frac{1}{C} \int_0^{t_1} i \, dt + v(0),$$

where $v(0)$ was the 'initial' capacitor voltage at time, $t = 0$. All circuits must be switched on (or rearranged) at some time and it is usually convenient to take the instant of switching as the reference time, $t = 0$. The question immediately arises as to how $v(0)$ can be determined from conditions prior to the operation of the switch, bearing in mind that the switching will have altered the circuit configuration. The answer lies in the principle of continuity of charge for circuits containing capacitance and continuity of flux linkage for circuits containing inductance. If the behaviour of a system of water tanks and interconnecting pipes were to be investigated, following the operation of a valve, it would be very reasonable to assume that the volume of water in each tank had not changed instantaneously as the valve was operated. At this stage, it is convenient to introduce a notation which will describe conditions immediately before and immediately after operating a switch. Assuming that the switch operates at $t = 0$, the notation $0-$ and $0+$ is used to denote an infinitesimally small period of time before and after its operation. For example, $v_C(0-)$ will signify a capacitor voltage immediately before a switch operation and $v_C(0+)$ the voltage immediately after.

In an electric circuit, current is rate of flow of charge with respect to time and, therefore, unless an infinite current flows (i.e. dq/dt is infinite), the charge in a given location must remain constant during the vanishingly short period between $t = 0-$ and $t = 0+$, hence,

$$q(0+) = q(0-).$$

Furthermore, because $q = Cv$ and assuming the capacitance does not change instantaneously

$$v_C(0+) = v_C(0-). \qquad \bullet$$

In the water-tank analogy, the volume of water (analogous to charge) would not change instantaneously nor, with a constant cross-sectional area (analogous to constant capacitance), would the water height (analogous to voltage) unless there were an infinitely large flow of water from or into the tank. Duality yields the corresponding statements for the inductor:

$$\psi(0+) = \psi(0-),$$

and, for constant inductance,

$$i_L(0+) = i_L(0-),$$

assuming that an infinite voltage does not exist across the inductor.

Example 2.11 *Using the Ohm and Kirchhoff laws and the continuity relationships, determine the following voltages and currents for the circuit shown in Fig. 2.22, assuming that the switch is closed at time $t = 0$ after having been open for a long time prior to $t = 0$.*

(i) $i_2(0-)$;
(ii) $v_C(0-)$;
(iii) $i_2(0+)$;
(iv) $i_3(0+)$;
(v) *change in current in R_1 on closing the switch.*

Fig. 2.22 Circuit for Example 2.11

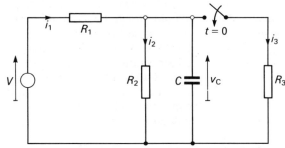

Before the switch is closed, steady conditions exist and C behaves as an open circuit with no current flowing in it.

(i) $i_2(0-) = \dfrac{V}{R_1 + R_2}$,

and

(ii) the voltage across $R_2 = i_2(0-)R_2 = \dfrac{VR_2}{R_1 + R_2}$.

This is also $v_C(0-)$.

After the switch is closed, currents will flow in C and R_3. Also at $t(0+)$,

$$v_C(0+) = v_C(0-) = \frac{VR_2}{R_1 + R_2}.$$

Therefore,

(iii) $i_2(0+) = \dfrac{v_C(0+)}{R_2} = \dfrac{V}{R_1 + R_2}$

(this is unchanged, since $v_C(0+) = v_C(0-)$,

and

(iv) $i_3(0+) = \dfrac{v_C(0+)}{R_3} = \dfrac{VR_2}{R_3(R_1 + R_2)}$.

Finally,

(v) The current in R_1 does *not* change since the voltage across it, $V - v_C$, remains unchanged. The current flowing in R_3 immediately after the switch is closed results from the charge flow from C.

2.4.2 Impulses

The results obtained in the previous subsection were based on the assumption that, for the capacitor, infinite current could not flow and, for the inductor, infinite voltage could not exist. In practical circuits, these constraints are imposed by other circuit elements and by imperfections in the components themselves. For example, if a charged capacitor were connected to a resistor through a switch (Fig. 2.23), the

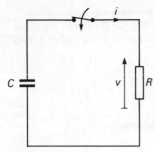

Fig. 2.23 Current and voltage in a CR circuit

current would be regulated for the resistor (by $i = v/R$) and by the fact that the voltage v, on closing the switch, must be the same as that across the capacitor, which is fixed by its initial charge. An infinite current would imply infinite voltage or zero resistance.

Notwithstanding circuit constraints, it is quite possible to connect a short circuit (ideally, a zero-resistance connecting wire) across the charged capacitor or to open circuit a connecting wire to an inductor through which a current is already flowing (Fig. 2.24). Apparently, these operations should violate the continuity principles discussed in the previous section by making $v_C(0+)$ or $i_L(0+)$ instantaneously fall to zero from initially non-zero values. In practice, circuit imperfections mean that v_C or i_L do not become zero immediately, but they do so very quickly. The effect is to produce a very large, short-duration current flow from the capacitor and a similar very large voltage variation across the inductor.

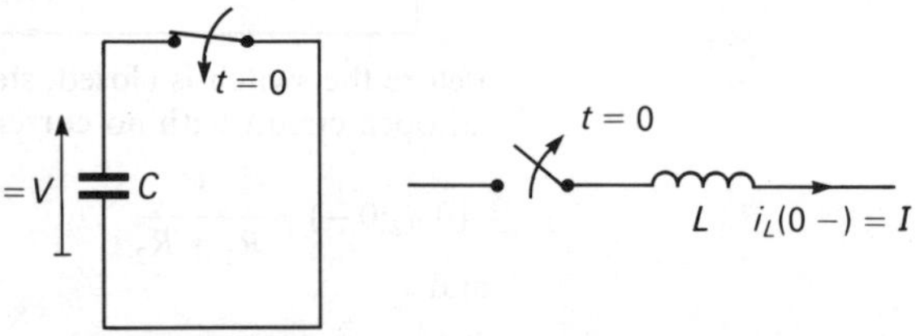

Fig. 2.24 A short-circuited capacitor and an open-circuited inductor

$$v_C(0-) = V \quad \quad C \quad \quad t = 0$$

$$t = 0 \quad \quad L \quad i_L(0-) = I$$

When the duration of a current flow or a voltage pulse is very short in comparison with the length of the timing period under consideration, it is known as an **impulsive** current or voltage. The true mathematical **impulse function**, $\delta(t)$, to be discussed in Chapter 9, has zero time duration and infinite amplitude, a condition towards which the practical impulse tends but never reaches. The magnitude or **strength** of an impulse is the area under the amplitude–time curve. When a capacitor discharges, the strength of the current impulse generated is equal to the loss of charge. Similarly, when the current in an inductor is interrupted, the strength of the voltage impulse is equal to the loss of flux linkage. For the capacitor, this may be demonstrated as follows: in Example 2.3 it was shown that a triangular voltage waveform across an ideal capacitor results in a square current waveform. A variation on this example is illustrated in Fig. 2.25(a) and (b), in which a trapezoidal voltage waveform results in rectangular current pulses.

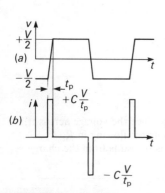

Fig. 2.25 In an ideal capacitor current flows only when the voltage changes

The relationship between the voltage and the current is governed, as before, by $i = C\,dv/dt$, from which it may be deduced that the amplitude of the current pulses is CV/t_p, where t_p is the duration of that part of the voltage waveform which sets up the current pulse and is therefore also the width of the current pulse. The area under the current pulse will be seen to be $(CV/t_p)t_p (= CV)$ which is the charge transferred to or from the capacitor in time t_p. If now the interval t_p is allowed to decrease, the pulses will become narrower and narrower and, at the same time, higher in amplitude. As they do so, however, the area will remain constant at CV. In the

limit, the width will be zero, the height infinite and the
impulse strength, as defined above, equal to CV, the charge
transferred.

2.4.3 A circuit containing two capacitors

The continuity principles and the impulse may be linked
through a discussion on a circuit containing two capacitors, a
resistor and a switch: Fig. 2.26(a) shows the circuit
arrangement before closing the switch with capacitor, C_1,
charged to a voltage, V_0, and capacitor, C_2, uncharged.
Fig. 2.26(b) shows conditions after closing the switch and
allowing a steady state to be reached; both capacitors are
now charged to a voltage, V, and no current is flowing in the
circuit. Fig. 2.26(c) and (d) shows the corresponding
conditions in two connected water tanks. As water flows from
the full tank into the empty tank on opening the valve, so the
uncharged capacitor charges until an equal voltage (height of
water in the tanks) exists across both.

Fig. 2.26 Connecting an
uncharged capacitor to a
charged capacitor

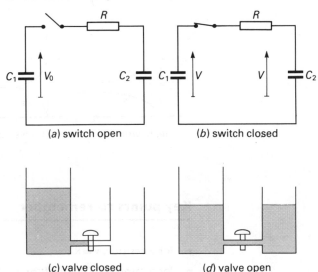

(a) switch open   (b) switch closed

(c) valve closed   (d) valve open

After the methods to be developed in Chapter 6 have been
studied, it will be possible to show that the waveform of the
current and the voltage across C_1 vary exponentially with
respect to time, but this is not important at this stage. On
closure of the switch the voltage levels adjust themselves, and
in the process a current flows. The new voltage levels are
given by equating the charge in the system before closing the
switch to that after it is closed. Thus $C_1 V_0 = (C_1 + C_2)V$ or
$V = [C_1/(C_1 + C_2)]V_0$. Energy is lost in the process, the
amount of the loss being given by $\frac{1}{2}C_1 V_0^2 - \frac{1}{2}(C_1 + C_2)V^2$
which, on substituting for V, gives $\frac{1}{2}[(C_1 C_2)/(C_1 + C_2)]V_0^2$: if
$C_1 = C_2$ for example, half the original energy is lost. The
energy is lost in the resistor but is independent of the value of
R and of the time taken for the charge transfer.†

† After Chapter 6 has been studied, it is an interesting exercise to
integrate an expression for the current between the time limits of 0
and ∞. This will yield the charge transferred; integrating the current
squared multiplied by R will yield the energy dissipated.

Graphs showing the manner in which the current and voltage vary with time may be sketched for decreasing values of R and these are shown in Fig. 2.27(a), (b) and (c). The final sketch shows the limiting (theoretical) case where R is zero and the capacitors are ideal. Here, the current becomes an impulse function and there is an instantaneous change in the value of the capacitor voltage. In all other cases, the capacitor voltage is continuous, showing no instantaneous change. It can be shown that,† for any value of R, the area under the current graph is equal to the charge transferred, $C_1(V_0 - V)$ or $[(C_1 C_2)/(C_1 + C_2)]V_0$. In the limiting case, this is the strength of the impulse.

Fig. 2.27 The effect of reducing circuit resistance in the CR circuit

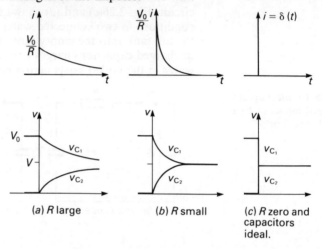

(a) R large   (b) R small   (c) R zero and capacitors ideal.

Key points to remember

- for a resistor, $v = Ri$;
- for a capacitor, $i = C\, dv/dt$ or $v = 1/C \int_0^t i\, dt$;
- for an inductor, $v = L\, di/dt$ or $i = 1/L \int_0^t v\, dt$;
- a mutually induced e.m.f. $M\, di/dt$ is set up in one coil by a changing flux set up by another;
- the transformer is a means of changing the amplitude of time-varying voltages and current;
- in a real system, capacitor voltage and inductor current are both continuous in time.

Further reading

Bobrow, L. S., *Elementary Linear Circuit Analysis*. Holt, Rinehart and Winston (1981).
Boylestad, R. L., *Introductory Circuit Analysis*. C. Merrill (1982).
Nilsson, J. W., *Electric Circuits* (2nd edn). Addison-Wesley (1986).

EXERCISES 2

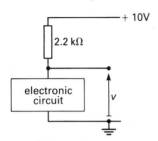

Fig. E2.1

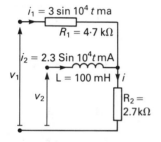

Fig. E2.2

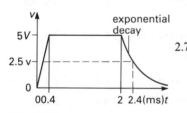

Fig. E2.3

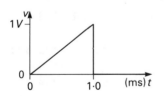

Fig. E2.4

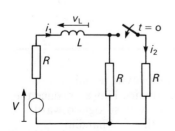

Fig. E2.5

2.1 A $2.2\,k\Omega$ resistor, forming part of an electronic circuit, has its upper terminal connected to a $+10\,V$ direct-voltage source as shown in Fig. E2.1. The direct potential of the lower resistor terminal is $+6\,V$ and there is also an alternating component of current $2\sin\omega t\,mA$ flowing in it. Write down an expression for the total current in the resistor and the voltage v across the electronic circuit.
Also determine the instantaneous and the mean power dissipation in the resistor.

2.2 Use the Kirchhoff current law to determine the current i in Fig. E2.2. Hence determine the potential difference across each circuit element and, using the Kirchhoff voltage law, determine the two circuit voltages v_1 and v_2.

2.3 Using the results of Exercise 2.2, determine the instantaneous power flow into the network as the sum of the two products, $v_1 i_1$ and $v_2 i_2$.
Also show that the mean value of this power over a period of $628\,\mu s$ is the same result as given by the mean value of $i_1^2 R_1 + i^2 R_2$ over the same period.

2.4 The switching voltage waveform shown in Fig. E2.3 is applied across the terminals of an ideal $0.1\,\mu F$ capacitor. Sketch the waveform of the current flowing.

2.5 Sketch a graph of the current in an ideal $1\,mH$ inductor across which the voltage is shown in Fig. E2.4. Assume the initial current is zero.

2.6 Using the results of Exercise 2.5, sketch a graph of the instantaneous power against time (using the same scale as Fig. E2.4). Show by integration that the total energy supplied is $\frac{1}{2}LI^2$ where I is the final value of the current.

2.7 An ideal transformer with no losses and perfect flux coupling has a primary inductance of $100\,mH$ and a mutual inductance of $50\,mH$. If a voltage $340\sin\omega t\,V$ is maintained across the primary winding with the secondary open circuited, determine the primary current and secondary voltage at a frequency of $50\,Hz$.
If a resistance of $17\,\Omega$ is now placed across the secondary winding, the primary voltage being maintained as above, determine the new primary current.

2.8 In the circuit shown in Fig. E2.5, the switch is closed at time $t=0$ after having been open for a long time. Determine the following in terms of the values shown on the diagram.

(i) $i_1(0-)$ (ii) $i_1(0+)$
(iii) $i_2(0-)$ (iv) $i_2(0+)$
(v) $v_L(0-)$ (vi) $v_L(0+)$.

Note: This question will be found easier after Section 4 of Chapter 3 has been studied.

2.9 An ideal $10\,\mu F$ capacitor is connected to the terminals of a heavy duty $12\,V$ battery. Describe the approximate shape of the capacitor–voltage and current waveform. How can the current waveform be quantified?
If the capacitor were removed from the battery and connected to an ideal $5\,\mu F$ capacitor sketch voltage and current waveforms for both capacitors.

3 Circuit analysis techniques

The principal learning objectives of this chapter are to:

		Section	Exercises
•	determine the effective value of resistors, capacitors or inductors in series and parallel groups;	2.1, 2.2	3.1
•	appreciate that sources can be represented in voltage and current-source forms;	3.1, 3.2	3.2, 3.3
•	explain the effects of high and low source impedance;	3.3	3.4
•	analyse simple resistive circuits using basic techniques;	4	3.5
•	apply voltage and current-divider methods;	5	3.6, 3.7
•	determine resistive-circuit voltages and currents using the mesh and nodal-analysis techniques;	6.1, 6.2	3.8
•	deduce and apply the Millman theorem;	6.3	3.9
•	understand that circuits may contain controlled sources;	6.4	3.10
•	explain the superposition principle;	7	3.11
•	state the Thévenin and Norton equivalent circuits;	8.1, 8.2	3.13
•	apply the Thévenin and Norton theorems;	8.3	3.12, 3.13
•	state and apply the principle of reciprocity;	8.4	3.14
•	state and apply the star–delta transformation.	8.5	3.15

3.1 Introduction

The chapter introduces a number of analysis techniques applicable at this stage to resistive circuits. However, once the techniques are established, it is a relatively straightforward matter to combine them with the methods of handling capacitors and inductors in order to provide a more general theory. The reason for the simplicity of the resistive-circuit analysis is the simplicity of the relationship between the voltage and the current as compared with the differential and integral relationships required to describe the behaviour of the capacitor or the inductor. Lower-case symbols are used throughout for the voltages and the currents. It is intended that these should stand for either direct or time-varying quantities as required.

The terms 'circuit' and 'network' appear, at times, to be used almost interchangeably. In this book, common usage will be observed in most cases; for example, a two-port network but a parallel-resonant circuit. However, as a general principle, any set of interconnected elements is treated as a **network** whereas a **circuit** would include a source, thus providing a path or 'circuit' for the current flow. It is generally assumed that the circuit elements comply with the linear, time-invariant conditions mentioned in Chapter 2.

3.2 Groups of circuit elements of a like kind

3.2.1 Resistive elements in series and in parallel

If a number of resistors are connected together in the **series-circuit** arrangement shown in Fig. 3.1, the total potential difference across the elements is the sum of the individual-element p.d.'s. As the same current flows in each element, the total p.d. is given by,

$$v_T = R_1 i + R_2 i + \cdots$$
$$= i(R_1 + R_2 + \cdots).$$

Now the total resistance of the circuit will be given by v_T/i and is therefore equal to $R_1 + R_2 + \cdots$. In general, the total resistance of a series circuit is equal to the sum of the individual resistances, i.e.

$$R_T = R_1 + R_2 + R_3 + \cdots.$$

If a parallel combination of resistive elements is considered (Fig. 3.2), the potential difference across each element will be the same and, from the Kirchhoff current law, the total current will be given by,

$$i_T = G_1 v + G_2 v + \cdots$$
$$= v(G_1 + G_2 + \cdots).$$

Now the total conductance of the circuit will be given by i_T/v and is therefore equal to $G_1 + G_2 + \cdots$. In general, the total conductance of a parallel circuit is equal to the sum of the conductances of the individual elements, i.e. $G_T = G_1 + G_2 + G_3 + \cdots$ or, using the resistance notation,

$$\frac{1}{R_T} = \frac{1}{R_1} + \frac{1}{R_2} + \frac{1}{R_3} + \cdots.$$

The resistance and conductance relationships are dual forms, as are the series and parallel forms of connection (see

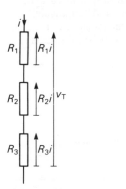

Fig. 3.1 Resistors in series

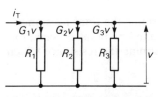

Fig. 3.2 Resistors in parallel

Table 1.1 in Chapter 1). When just two resistors are connected in parallel, $1/R_T = 1/R_1 + 1/R_2$ and, hence, $R_T = (R_1 R_2)/(R_1 + R_2)$. Thus, the total resistance of two resistors in parallel is given by the product of their resistances divided by the sum. This rule is widely used but applies only in the two-element case.

Combinations of series and parallel-connected circuit elements may be dealt with along similar lines as illustrated by the following examples.

Example 3.1

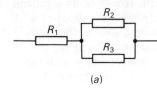

(a)

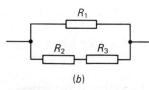

(b)

Fig. 3.3 Two combinations of resistors

Determine the total resistance (or conductance) of the two networks shown in Fig. 3.3(a) and (b).

(i) The total resistance R_T is given by the combination of R_1 in series with the parallel combination of R_2 and R_3. Thus,

$$R_T = R_1 + \frac{1}{G_2 + G_3}.$$

Alternatively, the expression may be written entirely in terms of resistance values:

$$R_T = R_1 + \frac{1}{(1/R_2) + (1/R_3)} = R_1 + \frac{R_2 R_3}{R_2 + R_3}.$$

(ii) This network is probably better treated using conductance:

$$G_T = G_1 + \frac{1}{R_2 + R_3} = G_1 + \frac{G_2 G_3}{G_2 + G_3}.$$

This result could have been obtained directly by inspection of the previous result because the network is the dual of that in part (i); the resulting expressions are therefore dual forms. Alternatively, working entirely in terms of resistance; the total resistance of circuit (ii) may be obtained using the 'product-over-sum' rule as follows:

$$R_T = \frac{R_1(R_2 + R_3)}{R_1 + (R_2 + R_3)}.$$

The technique is further illustrated by the following numerical example.

Example 3.2

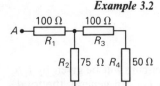

Fig. 3.4 Network for Example 3.2

Determine the resistance which would be measured across terminals A and B on the network shown in Fig. 3.4.

The series combination of R_3 and R_4 is 150 Ω, a conductance of 0.006 67 S. In parallel with R_2, the total conductance of the combination is $0.006\,67 + 0.013\,33 = 0.02$ S, or 50 Ω. Combined in series with R_1, the total resistance is $100 + 50 = 150$ Ω.

It is sometimes necessary to determine the total resistance of a group of elements from more than one point of view: for example, it may be required to determine the resistance which would be measured,

(i) across the terminals *AB*, and
(ii) across the terminals *AC* in Fig. 3.5.

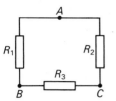

Fig. 3.5 A network which may be viewed in different ways

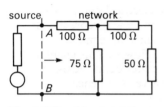

Fig. 3.6 'Looking into' the network at terminals AB

3.2.2 Inductive and capacitive elements

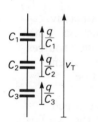

Fig. 3.7 Capacitors in series

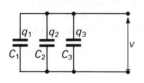

Fig. 3.8 Capacitors in parallel

Following the methods established above,

$$R_{AB} = \frac{R_1(R_2 + R_3)}{R_1 + R_2 + R_3}$$

and

$$R_{AC} = \frac{R_2(R_1 + R_3)}{R_1 + R_2 + R_3},$$

using the product-over-sum rule in each case. Expressions such as 'seen across terminals *AB*' or 'looking between terminals *AB*' are sometimes used in these situations. Another expression used when it is required to specify the resistance of a part of a network is 'looking into the network at the terminals *AB*'. For example, it might be said that the resistance 'looking into' that part of the circuit to the right of the terminals *AB* in Fig. 3.6 (using the result from Example 3.2) is 150 Ω. An arrow is often used to indicate which part of the circuit is to be considered, the implication being that any part of the circuit on the other side of the arrow should be ignored.

Although this chapter sets out to discuss only the resistive circuit element, it is convenient in this one instance to append expressions for series and parallel combinations of capacitors and of inductors. Large groups of interconnected capacitors are much less common in electronic systems than groups of resistors and the discussion is therefore limited to straightforward series and parallel combinations. For a number of capacitive elements in series (Fig. 3.7), across which the total p.d. is v_T, the charge on each will be the same and, hence, the voltage across each will be $q/C_1 + q/C_2 + \cdots$. Using the Kirchhoff voltage law,

$$v_T = \frac{q}{C_1} + \frac{q}{C_2} + \cdots.$$

Now, the total capacitance of the network will be given by $1/C_T = v_T/q$ and, therefore,

$$\frac{1}{C_T} = \frac{1}{C_1} + \frac{1}{C_2} + \frac{1}{C_3} + \cdots.$$

Capacitors arranged in parallel, Fig. 3.8, have the same voltage across each and, therefore, the total charge q_T is given by

$$q_T = q_1 + q_2 + \cdots$$

and the total capacitance, C_T, by $C_T v = q_T$, resulting in

$$C_T = C_1 + C_2 + C_3 + \cdots.$$

As is the case for the capacitor, large groups of inductors are relatively uncommon. However, expressions for ideal inductors in series and in parallel may be derived using duality: for inductors in series (which is the dual of capacitors in parallel),

$$L_T = L_1 + L_2 + L_3 + \cdots$$

and, for inductors in parallel,

$$\frac{1}{L_T} = \frac{1}{L_1} + \frac{1}{L_2} + \frac{1}{L_3} + \cdots.$$

3.3 Source representations

3.3.1 Introduction The concept of sources and sinks of electrical energy was discussed in Chapter 1. There, the source was represented simply by a circular symbol across which an e.m.f. *e* was indicated and from which a current *i* flowed. This chapter considers source representation in greater detail. Also, because the sink will always be resistive, and hence dissipative, the term **load** will be used.

Evidently, the source is a source of electrical energy but, because there are a variety of ways of manufacturing sources, some of which produce a nominally constant voltage irrespective of a wide range of current values, and some of which produce a nominally constant current irrespective of source voltage, it is usual practice to refer either to **voltage sources** or to **current sources**. The battery is a typical voltage source, maintaining an almost constant terminal voltage as the current is varied, whereas the transistor (see Chapter 12) is a typical current source, delivering an approximately constant current in spite of changes in load resistance which cause the terminal voltage to vary. Sometimes such sources are referred to as constant-voltage and constant-current sources but it is intended that 'constant' should be understood as being nominal.

It is useful to define two forms of ideal source which represent the (theoretical) limiting behaviour of the two types. Fig. 3.9(*a*) shows the **ideal voltage source** having the voltage–current characteristic of Fig. 3.9(*d*). An alternative representation is shown in Fig. 3.9(*b*). The e.m.f. is indicated by lower-case *e* to stand either for a direct or a time-varying voltage but in cases where it is required to emphasise that the e.m.f. is a direct quantity, the battery symbol in Fig. 3.9(*c*) may be used: this is often called a d.c. source. Fig. 3.10(*a*) represents the **ideal current source** having the current–voltage characteristic shown in Fig. 3.10(*c*). Fig. 3.10(*b*) is an alternative symbol for the current source; there is no special symbol for a direct-current source.

Fig. 3.9 An ideal voltage source and its characteristic

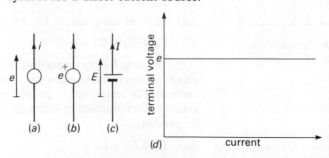

(*a*) (*b*) (*c*) (*d*)

Fig. 3.10 An ideal current source and its characteristic

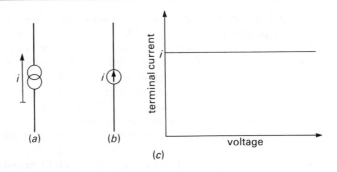

(a) (b) (c)

3.3.2 Practical voltage sources

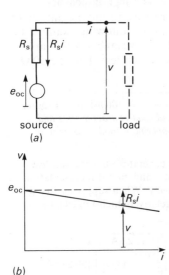

source
(a)

load

(b)

Fig. 3.11 A practical voltage source and its characteristic

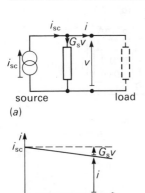

source
(a)

load

(b)

terminal voltage, v

Fig. 3.12 A practical current source and its characteristic

The ideal voltage-source representation implies that (in the limit) it would be possible to supply infinite current at the voltage level e. This would mean infinite power which is not practical, and in the real source the terminal voltage reduces as the current increases. To account for this fall in terminal voltage, which in a battery, for example, would correspond to the generation of heat, a resistance R_s, known as the **internal** or **source resistance**, is included in the source representation. The energy dissipated in this resistance accounts for the energy loss in the real device. Reference to Fig. 3.11 shows that the terminal voltage v may be expressed as the terminal voltage when $i = 0$ (which is equal to the ideal-source e.m.f. and is usually known as the **open-circuit e.m.f.** e_{oc}) less the potential drop across R_s, i.e.

$$v = e_{oc} - R_s i.$$

This is illustrated in Fig. 3.11(b).

The current-source representation is the dual of the voltage-source form with the **short-circuit current** replacing the open-circuit voltage and the source conductance (or resistance) in parallel with the ideal source. Fig. 3.12 shows the source representation and characteristic in which the load current is equal to the short-circuit current i_{sc} less the current flowing in the source conductance, i.e.

$$i = i_{sc} - G_s v.$$

The short-circuit current is that current which would flow in a short circuit placed across the source and is equal to the ideal-source current.

Notwithstanding the derivation of two forms of source representation, a particular real source may be represented by either form. Equivalence exists between the two forms when the open circuit e.m.f.'s are equal and when the short-circuit currents are the same. But, from Figs. 3.11 and 3.12

$$R_s = \frac{e_{oc}}{i_{sc}} \quad \text{and} \quad G_s = \frac{i_{sc}}{e_{oc}},$$

from which, for equivalence,

$$R_s = \frac{1}{G_s}; \quad e_{oc} = R_s i_{sc}; \quad i_{sc} = G_s e_{oc} \quad \text{or} \quad \frac{e_{oc}}{R_s}.$$

3.3.3 Source impedance

Often, the term **source impedance** is used rather than source resistance. The meaning of impedance is discussed in the next chapter but, as far as the present discussion is concerned, it may be regarded as a more general term than resistance, allowing for the possibility that there may be an inductive or a capacitive component as well as a resistive one. Nevertheless, the 'impedance' is often assumed to be resistive and source impedances of, say, 50 Ω or 75 Ω are quoted for signal generators which, lacking information to the contrary, must be assumed to be resistive. Another term sometimes used in this context is **output impedance**. This is also explained in the next chapter.

It will be apparent that the typical voltage source has a relatively small source resistance and that the typical current source has a low source conductance, i.e. a high source resistance. For these reasons the former is also known as a **low-impedance source** and the latter as a **high-impedance source**. These terms are, however, relative to the magnitude of the load impedance, as illustrated in the following example in which a signal generator is loaded by resistances which are, respectively, much greater than and much less than the 50 Ω source resistance.

Example 3.3

A signal generator has an open-circuit e.m.f. of 100 mV and a source resistance of 50 Ω. Sketch the source and load characteristics and suitable circuit representations when supplying a load resistance of (i) 1 kΩ, and (ii) 10 Ω.

When supplying a 1 kΩ load the 50 Ω generator appears as a low-impedance source with the characteristic and circuit representation shown in Fig. 3.13(a) and (b), respectively. When supplying the 10 Ω load the 50 Ω generator appears as a relatively high-impedance source, illustrated in Fig. 3.14.

Fig. 3.13 Solution to Example 3.2(i)

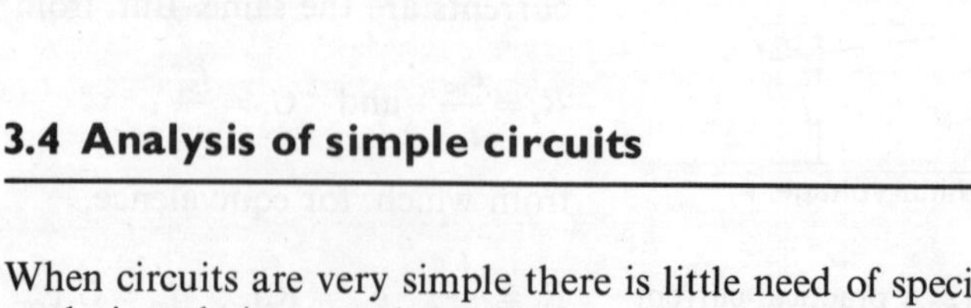

Fig. 3.14 Solution to Example 3.2(ii)

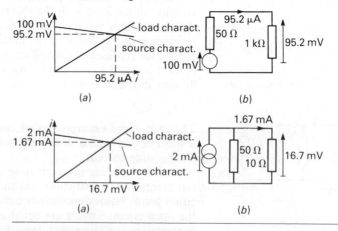

3.4 Analysis of simple circuits

When circuits are very simple there is little need of special analysis techniques and the Ohm and Kirchhoff laws may be

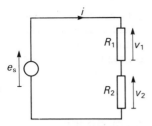

Fig. 3.15 A simple resistive circuit

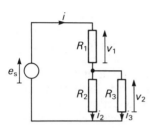

Fig. 3.16 A three-resistor circuit

applied directly. With some practice, the required results may be obtained with relatively little effort, in many cases by inspection of the circuit. For example, for the circuit shown in Fig. 3.15, the current may be determined by dividing the source e.m.f. by the total resistance of R_1 and R_2 in series. Thus

$$i = \frac{e_s}{R_1 + R_2}.$$

The p.d. across R_1 and R_2 (if required) may be obtained simply using $v_1 = R_1 i$ and $v_2 = R_2 i$. A further example of direct solution is provided by adding a resistor in parallel with R_2 in Fig. 3.15. This gives Fig. 3.16 for which,

$$i = \frac{e_s}{R_1 + R_2 R_3/(R_2 + R_3)}.$$

The new values of v_1 and v_2 will be given by multiplying the new value of i by the respective resistances, i.e. R_1 for v_1 and the parallel combination of R_2 and R_3 for v_2. The branch currents, i_2 and i_3 are given by v_2/R_2 and v_2/R_3, respectively. This is done numerically in Example 3.4.

Example 3.4   *For the circuit shown in Fig. 3.17, determine the voltages and currents, i, v_1, v_2, i_2 and i_3; e_s is a 10 V d.c. source.*

Working with milliamperes and kilohms:

$$\text{Total resistance} = 3.3 + \frac{5.6 \times 4.7}{5.6 + 4.7}$$

$$= 3.3 + 2.56 = 5.86 \text{ k}\Omega.$$

Then,

$$i = \frac{10}{5.86} = 1.71 \text{ mA},$$

$$v_1 = 3.3i = 5.63 \text{ V},$$

$$v_2 = 2.56i = 4.37 \text{ V},$$

$$i_2 = \frac{v_2}{5.6} = 0.78 \text{ mA},$$

$$i_3 = \frac{v_2}{4.7} = 0.93 \text{ mA}.$$

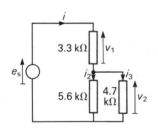

Fig. 3.17 Circuit for Example 3.4

(Alternatively, v_2 may be found by subtracting v_1 from e_s and i_3 may be found by subtracting i_2 from i.)

The basic units used in the calculation above are milliamperes and kilohms. This is typical of electronic-circuit calculations and the use of these units saves much unnecessary detail. The product of a current and resistance expressed in these units gives a result in volts. This procedure must, however, be used with care where other variables are involved.

These examples illustrate the type of circuit analysis which may be used for simple circuit configurations. In these cases, the determination of the circuit voltages and currents does not necessarily follow a formal procedure (except in the use of the stated laws); each configuration is treated individually. This may be contrasted with the procedure adopted in later sections, where a particular analysis technique follows a set pattern.

3.5 Potential (voltage) and current-divider methods

It is often possible to save some effort in the analysis of circuits of the type discussed in the previous section using the **potential** and **current-divider** techniques. Both follow directly from application of the Ohm and Kirchhoff laws.

If a voltage v_T is maintained across a chain of resistive elements in series (see Fig. 3.1), it will divide itself such that the voltage across each element is in proportion to the resistance of that element. This is because each element has the same current flowing in it and, hence, the voltage is directly proportional to the resistance. The voltage across the kth element in a series chain of n elements is therefore,

$$v_k = \frac{R_k}{R_1 + R_2 + \cdots + R_n} v_T.$$

By duality, the current i_k, flowing in the kth element of n resistive elements connected in parallel (see Fig. 3.2) into which a total current i_T flows, is

$$i_k = \frac{1/R_k}{1/R_1 + 1/R_2 + \cdots + 1/R_n} i_T.$$

Example 3.5   *For the circuit used in Example 3.4, apply the current-divider method to determine i_2 and i_3 using the value for i found in the example. Also find the voltages v_1 and v_2 using the potential-divider method.*

From the previous example, $i = 1.71\,\text{mA}$. Therefore,

$$i_2 = \frac{0.179}{0.179 + 0.213} 1.71 \quad \text{(working in mS)}$$

$$= 0.78\,\text{mA}.$$

$$i_3 = \frac{0.213}{0.179 + 0.213} 1.71$$

$$= 0.93\,\text{mA}.$$

Using potential-divider principle:

$$v_1 = \frac{3.3}{3.3 + 2.56} 10 \quad \text{(working in k}\Omega\text{)}$$

$$= 5.64\,\text{V}.$$

$$v_2 = \frac{2.56}{3.3 + 2.56} 10$$

$$= 4.37\,\text{V}.$$

3.6 Mesh and nodal-analysis methods

As the circuits to be analysed become more complex, the techniques discussed in the previous sections become increasingly difficult to implement. Often a number of equations may be set up (some of which may be redundant) and it is then a matter of manipulating these to obtain the required result; this can be a laborious process with each circuit problem requiring an individual solution technique.

There is a clear need for a more formal method of solution which can be applied by following a routine procedure, obtaining the required results with a minimum of algebraic and arithmetic effort. Apart from reducing the labour required, the probability of accidental error is also reduced. Furthermore, a routine procedure is more readily adaptable to machine methods of solution.

3.6.1 Mesh-current analysis

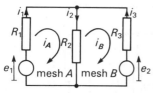

Fig. 3.18 Mesh current flow

In this technique, circuit meshes are identified as in Fig. 3.18 in which there are two independent meshes. Having identified the meshes, **mesh currents** or circulating currents are indicated (i_A and i_B in Fig. 3.18) and it is important that they be drawn in the same direction. In this case, a clockwise direction is selected. The **branch currents** (i.e. the currents in each branch of the circuit) are given by the sums of the mesh currents which are common to that branch with due regard being paid to the mesh-current directions. In Fig. 3.18, $i_1 = i_A$, $i_2 = i_A - i_B$ and $i_3 = -i_B$. The object of the method is to determine the mesh currents (and, hence, the branch currents and any required circuit voltages) by setting up equations involving i_A and i_B which equate the mesh e.m.f.'s to the mesh potential drops. As with the current directions, due regard must be paid to the polarities of the voltages and these follow the normal rules for sources and sinks, i.e. the current leaves the positive terminal of a source and enters the positive terminal of a sink. For a multi-source circuit, as in this example, it may not be possible to satisfy these conditions; if so, a source e.m.f. (such as e_2 in Fig. 3.18) into whose positive terminal a mesh current flows, must be taken to be negative when the equations are written down.

By reference to Fig. 3.18 in which the potential drops are shown:

for mesh A: $e_1 = R_1 i_A + R_2(i_A - i_B)$,

for mesh B: $-e_2 = -R_2(i_A - i_B) + R_3 i_B$.

Rearranging:

$$e_1 = (R_1 + R_2)i_A \qquad - R_2 i_B,$$
$$-e_2 = \qquad -R_2 i_A + (R_2 + R_3)i_B.$$

These equations may now be solved for i_A and i_B but, before doing this, it may be noted that the equations are in a form which can be written down directly simply by inspection of the circuit diagram: the general form of the equations will be seen to be:

Mesh e.m.f. = (self-resistance of the mesh × mesh current)

— (mutual resistance between the mesh and
an adjacent mesh

× the current in the adjacent mesh),

where

the **self-resistance** of a mesh is the resistance around the mesh, considering all the elements to be in series, and
the **mutual resistance** is that resistance which is common to a mesh and a neighbouring mesh.

It may be noted that the equations appear in this form only if the mesh currents 'circulate' in the same direction.

There are as many equations as there are independent meshes and the number of mutual-resistance terms depends on the number of meshes adjacent to the mesh under consideration. The following example illustrates how the method may be used.

Example 3.6   *Write down the mesh equations for the circuit shown in Fig. 3.19.*

Fig. 3.19 Circuit for
Example 3.6

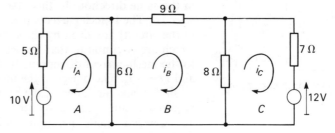

Identifying the three meshes A, B and C and following the rules established in the previous paragraph:

Mesh A: $10 = (5+6)i_A \qquad -6i_B$

$\qquad = \qquad 11i_A \qquad -6i_B;$

Mesh B: $0 = \qquad -6i_A + (6+9+8)i_B \qquad -8i_C$

$\qquad = \qquad -6i_A \qquad +23i_B \qquad -8i_C;$

Mesh C: $-12 = \qquad\qquad\qquad -8i_B + (8+7)i_C$

$\qquad = \qquad\qquad\qquad -8i_B \qquad +15i_C.$

(Solution of these equations is given in Example 3.7, below.)

Having seen that the equations may be set down very easily, it now remains to solve them. They are simultaneous equations which may be solved in a number of ways. Example 3.7 illustrates the use of Cramer's rule by which the unknown currents may be written down as the ratio of two determinants, the denominator being formed by an array of the coefficients, and the numerator by the same array but with the kth column replaced by the mesh e.m.f.'s when the kth current is required.

Example 3.7   *Solve the equations developed in Example 3.6 and hence determine the branch currents in the 7 Ω, 8 Ω and 9 Ω resistors.*

$$\Delta = \begin{vmatrix} 11 & -6 & 0 \\ -6 & 23 & -8 \\ 0 & -8 & 15 \end{vmatrix} = 11(23 \times 15 - 8 \times 8) + 6(-6 \times 15)$$
$$= 2550.$$

To obtain the specified branch currents, mesh currents i_B and i_C are required: thus,

$$i_B = \frac{\begin{vmatrix} 11 & 10 & 0 \\ -6 & 0 & -8 \\ 0 & -12 & 15 \end{vmatrix}}{\Delta} = -0.06 \text{ A}$$

and

$$i_C = \frac{\begin{vmatrix} 11 & -6 & 10 \\ -6 & 23 & 0 \\ 0 & -8 & -12 \end{vmatrix}}{\Delta} = -0.83 \text{ A}.$$

The branch currents are now given as follows:

current in the 7 Ω resistor

$$= i_C \quad = 0.83 \text{ A}, \quad \text{flowing upward;}$$

current in the 8 Ω resistor

$$= i_B - i_C = 0.77 \text{ A}, \quad \text{flowing downward;}$$

current in the 9 Ω resistor

$$= i_B \quad = 0.06 \text{ A}, \quad \text{flowing from right to left.}$$

3.6.2 Node-voltage analysis

Having studied the mesh-current procedure, the node-voltage method may be deduced using the duality principle. Initially, the circuit must be expressed in its dual form (unless already in this form) and this involves replacing all voltage-source representations by the equivalent current-source representation. The reverse would be true if the mesh-current method were to be used. Applying this to the circuit shown in Fig. 3.18, the redrawn circuit becomes as shown in Fig. 3.20.

Fig. 3.20 Fig. 3.18 redrawn for the node-voltage method

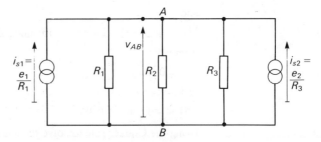

The circuit **nodes** may now be identified (*A* and *B* in the diagram) and one is selected as the reference node, *B* in this case. The nodal-voltage equation is now written as the dual of the mesh-current equation in the form,

source current into node

= (**self-conductance** joining the node × node voltage)

− (the **mutual conductance** between the node and an adjacent node

× the adjacent-node voltage).

In the particular case of Fig. 3.20, it happens that there are no adjacent nodes; hence there is only one node-voltage equation. However, in the general case the number of nodal equations is equal to the total number of nodes minus one, as illustrated in Example 3.8 below. Returning to Fig. 3.20, the single nodal equation is:

$$i_{s_1} + i_{s_2} = (G_1 + G_2 + G_3)v_{AB},$$

where conductances G_1, G_2 and G_3 are the reciprocals of R_1, R_2 and R_3 respectively. If, subsequently, it is required to determine branch currents, for example, then these may be found from the nodal voltages. Example 3.8 shows how this may be done using the same circuit as for Examples 3.6 and 3.7; as in those examples the branch currents are to be found.

Example 3.8 *Use the node-voltage method to determine the branch currents in the 7 Ω, 8 Ω and 9 Ω resistors in the circuit shown in Fig. 3.19.*

Fig. 3.21 Circuit for Example 3.8

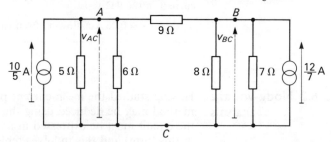

The circuit is redrawn in the current-source form in Fig. 3.21. Nodes are identified at points A, B and C and node C is selected as reference. By inspection of the diagram, the two nodal equations may now be written directly as:

$$\tfrac{10}{5} = (\tfrac{1}{5} + \tfrac{1}{6} + \tfrac{1}{9})v_{AC} - \tfrac{1}{9}v_{BC} \quad \text{for node } A,$$

and

$$\tfrac{12}{7} = -\tfrac{1}{9}v_{AC} + (\tfrac{1}{9} + \tfrac{1}{8} + \tfrac{1}{7})v_{BC} \quad \text{for node } B,$$

from which

$$2.0 = 0.48v_{AC} - 0.11v_{BC},$$

and

$$1.71 = -0.11v_{AC} + 0.38v_{BC}.$$

Using the Cramer rule to solve the equations;

$$v_{AC} = \frac{\begin{vmatrix} 2.0 & -0.11 \\ 1.71 & 0.38 \end{vmatrix}}{\Delta} \quad \text{and} \quad v_{BC} = \frac{\begin{vmatrix} 0.48 & 2.0 \\ -0.11 & 1.71 \end{vmatrix}}{\Delta},$$

where

$$\Delta = 0.48 \times 0.38 - 0.11 \times 0.11 = 0.17.$$

Substituting values; $v_{AC} = 5.61$ V and $v_{BC} = 6.16$ V. Having established the node voltages, the branch currents in the original circuit (Fig. 3.19) may now be determined as follows:

current in 7 Ω resistor

$$= 1.71 - \frac{v_{BC}}{7} = 0.83 \text{ A}, \quad \text{flowing upward};$$

current in 8 Ω resistor

$$= \frac{v_{BC}}{8} \qquad\qquad = 0.77 \text{ A}, \quad \text{flowing downward};$$

current in 9 Ω resistor

$$= \frac{v_{AC} - v_{BC}}{9} \quad = 0.06 \text{ A}, \quad \text{flowing from right to left}.$$

These branch-current values are the same as those found in Examples 3.6 and 3.7. The current in the 7 Ω branch (in Fig. 3.19) is given by the algebraic sum of the source current and the current in the 7 Ω branch in Fig. 3.21. This is a consequence of using the current-source form, with its two parallel current paths.

3.6.3 Millman theorem This is a useful theorem, enabling the potential of a common junction of several elements to be determined in terms of the conductance of the elements and the potentials at their other terminals. All potentials must relate to the same reference point but this need not be known or specified.

The theorem may be used to determine the node voltage in a two-node circuit such as Fig. 3.22(a). If each branch is redrawn in current-source form (Fig. 3.22(b)) and the Kirchhoff current law applied at the upper node, the source current flowing into the node is $i_1 + i_2 + i_3$ or $v_1/R_1 + v_2/R_2 + v_3/R_3$ (using equivalent voltage-source parameters). But this must equal the current leaving the node through R_1, R_2 and R_3, i.e. $v/R_1 + v/R_2 + v/R_3$. Equating the currents,

$$v/R_1 + v/R_2 + v/R_3 = v_1/R_1 + v_2/R_2 + v_3/R_3,$$

from which

$$v = \frac{v_1/R_1 + v_2/R_2 + v_3/R_3}{1/R_1 + 1/R_2 + 1/R_3}.$$

The theorem is also called the **parallel-generator theorem** and can be applied for any number of branches joining the node.

Fig. 3.22 Conversion of circuit to current-source form to derive the Millman theorem

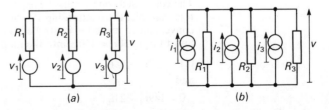

(a)   (b)

Example 3.9   *Determine the potential of the point P with respect to the 0 V reference shown in Fig. 3.23.*

(Working in kΩ.)

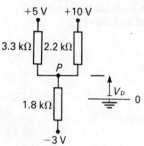

$$v_P = \frac{\sum Gv}{\sum G}$$

$$= \frac{(5/3.3) + (10/2.2) + (-3/1.8)}{(1/3.3) + (1/2.2) + (1/1.8)} = 3.35 \text{ V}.$$

It may be noted that the reference potential is quite arbitrary. If it were taken to be, say, -3 V instead of 0 V, the new value of v_P would be

$$v_P = \frac{(8/3.3) + (13/2.2)}{(1/3.3) + (1/2.2) + (1/1.8)} = 6.35 \text{ V},$$

3 V higher than before.

Fig. 3.23 Circuit for Example 3.9

3.6.4 Controlled sources

It is quite common to find that the circuit to be analysed contains **controlled sources**; these are voltage or current sources whose value is dependent upon other voltages or currents within the circuit. Fig. 3.24, used for Example 3.10 below, shows a voltage source which is dependent on a circuit voltage; other examples of controlled sources occur in later chapters. Controlled sources may be dealt with using the mesh and nodal techniques provided the dependent source is expressed as a function of one of the variables and the equations are modified accordingly. If the controlled source is not initially in this form (as in the example below), some manipulation will be needed to satisfy the requirements.

Example 3.10   *Determine the voltage v_o in the circuit shown in Fig. 3.24. Use the mesh-current method.*

Fig. 3.24 Circuit containing a controlled (voltage-dependent) source

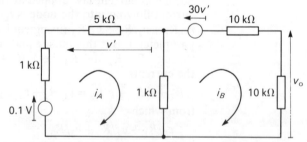

By inspection, the mesh equations (working in milliamperes, kilohms and volts) are

$$0.1 = 7i_A - i_B,$$

$$-30v' = -i_A + 21i_B.$$

The controlled source must be expressed as a function of i_A or i_B; in this example, the relationship $v' = 5i_A$ will effect the necessary conversion to make the controlled source a function of i_A. Substituting $30v' = 150i_A$ into the mesh equation gives

$$0.1 = 7i_A - i_B,$$

and

$$0 = 149i_A + 21i_B.$$

Working from these figures:

$\Delta = 7 \times 21 + 149 \times 1 = 296$,

and, therefore,

$$i_B = \frac{14.9}{296} = 0.05 \, \text{mA} \quad \text{and} \quad v_o = 0.5 \, \text{V}.$$

3.7 Superposition

In general, the **principle of superposition** states that the resultant voltage or current response in any given element in a linear circuit is the algebraic sum of the component responses due to each source e.m.f. (or source current) acting alone. It is emphasised that superposition applies only in linear circuits and does not apply for power. In determining the response to each source the other sources are 'set to zero', meaning that an e.m.f. is replaced by a short circuit or a current source by an open circuit; any source resistance (or conductance) must remain in the circuit. Example 3.11 illustrates the superposition principle.

Example 3.11 *Determine the voltage across the 1.8 kΩ resistor in the circuit shown in Fig. 3.25.*

Setting the 5 V source to zero, the voltage across the 1.8 kΩ resistor due to the 10 V source alone is

$$v'_{1.8} = \frac{1.16 \times 10}{2.2 + 1.16} = 3.46 \, \text{V}.$$

The 1.16 kΩ value is that resulting from 1.8 kΩ and 3.3 kΩ in parallel. Now, setting the 10 V source to zero, the voltage due to the 5 V source is

$$v''_{1.8} = \frac{0.99 \times 5}{3.3 + 0.99} = 1.15 \, \text{V}.$$

With both sources on, the total voltage is

$3.46 + 1.15 = 4.61 \, \text{V}.$

The result may be checked using the Millman theorem:

$$v_{1.8} = \frac{(5/3.3) + (10/2.2)}{(1/3.3) + (1/2.2) + (1/1.8)} = 4.61 \, \text{V}.$$

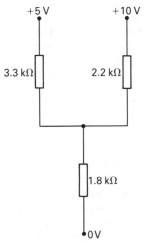

Fig. 3.25 Circuit for Example 3.11

3.8 Circuit theorems and reduction techniques

3.8.1 Introduction

The techniques discussed so far have been concerned with determining the general circuit-voltage and current distributions as effectively as possible. If it is required to investigate only one particular aspect of a circuit's behaviour, it may be possible to reduce the remainder of the network so that attention may be concentrated on the elements in

question. Examples of this reduction are given in the
following sections but, at this stage, the combination of two
resistors in parallel, previously discussed, may be cited as a
simple example of network reduction. In other cases, it may
be helpful to rearrange the circuit simply to make its analysis
(possibly using other techniques) easier. In all cases of
network reduction, it is emphasised that the elements,
whether resistive, capacitive or inductive, must be linear in
the sense, for example, that if the magnitude of the current is
doubled, the voltage will also double.

3.8.2 Thévenin and Norton equivalent circuits

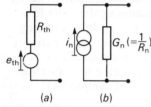

Fig. 3.26 Thévenin and
Norton representations

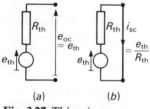

Fig. 3.27 Thévenin
equivalent open- and short-
circuited

If a linear network, consisting of any number of
interconnected sources and resistances, has two accessible
terminals, then connecting a load resistance across these
terminals will result in a defined current flow in that load and
a defined p.d. across it. The important point is that, as far as
the load is concerned, the network behaves as a simple source
which may be represented by either voltage- or current-source
forms, as shown in Fig. 3.26. The voltage-source
representation is known as the **Thévenin equivalent circuit** and
the current-source representation is the **Norton equivalent
circuit**. In acknowledgement of these titles, the suffices, th and
n are often used, as shown in the diagram. There is no
restriction on the value of the load resistance and open-circuit
and short-circuit loads are valid. Fig. 3.27 shows the two
operating conditions for the voltage-source representation and
from this diagram, it will be seen that e_{th} is the open-circuit
voltage and R_{th} is the open-circuit voltage divided by the
short-circuit current. Using the duality principle, the Norton
equivalent-circuit parameters, i_n and G_n, are given by the
short-circuit current and the short-circuit current divided by
the open-circuit voltage respectively.

3.8.3 Thévenin and Norton's theorems

Arising from these considerations, **Thévenin's theorem** may be
stated in the following form: as far as an externally connected
load is concerned, any linear network containing sources and
resistances, may be represented by a voltage-source having an
e.m.f. equal to the open-circuit voltage across the network's
terminals and a series resistance equal to that open-circuit
voltage divided by the current which would flow in a short
circuit across the terminals.

Norton's theorem may be stated in the form: as far as an
externally connected load is concerned, any linear network
containing sources and resistances, may be represented by a
current source having a source current equal to the short-
circuit current across the network's terminals and a parallel
conductance equal to that short-circuit current divided by the
open-circuit voltage across the terminals.

As an alternative to the open-circuit voltage/short-circuit
current definition, it is common practice to express R_{th} as the
resistance 'looking into' the network at the terminals with the
e.m.f.'s and source currents set to zero. The process of 'setting

to zero' involves replacing an e.m.f. by a short circuit and a current source by an open circuit; the source resistance (or conductance) must remain in the circuit.

As a general point, once the network is reduced, all information concerning individual elements is lost. It may be possible to exclude a particular element from the reduction process if this is necessary. Two examples follow using the Thévenin and Norton circuits. The first shows how, by applying the method in stages, the complexity of the problem and the amount of labour required may be reduced.

Example 3.12 *Determine the Thévenin and the Norton equivalent circuits as seen by the terminals AB of the network in Fig. 3.28.*

Inspection of the circuit shows that a break at *CD* will simplify the work. Thus, removing the 8 Ω and 9 Ω resistors, the voltage across *CD* is

$$v_{CD} = \frac{6}{5+6}\,10 = 5.45\text{ V} \quad \text{(using potential divider)}.$$

With a short circuit across *CD*,

$$i_{CD} = \frac{10}{5} = 2\text{ A}.$$

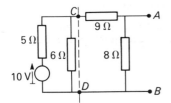

Fig. 3.28 Circuit for Example 3.12

The Thévenin equivalent circuit to the left of terminals *CD* is therefore a 5.45 V source in series with a 5.45/2 = 2.73 Ω resistance. Alternatively, the source resistance may be found by suppressing the e.m.f. to leave 5 Ω and 6 Ω in parallel, i.e. $R_{th} = (5 \times 6)/(5+6) = 2.73$ Ω. Using this representation and replacing the 8 Ω and 9 Ω resistors gives the reduced circuit shown in Fig. 3.29. Now the open-circuit voltage across *AB* is

$$\frac{8}{8+9+2.73}\,5.45 = 2.21\text{ V},$$

and the short-circuit current across *AB* is

$$\frac{5.45}{2.73+9} = 0.465\text{ A}.$$

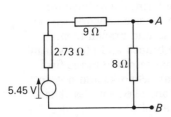

Fig. 3.29 Part solution to Example 3.12

Thus the Thévenin equivalent circuit to the left of terminals *AB* is a 2.21 V source in series with a 2.21/0.465 = 4.75 Ω resistance. The dual Norton equivalent circuit is shown in Fig. 3.30(*b*).

Fig. 3.30 Final solution to Example 3.12

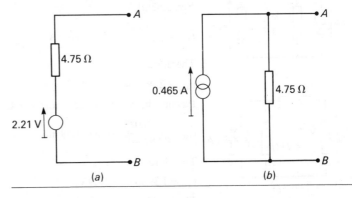

(a)   (b)

Although the derivation of the equivalent circuit may seem rather long, removal of the explanatory notes would reduce the length significantly. Furthermore, each stage in the calculation is relatively straightforward.

An application of this result is provided by the following example which is a commonly-used method for finding the current in (or the p.d. across) a given circuit element. By this method, the branch containing the element in question is removed and the Thévenin equivalent of the remaining part of the network is determined. The current may be found quite simply by reconnecting the branch to the terminals.

Example 3.13

Determine the current flowing in the 7 Ω resistance in the circuit shown in Fig. 3.19, the circuit used for Example 3.6. (The Thévenin equivalent circuit to the left of the terminals AB has already been found in Example 3.12, and this result may be used).

Using the Thévenin equivalent circuit from Example 3.12 and connecting the branch gives the reduced circuit shown in Fig. 3.31, whence

$$i = \frac{2.21 - 12}{4.75 + 7} = -0.83 \text{ A}.$$

This result is in agreement with that obtained in Example 3.7.

Fig. 3.31 Solution to Example 3.13

3.8.4 Reciprocity theorem

This theorem may be stated in the form: if a voltage (or current) source in one branch of a passive network sets up a current (or voltage) response in a second branch then, removing the source from the first branch and placing it in the second, will produce the original response in the first. Reciprocity applies to passive linear networks and not, in general, for networks containing controlled sources. The theorem is demonstrated by an example.

Example 3.14

Demonstrate the reciprocity theorem by determining the voltage across the 4.7 kΩ resistor in the circuit shown in Fig. 3.32(a) and then placing the 5 mA source across the 4.7 kΩ resistor, and determining the voltage across the 10 kΩ resistor.

(Working in milliamperes, millisiemens, kilohms and volts.) For Fig. 3.32(a),

$$i_{4.7} = \frac{0.145}{0.1 + 0.145} 5 = 2.96 \text{ mA}.$$

Therefore,

$$v_{4.7} = 2.96 \times 4.7 = 13.9 \text{ V}.$$

Placing the 5 mA source across the 4.7 kΩ resistor (Fig. 3.32(b)),

$$i_{10} = \frac{0.082}{0.082 + 0.213} 5 = 1.39 \text{ mA}.$$

Therefore,

$$v_{10} = 1.39 \times 10 = 13.9 \text{ V}.$$

This is the same as the voltage across the 4.7 kΩ resistor in Fig. 3.32(a).

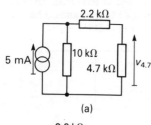

(a)

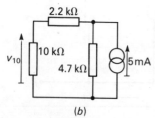

(b)

Fig. 3.32 Circuits in Example 3.14

3.8.5 The star–delta and delta–star transformations

For a given 'star-connected' network (Fig. 3.33(a)), there is an equivalent 'delta-connected' network (Fig. 3.33(b) and vice versa. Networks are equivalent when, replacing one by the other terminal for terminal, the currents and voltages in any circuit elements external to the terminals remains unchanged.

Fig. 3.33 Star–delta equivalence

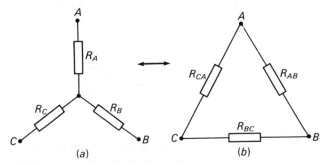

(a)   (b)

The same procedure may be applied to the T and π networks shown in Fig. 3.34(a) and (b) which are, respectively, the same as the star and delta networks. The transformation may be made by equating the resistance (or conductance) between a specified pair of terminals. For example, between terminals A and B in Fig. 3.33,

$$R_A + R_B = \frac{R_{AB}(R_{BC} + R_{CA})}{R_{AB} + R_{BC} + R_{CA}}.$$

Fig. 3.34 T–π equivalence

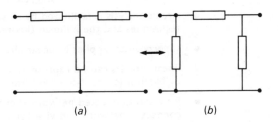

(a)   (b)

Completing the set of three equations and solving them simultaneously for R_A, R_B and R_C will give expressions for the star components in terms of the delta components. The detailed derivations are rather laborious but the results (quoted below) have a symmetry:

For delta-to-star transformation:

$$R_A = \frac{R_{CA} R_{AB}}{R_d}; \quad R_B = \frac{R_{AB} R_{BC}}{R_d}; \quad R_C = \frac{R_{BC} R_{CA}}{R_d},$$

where

$$R_d = R_{AB} + R_{BC} + R_{CA},$$

and, for star-to-delta transformation:

$$G_{AB} = \frac{G_A G_B}{G_s}; \quad G_{BC} = \frac{G_B G_C}{G_s}; \quad G_{CA} = \frac{G_C G_A}{G_s},$$

where

$$G_s = G_A + G_B + G_C.$$

An example of the application of these results is the determination of the resistance between A and B in Fig. 3.35(a). The star set of $7\,\Omega$, $8\,\Omega$ and $9\,\Omega$ resistors can be converted into a delta set as shown in Fig. 3.35(b). This can be then reduced to a single resistance using the normal rules for resistors in series and parallel.

Fig. 3.35 Example of star–delta transformation

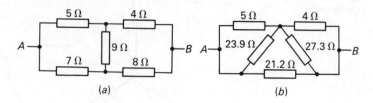

(a) (b)

Key points to remember

- for resistors in series $R_T = \sum R$; for resistors in parallel $1/R_T = \sum 1/R$;

- voltage or current-source representations of a practical source may be used depending on the circuit context;

- resistive circuits may be analysed using just the Ohm and Kirchhoff laws;

- to find voltage in series circuit, $v_k = (R_k/\sum R)v_T$ and, in a parallel circuit, current $i_k = ((1/R_k)/\sum (1/R))i_T$;

- circuit analysis is facilitated by mesh- and nodal-analysis techniques and the Millman theorem;

- superposition applies in linear circuits;

- linear circuits can be represented in Thévenin (voltage-source) or Norton (current-source) forms;

- for a star-connected network there is an equivalent delta-connected network and vice-versa.

Further reading

Bobrow, L. S., *Elementary Circuit Analysis*. Holt, Rinehart and Winston (1981).
Boylestad, R. L., *Introductory Circuit Analysis*. C. Merrill (1982).
Nilsson, J. W., *Electric Circuits* (2nd edn). Addison-Wesley (1986).
Van Valkenburg, M. E. and Kinariwala, B. K., *Linear Circuits*. Prentice-Hall (1983).

EXERCISES 3

3.1   (i) Determine the resistance across the terminals AB in the circuit shown in Fig. E3.1(a).

      (ii) Determine the capacitance across terminals AB in the circuit shown in Fig. E3.1(b).

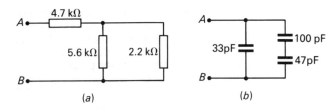

Fig. E3.1

3.2 Carry out open and short-circuit tests to show that the circuits in Fig. E3.2(a) and (b) are equivalent.

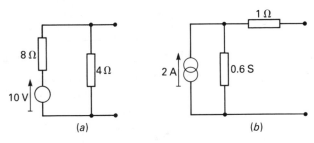

Fig. E3.2

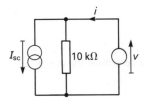

Fig. E3.3

3.3 Sketch a set of voltage-current characteristics (with voltage on the x axis) relating the voltage v to the current i in Fig. E3.3 as it is varied over the range 0–10 V and I_{sc} is set at a sequence of values, 0, 1 mA, 2 mA and 3 mA.

3.4 (i) A 600 Ω resistive source having an open-circuit e.m.f. of 2 V is connected to a load comprising

(a) a 10 kΩ resistance in series with a 30 Ω resistance; and
(b) a 10 kΩ resistance in parallel with a 30 Ω resistance.

Determine the load voltage in each case.
(ii) Check the value obtained in (i)(b) by representing the source in its current-source form and combining the three resistances in parallel.

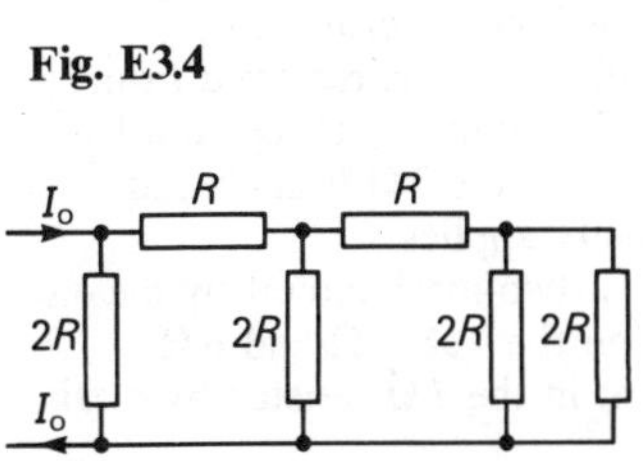

3.5 A resistor having an actual value of 4.7 kΩ is to be checked by connecting it to an ideal 10 V source and measuring the voltage across it and the current flowing in it: the voltmeter and ammeter have resistances of 100 kΩ and 50 Ω respectively. Calculate the percentage error in the measured value resulting from
(i) connecting the voltmeter across the ammeter and resistor compared with
(ii) connecting the voltmeter across the resistor alone.

3.6 The circuit shown in Fig. E3.4 is a **Wheatstone Bridge** circuit used for the measurement of resistance. The bridge is said to be 'balanced' when, by setting R_s, there is no potential difference between A and B.
Use the potential-divider method to show that, at balance, the resistance to be measured R_x is given by $R_x = (R_2/R_1)R_s$.

3.7 Use the current-divider principle to show that the current flowing in three successive vertical branches (starting on the left) in Fig. E3.5 is half that of its neighbour.

Fig. E3.4

Fig. E3.5

3.8   (i) Use the mesh-analysis method to determine the current flowing in the 7 Ω resistor in Fig. E3.6.

(ii) Repeat (i) using nodal analysis.

Note: Only 2 nodal equations are required.

3.9   Determine the potential of point *P* with respect to ground for the circuit shown in Fig. E3.7 using the Millman theorem.

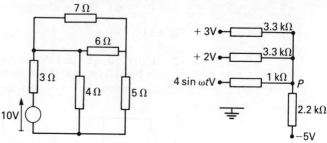

Fig. E3.6   **Fig. E3.7**

3.10   Determine the voltage ratio v_o/v_i for the network shown in Fig. E3.8. Note the presence of the controlled current source.

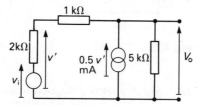

Fig. E3.8

3.11   Use of the superposition principle to determine the current in the 3 Ω resistor in Fig. E3.9.

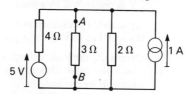

Fig. E3.9

3.12   By means of open and short-circuit tests determine the Thévenin and Norton equivalents of the circuit shown in Fig. E3.9 across the terminals *A* and *B* with the 3 Ω resistor removed. Hence determine the current in the 3 Ω resistor when reconnected into the circuit.

3.13   Taking the result of Exercise 3.10 as the open-circuit voltage across the output terminals, determine the short-circuit current and hence the Thévenin equivalent of the circuit as seen at the terminals. The equivalent voltage will be in terms of v_i.

3.14   If in the circuit in Fig. E3.6, the 10 V e.m.f. is removed from the 3 Ω branch and placed in the 7 Ω branch (acting from left to right), determine the new current in the 3 Ω branch and show that the principle of reciprocity applies.

3.15   Reduce the circuit in Fig. E3.6 to a two-mesh circuit by means of a delta-to-star transformation on the 4 Ω, 5 Ω and 6 Ω resistors and determine the current in the 7 Ω resistor by mesh analysis.

4 Sinusoidal waveforms and circuit analysis

The principal learning objectives of this chapter are to:

	Section	Exercises
• state the terminology associated with the sinusoid;	1.2	
• derive mean and r.m.s. values of sinusoid and other waveforms;	1.3	4.1
• appreciate the importance of the sinusoid;	1.4	
• evaluate the phasor technique for handling sinusoids;	2.1, Appendix 4A	4.2
• develop the phasor operator known as impedance;	2.2	4.3
• apply the phasor method to basic circuit analysis;	2.3	4.4, 4.5
• calculate power relationships in circuits;	3.1, 3.2	4.6
• understand the applications of admittance;	4	4.7
• apply the circuit theorems introduced in Chapter 3 and the phasor method to the solution of circuit problems;	5	4.8, 4.9, 4.10
• analyse simple three-phase systems;	6	4.10, 4.11
• appreciate the nature of the two-port representation of electrical devices;	7.1	
• determine the impedance, hybrid and transmission parameters of a device or system;	7.2–7.4	4.12
• use the transmission parameters to analyse transmission models;	7.4	(Chapter 5)
• develop a table showing the properties of the loaded two-port network.	7.5	4.12

4.1 The sinusoidal waveform

4.1.1 Introduction

Sinusoidal waveforms were used in Chapter 2 to illustrate voltage, current and power relationships in resistors, capacitors and inductors, and they were regarded there as one example of a range of periodic waveforms (which included triangular and pulse types). This chapter is devoted to the analysis of networks containing resistance, capacitance and inductance to which sinusoidal sources are applied. The importance of the sinusoid in network and system analysis is described in Section 4.1.4.

4.1.2 The nature of the sinusoid

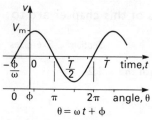

Fig. 4.1 Sinusoidal waveform on both time and angle axes

The waveshape, adjectivally known as **sinusoidal**, is drawn in Fig. 4.1. The time-varying waveform, or the mathematical expression describing it, is known as a **sinusoid**, the term being used in a general sense to describe any sinusoidal or cosinusoidal function of time. The sinusoid may be described by the expressions

$$v = V_m \sin(\omega t + \phi),$$

shown in Fig. 4.1, or

$$v = V_m \cos(\omega t + \phi),$$

depending on which is the more convenient in a particular context. The various symbols are discussed below in relation to Fig. 4.1. Although voltage is implied by the use of v in the expressions above, a current waveform is equally probable.

The waveform is alternating (i.e. its polarity or direction changes regularly) and it is **periodic**; this means that, after a certain time (known as the **period**, T), the amplitude variation repeats itself exactly. Each amplitude repetition is called one **cycle** and the number of cycles occurring per second is the **frequency**, whose quantity symbol is f, unit is hertz and unit symbol is Hz. Since each cycle occupies one period, the number of cycles per second is the reciprocal of the period, i.e. $f = 1/T$. The **angular frequency** (in radians per second) is ω, related to f and T by $\omega = 2\pi f$ or $\omega = 2\pi/T$. The angle ϕ is known as the **phase angle** and, to be consistent with ω in rad/s and t in seconds, ϕ should be expressed in rad. However, it is common practice to show ϕ in degrees, but with the degree symbol added. Although the waveforms are functions of time it can be convenient (in the next section, for example) to work in terms of angle. Basically, the sinusoidal function is the sine (or cosine) of an angle, but provided ω is constant it can be used to represent a sinusoidal function of time. The maximum value of the waveform, described by V_m (or I_m), is usually known as the peak value or amplitude.

4.1.3 Root-mean-square (r.m.s.) and mean values of a sinusoid

When specifying the amplitude of a sinusoid, it is common practice to state what is known as its **root-mean-square (r.m.s.) value** rather than its peak value; in fact, unless the peak value is specifically stated, the value is normally assumed to be r.m.s. Common use of the r.m.s. value results from the use of (sinusoidal) alternating supplies in energy-conversion processes such as occur in heaters and motors. Taking a resistive heating device for example, the mean power dissipated during one period T is given by

$$P = \frac{1}{T} \int_0^T Ri^2 \, dt,$$

where i is the instantaneous value of the current. For the sinusoid $i = I_m \sin \omega t$,

$$P = \frac{1}{T} \int_0^T RI_m^2 \sin^2 \omega t \, dt,$$

or, more conveniently, in terms of angle

$$P = \frac{1}{2\pi} \int_0^{2\pi} RI_m^2 \sin^2 \theta \, d\theta = \frac{1}{4\pi} RI_m^2 \left(\theta - \frac{\sin 2\theta}{2} \right)_0^{2\pi}$$

$$= \frac{RI_m^2}{2}.$$

Now, if a direct current I were used to effect the heating, the mean power would be RI^2 and it is therefore possible to define an **effective** or **r.m.s.** value of the sinusoidal current $I_{r.m.s.}$ by equating $RI_{r.m.s.}^2$ to $RI_m^2/2$ giving $I_{r.m.s.}^2 = I_m^2/2$ and therefore $I_{r.m.s.} = I_m/\sqrt{2}$. Thus, the r.m.s. value of a sinusoid = peak value$/\sqrt{2}$ and is independent of frequency. The upper-case symbol is normally used for the r.m.s. value.

Effective value is probably a better title than r.m.s. but the latter's use is now well established. Its basis is the general form of the expression from which the r.m.s. value of any periodic waveform $f(t)$ may be determined, i.e. the root of the mean of the square

$$\sqrt{\left[\frac{1}{T} \int_0^T (f(t))^2 \, dt \right]}.$$

The expression may be used to determine the r.m.s. value of the voltage or current for any periodic waveform; for example, the r.m.s. value of the waveform in Fig. 4.2 is $V_m/\sqrt{3}$. Another commonly occurring situation is that in which an alternating waveform has a direct-current or direct-voltage component added to it (Fig. 4.3). In this case, the general formula gives the r.m.s. value of the composite waveform as

$$\sqrt{(I_{dc}^2 + I_{rms}^2)},$$

where I_{dc} is the d.c. component and I_{rms} is the r.m.s. value of the alternating component alone.

The **mean** or **average** value of a voltage or current is given by integrating the function over a suitable time interval and dividing by that interval; for a periodic waveform the interval would normally be one period. The mean value of a sinusoid is zero (because integrating any sine or cosine wave over one period gives zero), but there are a number of applications in which it is required to determine the mean value of what is known as a **rectified** sinusoid, i.e. one whose instantaneous amplitude is always unidirectional. Fig. 4.4(a) and (b) shows half-wave and full-wave rectified sinusoids respectively. For these waveforms the mean value is not zero. For the half-wave rectified sinusoid, the mean value of the voltage waveform is given by integrating the sinusoid over a half-

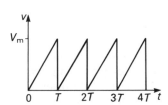

Fig. 4.2 A sawtooth waveform

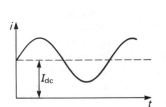

Fig. 4.3 A waveform with direct and alternating components

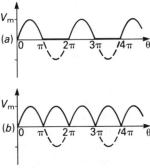

Fig. 4.4 Half- and full-wave rectification of a sinusoid

period and dividing by the whole period:

$$\text{mean value} = \frac{1}{2\pi} \int_0^\pi V_m \sin \theta \, d\theta$$

$$= \frac{V_m}{2\pi} [-\cos \theta]_0^\pi = \frac{V_m}{\pi} = 0.318 V_m.$$

For the full-wave rectified sinusoid, the mean value is given by integrating over a half-period and dividing by the half-period because the waveform repeats every half-period:

$$\text{mean value} = \frac{1}{\pi} \int_0^\pi V_m \sin \theta \, d\theta = \frac{2V_m}{\pi} = 0.636 V_m.$$

If in general usage a non-zero mean value of a sinusoidal waveform is quoted, it will refer to the half- or full-wave rectified waveform, usually the latter.

4.1.4 The importance of the sinusoid

The sinusoidally varying voltage and current waveform is of great importance in electrical and electronic-systems analysis. It is the 'natural' waveshape to use in an electrical-power transmission system because, whether the circuit elements are resistive, capacitive or inductive, the waveform of every voltage and current in the system will be sinusoidal, provided the elements are linear. This is because the differential and the integral of a sinusoid is another sinusoid of the same period and frequency, a property which waveforms such as the square wave, pulse or ramp function do not possess.

Not only is the sinusoid of importance in power-transmission systems but, as shown in Chapter 8, any periodic waveform can be expressed as the summation of a number of sinusoids of differing frequencies. The response of a linear network to a non-sinusoidal waveform may therefore be determined by calculating the response to each sinusoidal component and then summing these component responses; each input component will result in an output at the corresponding frequency but, in general, the circuit will modify the phase angle and the amplitude of each component in a different way, causing the waveshape of the composite output to be different from that at the input.

Implicit in the statement in the previous paragraph is the fact that the sinusoid exists at one frequency only. Although the significance of this property of the sinusoid may be rather obscure at this stage, it does mean that, for example, a sinusoidal 'carrier' wave from a radio transmitter can be unambiguously selected by tuning a receiver to that frequency. This is discussed in Chapter 10.

Another important aspect is the testing and specification of systems in terms of their performance with sinusoidal inputs; the frequency response of an amplifier for use in a sound-reproduction system is an example of this application.

As a final comment, it may be observed that the waveshape of many naturally occurring phenomena is sinusoidal; the current flow in a source-free RLC circuit or the motion of a swinging pendulum are two examples.

4.2 Sinusoidal analysis techniques

4.2.1 Methods for handling sinusoids

The circuit-analysis methods described in Chapter 3 involved the arithmetic processes of addition, multiplication, etc., but because the variables chosen were not time-varying and the circuits were resistive, the processes were straightforward. However, with sinusoidal variables the calculations become more difficult. Suppose, for example, that it were required to add two sinusoids, $3 \sin \omega t$ and $2 \sin(\omega t - 60°)$. Adding trigonometrically,

$$3 \sin \omega t + 2 \sin(\omega t - 60°)$$
$$= \sqrt{[(3 + 2 \cos 60°)^2 + (2 \sin 60°)^2]}$$
$$\times \sin\left(\omega t - \tan^{-1} \frac{2 \sin 60°}{3 + 2 \cos 60°} \right)$$
$$= 4.36 \sin(\omega t - 23.4°).$$

The operation is relatively involved. A simpler alternative is to represent the sinusoids by **phasors**, as shown in Fig. 4.5(b). The phasor is a quantity having magnitude and angle, known as the **modulus**† and **argument** respectively.‡ In the diagram the two phasors $3\underline{/0°}$ and $2\underline{/-60°}$ are summed graphically to obtain the resultant $4.36\underline{/-23.4°}$. As the magnitudes and angles of the component sinusoids were represented by the component phasors so the resultant phasor represents the resultant sinusoid $4.36 \sin(\omega t - 23.4°)$. The diagram is known as a **phasor diagram**.

Fig. 4.5 Addition of two sinusoids illustrated on (a) a waveform diagram and (b) using phasors

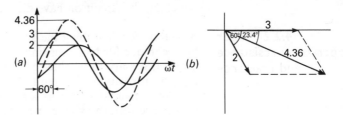

The phasor is represented by a **complex number** and the modulus-and-argument form of representation is known as the **polar form**. Fig. 4.6 relates the general number **A** to the sinusoid $A_m \sin(\omega t + \phi)$: the phasor is drawn on mutually perpendicular axes with length A and making an angle ϕ with the x axis. A firmer mathematical basis for the phasor is described in Chapter 6 but, for the present, phasor and

† There is always a slight difficulty in relating the phasor to the sinusoidal waveform because phasor magnitudes are normally taken to be r.m.s. values whereas the sinusoid must involve the peak value. However, it must be remembered that the phasor and the corresponding sinusoid are not mathematically identical.
‡ The phasor representation does not require that its angle should be the same as the phase angle of the sinusoid (ϕ in this case). However, it is convenient to make it so in this discussion and this is often the case. It is required that, when more than one phasor is used in a given circuit, the correct *relative* angles are maintained.

Fig. 4.6 Relationship between (a) waveform and (b) phasor; (c) shows a rotating phasor with projections onto the axes

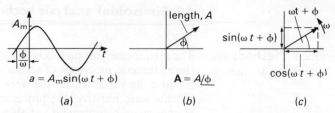

$$a = A_m \sin(\omega t + \phi)$$

(a)

$$\mathbf{A} = A\underline{/\phi}$$

(b)

(c)

sinusoid can be related by allowing a unit-length phasor to rotate at angular frequency ω (Fig. 4.6(c)); projections on to the horizontal and vertical axes then result in cosinusoidal and sinusoidal functions respectively. The phasor is represented in boldface type. Thus, boldface variables are complex quantities either representing or relating to sinusoidal quantities. Where the quantity symbol could imply other waveshapes (as well as sinusoidal) or where the notation specifically implies sinusoidal or where the modulus is implied, normal type is used. Where it is required to emphasise that modulus is involved, the modulus sign $|\ |$ is used.

The phasor representation of the sinusoid is used in the remainder of this and in later chapters in both the polar and the rectangular forms. Appendix 4A to this chapter outlines the principal properties of the complex number, relating polar and rectangular forms, and provides a summary of the required arithmetic processes. Before proceeding with the applications it is, however, important to emphasise that the technique applies only in what are known as 'steady-state' conditions, in which the circuit has been in operation for a long period and any transient effects associated with switching the circuit on have died away.

4.2.2 Phasor operators: resistance and reactance

A method for describing the sinusoid is only the first stage in the technique for handling sinusoidal-waveform problems; it is also necessary to be able to relate the various sinusoidal components within the circuit. Suppose that a sinusoidal voltage is maintained across a resistor. The current waveform is in phase with the voltage waveform and the ratio of their magnitudes is the value of the resistance R. If the sinusoids are now represented by phasors, as shown in the first entry in Table 4.1, their ratio will be $R\underline{/0°}$ or simply R. However, if the circuit element is either inductive or capacitive the differential relationship between the sinusoidal voltage and current results in a 90° phase shift between current and voltage and the ratio of the phasors will have a 90° angle as well as a magnitude: expressions are derived in Table 4.1. This ratio is known, in general, as the **impedance** of the circuit element. The symbol for impedance is $\mathbf{Z}$ and its unit is the ohm. Thus, the impedance of the ideal inductor is $\omega L\underline{/90°}$ or, using the alternative form explained in Appendix 4A, $j\omega L$. The magnitude of the expression is known as the **reactance** of the inductor. The symbol for reactance is X and its unit is also the ohm; thus, inductive reactance $X_L = \omega L$. The impedance of the capacitor (Table 4.1) is $-j/\omega C$ and the capacitive reactance is given by $X_C = 1/\omega C$; some references

Table 4.1. *Phasor operators for resistance, capacitance and inductance*

Circuit element	Circuit symbol	Waveforms	Relationships
Resistor			If $v = V \sin \omega t$, $i = \dfrac{v}{R} = \dfrac{V}{R} \sin \omega t$ and voltage and current are in phase Therefore, if $\mathbf{V} = V\underline{/0^\circ}$, $\mathbf{I} = \dfrac{V}{R}\underline{/0^\circ}$ and phasor operator, $\mathbf{Z} = \dfrac{\mathbf{V}}{\mathbf{I}} = R\underline{/0^\circ}$
Capacitor			If $v = V \sin \omega t$, $i = C\dfrac{\mathrm{d}v}{\mathrm{d}t} = \omega C V \cos \omega t$ and current leads the voltage by 90° Therefore, if $\mathbf{V} = V\underline{/0^\circ}$, $\mathbf{I} = \omega C V\underline{/90^\circ}$ and phasor operator, $\mathbf{Z} = \dfrac{\mathbf{V}}{\mathbf{I}} = \dfrac{1}{\omega C}\underline{/-90^\circ}$ Alternative forms: $-j/\omega C$ or $1/j\omega C$
Inductor			If $v = V \sin \omega t$ $i = \dfrac{1}{L}\int v\,\mathrm{d}t = \dfrac{V}{\omega L}(-\cos \omega t)$ and current lags the voltage by 90° Therefore, if $\mathbf{V} = V\underline{/0^\circ}$, $\mathbf{I} = \dfrac{V}{\omega L}\underline{/-90^\circ}$ and phasor operator, $\mathbf{Z} = \dfrac{\mathbf{V}}{\mathbf{I}} = \omega L\underline{/90^\circ}$ Alternative form: $j\omega L$

retain the minus sign to give $-1/\omega C$. Although impedance has modulus and argument it is not a phasor because it does not represent a sinusoid. However, because it relates two phasors it is known as a **phasor operator**.

4.2.3 Circuit-analysis techniques and impedance

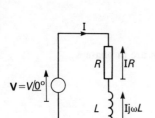

Fig. 4.7 A series RL circuit

To illustrate the basic procedures consider the circuit shown in Fig. 4.7. A sinusoidal voltage, represented by

$$\mathbf{V} = V\underline{/0^\circ},$$

is applied to resistance R and inductance L in series.

If the current is represented by phasor $\mathbf{I}$ then the potential differences across R and L are given by the product of the current and the impedances of the individual elements, i.e. $\mathbf{V_R} = \mathbf{I}R$ and $\mathbf{V_L} = \mathbf{I}j\omega L$. But, by the Kirchhoff voltage law, the total voltage

$$\mathbf{V} = \mathbf{V_R} + \mathbf{V_L} = \mathbf{I}R + \mathbf{I}j\omega L = \mathbf{I}(R + j\omega L).$$

Then the current

$$\mathbf{I} = \frac{\mathbf{V}}{R + j\omega L}$$

$$= \frac{V}{\sqrt{[R^2 + (\omega L)^2]}} \underline{\left/ -\tan^{-1}\frac{\omega L}{R}\right.}.$$

This short example illustrates a general procedure in which the voltages and currents are represented by phasors (in this case, voltage known and current unknown), the circuit equations are written down in complex form and the solution obtained by complex-algebraic manipulation.

The phasor operator $\mathbf{V}/\mathbf{I}$ $(= R + j\omega L)$ is the impedance of the resistance and inductance in series; in general, impedance may be expressed in the form $R \pm jX$, where R and X are the resistive and reactive components. If in the above example the resistance were $90\,\Omega$ and the inductance were $0.3\,\text{H}$, then at a frequency of $100\,\text{Hz}$, the impedance would be $90 + j(2\pi \times 100 \times 0.3) = 90 + j188 = 208\underline{/64^\circ}\,\Omega$. Further examples are given in Example 4.1.

In the analysis above the impedance is the sum of the individual circuit-element impedances in the series circuit. This method of determining the total impedance follows the same principle as that established for resistors in Section 3.2.1 of Chapter 3 where the essential procedure was also one of summing potential differences around the circuit. It follows that the procedure for summing resistors in parallel also applies; indeed, all the network reduction techniques and circuit theorems established in Chapter 3 for resistive networks can be applied to the steady-state sinusoidal analysis of networks containing resistance, inductance and capacitance, provided that resistance is represented by R, inductance by $j\omega L$ and capacitance by $1/j\omega C$ (or $-j/\omega C$).

This is the strength of the phasor method: complicated circuits can be analysed without recourse to differential and integral relationships. However, it must be remembered that the techniques only apply when sinusoidal waveforms are involved and then only when the circuit is operating in its steady-state condition.

Example 4.1 illustrates how the impedance of various networks can be determined. The networks are shown in Fig. 4.8.

Example 4.1

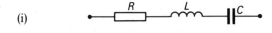

	Network	*Impedance*

(i)

$$\mathbf{Z} = R + j\omega L - \frac{j}{\omega C}$$

(ii)

$$\frac{1}{\mathbf{Z}} = \frac{1}{R} + j\omega C$$

or

$$\mathbf{Z} = \frac{R}{1 + j\omega CR}$$

(iii)

$$\frac{1}{\mathbf{Z}} = j\omega C + \frac{1}{R + j\omega L}$$

or, using the product-over-sum rule,

$$\mathbf{Z} = \frac{(R + j\omega L)/j\omega C}{R + j\omega L + 1/j\omega C}$$

(iv)

$$\mathbf{Z} = R_1 + \frac{j\omega L R_2}{R_2 + j\omega L}$$

Fig. 4.8

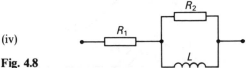

The following example illustrates a typical complex-phasor calculation. Further examples are given on pp. 80–82.

Example 4.2   *Calculate the currents i and i_R in the circuit shown in Fig. 4.9.*

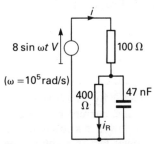

Fig. 4.9 Circuit for Example 4.2

Total impedance $= 100 + \dfrac{1}{1/400 + j\omega 47 \times 10^{-9}}$.

Substituting for ω:

$$\mathbf{Z} = 100 + 188\underline{/-62°}$$

$$= 100 + 88 - j166$$

$$= 251\underline{/-41.4°}\ \Omega.$$

Therefore

$$\mathbf{I} = \frac{8}{251\underline{/-41.4°}} = 0.032\underline{/41.4°}\ \text{A}.$$

$\mathbf{I_R}$ may be determined using the current-divider method:

$$= \frac{1/400}{1/400 + j\omega 47 \times 10^{-9}} \times 0.032\underline{/41.4°}$$

$$= 0.015\underline{/-20.6}\ \text{A}\quad \text{(working in peak values throughout)}.$$

Note: as in this example, results are often quoted in the complex form. It is understood that, for example, i as a function of time is $0.032 \sin(10^5 t + 41.4°)$ A.

4.3 Power relationships

4.3.1 Power and power factor

Following the procedure in Example 4.2, the modulus of the polar-form result may be used to determine the magnitude ratio of the sinusoidal voltage and current and the argument to determine the phase difference between the sinusoids.

The argument is dependent only on the circuit and is known as the **circuit phase angle**. This is an absolute quantity and is not relative as is the case in the voltage or current phasors. Thus, the phase angle of a circuit may be stated as 41°, for example, without further qualification, but the phase angle of the current would have to be specified as 41° with respect to a reference quantity, the source voltage in this case.

Positive impedance angles are said to be **lagging angles** because the circuit current lags (or is delayed with respect to) the circuit voltage. Negative impedance angles are **leading angles** because the current leads the voltage. Fig. 4.10 illustrates these points.

Fig. 4.10 Phase angle related to impedance

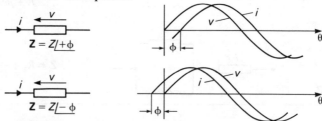

The power dissipation in a circuit across which there is voltage, $v = V_m \sin \omega t$ and in which the current, $i = I_m \sin(\omega t \pm \phi)$, flows is given by

$$P = \frac{1}{T}\int_0^T vi\, \mathrm{d}t = \frac{1}{T}\int_0^T V_m I_m \sin \omega t \sin(\omega t \pm \phi)\, \mathrm{d}t,$$

using the results obtained in Chapter 1. Evaluating this integral, gives

$$P = \frac{V_m I_m}{2}\cos \phi = \frac{V_m}{\sqrt{2}}\frac{I_m}{\sqrt{2}}\cos \phi$$
$$= VI \cos \phi,$$

where V and I are r.m.s. values. The factor by which the product of the r.m.s. voltage and the r.m.s. current must be multiplied in order to obtain the mean power is known as the **power factor** of the circuit. Thus the power factor is the cosine of the phase angle between the voltage and the current.

The value of the phase angle used in power calculations is the phase difference between the relevant voltage and current, and some care is necessary to ensure that the correct angle is used. This point is illustrated in the following worked example:

Example 4.3   *For the circuit shown in Fig. 4.9 (Example 4.2) determine:*

(i) the total power dissipation in the circuit;
(ii) the power dissipation in the 100 Ω resistor;
(iii) the power dissipation in the parallel C–R combination.

(i) r.m.s. value of source voltage (modulus V) $= \dfrac{8}{\sqrt{2}} = 5.66 \text{ V}$;

r.m.s. value of total current (modulus I) $= \dfrac{32}{\sqrt{2}} = 22.6 \text{ mA}$;

phase difference is $41.4°$.

$\therefore$ total power $= 5.66 \times 22.6 \cos 41.4° = 95.9 \text{ mW}$.

(ii) The voltage across the $100 \, \Omega$ resistor is $100I = 2.26 \text{ V}$.

$\therefore$ power in the $100 \, \Omega$ resistor $= 2.26 \times 22.6 \cos 0° = 51.0 \text{ mW}$,

since there is no phase difference between the voltage and the current in the resistor.

(iii) Probably the quickest way to determine the voltage across the $400 \, \Omega$ resistor is to subtract the $100 \, \Omega$ resistor voltage from the supply voltage:

i.e. $\mathbf{V}_{400} = 5.66\underline{/0°} - 2.26\underline{/+41.4°}$

$\qquad = (5.66 + j0) - (1.69 + j1.49)$

$\qquad = (3.97 - j1.49) = 4.24\underline{/-20.6°} \text{ V}$.

$\therefore$ power in the parallel C–R combination

$\qquad = 4.24 \times 22.6 \cos(-20.6° - (+41.4°)) = 44.9 \text{ mW}$.

Notes: 1. All the power in answer (iii) is in fact transferred to the $400 \, \Omega$ resistor, there being zero mean power in the capacitor; however, the method of calculation used is not based on this assumption. Alternatively, using $I_R^2 R$ gives $15/\sqrt{2} \times 10^{-6} \times 400 = 44.9 \text{ mW}$.

2. The power values in (ii) and (iii) together sum to the value in (i).

There are a number of variations on the method of calculating power, two of which are summarised below.

The expression $VI \cos \phi$ can be written as $IZI \cos \phi$ or $I^2 Z \cos \phi$. Thus, if the impedance of a circuit (or of part of a circuit) is known, the power delivered to this circuit is given by the r.m.s. current squared multiplied by the resistive component of the impedance $Z \cos \phi$. If the circuit in question is purely resistive, the power will be $I^2 R$ where R is the circuit resistance.

For the lower half of the circuit in Fig. 4.9, the impedance has been calculated as $(88 - j166) \, \Omega$ (in Example 4.2). The power is given by (r.m.s. current) squared times resistive component $(0.032/\sqrt{2})^2 \times 88 = 44.9 \text{ mW}$, agreeing with that example.

Another expression for the power in a circuit results from taking, in the general case, $\mathbf{V}$ as $V\underline{/\theta}$ and $\mathbf{I}$ as $I\underline{/\theta + \phi}$. Then carrying out a little trigonometric manipulation will show that the power, $VI \cos \phi$, is given by the real part of the product $\mathbf{V}$ times the complex conjugate of $\mathbf{I}$, i.e.

$$P = R_e[\mathbf{V}\mathbf{I}^*].$$

Again referring to Fig. 4.9 and Example 4.3, the real component of the product of the r.m.s. voltage and the complex conjugate of the r.m.s. current in the lower half of the circuit is

$$R_e[(3.96) - j1.49)(16.9 - j14.9) \times 10^{-3}]$$
$$= (67.1 - 22.2) \times 10^{-3}$$
$$= 44.9 \text{ mW}.$$

4.3.2 Active and reactive power

The power value referred to in the previous section (i.e. the mean power delivered to the resistor) is also known as **active** or **real power** P. This is in contrast with what is known as **reactive** or **wattless power** Q, measured in **voltampere (reactive)** (whose symbol is var) and given by $VI \sin \phi$ where $\phi = \text{arc cos(power factor)}$. Thus, if the product of the voltage and the current, known in this context as the **apparent power** S and measured in **voltampere** (symbol VA), is represented by one side of a right-angled triangle, the active and reactive powers can be represented by the other two sides as shown in Fig. 4.11. The magnitudes of the quantities are thus related by

$$(VI)^2 = (VI \cos \phi)^2 + (VI \sin \phi)^2.$$

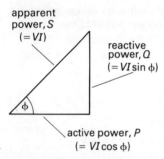

Fig. 4.11 Relationship between active and reactive quantities

Interest in apparent power arises because, although a given load may consume little active power as a result of having a low power factor, a significant current will still flow and power losses in transmission and generating equipment are proportional to the square of the current supplied rather than the active power supplied.

4.3.3 Maximum power transfer

In order to transfer maximum power from source to load, a particular relationship between source and load impedances should exist. Furthermore, there are degrees of maxima in the sense that a purely resistive load would have a resistance value which would cause maximum power to be transferred from a complex source as that resistance varied, but given an additional degree of freedom in the form of an independently variable reactive component in the load, even more power can be transferred. Four commonly met conditions are,

(i) load purely resistive and variable: maximum power extracted from a resistive source when $R_L = R_s$;

(ii) load purely resistive and variable: maximum power extracted from a complex source when $R_L = |Z_s|$;

(iii) load complex with magnitude (but not phase angle) variable: maximum power extracted from a complex source when $|Z_L| = |Z_s|$;

(iv) load complex with resistive and reactive components independently variable: maximum power extracted when Z_L is the complex conjugate of Z_s.

(i) gives conditions for absolute maximum power transfer from a resistive source to a resistive load and (iv) gives the corresponding condition for complex source and load.

Maximum-power transfer does not mean maximum efficiency of transfer. For example, a resistive source supplying an equal-value resistive load would have half the system power dissipation in the source. For power-distribution systems maximum-power conditions are therefore not aimed for.

4.4 Admittance, conductance and susceptance

When determining the effective resistance of a group of parallel resistors in Chapter 3, it was found to be convenient to use reciprocal resistance, namely conductance. In just the same way, it is convenient to use the reciprocal of impedance in the more general case: this reciprocal quantity is called **admittance** (symbol Y, unit siemens). The real component of admittance is the **conductance** G and the quadrature component is the **susceptance** B, i.e. $Y = G \pm jB$.

For individual circuit elements, the admittance form is the reciprocal of the impedance form, $1/R$ (or G) for resistance, $-j/\omega L$ for inductance and $j\omega C$ for capacitance. For elements in parallel these are summed as in part (ii) of Example 4.1. However, in the general case where an impedance has resistive and reactive components (i.e. $Z = R + jX$), the conductive component of the admittance is *not* in general the reciprocal of the resistive component, nor is the susceptive component the reciprocal of the reactive component. For example, a $2\,\Omega$ resistor in series with an inductor having a reactance of $3\,\Omega$ at the operating frequency, or a combination of circuit elements which is equivalent to this resistor and inductor in series, has an impedance of $(2 + j3)\,\Omega$. The equivalent admittance is $1/Z = 1/(2 + j3)$ which is equal to $(0.15 - j0.23)\,S$, i.e. real and imaginary components of 0.15 and $-j0.23$ respectively. If, incorrectly, the admittance were taken as having real and imaginary components of $\frac{1}{2}$ and $1/j3$ this would imply that the circuit may be composed of a $2\,\Omega$ resistance in parallel (rather than in series) with a $3\,\Omega$ reactance. In fact, using the correct figures, the series combination of the $2\,\Omega$ resistance and $3\,\Omega$ reactance is equivalent to the combination of a $1/0.15 = 6.7\,\Omega$ resistance in parallel with a $1/0.23 = 4.3\,\Omega$ inductive reactance.

The allied idea, briefly mentioned in the last paragraph, of combinations of circuit elements being equivalent to a resistor and inductor in series is also an important one. Although, in general, a circuit may consist of a number of circuit elements (possibly resistors, capacitors and inductors), the expression for impedance, however involved, may always be reduced to the basic rectangular form, $A + jB$. This is the same result as if the circuit were composed only of resistance A in series with reactance B and the circuit may therefore be regarded as equivalent to this series combination. Conversely, if the value $A + jB$ only is known, individual elements cannot be identified. A similar argument applies for the admittance form $G + jB$. It follows that when an impedance is in the form

$R + jX$ (or an admittance in the form $G + jB$), R and X (or G and B) are not necessarily associated with individual circuit elements.

4.5 The use of phasors in network analysis

Chapter 3 introduced a range of circuit analysis techniques which, at that stage, were applied only to resistive circuits and networks. In the following composite example these are combined with the phasor technique to analyse a circuit containing resistance and capacitance to which a sinusoidal forcing function is applied.

Example 4.4

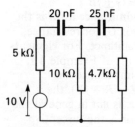

Fig. 4.12 Circuit for Example 4.4

For the circuit shown in Fig. 4.12 determine the current flowing in the 4.7 kΩ resistor at an angular frequency of 10^4 rad/s using

(i) *mesh analysis;*
(ii) *the Millman theorem;*
(iii) *the Thévenin theorem.*

(i) Fig. 4.13 shows the circuit prepared for mesh analysis with the reactances of the capacitor inserted (working throughout in kΩ). The mesh equations are formed by inspection of the circuit

$$10\underline{/0°} = (15 - j5)\mathbf{I}_a - (10)\mathbf{I}_b,$$

and

$$0 = -(10)\mathbf{I}_a + (14.7 - j4)\mathbf{I}_b.$$

The required current $\mathbf{I}_b$ is given by

$$\mathbf{I}_b = \frac{\begin{vmatrix} 15 - j5 & 10\underline{/0°} \\ -10 & 0 \end{vmatrix}}{\begin{vmatrix} 15 - j5 & -10 \\ -10 & 14.7 - j4 \end{vmatrix}}$$

$$= \frac{-(-10)10\underline{/0°}}{(15 - j5)(14.7 - j4) - (-10)(-10)} = 0.6\underline{/53°} \text{ A}.$$

Fig. 4.13 Circuit prepared for mesh analysis

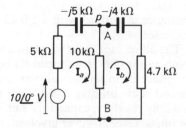

(ii) The Millman theorem determines the potential of a star point p shown in Fig. 4.13. Thus,

$$\mathbf{V}_p = \frac{10/(5 - j5)}{1/(5 - j5) + (1/10) + 1/(4.7 - j4)}$$

$$= 3.7\underline{/12.6°} \text{ V}$$

and the current in the 4.7 kΩ resistor is $\mathbf{V}_p$ divided by $(4.7 - j4)$

$$\therefore \quad \mathbf{I} = \frac{3.7\underline{/12.6^\circ}}{4.7 - j4}$$

$$= 0.6\underline{/53^\circ}\,\text{A}.$$

(iii) Disconnecting the 25 nF capacitor and the 4.7 kΩ resistor and determining the Thévenin equivalent to the left of AB:

open-circuit voltage $\mathbf{V}_{oc} = \dfrac{10}{5 - j5 + 10}\,10\underline{/0^\circ}$

(using potential divider)

$$= \frac{100}{15 - j5} = 6.32\underline{/18.4^\circ}\,\text{V}.$$

short-circuit current $\mathbf{I}_{sc} = \dfrac{10\underline{/0^\circ}}{5 - j5} = 1.41\underline{/45^\circ}\,\text{A}.$

The Thévenin equivalent circuit is therefore a voltage source of $6.32\underline{/18.4^\circ}$ V (angle is referred to the actual-circuit source voltage) and source resistance of $\mathbf{V}_{oc}/\mathbf{I}_{sc} = 4.48\underline{/-27^\circ} = (4 - j2.03)$ kΩ. The current in the reconnected 25 nF capacitor and 4.7 kΩ resistor is then

$$\frac{6.32\underline{/18.4^\circ}}{(4 - j2.03) + (4.7 - j4)} = 0.6\underline{/53^\circ}\,\text{A}.$$

4.6 Three-phase supplies

The 240 V domestic mains supply referred to in Chapter 1 is one phase of a three-phase supply system by which mains power is distributed. The supply comprises three equal-amplitude sources, each differing in phase with respect to the other by 120°. This is shown in Fig. 4.14 which illustrates a four-wire balanced three-phase source with **phase sequence** a–b–c: the sequence refers to the respective positions of the phasors, $\mathbf{V}_{bn}$ lagging $\mathbf{V}_{an}$ and $\mathbf{V}_{cn}$ lagging $\mathbf{V}_{bn}$. Fig. 4.14(a) shows zero-impedance sources with the three **phase voltages** $\mathbf{V}_{an}$, $\mathbf{V}_{bn}$ and $\mathbf{V}_{cn}$ at the terminals. These are shown relative to the neutral conductor but **line voltages** (i.e. line-to-line voltages) are also available; as shown in Fig. 4.14(b) these have a magnitude which is a factor of $\sqrt{3}$ (given by $2\cos 30^\circ$) greater than the phase voltages (i.e. 415 V when the phase voltage is 240 V) as well as a phase displacement.

Three-phase loads may be either star or delta connected: these forms of connection are illustrated in Fig. 3.33 and are also known as the **wye** and **mesh** connections. In the former case (see Example 4.5 below) the three branches are connected between respective phase terminals and neutral: in the latter case the three branches are connected across the three sets of line terminals ab, bc and ca.

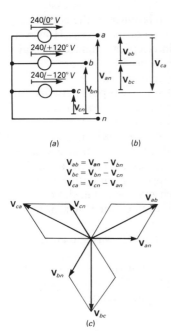

$\mathbf{V}_{ab} = \mathbf{V}_{an} - \mathbf{V}_{bn}$
$\mathbf{V}_{bc} = \mathbf{V}_{bn} - \mathbf{V}_{cn}$
$\mathbf{V}_{ca} = \mathbf{V}_{cn} - \mathbf{V}_{an}$

Fig. 4.14 An ideal three-phase source and its phasor representation

Example 4.5

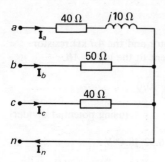

Fig. 4.15 A three-phase load

Determine the line and neutral currents flowing in the three-phase load shown in Fig. 4.15 when connected to a 415 V, three-phase supply with phase sequence a–b–c.

Note: in accordance with convention, the voltage magnitude quoted is the line rather than the phase voltage.

The line currents are given by the respective phase voltages divided by the phase impedances. The magnitude of the phase voltages is $415/\sqrt{3} = 240$ V. Thus,

$$\mathbf{I}_a = \mathbf{V}_{an}/\mathbf{Z}_a = 240\underline{/0°}/(40 + j10) = 5.82\underline{/-14°}\,\text{A},$$

$$\mathbf{I}_b = \mathbf{V}_{bn}/\mathbf{Z}_b = 240\underline{/-120°}/50 \quad = 4.80\underline{/-120°}\,\text{A},$$

$$\mathbf{I}_c = \mathbf{V}_{cn}/\mathbf{Z}_c = 240\underline{/+120°}/40 \quad = 6.0\underline{/+120°}\,\text{A}.$$

The neutral current $\mathbf{I}_n$ is the sum of the line currents:

$$\mathbf{I}_n = \mathbf{I}_a + \mathbf{I}_b + \mathbf{I}_c$$

$$= (5.65 - j1.41) + (-2.4 - j4.16) + (-3 + j5.2)$$

$$= 0.25 - j0.37 = 0.45\underline{/56°}\,\text{A}.$$

Note: the neutral current is quite small; in a perfectly balanced system (i.e. source and load) the neutral current is zero.

4.7 Two-port networks

4.7.1 Introduction

It was established in Chapter 2 that, whatever the behaviour within the bulk of the material from which a device such as a resistor was made, it could be represented as a two-terminal device. Its behaviour could then be described by the relationship between the potential difference across the terminals and the current flowing into them. In the case of the resistor it was a proportionate relationship, the constant of proportionality being the resistance of the device. However, many of the devices encountered in electrical engineering have three or four terminals and there is a need for a more sophisticated approach to their representation.

Fig. 4.16 shows an arrangement for a two-port network (or simply 'two-port') in which four terminals are grouped in pairs to form the two ports. The diagram shows the conventional reference polarities and directions for the voltages and currents associated with the two ports; it will be seen that the current reference directions are inward at both ports 1 and 2. A general-purpose upper-case notation is used for the voltages and currents, which may be either direct quantities or time-varying quantities represented by a non time-varying form.

Returning to the two-terminal resistor, it was shown that the voltage/current relationship could be expressed by the single statement, $V = RI$ (or $I = GV$). For the two-port, with its four variables, there are six ways in which any two can be expressed in terms of the other two. One example is:

$$V_1 = z_{11}I_1 + z_{12}I_2,$$

and

$$V_2 = z_{21}I_1 + z_{22}I_2.$$

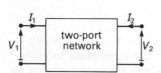

Fig. 4.16 Voltage and current reference directions for a two-port network

These equations express V_1 and V_2 as functions of the currents I_1 and I_2, and the coefficients are known as the **impedance parameters** because they have the dimensions of impedance. Thus, as the behaviour of the piece of resistive material was described by the parameter R (or G), the behaviour of the contents of the two-port is described by its four z parameters. These and two other sets, the hybrid parameters and the transmission parameters, are described in the following sections.

The representation of a two-port by parameters does not preclude the possibility of parameter variations, for example with temperature or frequency, just as the resistance of a resistor may so vary. However, it is the purpose of this section to discuss the concept of parameter representation rather than the properties of the parameters themselves. The networks are assumed to exhibit the linear, time-invariant conditions previously assumed for single circuit elements.

4.7.2 The z-parameter defining equations and equivalent circuits

The defining equations have already been introduced in Section 4.7.1 as those equations which express the two-port voltages V_1 and V_2 in terms of the port currents I_1 and I_2:

$$V_1 = z_{11}I_1 + z_{12}I_2,$$

$$V_2 = z_{21}I_1 + z_{22}I_2.$$

The reference directions of the voltages and currents are shown in Fig. 4.16. Related to these equations is an **equivalent circuit** which behaves in the same way as the two-port in the sense that replacing the actual two-port by its equivalent circuit would cause no change in the behaviour of the rest of the system of which the two-port forms a part. The form shown in Fig. 4.17 is derived directly from the parameter defining equations, although it is not the only circuit possible.

Fig. 4.17 Impedance parameter equivalent circuit

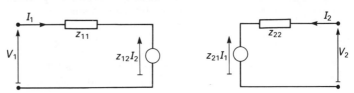

On the left-hand side of the circuit V_1 has two components $z_{11}I_1$ and $z_{12}I_2$; on the right, V_2 has two components $z_{21}I_1$ and $z_{22}I_2$. The components $z_{11}I_1$ and $z_{22}I_2$ are the potential differences across the impedances z_{11} and z_{22}, whilst the components $z_{12}I_2$ and $z_{21}I_1$ are current-dependent voltage sources.

The defining equations provide a direct clue to a method of determining the parameters. From the equation,

$$V_1 = z_{11}I_1 + z_{12}I_2,$$

it will be seen that if port 2 were open circuited, I_2 is zero and V_1 becomes $z_{11}I_1$. Thus

$$z_{11} = \left.\frac{V_1}{I_1}\right|_{I_2=0}.$$

This is the **input impedance** with port 2 open circuited, and is also denoted z_i. Similarly,

$$z_{22} = \frac{V_2}{I_2}\bigg|_{I_1 = 0}.$$

This is the **output impedance** with port 1 open circuited, also denoted z_o. The remaining parameters are given by

$$z_{12} = \frac{V_1}{I_2}\bigg|_{I_1 = 0}.$$

This is the **reverse transfer impedance** with port 1 open circuited, also denoted z_r, and

$$z_{21} = \frac{V_2}{I_1}\bigg|_{I_2 = 0}.$$

This is the **forward transfer impedance** with port 2 open circuited, also denoted z_f.

Example 4.6   *A step-down transformer operated with a sinusoidal input has z parameters as follows:*

$$z_{11} = 20 + j300 \ \Omega; \quad z_{12} = j135 \ \Omega;$$

$$z_{21} = j135 \ \Omega; \quad z_{22} = 6 + j75 \ \Omega.$$

Use Table 4.2 (p. 86) to determine the input impedance and primary–secondary voltage ratio when the secondary is loaded with a 10 Ω resistor. Recalculate the values with perfect coupling and negligible resistance.

$$\Delta z = z_{11}z_{22} - z_{12}z_{21}$$

$$= (20 + j300)(6 + j75) - (j135)^2$$

$$= -4155 + j3300.$$

The voltage-gain expression gives the ratio of secondary-to-primary voltage: this has a value

$$\frac{j135 \times 10}{-4155 + j3300 + (20 + j300)10} = 0.18\underline{/-33°}.$$

The input impedance is given by

$$\frac{-4155 + j3300 + (20 + j300)10}{6 + j75 + 10} = 95.7\underline{/45°} \ \Omega.$$

With perfect coupling the mutual impedance is given by $j\omega M$ where $M = \sqrt{(L_1 L_2)}$; i.e.

$$j\omega M = \sqrt{(j\omega L_1 \, j\omega L_2)} = \sqrt{(j300\,j75)} = j150 \ \Omega.$$

New impedance parameters are

$$z_{11} = j300 \ \Omega; \quad z_{12} = j150;$$

$$z_{21} = j150; \quad z_{22} = j75.$$

New $\Delta z = j300 \times j75 - j150 \times j150 = 0$. This gives a voltage ratio of

$$\frac{z_{21}Z_L}{z_{11}Z_L} = \frac{j150}{j300} = 0.5,$$

and an input impedance of

$$\frac{z_{11}Z_L}{z_{22} + Z_L} = \frac{j300 \times 10}{j75 + 10} = 39.6\underline{/7.6°} \ \Omega.$$

The magnitude of this impedance will be seen to be approximately equal to $n^2 R_L$, where n is the turns ratio ($= 2.0$) and $R_L = 10\,\Omega$. This is discussed in Chapter 2.

4.7.3 The hybrid parameters

Another form of two-port representation uses the **hybrid** *or* **h parameters** defined by:

$$V_1 = h_{11}I_1 + h_{12}V_2,$$

$$I_2 = h_{21}I_1 + h_{22}V_2.$$

Following the same general procedure as for the z parameters, the open and short-circuit definitions of the h parameters are as follows:

$$h_{11} = h_i = \left.\frac{V_1}{I_1}\right|_{V_2=0}, \quad h_{12} = h_r = \left.\frac{V_1}{V_2}\right|_{I_1=0},$$

$$h_{21} = h_f = \left.\frac{I_2}{I_1}\right|_{V_2=0}, \quad h_{22} = h_o = \left.\frac{I_2}{V_2}\right|_{I_1=0}.$$

The corresponding equivalent circuit is shown in Fig. 4.18.

Fig. 4.18 Hybrid parameter equivalent circuit

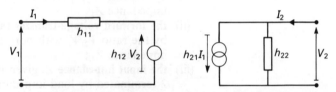

4.7.4 Transmission parameters

As its name suggests, this set of parameters finds application in the analysis of transmission networks. The defining equations are:

$$V_1 = AV_2 + BI_2,$$

and

$$I_1 = CV_2 + DI_2,$$

and are normally defined for current I_2 flowing out of port 2, as shown in Fig. 4.19. The parameters may be found using open and short circuit tests but an alternative method based on the matrix-algebraic notation is demonstrated in Example 4.7. In this method, applicable when a network of known configuration is to be expressed in two-port form, individual network elements are expressed in the matrix form

$$\begin{bmatrix} V_1 \\ I_1 \end{bmatrix} = \begin{bmatrix} A & B \\ C & D \end{bmatrix} \begin{bmatrix} V_2 \\ I_2 \end{bmatrix},$$

and, because the output-port variables for one 'network' become the input-port variables for the next, the overall parameter matrix is given by the product of individual-element matrices. By inspection it will be seen that for a single series impedance Z the parameter matrix is $\begin{bmatrix} 1 & Z \\ 0 & 1 \end{bmatrix}$ and for a single shunt admittance it will be $\begin{bmatrix} 1 & 0 \\ Y & 1 \end{bmatrix}$.

Example 4.7

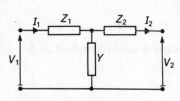

Fig. 4.19 Circuit for Example 4.7

Use a matrix multiplication method to determine the transmission parameters of the network shown in Fig. 4.19.

$$\begin{bmatrix} A & B \\ C & D \end{bmatrix} = \begin{bmatrix} 1 & Z_1 \\ 0 & 1 \end{bmatrix} \begin{bmatrix} 1 & 0 \\ Y & 1 \end{bmatrix} \begin{bmatrix} 1 & Z_2 \\ 0 & 1 \end{bmatrix}$$

$$= \begin{bmatrix} 1 + Z_1 Y & Z_1 \\ Y & 1 \end{bmatrix} \begin{bmatrix} 1 & Z_2 \\ 0 & 1 \end{bmatrix}$$

$$\therefore \quad \begin{bmatrix} A & B \\ C & D \end{bmatrix} = \begin{bmatrix} 1 + Z_1 Y & Z_1 + Z_2 + Z_1 Z_2 Y \\ Y & 1 + Z_2 Y \end{bmatrix},$$

using the usual rules for matrix multiplication. Often, as in the next chapter, networks of this form are symmetrical ($Z_1 = Z_2$), in which case A and D parameters are the same.

4.7.5 The loaded two-port network

In normal operation the two-port will be part of a larger system and this section describes four commonly-used properties of the two-port when connected between source and load:

(i) **the forward current-transfer ratio** or **current gain** A_i given by the ratio I_2/I_1 with port 2 terminated by load impedance Z_L;

(ii) **the forward voltage-transfer ratio** or **voltage gain** A_v given by the ratio V_2/V_1 with port 2 terminated by load impedance Z_L;

(iii) **the input impedance** Z_i given by the ratio V_1/I_1 with port 2 terminated by load impedance Z_L;

(iv) **the output impedance** Z_o given by the ratio V_2/I_2 with port 1 terminated by source impedance Z_s.

Table 4.2 lists expressions for these four properties in terms of the three sets of parameters. To illustrate how the table is obtained the current-gain expression in terms of the z parameters might be found as follows. For the reference directions involved (Fig. 4.20), V_2 and I_2 are related by $V_2 = -Z_L I_2$. Then, using equations, $V_2 = z_{21} I_1 + z_{22} I_2$ and, substituting for V_2,

$$-Z_L I_2 = z_{21} I_1 + z_{22} I_2,$$

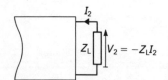

Fig. 4.20 Voltage–current relationship for a two-port load

Table 4.2. *Properties of the loaded two-port*

Current gain A_i	$\dfrac{-z_{21}}{z_{22} + Z_L}$	$\dfrac{h_{21}}{1 + h_{22} Z_L}$	$\dfrac{-1}{D + C Z_L}$
Voltage gain A_v	$\dfrac{z_{21} Z_L}{\Delta z + z_{11} Z_L}$	$\dfrac{-h_{21} Z_L}{h_{11} + \Delta h Z_L}$	$\dfrac{Z_L}{B + A Z_L}$
Input impedance Z_i	$\dfrac{\Delta z + z_{11} Z_L}{z_{22} + Z_L}$	$\dfrac{h_{11} + \Delta h Z_L}{1 + h_{22} Z_L}$	$\dfrac{A Z_L + B}{C Z_L + D}$
Output impedance Z_o	$\dfrac{\Delta z + z_{22} Z_s}{z_{11} + Z_s}$	$\dfrac{h_{11} + Z_s}{\Delta h + h_{22} Z_s}$	$\dfrac{D Z_s + B}{C Z_s + A}$

Note: $\Delta x = x_{11} x_{22} - x_{12} x_{21}$.

giving current gain

$$A_i = \frac{I_2}{I_1} = -\frac{z_{21}}{z_{22} + Z_L}.$$

Key points to remember

- sinusoids are quantified by amplitude (instantaneous and r.m.s.), frequency and phase angle;
- sinusoids may be represented by complex numbers (phasors) having magnitude and angle;
- steady-state sinusoidal circuit analysis can be performed with phasors and phasor operators, R for resistance, $j\omega L$ for inductance and $1/j\omega C$ for capacitance; the analysis becomes an exercise in complex algebra;
- all the general procedures developed in Chapter 3 for resistive circuits can be applied to sinusoidal analysis of networks containing inductance and capacitance as well as resistance;
- mean power is given by $VI\cos\phi$ and related expressions; power transfer to a load is dependent on both load and source impedance;
- mains power is distributed by a three-phase supply having three source voltages, mutually displaced by $120°$;
- certain devices can be represented by two-port networks with associated parameter sets;
- the behaviour of devices within a circuit can be specified in terms of the two-port parameters.

Further reading

Bobrow, L. S., *Elementary Circuit Analysis.* Holt, Rinehart and Winston (1981).
Van Valkenburg, M. E. and Kinariwala, B. K., *Linear Circuits.* Prentice-Hall (1983).

Appendix 4A Complex numbers

Polar and rectangular forms

A **complex number** is a number which has an angle as well as magnitude. The number $\mathbf{A} = A\underline{/\theta}$ in Fig. 4A.1(a) is such a number expressed in what is known as the **polar** form with **modulus** A and **argument** θ.

Alternatively, Fig. 4A.1(b) shows the **rectangular form** of representation in which the number is resolved into an **in-phase** or **real** component a and a **quadrature** or **imaginary** component b. The number is written as $\mathbf{A} = a + jb$ where the j preceding b indicates that it is an imaginary component.

Fig. 4A.1 Polar and rectangular form representations of a complex number

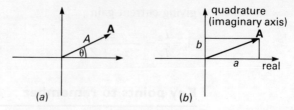

(a)   *(b)*

Conversion from polar to rectangular forms is effected through the relationship (see Fig. 4A.1):

$$a = A \cos \theta,$$

$$b = A \sin \theta,$$

from which

$$a + jb = A \cos \theta + jA \sin \theta.$$

Also,

$$A^2 = a^2 + b^2,$$

and

$$\theta = \tan^{-1}(b/a),$$

from which

$$A\underline{/\theta} = \sqrt{(a^2 + b^2)}\underline{/\tan^{-1}(b/a)}.$$

The *j* operator

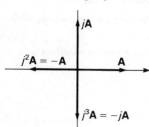

Fig. 4A.2 The effect of successively multiplying by *j*

Although *j* is introduced above simply as a prefix to the quadrature component of **A**, it is properly described as a mathematical **operator**, the 'operation' being rotation through 90°. Thus, whereas the number 3 is a real number (i.e. $3\underline{/0°}$), *j*3 is an imaginary number ($3\underline{/90°}$).

As an operator, *j* can be treated as a normal algebraic symbol in the sense that, for example, $j3 \times j4 = j^2 12$. However, as illustrated in Fig. A4.2, j^2 represents two 90° rotations and is therefore equivalent to -1. Similarly, j^3 is equivalent to a 270° (or a $-90°$) rotation. Also, the reciprocal of *j* is $-j$ and vice versa, division by *j* being equivalent to a $-90°$ rotation.

Complex number arithmetic

The rules are as follows.

(a) Polar form:

multiplication $(A\underline{/\theta})(B\underline{/\phi}) = AB\underline{/\theta + \phi},$

division $\dfrac{A\underline{/\theta}}{B\underline{/\phi}} = \dfrac{A}{B}\underline{/\theta - \phi}.$

square root $\sqrt{(A\underline{/\theta})} = \sqrt{(A)}\underline{/\theta/2}.$

Addition and subtraction cannot be carried out in polar form; rectangular form must be used:

(b) Rectangular form:

addition $(a + jb) + (c + jd) = (a + c) + j(b + d),$

subtraction $(a + jb) - (c + jd) = (a - c) + j(b - d),$

multiplication $(a + jb) \times (c + jd) = ac + j^2 bd + j(bc + ad)$

$$= ac - bd + j(bc + ad),$$

division

$$\frac{(a+jb)}{(c+jd)} = \frac{(a+jb) \times (c-jd)}{c^2+d^2}$$

$$= \frac{ac+bd+j(bc-ad)}{c^2+d^2}.$$

Mathematical form of the polar form

The A/θ notation used above and in Chapter 4 is simply a shorthand notation. As discussed extensively in Chapter 6, the correct form for A/θ is $A\,e^{j\theta}$ which is mathematically identical to the rectangular form $A\cos\theta + jA\sin\theta$. Stated formally,

$$A\,e^{\pm j\theta} = A\cos\theta \pm jA\sin\theta,$$

or, rearranging,

$$A\cos\theta = \tfrac{1}{2}A(e^{j\theta} + e^{-j\theta}),$$

and

$$A\sin\theta = \frac{A}{j2}(e^{j\theta} - e^{-j\theta}).$$

EXERCISES 4

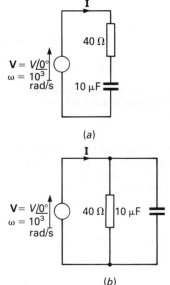

(a)

(b)

Fig. E4.1

In figure (a): I, 40 Ω, $V = V/\underline{0^\circ}$, $\omega = 10^3$ rad/s, 10 μF

In figure (b): I, $V = V/\underline{0^\circ}$, $\omega = 10^3$ rad/s, 40 Ω, 10 μF

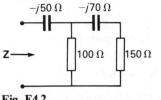

$-j50\ \Omega$ $-j70\ \Omega$ Z →   100 Ω   150 Ω

Fig. E4.2

4.1 Derive the mean and r.m.s. value of the waveform drawn in Fig. 4.2 in Section 4.1.3.

4.2 Two sinusoids are given by

$$a_1 = 4\sin(\omega t + 60^\circ),$$

$$a_2 = 6\sin(\omega t - 40^\circ).$$

(a) Determine their sum
  (i) by adding phasors graphically on a phasor diagram, and
  (ii) by expressing the phasors in rectangular form and adding.

(b) Determine the difference $A_1 - A_2$ by the two methods in (a).

(c) Determine the product $A_1 \times A_2$ by expressing the phasors in the polar form.

(d) Determine the quotient A_1/A_2 by expressing the phasors in the polar form.

4.3 A current $i = 3\sin 10^4 t$ mA flows in an ideal 10 mH inductance. Using the relationship $v = L\,di/dt$, determine the voltage waveform and deduce a value for the inductive reactance X_L.

4.4 (a) A sinusoidal voltage (represented by **V**) is applied across a resistor and capacitor in series (Fig. E4.1(a)). The current is represented by phasor **I**. Apply the Kirchhoff voltage law to determine **V** as a function of **I** and hence determine the circuit impedance $\mathbf{Z}(= \mathbf{V}/\mathbf{I})$.

(b) For the parallel circuit in Fig. E4.1(b), apply the Kirchhoff current law to determine **I** as a function of **V** and hence determine the circuit impedance $\mathbf{Z}(= \mathbf{V}/\mathbf{I})$.

4.5 (a) Using standard rules for determining the overall impedance of groups of circuit elements in series and parallel, determine the impedance **Z** of the network in Fig. E4.2.

(b) Use the impedance value to determine the current (in phasor form) which would be supplied by a 10 V sinusoidal source having a 50 Ω resistive source impedance and, using the current-divider rule, the phasor current in the 100 Ω resistor.

4.6   Assuming that the specified source voltage is an r.m.s. value, use the results of Exercise 4.5(*b*) to determine the following:

   (i) the total power supplied;
   (ii) the power in the 100 Ω resistor;
   (iii) the power in the 150 Ω resistor;
   (iv) the total reactive power, showing that

$$(\text{apparent power})^2 = (\text{active power})^2 + (\text{reactive power})^2.$$

4.7   Given that the admittance of a two-component network is $(2.5 + j4.2)\,\text{mS}$, determine the component values of both a parallel and a series network having this admittance at a frequency of 10 kHz.

4.8   Check the value of the currents obtained in Exercise 4.5(*b*) using the mesh-analysis method.

4.9   By determining the Thévenin equivalent of the network (Fig. E4.3) to the left of terminals *a* and *b* show that maximum power will be transferred to the 40 Ω load. Determine the magnitude of the power.

Fig. E4.3

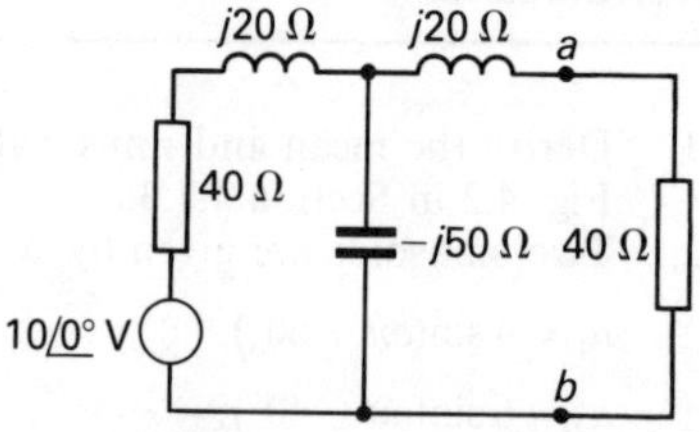

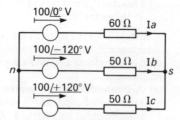

4.10   Fig. E4.4 represents a three-phase three-wire star connected system with a small degree of unbalance in the load. Determine the three line currents

   (i) using mesh analysis, and
   (ii) determining the potential at the load star point *s* (relative to the source neutral *n*) using the Millman theorem and then deducing the line currents from the potential differences and the branch resistances.

Fig. E4.4

4.11   A three-phase supply is connected to a three-phase balanced load. Show that, for both star and delta connected loads, the power delivered to the load is $\sqrt{(3)}V_L I_L \cos \phi$, where V_L and I_L are the magnitudes of the line voltage and current and $\cos \phi$ is the power factor of each branch of the load.

4.12   Tests on an electronic device having two ports gave the following result:

   (i) with output short circuited, $I_1 = 5\,\mu\text{A}$; $I_2 = 1\,\text{mA}$; $V_1 = 25\,\text{mV}$; and
   (ii) with input open circuit, $V_2 = 2\,\text{V}$; $I_2 = 40\,\mu\text{A}$; $V_1 = 0$.

(*a*) Determine the hybrid parameters and draw an equivalent circuit for the device.
(*b*) Determine a value for the voltage gain of the device when loaded with a 10 kΩ resistance
  (i) by substituting values into the appropriate expression in Table 4.2, and
  (ii) working directly from the equivalent circuit with the 10 kΩ load resistance added.

(Exercises on transmission parameters appear in Chapter 5.)

5 Transmission networks and lines

The principal learning objectives of this chapter are to:

	Section	Exercises
• recognise the need for correct network termination;	1.1	
• deduce values for image, iterative and characteristic impedance;	1.1	1, 2
• derive the propagation coefficient of a network;	1.2, 1.3	2, 4
• design a passive attenuator;	1.3	2
• determine the insertion loss of a network;	1.4	3
• explain the existence of travelling and standing waves in a cascaded, lumped network;	2.1–2.6	4, 5
• predict the effect of line mistermination on transmitted pulses;	2.7	6
• derive line equations which predict the behaviour of distributed transmission lines;	3.1	
• predict line behaviour from the line equations;	3.2–3.6	7, 8
• appreciate the need for line matching;	3.6	12
• explain the principle of the Smith chart line calculator;	4.1–4.2	
• apply the chart to the determination of line behaviour.	4.3	9–12

5.1 Lumped networks

5.1.1 Terminating impedance

The need to terminate a network in a specified way is sometimes overlooked. For example, a 20 dB attenuator may be placed in a system with the object of reducing the signal level. However, the actual attenuation will depend not only on the attenuator but also on the terminating impedance. This section considers three particular terminating conditions.

For a given two-port network, it is possible to determine

an impedance which, when connected across port 2 gives an input impedance of the same value at port 1. Fig. 5.1(*a*) shows such an impedance, called the **iterative impedance** and designated Z_{it_1}.† Fig. 5.1(*b*) shows the second iterative impedance Z_{it_2} which, when connected across port 1, gives the same impedance at port 2.

Fig. 5.1 Iterative impedance

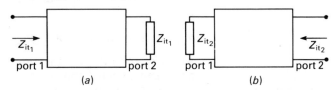

(*a*)   (*b*)

As demonstrated in Fig. 5.2, any number of suitably terminated networks may be cascaded and the input impedance is always Z_{it_1}. Similarly, the output impedance is always Z_{it_2}.

Fig. 5.2 Iterative impedances in a cascaded network

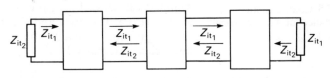

Example 5.1

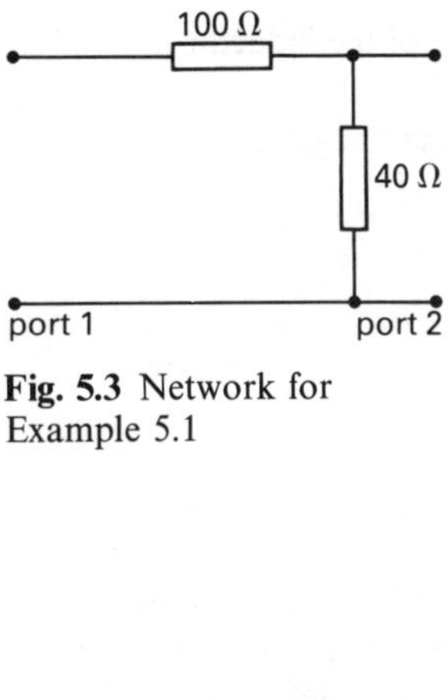

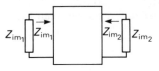

Fig. 5.3 Network for Example 5.1

Determine the iterative impedance Z_{it_1} for the network shown in Fig. 5.3.

With a resistance R_{it_1} connected across the 40 Ω resistance (i.e. across port 2), the input impedance is R_{it_1}, i.e.

$R_{it_1} = 100 + 40R_{it_1}/(40 + R_{it_1})$.

∴ $R_{it_1}^2 - 100R_{it_1} - 4000 = 0$,

and

∴ $R_{it_1} = 131\,\Omega$ (ignoring the negative solution).

Image impedance is concerned with matching a network's input impedance to its source impedance and its output impedance to its load impedance.

Fig. 5.4 shows the two image impedances Z_{im_1} and Z_{im_2} in accordance with the definitions given above.

Image impedance may be expressed in terms of the parameter sets. Using Table 4.2 and substituting Z_{im_1} for Z_s and Z_{in}, and Z_{im_2} for Z_L and Z_o gives
$Z_{im_1} = (AZ_{im_2} + B)/(CZ_{im_2} + D)$ and
$Z_{im_2} = ((DZ_{im_1} + B)/(CZ_{im_1} + A))$ in terms of the transmission parameters. Solving these two equations gives
$Z_{im_1} = \sqrt{(AB/CD)}$ and $Z_{im_2} = \sqrt{(BD/AC)}$.
Another method for determining image impedance is by means of network input and output impedances with the other port either open or short circuited. Thus, if Z_{ioc} is the input impedance with the output port open circuited and Z_{isc}

Fig. 5.4 Image impedance

---

† A general-purpose notation is used for impedance. Where sinusoidal operation is specifically implied, phasor and phasor-operator notation (boldface type) is used.

is the input impedance with the output port short circuited,

$$Z_{\text{ioc}} = \frac{A}{C} \quad \text{and} \quad Z_{\text{isc}} = \frac{B}{D} \quad \text{(from Table 4.2)},$$

and

$$Z_{\text{im}_1} = \sqrt{(AB/CD)} = \sqrt{(Z_{\text{ioc}} \cdot Z_{\text{isc}})}.$$

Similarly,

$$Z_{\text{im}_2} = \sqrt{(BD/AC)} = \sqrt{(Z_{\text{ooc}} \cdot Z_{\text{osc}})},$$

where Z_{ooc} and Z_{osc} are the output impedances with the input port open circuited and short circuited respectively.

For a symmetrical network the two iterative and the two image impedances all have the same value and are known as the **characteristic impedance** Z_0. In accordance with the previous definitions its properties are summarised by Fig. 5.5. Because the A and D transmission parameters are equal for a symmetrical network, the previous expressions for Z_{im} lead to $Z_0 = \sqrt{(B/C)}$. The open and short-circuit definitions used for the image impedance also apply to characteristic impedance, and hence, alternatively, $Z_0 = \sqrt{(Z_{\text{sc}} Z_{\text{oc}})}$.

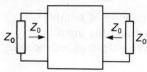

Fig. 5.5 Characteristic impedance for a symmetrical network

Example 5.2

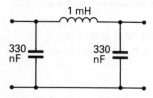

Fig. 5.6 Network for Example 5.2

Determine the characteristic impedance of the network shown in Fig. 5.6 at an operating frequency of 6 kHz. using the expression

$$\mathbf{Z}_0 = \sqrt{(\mathbf{Z}_{\text{ioc}} \mathbf{Z}_{\text{isc}})}.$$

At the operating frequency the impedance of the inductor is $j37.7\,\Omega$ and that of each capacitor is $-j80.4\,\Omega$.

$$\mathbf{Z}_{\text{ioc}} = -j80.4(j37.7 - j80.4)/(-j80.4 + j37.7 - j80.4)$$

$$= -j28.0\,\Omega.$$

$$\mathbf{Z}_{\text{isc}} = -j80.4 \times j37.7/(-j80.4 + j37.7)$$

$$= +j70.7\,\Omega.$$

Therefore,

$$\mathbf{Z}_0 = \sqrt{(\mathbf{Z}_{\text{ioc}} \cdot \mathbf{Z}_{\text{isc}})} = 44.5\underline{/0°}\,\Omega.$$

5.1.2 Propagation coefficient

For a symmetrical network terminated by its characteristic impedance, the **propagation coefficient** γ is a complex number whose real component α is an **attenuation coefficient**, defined as the natural logarithmic ratio of the input and output-voltage magnitudes, and whose imaginary component β is a **phase coefficient**, defined as the phase difference between the input and output voltages.

With reference to Fig. 5.7,

$$\gamma = \alpha + j\beta,$$

where

$$\alpha = \ln|V_1/V_2|,$$

and

$$\beta = \arg \mathbf{V}_1/\mathbf{V}_2,$$

where $\mathbf{V}_1$ and $\mathbf{V}_2$ are phasors representing sinusoidal

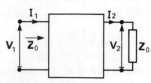

Fig. 5.7 A network terminated by its characteristic impedance

quantities. The unit of α is the neper (abbreviated to Np) and the unit of β is the radian. The composite relationship,

$$\gamma = \alpha + j\beta = \ln|V_1/V_2| + j \arg \mathbf{V}_1/\mathbf{V}_2$$
$$= \ln \mathbf{V}_1/\mathbf{V}_2$$

may be taken as a mathematical definition of the propagation coefficient.

Alternatively, it may be more convenient to define γ by the relationship

$$e^\gamma = \mathbf{V}_1/\mathbf{V}_2.$$

Expanding,

$$e^\gamma = e^\alpha \underline{/\beta} = |V_1/V_2|\underline{/\arg(\mathbf{V}_1/\mathbf{V}_2)},$$

from which

$$e^\alpha = |V_1/V_2| \quad \text{and} \quad \beta = \arg(V_1/V_2),$$

corresponding to the original definitions.

The commonly used logarithmic measure of ratio is the decibel (Appendix B) and it is possible to convert from the natural-logarithmic measure to the dB through the conversion, $2.303 \text{ Np} \equiv 20 \text{ dB}$ or $1 \text{ Np} \equiv 8.686 \text{ dB}$.

5.1.3 Propagation coefficient in terms of parameters

Having defined the propagation coefficient, it is necessary to relate it to the network elements. This can be conveniently done by expressing γ as a function of a set of parameters which themselves can then be related to the elements using methods outlined in Chapter 4. The transmission parameters will be used.

Thus, from Table 4.2, for a network terminated in $\mathbf{Z}_0$,

$$\mathbf{V}_1/\mathbf{V}_2 = \mathbf{B}/\mathbf{Z}_0 + \mathbf{A}.$$

But, $\mathbf{Z}_0 = \sqrt{(\mathbf{B}/\mathbf{C})}$ and, hence $\mathbf{V}_1/\mathbf{V}_2 = \sqrt{(\mathbf{BC})} + \mathbf{A}$. Also noting that for a symmetrical reciprocal network, $\mathbf{BC} = \mathbf{A}^2 - 1$, $\mathbf{V}_1/\mathbf{V}_2 = \sqrt{(\mathbf{A}^2 - 1)} + \mathbf{A}$. The natural logarithm of this ratio is γ and, by use of a standard algebraic identity,

$$\gamma = \ln \mathbf{V}_1/\mathbf{V}_2 = \ln[\sqrt{(\mathbf{A}^2 - 1)} + \mathbf{A}]$$
$$= \cosh^{-1} \mathbf{A},$$

or,

$$\cosh \gamma = \mathbf{A}.$$

Thus, if the A parameter is known (or its equivalents, z_{11}/z_{21} and $-\Delta h/h_{21}$), the phase and magnitude response of the terminated network can be predicted. However, because γ may be complex in the general case, the apparent simplicity of the relationship can be misleading. Applications of the relationship, as well as the parameter/network-element relationships, are therefore illustrated by the following representative examples.

Example 5.3   *A resistive T attenuator has the component values shown in Fig. 5.8. Determine the characteristic impedance and the attenuation which the network would introduce when terminated by its characteristic impedance.*

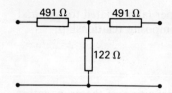

Fig. 5.8 Network for Example 5.3

The transmission parameters are given by:

$$\begin{bmatrix} A & B \\ C & D \end{bmatrix} = \begin{bmatrix} 1 & 491 \\ 0 & 1 \end{bmatrix}\begin{bmatrix} 1 & 0 \\ 1/122 & 1 \end{bmatrix}\begin{bmatrix} 1 & 491 \\ 0 & 1 \end{bmatrix} = \begin{bmatrix} 5.03 & 2960 \\ 8.2 \times 10^{-3} & 5.03 \end{bmatrix}.$$

Characteristic impedance, $Z_0 = \sqrt{(B/C)} = 600\,\Omega$. Propagation coefficient γ is given by $\cosh\gamma = A = 5.03$ and, therefore, $\gamma = \cosh^{-1} 5.03 = 2.3$. Since γ is real, there is no phase shift (as may be expected in a resistive network) and $\alpha = 2.3\,\mathrm{Np}$ or $20\,\mathrm{dB}$. With unknown resistance values, the formulae can be applied to predict these values from given values of characteristic impedance and attenuation.

Example 5.4

Determine an expression for γ for the network shown in Fig. 5.9 when terminated by its characteristic impedance and hence evaluate α and β at frequencies, (i) $f = 5\,kHz$ and (ii) $f = 50\,kHz$. Take $L = 3.6\,mH$ and $C = 22\,nF$.

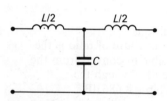

Fig. 5.9 Network for Example 5.4

Using the results obtained in Example 4.7 in Chapter 4, the A transmission parameter is $1 + \mathbf{ZY}$. For this network this becomes $1 + (j\omega L j\omega C/2)$ or $1 - (\omega^2 LC/2)$. Hence, $\cosh\gamma = 1 - \omega^2 LC/2$ or $\gamma = \cosh^{-1}(1 - \omega^2 LC/2)$. Inspection of this expression indicates that, for all values of ω, $\cosh\gamma$ is less than 1; thus γ cannot be a real number (for which $\cosh\gamma$ is always greater than 1).

(i) At $f = 5\,\mathrm{kHz}$, $\cosh\gamma = 0.96 + j0$. Writing $\cosh\gamma$ as $\cosh(\alpha + j\beta) = \cosh\alpha\cos\beta + j\sinh\alpha\sin\beta$, $\cosh\alpha\cos\beta = 0.96$ and $\sinh\alpha\sin\beta = 0$. Solving, $\alpha = 0$ and $\beta = 0.28\,\mathrm{rad}$, i.e. there is no attenuation but a phase shift of $16°$.

(ii) At $f = 50\,\mathrm{kHz}$, $\cosh\gamma = -2.9$. From the $\cosh\gamma$ expansion, $\cosh\alpha\cos\beta = -2.9$ and $\sinh\alpha\sin\beta = 0$. Solving, $\alpha = 1.73\,\mathrm{Np}$; $\beta = \pi\,\mathrm{rad}$, i.e. the network introduces an attenuation $15\,\mathrm{dB}$ with a phase shift of $180°$.

The network discussed in the example above behaves as a simple **low-pass filter**. Attenuation is zero up to a frequency at which $\cosh\gamma = -1.0$ (where $\omega^2 LC/2 = 2$ or $f = 1/\pi\sqrt{(LC)}$) after which it increases. The frequency range, $0 \to 1/\pi\sqrt{(LC)}$, is known as the **pass band**, the upper limit being the **cut-off frequency**.

5.1.4 Insertion loss

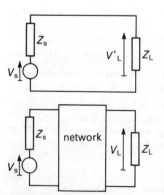

Fig. 5.10 Source and load without and with network inserted

The attenuation coefficient α, discussed in the previous section, applies in situations where a symmetrical network is operated between impedances equal to its characteristic impedance. Because Z_0 is defined by the network, the attenuation which it will introduce is completely defined by the network. Thus, a 20 dB attenuator may be sold knowing that, provided the user operates it between its characteristic impedances, it will in fact cause a signal attenuation of 20 dB. If, however, it is not properly terminated then the signal attenuation will not be 20 dB.

In the general case, where a network is operated between any two impedances, the attenuation may be specified by the **insertion loss**. This loss is defined (usually in decibels) as the ratio of the power in a load impedance without the network in circuit to that with the network in circuit; source and load impedances must be specified. Fig. 5.10 shows the operating conditions. Thus, insertion loss (in dB) $= 10\log_{10} P'/P$ where

P^1 and P are respectively, the load power without and with the network inserted into the system. Since power is proportional to the square of voltage in a given impedance, insertion loss $= 20 \log_{10} |V_L'/V_L|$ dB, and, because $V_L' = Z_L V_s/(Z_s + Z_L)$, loss $= 20 \log_{10} |Z_L V_s/(Z_s + Z_L) V_L|$.

5.2 Travelling waves, standing waves and reflections

5.2.1 Introduction

Section 3 of this chapter analyses the behaviour of transmission media such as a length of coaxial cable. From a low-frequency viewpoint the high-frequency behaviour of this and other transmission media is, at first sight, unusual. For example, connecting a 10 V low-frequency or direct-voltage source to a length of cable results in 10 V (or possibly slightly less) appearing across a load connected to the other end. It will be shown that in the high-frequency case, dependent on the load impedance and the ratio of line length to wavelength, the load voltage can vary over a wide range above and below the 10 V source-terminal voltage. More unusual is the length of open-circuited cable which, at the source terminals, appears almost to be a short circuit. These, and other effects, are accounted for by inductance and capacitance distributed over the length of the line.

In this present section, the distributed-line concept is introduced as an extension of the lumped-network theory developed in Chapter 4 and Section 1 of this chapter. In this way, the principles of travelling and standing waves are introduced without the need to derive the formal distributed-line equations. These are, however, derived in Appendix 5A and analysed in Section 5.3.

Between the extremes at very low and very high frequencies, transmission systems (such as, for example, 50 Hz power-supply lines) can be analysed by regarding the lines as T or π lumped networks and using the transmission-parameter techniques of Chapter 4 to determine the input/output voltage and current relationships. For example, given a specified load voltage and current (or load voltage, power and power factor) the source voltage may be determined using the defining equation $\mathbf{V}_1 = \mathbf{A}\mathbf{V}_2 + \mathbf{B}\mathbf{I}_2$ where the $\mathbf{A}$ and $\mathbf{B}$ transmission parameters are determined as in Examples 4.7 and 5.4.

5.2.2 A reactive network

In Example 5.4 it was found that, at the lower frequency, the reactive elements in the T network introduced a phase shift of $16°$ but produced no attenuation of the signal. Also as a result of termination by the characteristic impedance, the input impedance of each section is $\mathbf{Z}_0$ and it is therefore possible to cascade a whole series of networks and still maintain the correct terminating conditions for each. Fig. 5.11 shows a set of cascaded networks with small sketches of the sinusoidal waveforms which may be observed

Fig. 5.11 Cascaded LC networks

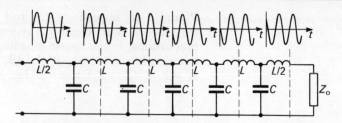

(on the same time scales) at the points of intersection: there is a phase shift of 16° at each intersection but no amplitude change. The phase shifts are not drawn to scale.

5.2.3 Travelling waves

The progressive retardation of phase in Fig. 5.11 is equivalent to a progressive time delay whose value is the phase shift divided by the angular frequency ($= \beta/\omega$ seconds per section). Inasmuch as the signal is delayed, it may be considered to have a **phase velocity** v_p whose value is the reciprocal of the delay, i.e. ω/β sections per second: if it takes 1 hour to travel 30 miles (a delay of 1 hour per 30 miles) the velocity is 30 miles per hour. The signal is said to be a **travelling wave**, specifically, in this case, a **forward travelling wave** moving from source to termination. In general, travelling waves exist in any transmission medium in which there is phase change with respect to distance.

Allied to the travelling-wave concept is that of **wavelength**. One wavelength is that distance required to cause a signal-phase change of 2π radians (or 360°). It follows that wavelength and phase shift are related through $\beta\lambda = 2\pi$ or $\beta = 2\pi/\lambda$ and, because phase velocity is ω/β,

$v_p = \omega\lambda/2\pi$ or $f\lambda$,

i.e. phase velocity = frequency × wavelength.

Example 5.5

Calculate the characteristic impedance of the single T section shown in Fig. 5.9 with $L = 3.6\,mH$, $C = 22\,nF$ and an operating frequency of $5\,kHz$. If a number of such sections are cascaded and terminated by this characteristic impedance, calculate the delay over 20 sections, the phase velocity and the wavelength.

Using the result obtained in Example 4.7,

$$Z_0 = \sqrt{(\mathbf{B}/\mathbf{C})} = \sqrt{[(L(1 - \omega^2 LC/4)/C)]}.$$

Substituting values:

$$Z_0 = 405\sqrt{[(1 - 0.02)]}$$

$$= 401\,\Omega.$$

Delay/section $= \beta/\omega$ and, from Example 5.4, $\beta = 0.28$ rad. Therefore,

delay over 20 sections $= 20 \times 0.28/2 \times 5 \times 10^3 = 178\,\mu s$.

Phase velocity, $v_p = \omega/\beta = 1.12 \times 10^5$ sections/s.

Wavelength $= v_p/f = 1.12 \times 10^5/5 \times 10^3 = 22.4$ sections.

Note: the wavelength is not an integral number of sections because the phase shift is not exactly 360° (relative to source) at an intersection. When dealing with a true distributed line, the point at which the phase shift is 360° would be precisely identifiable. For example, if the phase velocity were 1.12×10^5 m/s, the wavelength would be 22.4 m.

5.2.4 Reflections   If the set of cascaded networks is terminated by an impedance whose value is not equal to the characteristic impedance there is a **reflection** of the forward travelling voltage wave at the termination and the **reflected travelling wave** thereby set up interacts with the forward wave to produce a **standing wave**. The situation is similar to that which occurs when a stone is thrown into a pond and a forward wave travels radially away from the stone. On meeting the pond wall, a reflected wave is set up which then travels back toward the 'source', creating an interference pattern with the forward wave on the water's surface.

The correctly terminated cascaded networks behave in the same way as a pond with no walls, i.e. an infinite expanse of water, and only the forward travelling wave exists. In fact, forward travelling voltage and current waves exist and their ratio is Z_0. The reflected wave caused by a discontinuity in the transmission path (i.e. a termination not equal to Z_0) also consists of voltage and current waves but, in this case, their ratio is $-Z_0$; this is demonstrated mathematically in Section 5.3.3.

The ratio of reflected and forward waves is the **reflection coefficient** and can be specified at any point in the transmission path. Furthermore, at the terminating impedance Z_t, the ratio of the total voltage (forward and reflected) to the total current (forward and reflected) must satisfy the $V/I = Z$ relationship. Therefore, using the phasor notation,

$$(V_f + V_r)/(I_f + I_r) = Z_t,$$

where V_f and I_f are the forward-travelling voltage and current at the termination, V_r and I_r are the reflected-travelling voltage and current at the termination, and Z_t is the terminating impedance. Also, noting that $V_f/I_f = Z_0$ and $V_r/I_r = -Z_0$, the relationship may be written in the form,

$$V_f + V_r = Z_t(V_f/Z_0 - V_r/Z_0),$$

which, rearranged, gives the voltage reflection coefficient at the termination,

$$\rho_{vt} = V_r/V_f = (Z_t - Z_0)/(Z_t + Z_0).$$

The current reflection coefficient at the termination is similarly given by

$$\rho_{it} = I_r/I_f = -(Z_t - Z_0)/(Z_t + Z_0).$$

Example 5.6   *Determine values for the voltage and current travelling waves at the termination for the arrangement in Example 5.5 when terminated by a 600 Ω resistor and supplied by a sinusoidal source such that the termination voltage is $5\underline{/0°}$ V.*

With $Z_0 = 401\ \Omega$ and $Z_t = 600\ \Omega$, the voltage reflection coefficient, $\rho_{vt} = (Z_t - Z_0)/(Z_t + Z_0) = 0.199$. Thus, with $V_f + V_r = 5$ V and $V_r/V_f = 0.199$,

$$V_f = 4.17\underline{/0°}\ V \quad \text{and} \quad V_r = 0.83\underline{/0°}\ V.$$

Also,

$$\mathbf{I}_f = \mathbf{V}_f/\mathbf{Z}_0 = 10.4\underline{/0^\circ}\ \text{mA}$$

and

$$\mathbf{I}_r = -\mathbf{V}_r/\mathbf{Z}_0 = -2.1\underline{/0^\circ}\ \text{mA or } 2.1\underline{/180^\circ}\ \text{mA}.$$

In Example 5.6, as a consequence of the terminating impedance and $\mathbf{Z}_0$ being resistive, the reflection coefficient is a real number and $\mathbf{V}_f$ and $\mathbf{V}_r$ are in phase at the termination. However, because forward and reflected waves change phase with position and these changes are in the opposite sense, the in-phase condition exists only at the termination (or at multiples of one half-wavelength from it). This aspect is explored in the following section.

5.2.5 Standing waves

The interaction of the forward and reflected travelling waves to produce a standing wave is demonstrated in this section by reference to a cascaded set of networks terminated in a short circuit. Initially, however, Fig. 5.12(a) shows a set of phasors representing the sinusoidal voltages which would be measured at each intersection if the networks were correctly terminated by $\mathbf{Z}_0$. These represent the forward-travelling voltage wave and show a gradual retardation of phase on moving from source to termination. It is assumed that the magnitude is constant, consistent with zero line losses.

Fig. 5.12 Phasor representation of forward, reflected and standing waves

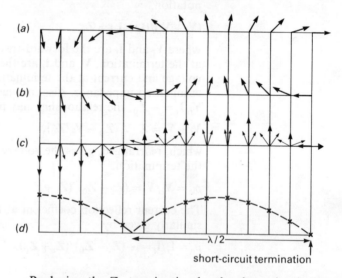

short-circuit termination

Replacing the Z_0 termination by the short circuit sets up a reflected-travelling wave, a set of phasors for which are shown in Fig. 5.12(b). Forward and reflected phasors are equal in magnitude and are in phase opposition at the termination, consistent with their resultant being zero (across the short circuit!) and with the voltage-reflection coefficient value, $(0 - Z_0)/(0 + Z_0) = -1$. Also, the change of phase with position is in the opposite sense for the two waves; whereas the forward wave retards from source to termination, the reflected wave retards from termination to source.

The resultant of forward and reflected waves is shown in Fig. 5.12(c) and, as a result of the differing phases, varies in magnitude. This is the **standing wave**. Fig. 5.12(d) is a graph of the magnitude of the standing voltage wave. With the passage of time, both phasors rotate (anticlockwise) with the same angular velocity and therefore the relative positions of forward and reflected waves remain unchanged. Thus the signal-magnitude variation remains stationary with respect to position and is, accordingly, a **standing wave pattern**. Because the positional rotation of each component phasor is 360° in one wavelength, their relative rotation is 360° every half-wavelength. In fact, one method for measuring the frequency of high-frequency signals involves determining the distance between adjacent minima using an air-spaced transmission line, for which the phase velocity is 3×10^8 m/s, and then calculating frequency from $f\lambda = 3 \times 10^8$ where λ is twice the adjacent-minima spacing.

The principle applies equally for terminations containing resistive and combinations of resistive and reactive components. For example, a cascaded set of networks for which $\mathbf{Z}_0 = 50\underline{/0°}$ and terminated in an impedance $(70 - j30)\ \Omega$ has a voltage reflection coefficient given by

$$\rho_{vt} = (\mathbf{Z}_t - \mathbf{Z}_0)/(\mathbf{Z}_t + \mathbf{Z}_0) = 0.29\underline{/-42°}.$$

Then, at the termination, the reflected voltage-wave magnitude will be 0.29 that of the forward wave and it will lag by 42°.

5.2.6 Standing-wave ratio (SWR)

As the forward and reflected waves go in and out of phase with each other, the standing wave exhibits maxima and minima. The ratio of the maxima to the minima is the **standing-wave ratio** S, or s ($= 1/S$), usually abbreviated to VSWR for voltage and ISWR for current. Because $|V_{max}|$ is the sum of the magnitudes of the forward and the reflected voltages (i.e. $|V_f| + |V_r|$) and $|V_{min}|$ is the difference in magnitudes, ($|V_f| - |V_r|$),

$$S = (|V_f| + |V_r|)/(|V_f| - |V_r|)$$

$$= (1 + |V_r|/|V_f|)/(1 - |V_r|/|V_f|)$$

$$= (1 + |\rho_v|)/(1 - |\rho_v|),$$

where $|\rho_v|$ is the magnitude of the reflection coefficient.

It is implicit in this relationship that $|\rho_v|$ is constant at least between adjacent maxima and minima. This is true for the conditions described so far in which there are no line losses. If losses do exist, S will vary over the length of the line, becoming smaller on moving towards the source as $|V_f|$ increases and $|V_r|$ decreases.

5.2.7 Pulse transmission

The effect of mistermination of a line with a continuous sinusoidal input is the generation of a standing-wave pattern resulting from the interaction of forward and reflected travelling waves. If the input is a discrete pulse and the transmission path meets the criteria for distortionless transmission described in Section 8.5.2 of Chapter 8, a

forward-travelling pulse will proceed from source to
termination without distortion. Provided that the termination
is resistive, and the reflection coefficient is therefore real, a
reflected pulse of the same shape as the forward pulse will be
established at the termination and will travel back towards
the source. Its magnitude is given by the magnitude of the
forward pulse multiplied by the reflection coefficient at the
termination and may be either positive or negative.

Fig. 5.13 shows the waveforms which would be observed at
source and termination in these ideal conditions. The data is
that previously used in Example 5.6 where $\rho_{vt} = 0.2$. The
incident pulse travels from source to termination, where a
reflected pulse of amplitude, $\rho_{vt}5$ ($= 0.2 \times 5 = 1.0$ V), is set up.
The sum of the forward and reflected pulses is observed. The
reflected pulse travels back to the source and, assuming that
its impedance is Z_0, the pulse is observed at that point, there
being no further reflection.

Fig. 5.13 Reflected pulses

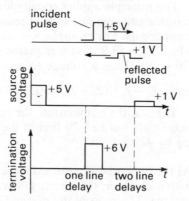

The assumption that the cascaded network meets the ideal
transmission conditions of constant or zero attenuation and a
linear phase-frequency characteristic is not in fact met.
However, provided the significant harmonics of the pulse (see
Chapter 8) have frequencies not exceeding approximately half
the cut-off frequency ($f_c = 1/\pi\sqrt{(LC)}$) of the lumped network,
the approximation is reasonably close. At these low
frequencies, $\alpha \simeq 0$, $\beta \simeq \omega\sqrt{(LC)}$ and $Z_0 \simeq \sqrt{(L/C)}$, results
which may be deduced from the expressions for γ and Z_0
used in Examples 5.4 and 5.5. With a phase shift of $\omega\sqrt{(LC)}$
the phase delay, β/ω, becomes $\sqrt{(LC)}$ which is independent
of frequency. The loss-free distributed line analysed in the
next section does not exhibit cut off and, in this sense, no
assumptions are necessary.

The concept of pulse reflections is further illustrated by a
general example:

Example 5.7 *Sketch source and load-voltage waveforms existing on a line having a
characteristic impedance of 50 Ω and delay of 5 μs (and satisfying the
ideal phase and attenuation requirements) when a 5 V, 2 μs pulse is
transmitted along it. Assume terminating conditions as follows:*

(i) termination resistance, 50 Ω; source resistance, 50 Ω;
(ii) termination resistance, 100 Ω; source resistance, 50 Ω;
(iii) termination resistance, 30 Ω; source resistance, 30 Ω.

(i) In this case, there is no reflection at source or termination and the pulse is simply delayed (Fig. 5.14(a)).

(ii) Termination reflection coefficient,

$\rho_{vt} = (100 - 50)/(100 + 50) = \frac{1}{3}$. There is a reflected pulse of amplitude $\frac{5}{3}$ V from termination to source and, because the source is matched, there are no further reflections (Fig. 5.14(b)).

(iii) Termination reflection coefficient,

$\rho_{vt} = (30 - 50)/(30 + 50) = -\frac{1}{4}$ and source reflection coefficient $= -\frac{1}{4}$. In this case, there are repeated reflections from termination to source and source to termination. Each reflected pulse is $\frac{1}{4}$ the amplitude of the incident pulse and is inverted. In all cases, the observed pulse is the algebraic sum of incident and reflected pulses (Fig. 5.14(c)).

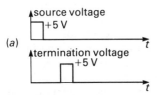

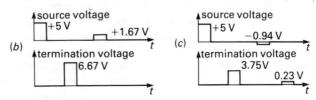

Fig. 5.14 Solution for Example 5.7

5.3 The distributed line

5.3.1 Introduction

The cascade of lumped networks introduces phase change with respect to distance and it is this property which causes travelling waves, standing waves and reflections. Transmission media such as open-pair wires and coaxial cables have inductance and capacitance distributed over their length and therefore introduce phase shift with respect to distance, and as a consequence, travelling waves.

Appendix 5A develops the distributed-line equations starting with an incremental section of line containing inductance, capacitance and, in general, resistance and conductance. The result of this derivation may be summarised as follows.

In Fig. 5.15,

$$V_x = \tfrac{1}{2}V_t[(1 + Z_0/Z_t)\,e^{\gamma x} + (1 - Z_0/Z_t)\,e^{-\gamma x}],$$

$$I_x = \tfrac{1}{2}\frac{V_t}{Z_0}[(1 + Z_0/Z_t)\,e^{\gamma x} - (1 - Z_0/Z_t)\,e^{-\gamma x}],$$

where

$$Z_0 = \sqrt{[(R + j\omega L)/(G + j\omega C)]},$$

and

$$\gamma = \sqrt{[(R + j\omega L)(G + j\omega C)]}.$$

R, L, G and C represent the physical properties of the line (see Appendix 5A). The equations are interpreted in the following sections.

Fig. 5.15 Voltage and current reference directions for a distributed line

5.3.2 The significance of γ as applied to distributed lines

Inasmuch as the real component α represents attenuation and the imaginary component β represents phase shift, γ has the same significance as in Section 5.1.2. However, two features of the line equations differ from the previously used notation: one is the coupling of γ with x and the other is the appearance of the factors, $e^{\gamma x}$ and $e^{-\gamma x}$ in the same expression.

Multiplication of γ by x implies that the attenuation and phase shift are both functions of x, the distance of the point under consideration from the termination. Thus $e^{\gamma x} = e^{\alpha x} e^{j\beta x}$ (or $e^{\alpha x}/\underline{\beta x}$) represents a unit-amplitude phasor at $x = 0$ whose magnitude increases as x increases (by α Np/m) and whose phase angle advances (by β rad/m) as x increases. This is shown in Fig. 5.16(a) and represents a forward-travelling phasor, 'forward' meaning towards the termination in the (assumed) direction of decreasing x.

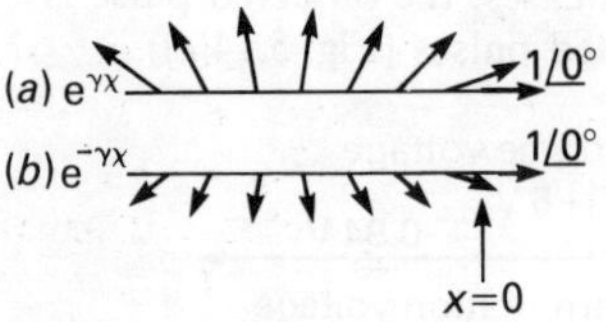

The appearance of the factor $e^{-\gamma x} = e^{-\alpha x} e^{-j\beta x}$ (or $e^{-\alpha x}/\underline{-\beta x}$) will be seen to represent a phasor decreasing in magnitude and advancing in phase with x. As shown in Fig. 5.16(b), this is a reflected travelling phasor.

The magnitudes of the attenuation and phase constants are given by the real and imaginary components of $\sqrt{[(R + j\omega L)(G + j\omega C)]}$. A typical calculation is illustrated in Example 5.8, in which are included the following basic relationships, previously discussed:

phase velocity, $v_p = \omega/\beta$;

wavelength, $\lambda = 2\pi/\beta$.

Fig. 5.16 Significance of $e^{\gamma x}$ and $e^{-\gamma x}$

Example 5.8   *A transmission line has the following primary constants: $R = 40$ mΩ/m, $L = 2$ μH/m, $C = 6$ pF/m and $G = 1$ nS/m. Calculate the attenuation and phase coefficients at 1 kHz and hence determine, (i) wavelength and (ii) the attenuation which a signal would experience over 10 km of correctly terminated line.*

$R + j\omega L = (40 + j12.6) \times 10^{-3} = 41.9 \times 10^{-3}/\underline{17.5°}$,

$G + j\omega C = (1 + j37.7) \times 10^{-9} = 37.7 \times 10^{-9}/\underline{88.5°}$.

Therefore,

$\gamma = \sqrt{[(R + j\omega L)(G + j\omega C)]}$

$\quad = \sqrt{[41.9 \times 37.7 \times 10^{-12}/\underline{17.5° + 88.5°}]}$

$\quad = \sqrt{[1580 \times 10^{-12}]/\underline{53°}}$

$\quad = (23.9 + j31.7) \times 10^{-6}/m$.

Note: the angle is halved when taking the square root.

(i) Wavelength $= 2\pi/\beta = 2\pi/31.7 \times 10^{-6} = 198$ km;

(ii) attenuation (in dB) over 10 km of line

$\quad = 10 \times 10^3 \times 23.9 \times 10^{-6} \times 8.68$

$\quad = 2.07$ dB.

5.3.3 The significance of Z_0 as applied to distributed lines

The characteristic impedance Z_0 appears in both line equations and there are a number of interesting conclusions which can be drawn.

(i) When the line is correctly terminated, substituting

$Z_t = Z_0$ into the equations gives:

$V_x = V_t e^{yx}$ and $I_x = I_t e^{yx}$.

It will be seen that the reflected travelling-wave components disappear, confirming that correct termination eliminates reflections.

(ii) The ratio V_x/I_x (when $Z_t = Z_0$) is Z_0, indicating that, when correctly terminated, the impedance at all points on the line is equal to the characteristic impedance, Z_0.

(iii) If the forward and reflected components of the expressions for V_x and I_x are considered separately, the ratio of the forward components, V_f/I_f will be seen to be Z_0 and the ratio of the reflected components, $V_r/I_r = -Z_0$. This is true for any load and, for this reason, Z_0 is sometimes known as the **surge impedance**.

Example 5.9   *Using the data for Example 5.8, determine the characteristic impedance of the line at (i) 1 kHz and (ii) at 100 kHz. Assume that the primary constants have the same values at both frequencies.*

At 1 kHz (using results from Example 5.8)

$Z_0 = \sqrt{[(R + j\omega L)/(G + j\omega C)]}$

$\quad = \sqrt{[(41.9 \times 10^{-3}/17.5°)/(37.7 \times 10^{-9}/88.5°)]}$

$\quad = \sqrt{[1.11 \times 10^6]/-35.5°}$

$\quad = 1.05/-35.5°\ \text{k}\Omega.$

At 100 kHz, $R \ll \omega L$ and $G \ll \omega C$ and Z_0 becomes

$\sqrt{(L/C)} = \sqrt{(2 \times 10^{-6}/6 \times 10^{-12})}$

$\quad = 577/0°\ \Omega.$

5.3.4 Special conditions

There are certain special conditions of line operating behaviour, two of which are the **loss-free** and the **distortionless** conditions. In the loss-free condition, R and G are considered to be negligible in comparison with ωL and ωC, respectively, the condition usually being associated with high-frequency operation. Making this assumption, $\gamma = j\omega\sqrt{(LC)}$, α is negligible (i.e. negligible attenuation) and $\beta = \omega\sqrt{(LC)}$, giving a linear phase/frequency characteristic. Also, $Z_0 = \sqrt{(L/C)}$ and is resistive and independent of frequency. The line equations thus become

$V_x = \tfrac{1}{2}V_t[(1 + Z_0/Z_t)/\beta x + (1 - Z_0/Z_t)/-\beta x]$,

and

$I_x = \tfrac{1}{2}\dfrac{V_t}{Z_0}[(1 + Z_0/Z_t)/\beta x + (1 - Z_0/Z_t)/-\beta x]$.

Substituting expressions for L and C (Appendix 5A) into the loss-free expressions for Z_0 and β gives $Z_0 = (\sqrt{(\mu/\varepsilon)}/2\pi) \ln(b/a)$ and $\beta = \omega\sqrt{(\mu\varepsilon)}$ which, for an air-spaced line, gives a phase velocity of $1/\sqrt{(\mu_0\varepsilon_0)} = c = 3 \times 10^8$ m/s.

In many situations, it is possible to obtain a good approximation to the actual behaviour of a transmission line by assuming loss-free conditions with its consequent simplifications. Frequently, losses are such that, even though the attenuation effect must be taken into account when dealing with very long lines, they have only a second-order effect on characteristic impedance and phase coefficient (as compared with the loss-free case) and hence on standing-wave patterns and input impedance.

The distortionless condition is one which is more likely to be engineered rather than one which occurs as a natural consequence of a particular operating condition. In situations in which the loss-free condition, with its attendant advantages, does not apply, the product LG may be deliberately made equal to CR, in which case β can be shown to be $\omega\sqrt{(LC)}$. Thus, as explained in Section 8.5.2 in Chapter 8, phase distortion may be avoided even though R and G are not negligible.

Example 5.10   *A loss-free air-spaced line, length 4 m and having a characteristic impedance of 50 Ω is terminated with a 100 Ω resistor. Determine the input voltage and current at a frequency of 100 MHz if the termination voltage is 4 V.*

Because the line is air spaced, the phase velocity is the velocity of electromagnetic waves in free space, $c(= 3 \times 10^8 \text{ m/s})$. Therefore, wavelength, $\lambda = c/f = 3 \times 10^8/100 \times 10^6 = 3$ m. The physical line length is 4 m and therefore its electrical length is $\frac{4}{3}$ wavelength. βx is then $2\pi \times (\frac{4}{3})$ rad or $360 \times \frac{4}{3}° \equiv 120°$.

$$\mathbf{V}_{\text{in}} = 2[(1 + \tfrac{50}{100})\underline{/120°} + (1 - \tfrac{50}{100})\underline{/-120°}]$$

$$= 2(-1.0 + j0.866) = 2.64\underline{/139°} \text{ V}.$$

$$\mathbf{I}_{\text{in}} = 0.04[(1 + \tfrac{50}{100})\underline{/120°} - (1 - \tfrac{50}{100})\underline{/-120°}]$$

$$= 0.04(-0.5 + j1.73) = 0.072\underline{/106°} \text{ A}.$$

The input impedance is then given by

$$\mathbf{V}_{\text{in}}/\mathbf{I}_{\text{in}} = (2.65\underline{/139°})/(0.072\underline{/106°}) = 36.7\underline{/33°} \text{ Ω}.$$

5.3.5 Reflection coefficient

This is defined as the ratio of the reflected and forward travelling waves. From the line equations, voltage reflection coefficient

$$\rho_{vx} = \mathbf{V}_r/\mathbf{V}_f = [(1 - \mathbf{Z}_0/\mathbf{Z}_t)/(1 + \mathbf{Z}_0/\mathbf{Z}_t)] \, e^{-2\gamma x},$$

and current reflection coefficient

$$\rho_{ix} = \mathbf{I}_r/\mathbf{I}_f = -[(1 - \mathbf{Z}_0/\mathbf{Z}_t)/(1 + \mathbf{Z}_0/\mathbf{Z}_t)] \, e^{-2\gamma x} = -\rho_{vx}.$$

Since reflected and forward voltages exist at all points on the line, the reflection coefficients may be defined for all values of x. In particular, at the termination (where $x = 0$) the reflection coefficients $\rho_{vx} = -\rho_{ix} = (\mathbf{Z}_t - \mathbf{Z}_0)/(\mathbf{Z}_t + \mathbf{Z}_0)$; this is the expression used in Section 5.2.4. For the loss-free line, $e^{-2\gamma x} = e^{-2\beta x}$, or $1\underline{/-2\beta x}$, and the reflection coefficients become

$\rho_{vx} = -\rho_{ix} = [(\mathbf{Z}_t - \mathbf{Z}_0)/(\mathbf{Z}_t + \mathbf{Z}_0)]\underline{/-2\beta x}$. In this case, the magnitude of the coefficient is constant (with respect to position on the line) but the angle retards on moving from termination to source; the angle changes through $360°$ in a half-wavelength. Following the same argument as in Section 5.2.5, the voltage maxima occur when the angle of the reflection coefficient is $0°$ (i.e. $\mathbf{V}_f$ and $\mathbf{V}_r$ in phase). Voltage minima occur when the angle is $180°$ when $\mathbf{V}_f$ and $\mathbf{V}_r$ are in antiphase. Also as before, $\text{VSWR} = (1 + |\rho_{vx}|)/(1 - |\rho_{vx}|)$.

5.3.6 Line impedance

The impedance looking towards the load (Fig. 5.17) at any point on a line, distance x from the load is given by

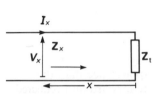

Fig. 5.17 Impedance looking towards the termination

$$\mathbf{Z}_x = \frac{\mathbf{V}_x}{\mathbf{I}_x} = \frac{\dfrac{\mathbf{V}_t}{2}[(1 + \mathbf{Z}_0/\mathbf{Z}_t)\,e^{\gamma x} + (1 - \mathbf{Z}_0/\mathbf{Z}_t)\,e^{-\gamma x}]}{\dfrac{\mathbf{V}_t}{2\mathbf{Z}_0}[(1 + \mathbf{Z}_0/\mathbf{Z}_t)\,e^{\gamma x} + (1 - \mathbf{Z}_0/\mathbf{Z}_t)\,e^{-\gamma x}]}$$

$$= \mathbf{Z}_0 \frac{1 + [(1 - \mathbf{Z}_0/\mathbf{Z}_t)/(1 + \mathbf{Z}_0/\mathbf{Z}_t)]\,e^{-2\gamma x}}{1 - [(1 - \mathbf{Z}_0/\mathbf{Z}_t)/(1 + \mathbf{Z}_0/\mathbf{Z}_t)]\,e^{-2\gamma x}}$$

$$= \mathbf{Z}_0 \frac{1 + \rho_{vx}}{1 - \rho_{vx}}.$$

As with the line equations, this is one of a number of expressions for input impedance, each having a very different appearance. An alternative form is described in the next section.

Impedance may be calculated as the ratio of the voltage to the current; for example, using the figure from Example 5.10, $\mathbf{Z}_{in} = 36.7\underline{/33°}\ \Omega$. Alternatively, again using the data from Example 5.10, the reflection-coefficient formula gives

$$\rho_{vin} = [(100 - 50)/(100 + 50)]\underline{/-240°} = 0.33\underline{/120°}.$$

Therefore,

$$\mathbf{Z}_{in} = \mathbf{Z}_0(1 + \rho_{vin})/(1 - \rho_{vin})$$

$$= 50(1 + 0.33\underline{/120°})/(1 - 0.33\underline{/120°})$$

$$= 36.7\underline{/33°}\ \Omega.$$

A topic closely associated with line impedance is that of **impedance matching**. Matching is the process of terminating a line with an effective impedance equal to the characteristic impedance, even though the actual terminating impedance may not be Z_0.

The principal advantages of matching may be summarised as follows:

   (i) multiple reflected pulses are eliminated;
   (ii) standing waves are eliminated. This removes the possibility of excessively high voltages and currents occurring at voltage (current) maxima;
   (iii) makes the line input impedance predictably equal to the characteristic impedance irrespective of line length. Furthermore, if Z_0 is resistive, the input impedance is always resistive and independent of line length and frequency.

Matching is discussed in detail in Davidson (1978).

5.3.7 The hyperbolic form of the line equations

It is common practice to express the distributed-line equations in the hyperbolic form rather than the exponential form. Using the equations derived in Appendix 5A, and regrouping the exponential terms,

$$V_x = \frac{V_t}{2}(e^{\gamma x} + e^{-\gamma x}) + \frac{V_t Z_0}{2Z_t}(e^{\gamma x} - e^{-\gamma x}),$$

$$I_x = \frac{V_t}{2Z_0}(e^{\gamma x} - e^{-\gamma x}) + \frac{V_t}{2Z_t}(e^{\gamma x} + e^{-\gamma x}).$$

Substituting I_t for V_t/Z_t

$$V_x = V_t \cosh \gamma x + Z_0 I_t \sinh \gamma x,$$

$$I_x = \frac{V_t}{Z_0} \sinh \gamma x + I_t \cosh \gamma x.$$

These equations, although of neater appearance than the exponential form, disguise the separate forward and reflected-travelling components which are apparent in the latter.

A line-impedance expression can be deduced in the following way. Substituting $V_t/I_t = Z_t$ and dividing throughout by $\cosh \gamma x$,

$$Z_x = Z_0(Z_t + Z_0 \tanh \gamma x)/(Z_t \tanh \gamma x + Z_0).$$

For the loss-free line, $\gamma = j\beta$ and $\tanh \gamma x$ becomes $j \tan \beta x$, giving

$$Z_x = Z_0(Z_t + jZ_0 \tan \beta x)/(jZ_t \tan \beta x + Z_0),$$

and, for the special case of the short-circuited loss-free line, $Z_t = 0$ and hence, $Z_x = jZ_0 \tan \beta x$.

5.4 Use of an impedance-chart calculator: the Smith chart

5.4.1 Introduction and a simple application

Calculations such as those illustrated in Section 5.3.6, although based on the relatively straightforward relationships,

impedance $Z_x = Z_0(1 + \rho_{vx})/(1 - \rho_{vx})$

and

voltage reflection coefficient $\rho_{vx} = [(Z_t - Z_0)/(Z_t + Z_0)] e^{-2\gamma x},$

can become tedious, particularly when Z_t has reactive and resistive components. In order to overcome this problem, a chart calculator, generally known as a **Smith chart**, has been developed which enables these relationships to be determined graphically. Although at first sight it may appear complex, it is not difficult to use and the purpose of this introductory section is to demonstrate how the results of Example 5.10 may be obtained from the chart. Having demonstrated its use in a simple application, the principle is described in the following section. It is implicit in this discussion that the line is loss free, and that Z_0 is resistive.

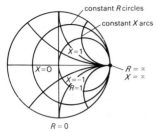

Fig. 5.18 Normalised constant-resistance and constant-reactance circles on a Smith chart

Fig. 5.19 A complete Smith chart illustrating how $\mathbf{Z}_{in}$ is determined from $\mathbf{Z}_t$ and the wavelength (with permission, © Phillip H. Smith, Analog Instruments Co., Box 808, New Providence, NJ, USA)

The chart consists of a grid made up of circles and arcs of circles representing resistive and reactive components of impedance (Fig. 5.18). In order to make the chart usable for lines having a range of differing characteristic impedances, all impedance values are **normalised** by dividing by Z_0 before plotting on the chart. Z_0 must be resistive in this case. Thus, the general impedance $\mathbf{Z} = R + jX$ becomes $\mathbf{z} = \mathbf{Z}/Z_0 = R/Z_0 + jX/Z_0$ after normalising. In Example 5.10, for example, the $100\,\Omega$ termination on the $50\,\Omega$ line would become a normalised load impedance of $2 + j0$, shown as $\mathbf{z}_t$ on the chart in Fig. 5.19. Around the circumference of the chart there are two wavelength scales with their origins on the left-hand side of the chart. Scale values 'toward the generator' (clockwise) and 'toward the load' (anticlockwise) are shown, one rotation around the chart representing one half-wavelength. Returning to Example 5.10, the object was to determine the input impedance of a line $\frac{4}{3}\lambda$ long. To do this it is necessary to move 1.33λ from the load toward the

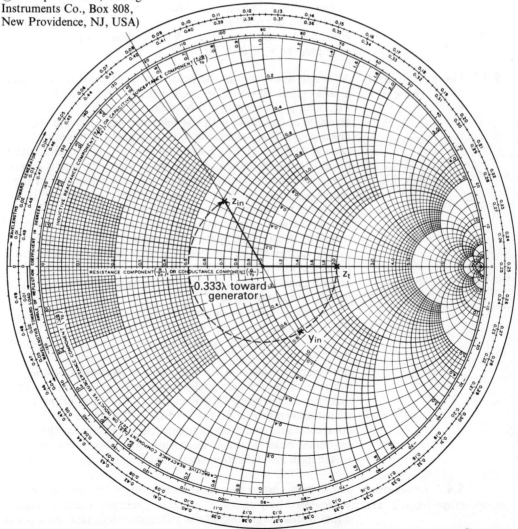

generator on a constant-radius circle centred on the centre of the chart. (In practice, it is only necessary to move 0.33 λ because one wavelength means two complete rotations, which need not be shown.)

Fig. 5.19 shows the normalised impedance value, z_{in} resulting from this rotation. Reading the resistance and reactance scales gives $z_{in} = 0.61 + j0.40$, from which $Z_{in} \simeq 36.7\underline{/33°}\ \Omega$, the same result as obtained in Example 5.10.

The input impedance has been obtained by a single construction line on the chart. If required, the voltage reflection coefficient can also be scaled from the chart; its angle is given by the circumferential scale inside the wavelength scales, from which the reflection-coefficient angles at termination and input will be seen to 0° and 120°, respectively, again agreeing with Example 5.10. The reflection-coefficient magnitude (which is constant on this loss-free line) is given by the radius of the construction line, scaled so that the outer-chart radius is unity. Scaling from the chart gives $\rho_v = 0.33$, as in Example 5.10.

The voltage-standing-wave ratio can also be read from the chart using the resistance scale to the right of the centre point. This scale doubles as a VSWR scale and in this example, the VSWR is 2.0.

5.4.2 The principle of the chart

Although not drawn in the polar form, the chart is essentially a polar graph of reflection coefficient. As illustrated in Fig. 5.20, ρ_{vx} is represented by a line of length $|\rho_{vx}|$ making an angle of $(\phi - 2\beta x)$ with the reference axis, ϕ being the phase angle of ρ_{vx} when $x = 0$, i.e. the angle of the term $(Z_t - Z_0)/(Z_t + Z_0)$. For a loss-free line, $|\rho_{vx}|$ is constant with respect to x and, therefore, movement along the line is represented by rotation of a constant-amplitude phasor about the centre point on the chart. Movement from termination to generator (x increasing) is indicated by clockwise rotation of the phasor and movement to the termination by anticlockwise rotation. Because the angle of the reflection coefficient varies as $2\beta x$ (rather the βx), a 360° change in reflection coefficient implies a 180° change in βx and, therefore, one rotation around chart is equivalent to a movement of half a wavelength along the line.

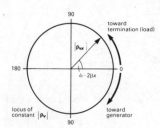

Fig. 5.20 Reflection coefficient shown on a Smith chart

By means of the previously established relationship, $Z_x = Z_0(1 + \rho_{vx})/(1 - \rho_{vx})$, from which $z_x = Z_x/Z_0 = (1 + \rho_{vx})/(1 - \rho_{vx})$, it is possible to superimpose an impedance 'grid' on the polar reflection-coefficient graph. Specifically, it can be shown that, if $z = r + jx$, lines of constant r and x describe circles (or part circles) on a polar graph of ρ_{vx}. This aspect is explained in Davidson (1978). The form of the grid is that shown in Fig. 5.18, with Fig. 5.19 showing the composite grid and reflection-coefficient phasors for the particular example under discussion. Also shown are the wavelength and reflection-coefficient-angle scales.

5.4.3 Additional information from chart

It has been shown that movement along a loss-free line is represented by rotation around the chart at a constant radius equal to the magnitude of the reflection coefficient. At a point on the line (or at the corresponding position on the chart) where the angle of the reflection coefficient is zero, the forward and reflected-voltage waves are in phase. At these points, the voltage is a maximum and the current is a minimum.

Moving a quarter-wavelength towards generator (or termination) sets the angle of the reflection coefficient at 180°, forward and reflected-voltage waves are in antiphase and there is a voltage minimum (or current maximum). Thus, as illustrated in Fig. 5.21, with the numerical values derived from Section 4.1, positions of maxima and minima can be located on the line.

Fig. 5.21 Relating voltage maxima and minima to position on the Smith chart

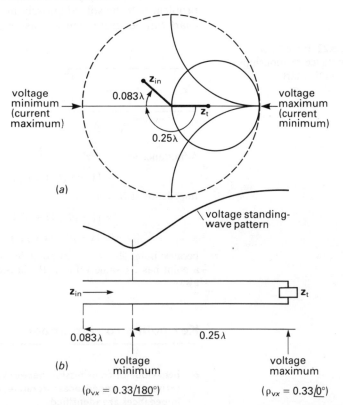

(a)

(b)

$(\rho_{vx} = 0.33\underline{/180°})$ $(\rho_{vx} = 0.33\underline{/0°})$

It is also possible to determine the VSWR: when forward and reflected-voltage waves are in phase and the angle of the reflection coefficient is 0° (i.e. ρ_{vx} is real and positive), the expression for the impedance $z = (1 + \rho_{vx})/(1 - \rho_{vx})$, has the same value as $(1 + |\rho_{vx}|)/(1 - |\rho_{vx}|)$ and this is the value of the VSWR on the line. Thus, the resistance scale along the 0° reflection-coefficient axis may be used as a VSWR scale.

Finally, the Smith chart may be used as an **admittance chart** as well as an impedance chart. The way in which this may be done can be appreciated by reference to Fig. 5.22 in which the impedance at point A on a line has a particular value, $z' = (1 + \rho'_{vx})/(1 - \rho'_{vx})$. The admittance at this point would be $(1 - \rho'_{vx})/(1 + \rho'_{vx})$ and this is also the value of the impedance at point B $\lambda/4$ away where the reflection-coefficient angle has changed through 180° and $\rho''_{vx} = -\rho'_{vx}$.

Effectively, therefore, to convert from impedance to admittance, or from admittance to impedance, the value can be found diagonally opposite the original point. For example, in Fig. 5.19, the conductive component of the normalised admittance, y_{in} is 1.14 and the inductive-susceptance component is 0.74, these values being read off the chart diagonally opposite z_{in}. That the value of y_{in} is $1/z_{in} = (1/0.734\underline{/33°})$ may be verified by normal complex-algebraic inversion. It is emphasised that the movement through $\lambda/4$ in Fig. 5.22 is intended only to justify the method; either impedance or admittance is a valid description of the voltage–current ratio at any point on the line. Furthermore, if a problem is to be solved entirely in the admittance form, the chart can be treated entirely as an admittance chart.

Fig. 5.22 Impedance–admittance relationships on the Smith chart

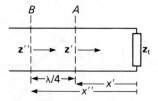

Admittance at $A = 1/z'$

$$= (1 - \rho'_{vx})/(1 + \rho'_{vx}).$$

Impedance at $B = z''$

$$= (1 + \rho''_{vx})/(1 - \rho''_{vx})$$

$$\text{or } (1 - \rho'_{vx})/(1 + \rho'_{vx}),$$

because point A is $\lambda/4$ from point B. Thus, the admittance at a point has the same value as the impedance at a point $\lambda/4$ away.

Key points to remember

- behaviour of transmission networks is dependent on their terminating impedances; iterative, image and characteristic impedances are identified;

- when terminated by its characteristic impedance, the magnitude and phase responses of a transmission network are given by the propagation coefficient;

- where a network or transmission system introduces phase change with respect to position, travelling waves exist;

- for a travelling wave, phase velocity is given by ω/β;

- mistermination sets up reflected wave (V_r/V_f at termination = $(Z_t - Z_0)/(Z_t + Z_0)$), manifesting itself as discrete reflections with a pulse input and standing waves with a sinusoidal input;

- special case of loss-free line gives $\alpha = 0$ and $\beta = \omega\sqrt{(LC)}$;

- line impedance $Z_x = Z_0(1 + \rho_{vx})/(1 - \rho_{vx})$;

- the Smith chart is essentially a polar plot of reflection coefficient with an impedance grid superimposed.

Further reading

Davidson, C. W., *Transmission Lines for Communications.* Macmillan (1978).

Open University, *Channels and Lines* (Unit No. T321). Open University Press (1976).

Young, P. H., *Electronic Communication Techniques.* C. Merrill (1985).

Appendix 5A Distributed transmission line equations

Fig. 5A.1 shows an incremental section of line, representing part of a line whose properties are uniformly distributed over its entire length. The section is taken to be distance x from the termination. Line voltage and current, $\mathbf{V}_x$ and $\mathbf{I}_x$, are shown, together with the incremental voltage and current, $\delta\mathbf{V}_x$ and $\delta\mathbf{I}_x$, associated with the incremental section, length, δx. The basic properties of the line are represented by the circuit elements, $L\delta x$, $R\delta x$, $C\delta x$ and $G\delta x$ representing, respectively, the loop inductance, loop resistance and the capacitance and conductance of the incremental section, L, R, C and G being the **primary constants** per unit length of line. For the coaxial cable at high frequencies, for example, the constants are as follows:

$$L = \frac{\mu}{2\pi}\ln(b/a), \quad R = \frac{1}{2\pi\delta\sigma}(1/a + 1/b),$$

$$C = 2\pi\varepsilon/\ln(b/a) \quad \text{and} \quad G = 2\pi\sigma/\ln(b/a),$$

where μ, σ and ε are, respectively, the permeability, conductivity and permittivity of the material under consideration in each case. δ is the **skin depth**† of the conductor given by $\sqrt{(2/\omega\mu\sigma)}$ at frequency ω. b and a are the outer and inner-conductor radii respectively.

Fig. 5A.1 An incremental section of a distributed line

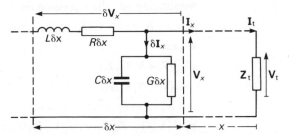

The analysis is carried out using the phasor technique for the voltages and currents and the results are therefore applicable to steady-state sinusoidal operation. It is common practice to retain the time variable in the analysis in order to demonstrate the existence of the travelling wave, whose phase angle is a function of both time and position. However, consistent with the diagrams in Section 5.2.5;

---

† At high frequencies, current flows near the surface of conductors and the quoted results are based on this assumption. **Skin effect** is discussed in Davidson (1978), in which the expression for δ is also derived.

the phasor form is used. From Fig. 5A.1,

$\delta \mathbf{V}_x = (R\delta x + j\omega L\delta x)\mathbf{I}_x$ (neglecting $\delta \mathbf{I}_x$ in comparison with $\mathbf{I}_x$).

Hence,

$\delta \mathbf{V}_x / \delta x = (R + j\omega L)\mathbf{I}_x$

and, in the limit,

$d\mathbf{V}_x / dx = (R + j\omega L)\mathbf{I}_x.$

Differentiating,

$d^2\mathbf{V}_x / dx^2 = (R + j\omega L) \, d\mathbf{I}_x / dx.$

But, also from the diagram,

$\delta \mathbf{I}_x = (G\delta x + j\omega C\delta x)\mathbf{V}_x,$

whence,

$d\mathbf{I}_x / dx = (G + j\omega C)\mathbf{V}_x.$

Substituting into the expression for $d^2\mathbf{V}_x / dx^2$ gives

$d^2\mathbf{V}_x / dx^2 = (R + j\omega L)(G + j\omega C)\mathbf{V}_x = \gamma^2 \mathbf{V}_x,$

where $\gamma = \sqrt{[(R + j\omega L)(G + j\omega C)]}$, being the **propagation coefficient** per unit length. A solution to this equation is

$\mathbf{V}_x = a\,e^{\gamma x} + b\,e^{-\gamma x},$

where a and b are constant coefficients, and, because

$\mathbf{I}_x = (d\mathbf{V}_x / dx)/(R + j\omega L),$

$\mathbf{I}_x = a\gamma\,e^{\gamma x}/(R + j\omega L) - b\gamma\,e^{-\gamma x}/(R + j\omega L)$

$\quad = a\,e^{\gamma x}/\mathbf{Z}_0 - b\,e^{-\gamma x}/\mathbf{Z}_0,$

where $\mathbf{Z}_0 = (R + j\omega L)/\gamma = \sqrt{[(R + j\omega L)/(G + \omega C)]}$, being the **characteristic impedance** of the line.

The constant coefficients can be determined by reference to the boundary conditions:

(i) $\mathbf{V}_x = \mathbf{V}_t$ when $x = 0$;

(ii) $\mathbf{I}_x = \mathbf{I}_t = \mathbf{V}_t / \mathbf{Z}_t$ when $x = 0$.

Substituting into the expression for $\mathbf{V}_x$ and $\mathbf{I}_x$,

$\mathbf{V}_t = a + b$ and $\mathbf{V}_t / \mathbf{Z}_t = a/\mathbf{Z}_0 - b/\mathbf{Z}_0,$

whence

$a = \tfrac{1}{2}(\mathbf{V}_t + \mathbf{V}_t \mathbf{Z}_0/\mathbf{Z}_t),$

$b = \tfrac{1}{2}(\mathbf{V}_t - \mathbf{V}_t \mathbf{Z}_0/\mathbf{Z}_t),$

and substituting these coefficients into the expressions for $\mathbf{V}_x$ and $\mathbf{I}_x$,

$\mathbf{V}_x = \tfrac{1}{2}\mathbf{V}_t[(1 + \mathbf{Z}_0/\mathbf{Z}_t)\,e^{\gamma x} + (1 - \mathbf{Z}_0/\mathbf{Z}_t)\,e^{-\gamma x}],$

$\mathbf{I}_x = \tfrac{1}{2}(\mathbf{V}_t/\mathbf{Z}_0)[(1 + \mathbf{Z}_0/\mathbf{Z}_t)\,e^{\gamma x} - (1 - \mathbf{Z}_0/\mathbf{Z}_t)\,e^{-\gamma x}].$

These are known as the **line equations** and are one of a number of forms in which the distributed-line behaviour can be expressed. Section 5.3.7 shows an alternative hyperbolic form.

EXERCISES 5

5.1 Determine the image impedances of the network shown in Fig. E5.1,

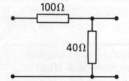

Fig. E5.1

(i) using transmission parameter definitions, and
(ii) open and short-circuit tests.

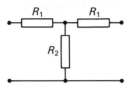

Fig. E5.2

5.2 Derive the transmission parameters for the network shown in Fig. E5.2 and hence obtain expressions for propagation coefficient and characteristic impedance in terms of R_1 and R_2. Hence determine values for R_1 and R_2 which would give an attenuation of 10 dB when terminated by a characteristic impedance of 50 Ω.

5.3 For the network shown in Fig. E5.1 determine insertion loss when inserted between its image impedances.

5.4 Determine the **A** parameter of the network shown in Fig. 5.6 at a frequency of 6 kHz and for a correctly terminated cascade of 30 such networks determine the following:

(i) overall delay;
(ii) phase velocity;
(iii) wavelength.

5.5 Sketch phasor diagrams for the voltage and current travelling and standing waves on a cascaded network for which
$\mathbf{Z}_0 = 50\underline{/0°}$ Ω and $\mathbf{Z}_t = (70 - j30)$ Ω.
What is the value of the VSWR?

5.6 A single 5 V, 2 μs pulse is fed from a 600 Ω resistive source through an ideal 50 Ω transmission channel to a resistive load of 200 Ω. If the channel delay is 5 μs, sketch the load-voltage waveform for a 20 μs period after the pulse is transmitted. Assuming the pulse at the load is detected by a detector with a +3 V threshold level, what are the minimum and the maximum values of terminating resistance which will avoid false readings.

5.7 (a) Derive the hyperbolic form of the distributed transmission-line equations from the exponential form and hence show that the input impedance of a short circuited loss-free line is purely reactive and has a magnitude $Z_0 \tan \beta l$.
(b) Determine the input impedance of a short-circuited 50 Ω loss-free line 0.48 wavelength long and sketch the voltage-standing-wave pattern on the line when fed from a 100 mV sinusoidal source, indicating the maximum voltage existing on the line.

5.8 Using the loss-free, air-spaced distributed-line voltage equation for $\mathbf{V}_x$ in terms of $\mathbf{V}_t$, $\mathbf{Z}_t$, $\mathbf{Z}_0$ and β, deduce the voltage standing wave pattern on a 40 cm length of line terminated by a resistance of 50 Ω shunted by a capacitance of 4 pF at a frequency of 900 MHz. Show the positions of the minima as well as the magnitude of the maxima and minima, assuming the magnitude of the termination voltage is 2 V and $\mathbf{Z}_0 = 50$ Ω.

5.9 A 2 m length of 75 Ω loss-free cable having a dielectric with a relative permittivity of 3 is terminated with a resistance of 50 Ω. Use the Smith chart to determine the input impedance, voltage reflection coefficient at the termination and the VSWR at a frequency of 80 MHz. (See Section 5.3.4 to determine the effect of the dielectric.)

5.10 Using the data in Exercise 5.8 check the VSWR and the position of the minima using a Smith chart.

5.11 The following data were determined on a 50 Ω loss-free air-spaced transmission line: minima occurred at distances of 37.5 cm and 67.5 cm back from the termination towards the source and the VSWR was 2. Determine the equivalent series resistance and capacitance of the termination at the operating frequency.

5.12 Use the Smith chart to show that a 50 Ω loss-free line

terminated by $100\underline{/0°}\,\Omega$ can be matched approximately by placing a 0.15 wavelength short-circuited 'stub' of similar line in parallel with the main line at a point 0.152 wavelength from the termination.

6 Time response

The principal learning objectives of this chapter are to:

		Section	Exercise
•	appreciate the nature of the time response of basic systems;	1	6.1
•	derive the natural and forced components of response of a first-order network;	2.1–2.4	6.2
•	explain the terms transient response and time constant;	2.5	6.3
•	derive and apply a general phasor and phasor operator;	3.1, 3.2	6.4
•	determine various network functions;	3.3	6.5
•	deduce a pole-zero diagram from the network function;	3.4	6.6, 6.7
•	relate natural and forced responses to the poles and zeros;	3.5, 3.6	6.8, 6.9
•	explain the basis of the Laplace-transform method of circuit analysis;	4.1, 4.2	
•	deduce the transforms of functions of time;	4.3, 4.4	6.10
•	apply the transform technique to circuit analysis.	4.5	6.11, 6.12

6.1 Introduction

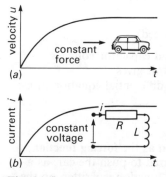

Fig. 6.1 Analogous first-order mechanical and electrical systems

The nature of the time response of many mechanical systems is so familiar that the senses are conditioned to anticipate them. For example, when pushing a car, it is expected that the vehicle will take a few moments to reach the required speed and it would be very surprising if it immediately started moving at that speed. Fig. 6.1(a) shows a typical speed-time graph for a car. The graph is characteristic of a **first-order system** in which there is only one energy-storage element in the system and whose performance is therefore characterised by a first-order differential equation. Fig. 6.1(b) shows a first-order electrical system and its corresponding current-time graph. As may be expected, second and higher-order systems will be encountered: for example, Fig. 6.2 shows analogous second-order electrical and mechanical systems together with their common response.

Fig. 6.2 Second-order systems and their time responses

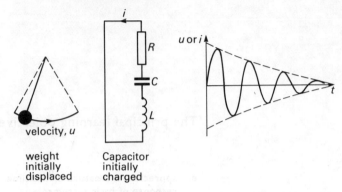

velocity, *u*

weight initially displaced

Capacitor initially charged

The energy-storage elements in the electrical system are capacitance and inductance and, following the treatment in Chapter 2, the response of circuits containing these elements may be determined using the relationships $i = C\, dv/dt$ and $v = L\, di/dt$, together with $v = Ri$ for the resistor and the Kirchhoff laws relating circuit voltages and currents. However, one of the primary purposes of this chapter is to develop more convenient methods of analysis and thus, as the chapter proceeds, it will become possible to avoid the differential and integral relationships and to use relatively straightforward algebraic methods in conjunction with the circuit-analysis techniques developed in Chapter 3.

6.2 The series CR circuit: a first-order system

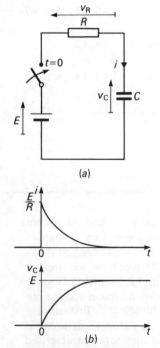

(a)

(b)

Fig. 6.3 Response of CR circuit to applied direct voltage

It is convenient to introduce the subject of the time response of networks with a simple circuit and, fortunately, one which is of practical relevance. The circuit to be discussed is shown in Fig. 6.3 and the aim is to discover how the capacitor voltage varies with time following closure of the switch at time $t = 0$. Applying the Kirchhoff voltage law around the loop gives:

$$v_R + v_C = E \quad \text{(after the switch is closed)},$$

where v_R and v_C are the resistor and capacitor voltages respectively. Substituting $i = C\, dv_C/dt$ gives $v_R = Ri = RC\, dv_C/dt$ resulting in a differential equation in v_C:

$$CR \frac{dv_C}{dt} + v_C = E.$$

E is the source e.m.f. and is known as the **forcing function**, being analogous to the force required to push the car; as a matter of convenience, the forcing function is written on the right-hand side of the equation. The general forms of the current and capacitor-voltage responses are shown in

Fig. 6.3(*b*) but before solving the equation to justify these shapes some general aspects of system responses are discussed.

6.2.1 Natural, forced and complete response

Assuming that the capacitor is initially uncharged, the variation in the voltage v_C and the current i with respect to time is shown in Fig. 6.3(*b*). After closing the switch, the voltage builds up from zero to its final steady-state value E and there is a current flow whilst this takes place. At the end of the period v_C is constant at E and, because $i = C\,dv/dt$, the current flow ceases and the capacitor behaves as an open circuit. This complete response can be resolved into two components. The **forced response** is that component of the total response which is dependent on the forcing function (the battery voltage in this case) and the circuit elements. It is the response which would exist if the forcing function had always been connected to the network. In this example the capacitor-voltage forced response is therefore E. Forced response is also called the **steady-state response**, being that to which the capacitor voltage eventually settles. However, the forcing function is not in fact connected until the switch is closed and it is unlikely that, at the point of switching, the 'initial' condition of the energy-storage elements in the network (i.e. the capacitor voltage) will match the conditions which the forcing function would seek to impose at that time. To bridge this mismatch an additional component of response arises. This is the **natural response**, existing for the period of adjustment only. Its form is dependent on the network elements alone and its magnitude is dependent on the mismatch between the initial conditions and the forced response at the time of switching. The **total response** is the sum of the natural and forced components. The natural and forced components correspond with the complementary function and particular integral components of the total response.

A special case occurs when the forcing function is zero. Then, the forced response does not exist and the total response is also the natural response which, in this case, is dependent only on the network elements and the initial conditions and is known as the **zero-input response**. An example is the freely swinging pendulum (Fig. 6.2) which is given an initial displacement and is then released. The response is shown in Fig. 6.2. The same graph represents the natural current response of an RLC network subject to an initial 'displacement' in the form of an initial charge on the capacitor.

Another term used is the **zero-state response**; this is the complete response (natural and forced) of a network or system having all initial conditions at zero.

6.2.2 Determination of the natural response

Because the form of the natural response is independent of the forcing function, it may be determined by setting E to zero in the differential equation developed for the circuit in Fig. 6.3. Effectively, the circuit becomes that shown in

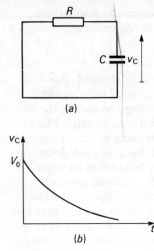

(a)

(b)

Fig. 6.4 Natural response of a CR circuit

Fig. 6.4. The differential equation is now:

$$CR\frac{dv_C}{dt} + v_C = 0.$$

The solution of this equation may be found by the standard procedure of forming an **auxiliary** or **characteristic equation**. A solution, $v_C = V_n e^{s_n t}$ where V_n is a constant and s_n is a circuit parameter, is assumed which, substituting into the equation, gives

$$s_n CR V_n e^{s_n t} + V_n e^{s_n t} = 0.$$

$$\therefore \quad (s_n CR + 1)v_C = 0.$$

Assuming that v_C is not zero, $s_n CR + 1 = 0$ and this is the auxiliary equation. The root of this equation (a single root for this first-order equation) is $s_n = -1/CR$ giving a solution $v_C = V_n e^{-t/CR}$.

To determine the constant V_n, initial conditions are used; if, for example, $v_C(0) = V_0$, $V_n = V_0$ and v_C becomes $V_0 e^{-t/CR}$. The shape of the natural response (Fig. 6.4(b)) will be seen to be a decaying exponential, an effect commonly known as an **exponential discharge** (of a capacitor).

6.2.3 Determination of the forced response

To determine the forced response the complete equation is considered:

$$CR\frac{dv_C}{dt} + v_C = E.$$

A standard method of solution, known as the *D*-operator method, may be used. In this method, differentiation of a variable, v_C in this case, is represented by the operational notation Dv_C. Thus, Dv_C represents dv_C/dt, $D^2 v_C$ represents $d^2 v_C/dt^2$, and so on.

The equation then becomes

$$CRDv_C + v_C = E,$$

or,

$$(CRD + 1)v_C = E,$$

whence

$$v_C = \frac{1}{CRD + 1} E.$$

The term $1/(CRD + 1)$ can be expanded by means of the Binomial theorem:

$$(1 + CRD)^{-1} = 1 + (-1)CRD + \frac{(-1)(-2)(CRD)^2}{2!} + \cdots$$

and the expression for v_C becomes

$$v_C = (1 - CRD + \cdots)E$$

$$= E \quad \text{(because the first and all the higher derivatives are zero).}$$

The forced response is therefore E.

6.2.4 The complete response

The complete response is given by the sum of the two component responses, natural and forced, which have been obtained using the two relationships,

$$(s_n CR + 1)v_C = 0$$

to give the natural component of the response, $v_{Cn} = V_n e^{-t/CR}$,

$$(DCR + 1)v_C = E$$

to give the forced component of the response, $v_{Cf} = E$.

The complete response is, therefore, $v_C = E + V_n e^{-t/CR}$ for $t \geqslant 0$. With the forced component present, a new value for the constant V_n may now be evaluated: if the initial value of the capacitor voltage is zero, i.e. $v_C(0) = 0$, substituting this into the equation gives $0 = E + V_n$, whence $V_n = -E$. Substituting this value into the solution gives, finally,

$$v_C = E(1 - e^{-t/CR}) \quad \text{for } t \geqslant 0.$$

Fig. 6.5 shows the two component responses and the resultant complete response, together with the step-input voltage for reference.

Fig. 6.5 Natural, forced and complete responses of a CR circuit

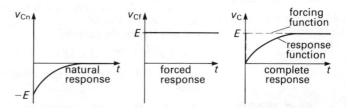

If it is required, the current response may be determined by $i = C\, dv/dt$. Thus $i = EC(-1/CR \cdot -e^{-t/CR}) = (E/R)e^{-t/CR}$ and this is the mathematical description of the waveshape shown in Fig. 6.3(b). Two examples follow: in the first, the natural response resulting from the discharge of an initially charged capacitor through a resistor is found. In the second, the complete response of a series CR circuit to a linearly increasing ramp voltage is determined.

Example 6.1

Determine the voltage variation across the capacitor in the circuit in Fig. 6.6(a) following closure of the switch. C is initially charged to a p.d. of +5 V.

There is no forcing function and the forced response is zero. The complete response is given by the natural response,

$$v_C = V_n e^{-t/CR} \quad \text{for } t \geqslant 0.$$

Initially, $v_C = +5$ when $t = 0$ and, substituting these conditions into the equation, $+5 = V_n$. With this value for V_n and substituting

Fig. 6.6 Network and response for Example 6.1

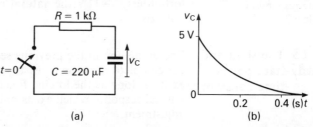

numerical values for C and R,

$$v_C = 5e^{-4.5t} \quad (t \geqslant 0).$$

This response is sketched in Fig. 6.6(b).

Example 6.2   *Determine the complete capacitor-voltage response for the circuit shown in Fig. 6.7. The capacitor is initially charged to $+5\,V$ and the forcing function e is a linearly increasing ramp voltage having a slope of $5 \times 10^6\,V/s$ for $t > 0$.*

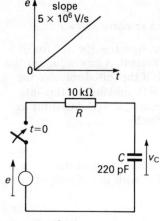

Fig. 6.7 Circuit for Example 6.2

The form of the circuit is the same as in the previous example and the natural response is therefore given by

$$v_{Cn} = V_n e^{-t/CR}$$

where V_n is a constant yet to be determined.
    The forced response is given by

$$v_{Cf} = (1 - CRD + \cdots)e,$$

where e is the ramp forcing function of slope k given by $e = kt$. Then

$$v_{Cf} = (1 - CRD + \cdots)kt \quad \text{(as in Section 6.2.3)}$$
$$= kt - kCR,$$

In this case, the first derivative is not zero, although the higherorder derivatives are. Combining v_{Cn} and v_{Cf} and substituting values for CR and k gives the complete response:

$$v_C = V_n e^{-4.54 \times 10^5 t} + 5 \times 10^6 t - 5 \times 10^6 \times 2.2 \times 10^{-6}$$

for $t \geqslant 0$. Substituting the initial condition, $v_C = +5\,V$ when $t = 0$, gives

$$+5 = V_n - 11,$$

from which

$$V_n = 16\,V,$$

and the complete response is

$$v_C = 16e^{-4.5 \times 10^5 t} + 5 \times 10^6 t - 11\,V \quad (t \geqslant 0).$$

The two component responses and the complete response are sketched in Fig. 6.8. The forcing function is shown for reference on the sketch of the complete response.

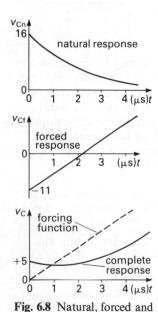

Fig. 6.8 Natural, forced and complete responses in Example 6.2

The results of this example (Fig. 6.8) show how the natural response matches the initial state of the network to the conditions which would be imposed by the forcing function. At time $t = 0$ the forced response has a value of $-11\,V$ and, because the initial capacitor voltage is $+5\,V$, a natural-response component of $5.0 - (-11) = 16\,V$ appears to bridge the mismatch. Had the initial capacitor voltage been, fortuitously, $-11\,V$ the natural response component would not exist.

6.2.5 Transient and steady-state periods: time constant

The discussion in the previous sections has established that the complete response consists of the forced response, which exists as long as the forcing function is connected, and the natural response which exists only during the period of adjustment.

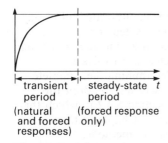

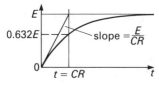

transient period (natural and forced responses) | steady-state period (forced response only) t

Fig. 6.9 Transient and steady-state periods of a charging curve

E

$0.632E$ — slope $= \dfrac{E}{CR}$

0 — $t = CR$ — t

Fig. 6.10 Time constant of a CR circuit

It is common practice to call the natural response the **transient response** and, as previously mentioned, the forced response the **steady-state** response. There is no problem with the latter because, as illustrated in Fig. 6.9, only the forced response exists in the steady-state period. However, during the transient period, both forced and natural components exist and if the term 'transient response' is used in this way, it is necessary to distinguish between 'transient response' and 'response during the transient period'.

A problem may arise in determining just when the transient period finishes and the steady-state period starts: how small does the natural component need to be in order to be neglected? There is no absolute answer, the division depending on the context of the system in which the circuit is used. However, a measure of this time period is provided by the circuit **time constant**, τ. For the single-energy storage system under discussion, time constant is defined as the time which would be needed for the variable (the capacitor voltage in this case) to reach its final value if its initial rate of change were maintained. Fig. 6.10 illustrates this idea. To determine the time constant in this case, v_C may be differentiated with respect to time:

$$\frac{dv_C}{dt} = \frac{E}{CR}\, e^{-t/CR}.$$

Then, at $t = 0$, the initial rate of increase of v_C is E/CR. The diagram shows that the time required to reach the final value, is $E/(E/CR) = CR$. The unit is the second, being the product of coulomb/volt and volt/ampere. Thus, for a series CR combination, the time constant is equal to the product of the resistance and the capacitance.

It will be evident that a time period equal to the time constant is unlikely to be a sufficiently accurate indication of the transient-period duration. As a rule of thumb, a period equal to 5τ is sometimes used. Thus, substituting $t = \tau$ into $v_C = E(1 - e^{-t/\tau})$ gives $v_C = 0.632E$ but $v_C = 0.993E$ when $t = 5\tau$. Although v_C reaches only 63.2% of its final value in the time period equal to one time constant, it reaches 99.3% in period 5τ.

6.3 Forced and natural response related to network poles and zeros

6.3.1 Introduction

In the previous section the principles described in Chapters 1 and 2 were combined to determine the response of a simple CR network. The resulting differential equation was solved using an auxiliary equation and the D-operator method to yield, respectively, the natural and forced components of response. This is one approach but there are alternatives, one of which is the Laplace-transform method. Using this technique, natural and forced components of response are determined and the initial conditions incorporated all in one step. Although it is a relatively sophisticated concept, the transform method is often used even at an introductory level because, for a wide range of problems, it provides a convenient mechanistic means of determining the complete time response of networks. Readers wishing to adopt this approach may proceed directly to Section 6.4.2 in which this problem-solving approach is explained. Chapter 8 then provides some background to transform methods.

A route providing greater insight into the behaviour of systems is presented in the following subsections. These introduce the concept of poles and zeros which are related to the natural and forced responses (including the phasor method). These sections also form a prerequisite to the study of frequency response and the stability of networks discussed in Chapters 7 and 14.

6.3.2 Forced response to exponential forcing functions: the phasor method

In the determination of the forced response in Section 6.2.3 above, the relationship

$$v_C = \frac{1}{CRD + 1} E$$

was developed: in that case E was the forcing function. It is now proposed that a general forcing function $F e^{s_f t}$ (where both F and s_f may be complex in the general case) be used as the basis of a **generalised phasor** method. A range of time functions can be represented by the exponential form, an important example being the cosinusoidal function $\cos \omega t$ which may be expressed in the complex exponential form $\frac{1}{2}(e^{j\omega t} + e^{-j\omega t})$. Because of the importance of this function it is considered in detail in Appendix 6A in which the phasor method (as used in Chapter 4) is developed graphically from the exponential form.

Returning to the general forcing function $F e^{s_f t}$, the effect of the D operator upon it is effectively to replace D by s_f.

$$DF e^{s_f t} = \frac{d}{dt} F e^{s_f t} = s_f F e^{s_f t},$$

a relationship which also holds for functions of D so that, for example,

$$v_C = \frac{1}{CRD + 1} F e^{s_f t} = \frac{1}{s_f CR + 1} F e^{s_f t}.$$

Evidently, v_C has the form $V_C e^{s_f t}$ where $V_C = (1/(s_f CR + 1))F$ and is a complex quantity representing the capacitor-voltage response. Relating to the terminology of Chapter 4, V_C and F will be seen to be effectively phasors related to each other through the phasor operator, $1/(s_f CR + 1)$, where, in this case, s_f (which may be real, imaginary or complex) has replaced $j\omega$. The following example illustrates the procedure by which V_C may be determined for a cosinusoidal forcing function and how the corresponding time function v_C is then found.

Example 6.3   *Determine the capacitor-voltage forced response if the ramp voltage in Example 6.2 is replaced by the cosinusoidal forcing function, 50 cos ωt, where ω = 10⁶ rad/s.*

The important step in the application of the phasor method is the representation of the forcing function by the exponential form: in this case, $50 \cos \omega t$ can be expressed as $25e^{j\omega t} + 25e^{-j\omega t}$, and setting $s_f = \pm j\omega$ in the phasor operator $1/(s_f CR + 1)$ yields

$$V_C = \frac{25}{j\omega CR + 1} + \frac{25}{-j\omega CR + 1}.$$

Substituting values and working in the polar form,

$$V_C = \frac{25}{2.42\underline{/66°}} + \frac{25}{2.42\underline{/-66°}}$$

$$= 10.3\underline{/-66°} + 10.3\underline{/+66°} \text{ V}.$$

To express v_C as a function of time, V_C must be multiplied by $e^{s_f t}$, i.e. $v_C = V_C e^{s_f t}$, where $s_f = \pm j\omega$ in this case. Then

$$v_C = 10.3\underline{/-66°}\, e^{j\omega t} + 10.3\underline{/+66°}\, e^{-j\omega t},$$

and, noting that $\underline{/66°}$ is equivalent to $e^{j66°}$,

$$v_C = 10.3 e^{j(\omega t - 66°)} + 10.3 e^{-j(\omega t - 66°)}$$

$$= 20.6 \cos(\omega t - 66°) \text{ V}.$$

It will be seen that the phasor method can be used for sinusoidal voltages and currents because the sinusoid can be expressed in the exponential form. In fact, there are two exponential components, differing only in the minus sign in front of $j\omega t$, and each line of the solution therefore contains an expression and its complex conjugate. It might be concluded that it would be possible to obtain the same result if only one term of double the magnitude were considered, i.e. $50 \cos \omega t$ represented by $50e^{j\omega t}$ instead of $25e^{j\omega t} + 25e^{-j\omega t}$. Then

$$V_C = \frac{50}{j\omega CR + 1} = \frac{50}{2.42\underline{/66°}} = 20.6\underline{/-66°} \text{ V}$$

in the phasor form, and

$$v_C = 20.6\underline{/-66°}\, e^{j\omega t}$$

which then represents $20.6 \cos(\omega t - 66°)$ V as a function of time.

There are two distinct aspects to the use of the phasor to represent the sinusoidal voltage or current: there is the general technique by which a response R is given in complex form by $R = H(s_f)F$, where $H(s_f)$ is a function of s_f derived from the network and F represents the forcing function, and there is the representation of the sinusoid by the single exponential term $e^{j\omega t}$. The latter aspect is explored graphically in Appendix 6A in which are described several representations of the sinusoid.

Although principally applied to sinusoidal analysis (with $s_f = j\omega$) the phasor principle is applicable to certain other

Fig. 6.11 Responses for various values of *s*

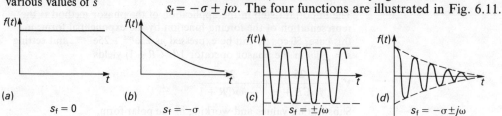

(a) $s_f = 0$

(b) $s_f = -\sigma$

(c) $s_f = \pm j\omega$

(d) $s_f = -\sigma \pm j\omega$

forcing functions. For example, for the direct forcing function $s_f = 0$ (because $e^0 = 1$), for the real exponential $s_f = -\sigma$ (where σ is a real number) and for the decaying sinusoid $s_f = -\sigma \pm j\omega$. The four functions are illustrated in Fig. 6.11.

6.3.3 The network function

Although the discussion has centred on the series *CR* network and the determination of the capacitor voltage, one of the virtues of the phasor method is the ease with which it is possible to handle quite complicated circuits, comprising any combination of resistance, capacitance and inductance. The aim of this subsection is to show how this may be done.

It is convenient to start with the series *LCR* network shown in Fig. 6.12. If the current is assumed to be given by $i = Ie^{st}$, the voltage across each element is then given by the following relationships:

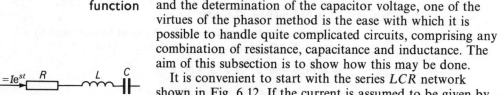

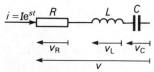

Fig. 6.12 Series RLC network in which current is an exponential function of time

$$v_R = RIe^{st}; \quad v_L = L\frac{\mathrm{d}(Ie^{st})}{\mathrm{d}t} = sLIe^{st};$$

$$v_C = \frac{1}{C}\int Ie^{st}\,\mathrm{d}t = \frac{1}{sC}I^{st}.$$

The total voltage drop across the three elements is then,

$$v = v_R + v_L + v_C = \left(R + sL + \frac{1}{sC}\right)i$$

and a **generalised impedance** $Z(s) = v/i$ can be expressed in the form $R + sL + 1/sC$. A general relationship may thus be stated in the form $r(t) = Z(s)f(t)$ where $r(t)$ and $f(t)$ are the response and forcing functions respectively, both of which contain the factor e^{st}.

In effect, the total impedance of the series circuit is given by the sum of the individual impedances of each circuit element:

$Z(s) = R$ for resistance, R,

$Z(s) = sL$ for inductance, L,

and

$Z(s) = \dfrac{1}{sC}$ for capacitance, C.

Alternatively, as explained in Chapter 4, the admittance forms, $1/R$, $1/sL$ and sC, may be used. It will be seen that the same principle has been used to determine the impedance as was used to find the total resistance of the resistive series circuit in Chapter 3. It may be inferred that all the techniques and theorems developed there may be applied in this more general case but with due allowance being made for the nature of the circuit element. This is the strength of the general phasor method. Furthermore, although the derived expression was in the form of impedance, expressions may be impedances, admittances or dimensionless ratios of voltages or currents. The general term, **network function** $H(s)$ is then used to include all of these possibilities. In particular cases, the network function may be an impedance function $Z(s)$, an admittance function $Y(s)$, or a ratio function, for which symbols such as $G(s)$ may be used. It is emphasised that these functions apply only when the voltages and currents vary exponentially with time, the sinusoidal waveform being a particular example, in which $s = j\omega$. So common is the sinusoidal case that impedance is often taken to imply just that; it is usual to find $\mathbf{Z}$ (alone) used for the impedance to sinusoidal waveforms and $Z(s)$ for the generalised impedance.

Example 6.4

Determine the network function describing the ratio v_C/v (where $v = Ve^{st}$) for the network shown in Fig. 6.13.

The impedance of the CR parallel combination is

$$\frac{1}{\dfrac{1}{R_2} + sC} = \frac{R_2}{1 + sCR_2}.$$

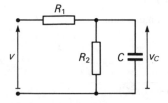

Fig. 6.13 Network for Example 6.4

Using the potential-divider method:

$$\frac{v_C}{v} = \frac{\dfrac{R_2}{1 + sCR_2}}{R_1 + \dfrac{R_2}{1 + sCR_2}}$$

$$= \frac{R_2}{R_1 + sCR_1R_2 + R_2}.$$

6.3.4 Poles and zeros

The network function is a function of s (which in general is complex) and it may be illustrated on a diagram, commonly known as an *s***-plane diagram** or **pole-zero diagram**. To effect this representation the function may be written as the ratio of two polynomials:

$$H(s) = K\frac{s^n + a_{n-1}s^{n-1} + \cdots + a_1s + a_0}{s^m + b_{m-1}s^{m-1} + \cdots + b_1s + b_0}.$$

This may be factorised to give:

$$H(s) = K\frac{(s - z_1)(s - z_2) \cdots (s - z_n)}{(s - p_1)(s - p_2) \cdots (s - p_m)},$$

where $z_1, z_2, \ldots, z_n$ are the roots of the equation formed by equating the numerator to zero and $p_1, p_2, \ldots, p_m$ are the roots of the equation formed by equating the denominator to zero. Setting s equal to z_1 or $z_2, \ldots,$ or z_n will make the numerator (and hence $H(s)$) zero and these are known as the **zeros** of the network function. Setting s equal to p_1 or $p_2, \ldots,$ or p_m will make the denominator zero (and hence $H(s)$

infinite) and these are known as the **poles** of the network function. The values of s $(= \sigma + j\omega$, in general), given by $s = p_1, p_2$, etc., and by $s = z_1, z_2$, etc., may be displayed graphically on the complex plane with σ along the real axis and ω along the imaginary axis. Poles are indicated by '$\times$' on this plane and zeros by '$\bigcirc$'. Fig. 6.14 shows the pole-zero diagram for the network function

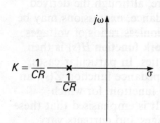

$$H(s) = \frac{1}{sCR + 1} = \frac{1}{CR}\frac{1}{s + 1/CR}.$$

Fig. 6.14 Pole-zero diagram for a CR network

In this simple example, there are no zeros but a pole occurs at $s = -1/CR$ (which is real and negative). The factor $1/CR$ in the numerator is simply a multiplying factor and is shown as $K = 1/CR$ to the left of the plane.

Two examples illustrate pole-zero diagrams for typical networks:

Example 6.5   *Determine an expression for the current i in Fig. 6.15(a) in terms of e and C and R when $e = Ee^{st}$. Hence write down a network function relating i and e and draw a pole-zero diagram.*

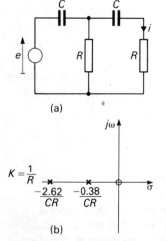

(a)

(b)

Fig. 6.15 Circuit and pole-zero diagram for Example 6.5

Using the mesh-analysis method and Cramer's rule:

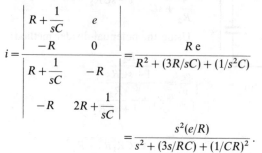

$$i = \frac{\begin{vmatrix} R + \dfrac{1}{sC} & e \\[2mm] -R & 0 \end{vmatrix}}{\begin{vmatrix} R + \dfrac{1}{sC} & -R \\[2mm] -R & 2R + \dfrac{1}{sC} \end{vmatrix}} = \frac{Re}{R^2 + (3R/sC) + (1/s^2C)}$$

$$= \frac{s^2(e/R)}{s^2 + (3s/RC) + (1/CR)^2}.$$

The ratio i/e is the admittance function,

$$Y(s) = \frac{s^2/R}{s^2 + (3s/CR) + (1/CR)^2}.$$

Factorising the denominator, the network function may be expressed in the form,

$$Y(s) = \frac{1}{R}\frac{s^2}{(s + (2.62/CR))(s + (0.38/CR))}.$$

There is a double zero at $s = 0$ and poles at $s = -2.62/CR$ and $s = -0.38/CR$. These are shown in Fig. 6.15(b).

Example 6.6   *Determine the admittance network function for the network shown in Fig. 6.12 and draw a pole-zero diagram for $R = 100\ \Omega$, $L = 36\ mH$ and $C = 0.1\ \mu F$.*

The impedance function $Z(s) = R + sL + 1/sC$. Therefore,

$$Y(s) = \frac{1}{R + sL + (1/sC)}$$

$$= \frac{1}{L}\frac{s}{s^2 + (sR/L) + (1/LC)}.$$

Substituting values,

$$Y(s) = 27.8 \frac{s}{s^2 + 2.78 \times 10^3 s + 2.78 \times 10^8}.$$

The roots of the denominator (the poles) are

$$s_1 = -1.39 \times 10^3 + j16.6 \times 10^3,$$

and

$$s_2 = -1.39 \times 10^3 - j16.6 \times 10^3.$$

The numerator is zero when $s = 0$ and, therefore, there is a zero at $s = 0$. Fig. 6.16 shows the pole-zero diagram.

Fig. 6.16 Pole-zero diagram: solution to Example 6.6

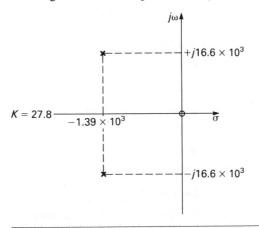

6.3.5 Forced response related to the pole-zero diagram

In the development of the generalised phasor method in Section 6.3.2 the relationship $R = H(s_f)F$ was deduced as the basic phasor relationship linking the phasor response R to the phasor forcing function F. $H(s_f)$ was subsequently identified as the network function and, with this in its factored form,

$$R = K \frac{(s_f - z_1)(s_f - z_2) \cdots}{(s_f - p_1)(s_f - p_2) \cdots} F.$$

The phasor response will be seen to be the result of multiplying the forcing-function phasor by a series of factors $(s_f - z_1)$, $(s_f - z_2)$, ... and dividing by $(s_f - p_1)$, $(s_f - p_2)$, ... These factors describe the lines joining the forcing-function value of s to the network-function zeros and poles respectively. This is illustrated in the following example in which $s_f = +j20 \times 10^3$ corresponding to the cosinusoidal forcing function $50 \cos 20 \times 10^3 t$ V.

Example 6.7   *Determine the forced current response of the series RLC network whose pole-zero diagram is drawn in Fig. 6.16 given that the forcing function is $50 \cos 20 \times 10^3 t$ V. (Diagram is not drawn to scale.)*

The pole-zero diagram is redrawn in Fig. 6.17 with the phasors joining the zero and the poles to the points $s_f = +j20 \times 10^3$. The forced response (in phasor form) is,

$$K \frac{s_f - z_1}{(s_f - p_1)(s_f - p_2)} V = K \frac{M_1}{M_2 M_3} V.$$

Fig. 6.17 Pole-zero diagram
leading to solution to
Example 6.7

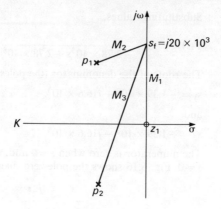

Substituting values, $K = 27.8$

$s_f - z_1 = 20 \times 10^3\underline{/90°}$,

$s_f - p_1 = 3.67 \times 10^3\underline{/67.8°}$,

$s_f - p_2 = 36.6 \times 10^3\underline{/87.8°}$,

and

$\mathbf{V} = 50\underline{/0°}$ V.

Then

$\mathbf{I} = 0.207\underline{/-65.5°}$ A.

Checking against the result obtained using the method developed in
Chapter 4, $\mathbf{I} = \mathbf{V}/(R + j\omega L + 1/j\omega C)$. Substituting values, $\mathbf{V} = 50$ V,
$R = 100\ \Omega$, $L = 36$ mH, $C = 0.1\ \mu F$,

$\mathbf{I} = 0.207\underline{/-65.6°}$ A.

Although the sinusoidal forcing function is most commonly
used the method works for any exponential forcing function.
Example 6.8 determines a forced response to a forcing
function $4e^{-7t}$ V.

Example 6.8   *Determine the forced response of the capacitor voltage in the network*
shown in Fig. 6.18(a) to the real exponential forcing function, $4\,e^{-7t}$ V.

Fig. 6.18 Circuit and pole-
zero diagram for
Example 6.8

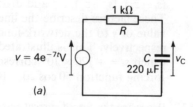

(a)

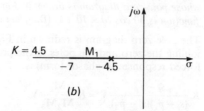

(b)

The network function is

$$\frac{1/sC}{R + 1/sC} = \frac{1}{CR} \frac{1}{s + 1/CR}.$$

Substituting values, the pole-zero diagram shown in Fig. 6.18(*b*) results. The forced capacitor-voltage response in the general phasor form is then given by $V_C = (K/M_1)E$, where $K = 4.5$, $E = 4$ and M_1 is the line joining $s_f(= -7)$ to the pole (at $s = -4.5$). Thus

$$V_C = \frac{4.5}{-2.5} 4 = -7.4.$$

To obtain the result as a function of time, $e^{s_f t}$ must be reinserted to give $v_C = -7.4\,e^{-7t}\,V$.

Note: this result is the forced component of response only and happens to be negative in this case. If the forcing function were suddenly applied to the network a natural component would also exist, matching the magnitude of the forced component to the condition of the capacitor at the time of connection.

6.3.6 Natural response related to the pole-zero diagram

In Section 2.2 of this chapter the natural response of a network was determined from the auxiliary equation. For example, if an equation has two (different) roots s_{n_1} and s_{n_2}, the natural response is given by

$$r_n(t) = K_{n_1} e^{s_{n_1} t} + K_{n_2} e^{s_{n_2} t}.$$

The equation itself is formed from the differential equation by setting the forcing function to zero and the same procedure is now applied to the network-function relationship to show that the roots of the equation are in fact the poles of the network function.

The general relationship between the response function $r(t)$ and the forcing function $f(t)$ in terms of the network function $H(s)$ may be formally stated as,

$$r(t) = H(s)f(t),$$

where $f(t)$, and hence $r(t)$, must contain the factor e^{st}. If $H(s)$ is now expressed as the ratio of two polynomials in s such that

$$r(t) = \frac{B(s)}{D(s)} f(t),$$

then

$$D(s)r(t) = B(s)f(t).$$

Setting the forcing function to zero will yield the roots s_{n_1} and s_{n_2}. Thus, if $f(t) = 0$,

$$D(s)r(t) = 0,$$

from which, provided $r(t)$ is itself not zero,

$$D(s) = 0.$$

But the poles of the network are given by setting $D(s)$ to zero and, therefore, the roots s_{n_1} and s_{n_2} are in fact the poles. It follows that the natural response is given by,

$$r_n(t) = K_{n_1} e^{p_1 t} + K_{n_2} e^{p_2 t} + \cdots,$$

where $p_1, p_2, p_3, \ldots$ are the poles of the network function.

The form of the natural response depends on the pole positions on the complex plane and a graphical summary of the relationships is given in Fig. 6.19. In this diagram the complex and imaginary poles occur in conjugate pairs, indicating a sinusoidal waveshape. Unlike the networks described so far, there is a class of networks which can have poles in the right-hand half plane, leading to a response which increases in amplitude as time proceeds. This aspect is explored further in Chapter 14.

Fig. 6.19 Relationship between the form of the natural response and pole position

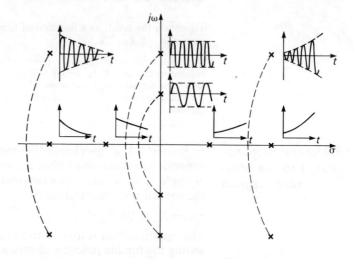

To relate the response shapes shown in Fig. 6.19 to an actual network, the natural current response of the *RLC* series network whose pole-zero diagram is illustrated in Fig. 6.16 is a decaying sinusoid, corresponding with the pair of conjugate poles having negative real parts. This form of response (which is known as an **underdamped** response) is shown in Fig. 6.20, together with typical responses for two other identifiable response forms. All are derived from the general expression for the admittance function whose poles are given by $s^2 + (sR/L) + (1/LC) = 0$:

$$p_1 = \frac{-R/L + \sqrt{[(R/L)^2 - (4/LC)]}}{2}$$

Fig. 6.20 Response of RLC network for various degrees of damping

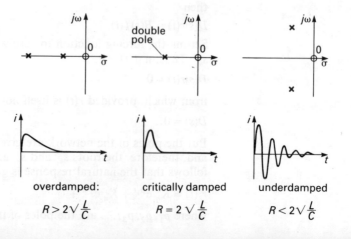

overdamped:

$R > 2\sqrt{\dfrac{L}{C}}$

critically damped

$R = 2\sqrt{\dfrac{L}{C}}$

underdamped

$R < 2\sqrt{\dfrac{L}{C}}$

and

$$p_2 = \frac{-R/L - \sqrt{[(R/L)^2 - (4/LC)]}}{2}.$$

Inspection of these roots shows that they may be real, complex or real and equal according to whether $(R/L)^2$ is greater than, less than or equal to $4/LC$. Expressions for these waveforms are derived in Example 6.12.

6.4 The Laplace transform

6.4.1 Introduction

The network function involves the circuit elements and the variable s which may be zero, real, imaginary or, in general, complex. In the solution of a particular problem, particular values of s are involved: those obtained by equating the denominator of the network function to zero (the poles of the network function) are used to obtain the natural response and those derived from the forcing function (e.g. $s = +j\omega$ for the sinusoid) to obtain the forced response. Obtaining the forced response in this way was seen as a more general form of the phasor technique introduced in Chapter 4.

Because the same form of the response, e^{st}, applied for the natural and forced components (even though s took on a different value in each case) the same network function could be used. Furthermore, because the effect of differentiation with respect to time means multiplication by s (i.e. $(d/dt)e^{st} = se^{st}$) and integration means division by s ($\int e^{st}\,dt = (1/s)e^{st}$) the network function is a straightforward algebraic function of s, and the circuit-analysis methods developed in Chapter 3 for resistive circuits can be more widely applied. Also of interest is the removal of the time variable, an aspect discussed in Appendix 6A. There it is shown how multiplying a rotating phasor by $e^{-j\omega t}$ (e^{-st} in general) renders the phasor stationary. This will be seen to be a feature of the Laplace transform definition in the next section.

6.4.2 Basic principles

The basis of the Laplace transform method is the transformation of a function of time $f(t)$ into a function of a complex variable s by means of the transform integral:

$$F(s) = \int_0^\infty f(t)e^{-st}\,dt.$$

As defined, $F(s)$ is the **unilateral Laplace transform**, for which the lower limit of integration is at $t = 0-$, and the principal aim of this chapter is to show how it may be used as a tool for the determination of the time response of networks. In this form $f(t)$ is zero for $t < 0$.

In contrast with the generalised-phasor method, the transformed function of time becomes a function of the new variable, in the same way as the original function was a function of the time variable t; s does not take on particular values any more than, for example, a particular value for t is implied in a statement such as $f(t) = 1 - \cos \omega t$. Thus, the phasor method is not a transform method in this sense. Having transformed the time function into a function of s, all the operations are algebraic and the circuit analysis is relatively straightforward. Having performed the analysis, the result is transformed back into a function of time. The transformation is said to be made from the **time domain** into the **complex frequency domain** and back again. This terminology is explained in Chapter 8.

The whole process is illustrated in Fig. 6.21 where a **step input** voltage of height E, denoted $Eu(t)$, is transformed into a function of s and then multiplied by a transfer function $G(s)$ (which, in this case with zero initial capacitor charge has the same form as the network function) to give the transformed zero-state response function $R(s)$. To obtain the solution, $R(s)$ is transformed back into a function of time. The detailed procedures of the transformation into and out of the complex-frequency domain are explained in the following sections.

Fig. 6.21 Basic procedure in determining time response using the Laplace transform technique

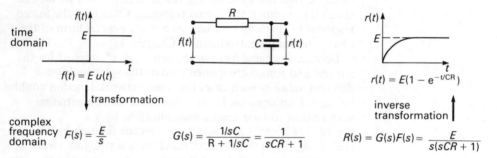

$$f(t) = E u(t)$$

$$F(s) = \frac{E}{s}$$

$$G(s) = \frac{1/sC}{R + 1/sC} = \frac{1}{sCR + 1}$$

$$r(t) = E(1 - e^{-t/CR})$$

$$R(s) = G(s)F(s) = \frac{E}{s(sCR + 1)}$$

It will be seen that the solution contains both natural and forced components of response and this is an important property of the transform technique not shared by the phasor method. In order to obtain the complete response it is of course necessary to insert any non-zero initial conditions into the solution and the way in which this is done is explained in the following sections.

6.4.3 Transformation of basic time functions and general properties

In the illustration in Fig. 6.21 the step function of time $Eu(t)$ was transformed to E/s in the frequency domain. This is one of a range of basic Laplace transforms (Table 6.1) derived from the defining integral. To be consistent with previously used notations, upper-case symbols are used to denote functions of frequency with the lower-case forms for functions of time. Further, to emphasise this notation, the function $-s$ and function $-t$ notation is used throughout. Thus, $F(s) = \mathscr{L}[f(t)]$, where the script $\mathscr{L}$ is read as 'the Laplace transform of...'. Inversely, $f(t) = \mathscr{L}^{-1}[F(s)]$. Also used are $V(s)$ and $I(s)$ when the variables are voltages or currents respectively. Thus, for example, $V(s) = \mathscr{L}[v(t)]$.

A range of basic transforms is derived as follows.

(a) The unit impulse: $f(t) = \delta(t)$. This function is introduced in Section 4 of Chapter 2 and is defined in Section 1.1 of

Chapter 9, as having zero width, infinite amplitude and unit area.

$$F(s) = \mathcal{L}[f(t)] = \int_{0-}^{\infty} \delta(t) e^{-st} \, dt.$$

Because the function is zero except at $t = 0$ (at which time $e^{-st} = 1$), $F(s)$ becomes $\int_{0-}^{\infty} \delta(t) \, dt$ and its value is the area under the graph of the function, i.e. $\mathcal{L}[\delta(t)] = 1$.

(b) *The unit-amplitude exponential:* $f(t) = e^{s_1 t}$, $(t \geqslant 0)$.

$$F(s) = \mathcal{L}[f(t)] = \int_0^{\infty} e^{s_1 t} e^{-st} \, dt$$

$$= \int_0^{\infty} e^{-(s-s_1)t} \, dt$$

$$= \frac{-1}{s-s_1} \left[e^{-(s-s_1)t} \right]_0^{\infty}$$

$$= \frac{1}{s-s_1}.$$

A number of special cases follow from this result:

(i) *Unit step:* $f(t) = u(t)$. In this case there is no 'decay' as such and $s_1 = 0$. Hence $\mathcal{L}[u(t)] = 1/s$.

(ii) *Real decay:* $f(t) = e^{-\alpha t}$ for $t \geqslant 0$ where α is real and positive. In this case $s_1 = -\alpha$ and $\mathcal{L}e^{-\alpha t} = 1/(s+\alpha)$.

(iii) *Hyperbolic function:* $f(t) = \cosh \beta t = \frac{1}{2}(e^{\beta t} + e^{-\beta t})$ for $t \geqslant 0$, where β is real and positive. Setting $s_1 = \pm \beta$ gives

$$\mathcal{L}[\cosh \beta t] = \frac{1}{2}\left(\frac{1}{s_1 - \beta} + \frac{1}{s_1 + \beta} \right) = \frac{s}{s^2 - \beta^2}.$$

(iv) *Sinusoidal function:* $f(t) = \cos \omega t = \frac{1}{2}(e^{j\omega t} + e^{-j\omega t})$ for $t \geqslant 0$, where ω is real and positive. Putting $s_1 = \pm j\omega$,

$$\mathcal{L}[\cos \omega t] = \frac{1}{2}\left(\frac{1}{s - j\omega} + \frac{1}{s + j\omega} \right) = \frac{s}{s^2 + \omega^2}.$$

(c) *Unit-slope ramp:* $f(t) = t$ for $t \geqslant 0$.

$$F(s) = \mathcal{L}[f(t)] = \int_0^{\infty} t e^{-st} \, dt$$

$$= \left[-\frac{t}{s} e^{-st} \right]_0^{\infty} - \int_0^{\infty} -\frac{1}{s} e^{-st} \, dt$$

(integrating by parts)

$$= \frac{1}{s^2}.$$

Table 6.1 summarises these results and is followed immediately by Table 6.2 which lists a number of general properties of the Laplace transform. Combinations of the basic-function transforms and the theorems enable a wide range of functions to be handled. Examples are given after the tables. Although proofs of the general properties are not

Table 6.1. *Basic transform pairs*

	$f(t)$ for $t \geqslant 0$	$F(s)$
Unit impulse	$\delta(t)$	1
Unit step	$u(t)$	$1/s$
Real decay	$e^{-\alpha t}$	$1/(s+\alpha)$
Hyperboloid	$\cosh \beta t$	$s/(s^2 - \beta^2)$
	$\sinh \beta t$	$\beta/(s^2 - \beta^2)$
Sinusoid	$\cos \omega t$	$s/(s^2 + \omega^2)$
	$\sin \omega t$	$\omega/(s^2 + \omega^2)$
Unit-slope ramp	t	$1/s^2$

Table 6.2. *General transform properties*

	Time domain	*Frequency domain*
Amplitude scaling	$Af(t)$	$AF(s)$
Time scaling	$f(at)$	$(1/a)F(s/a)$
Time shift	$f(t-a)u(t-a)$	$e^{-as}F(s)$ $(a > 0)$
Frequency shift (time damping)	$e^{-at}f(t)$	$F(s+a)$
Multiplication by t	$tf(t)$	$-dF(s)/ds$
Initial-value theorem	$\lim_{t \to 0+} f(t)$	$\lim_{s \to \infty} sF(s)$
Final-value theorem	$\lim_{t \to \infty} f(t)$	$\lim_{s \to 0} sF(s)$ $(F(s)$ to have no poles in the right-hand half plane)

given they may be justified fairly easily by means of the defining integral or are available in a number of references.

Example 6.9   *Determine $F(s)$ for the following functions of time: (i) $6\,e^{-5t}$; (ii) $5\cos 3t + 2\sin 3t$; (iii) $10\,e^{-7t}\sin 4t$; (iv) $t\,e^{-5t}$; (v) a rectangular pulse of 100 ms duration and 5 units high.*

(i) $6/(s+5)$, using real decay and amplitude scaling;

(ii) $5s/(s^2+9) + 6/(s^2+9) = (5s+6)/(s^2+9)$, using sinusoid, amplitude scaling and linear superposition;

(iii) $10[4/((s+7)^2 + 16)] = 40/(s^2 + 14s + 65)$, using sinusoid, amplitude scaling and frequency shift;

(iv) $(-d/ds)(1/(s+5)) = 1/(s+5)^2$, using real decay and multiplication by t;

(v)   for the rectangular pulse, $f(t) = 5u(t) - 5u(t-0.1)$, whose transform is $5/s - 5e^{-0.1s}/s = 5(1-e^{-0.1s})/s$, using step, time shift and superposition.

Example 6.10   *Determine $f(t)$ for the following functions of s. (i) $2/(s-2)$; (ii) $4/(s^2-4)$; (iii) $6/(s^2+8s+25)$; (iv) $6/s^4$; (v) $5/(s+3)^2$; (vi) $1 + e^{-s} + e^{-2s} + e^{-3s} + \cdots$.*

(i) $2\,e^{2t}$, using amplitude scaling and real decay;

(ii) $2\sinh 2t$, using amplitude scaling and hyperboloid;

(iii) completing the square gives $F(s) = 6/((s+4)^2 + 9)$ for which $f(t)$ is $2e^{-4t}\sin 3t$, using amplitude scaling, sinusoid and frequency shift;

(iv) t^3. The original function of s is one which results from repeated differentiation of the function $1/s$. This means that the function of time is the inverse transform of $1/s$ multiplied by t as many times as $1/s$ was differentiated; in this example three differentiations are involved;

(v) $5te^{-3t}$, using amplitude scaling, real decay and multiplication by t. The general principle involved in the note against (iv) above also applies in this case;

(vi) $\delta(t) + \delta(t-1) + \delta(t-2) + \delta(t-3) + \cdots$, using unit impulse and time shifting.

Example 6.11

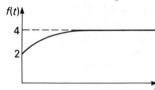

Fig. 6.22 Time function for Example 6.11

Sketch a graph of the time function $f(t) = (4 - 2e^{-2t})u(t)$ and hence determine its value at $t = 0+$ and $t = \infty$. Also determine $F(s)$ and use the initial and final-value theorems to check the values.

The sketch of the function is shown in Fig. 6.22. Using Table 6.1, $F(s) = (4/s) - (2/(s+2))$. Using the initial-value theorem,

$$\lim_{s \to \infty} sF(s) = \lim_{s \to \infty} (4 - 2s/(s+2)) = 4 - 2 = 2.$$

Using the final-value theorem,

$$\lim_{s \to 0} sF(s) = \lim_{s \to 0} (4 - 2s/(s+4)) = 4.$$

Both results are consistent with the sketch.

6.4.4 Laplace transform of a derivative and transformed circuit elements

In Fig. 6.21 the response $R(s)$ was obtained by multiplying the forcing function $F(s)$ by the transfer function $G(s)$, the latter obtained using normal network-analysis rules with the resistor represented by R and the capacitor by $1/sC$. This form of representation may be justified by applying the transform defining integral to the voltage–current relationship for each circuit element. This is demonstrated as follows.

For the resistor, $v(t) = Ri(t)$ and, R being constant, the first entry in Table 6.2 applies resulting in $V(s) = RI(s)$ or $V(s)/I(s) = R$. For the capacitor $i(t) = C\,dv(t)/dt$ and it is necessary to transform a derivative. In general terms the transform of the derivative $f'(t)$ of the function $f(t)$ is given by

$$\mathscr{L}[f'(t)] = \int_0^\infty f'(t)\,e^{-st}\,dt$$

$$= [e^{-st}f(t)]_0^\infty + s\int_0^\infty f(t)\,e^{-st}\,dt$$

(integrating by parts)

$$= -f(0) + sF(s),$$

where $f(0)$ is the value of $f(t)$ when $t = 0$ and $F(s) = \mathscr{L}[f(t)]$. Thus, the transform of the first derivative of a function whose transform is $F(s)$ and whose initial value is $f(0)$, is $sF(s) - f(0)$. Higher order derivatives may be transformed in a similar way giving, in general,

$$\mathscr{L}[f^n(t)] = s^n F(s) - s^{n-1}f(0) - s^{n-2}f'(0) \cdots f^{n-1}(0).$$

The result may be applied immediately to the capacitor:

$$i(t) = C\,dv(t)/dt,$$

$$\therefore \quad I(s) = C(sV(s) - v(0)),$$

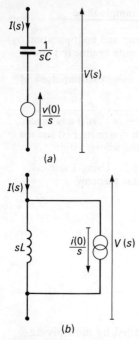

(a)

(b)

Fig. 6.23 Capacitance and inductance with non-zero initial conditions

where $I(s)$ and $V(s)$ are the transform of $i(t)$ and $v(t)$ and $v(0)$ is the initial value of $v(t)$. If the expression is rearranged it becomes

$$V(s) = \frac{I(s)}{sC} + \frac{v(0)}{s},$$

and the transformed potential difference across the capacitor will be seen to be in the form of a transformed current multiplied by a reactance $1/sC$ to which is added an initial-condition term $v(0)/s$. The relationship is illustrated in Fig. 6.23(a) which is sometimes known as the **transformed-circuit** representation of a charged capacitor.

A similar procedure may be used for the inductor:

$$v(t) = L\, di(t)/dt,$$

$$\therefore \quad V(s) = L(sI(s) - i(0)).$$

Rearranging,

$$I(s) = \frac{V(s)}{sL} + \frac{i(0)}{s},$$

and the transformed current in the inductor will be seen to be in the form of a transformed voltage divided by an impedance sL to which is added an initial-condition term $i(0)/s$. The relationship is illustrated in Fig. 6.23(b). Alternatively, the transform of an integral may be used to give the same results. Thus, for the capacitor for example,

$$v(t) = \frac{1}{C}\int_0^t i(\tau)\, d\tau + v(0)$$

transforms directly to

$$V(s) = \frac{I(s)}{sC} + \frac{v(0)}{s},$$

the transform of an integral of a function effectively dividing its transform by s whereas the transform of a derivative of a function multiplies its transform by s.

6.4.5 Circuit analysis

The essential procedure in Fig. 6.21 is to obtain a response function $R(s)$ by multiplying a forcing function $F(s)$ by a network function $H(s)$. The response, as a function of time, is then obtained from the inverse transform of $R(s)$. The response so obtained is the zero-state response. To allow for non-zero initial conditions it is necessary to work from the differential equation or to use the transformed network method explained in the previous subsection. The procedure is further illustrated by another straightforward example. Suppose it is required to determine the voltage appearing across a coil of inductance 0.1 H and negligible resistance in parallel with a 20 Ω resistor into which a constant current of 2 A is switched. The transformed forcing function (a step function) is $2/s$ and the network function (for resistance and inductance is parallel) is $(20 \cdot s0.1)/(20 + s0.1)$ giving a voltage response

$$V(s) = I(s)Z(s)$$

$$= \frac{2}{s} \frac{20 \cdot s0.1}{20 + s0.1} = \frac{4}{20 + s0.1}$$

$$= \frac{40}{s + 200}.$$

The inverse transform $v(t)$ is then, by reference to Table 6.1,

$$v(t) = 40e^{-t/200} \text{ V}.$$

In this example the inverse transform was determined from Tables 6.1 and 6.2 by inspection. This was because it was a simple combination of a real decay and an amplitude scaling function. In Example 6.10 a number of less obvious inverse transforms were determined and it is likely that, sooner or later, the need to obtain the inverse transform of even more complicated functions will arise. Differing approaches to this problem are possible; one is to use a more extensive table and another is to decompose the function into a number of simple functions. Because the former method still leaves the difficulty of rearranging a given expression into the right form to fit the table, the latter approach is adopted here. Furthermore, even with an extended table, it is likely that there will be occasions when the latter method is required and it must therefore be understood in any case.

The basis of the method is the expansion of a given function of s into a series of single-pole terms. For example, $F(s) = (s + 2)/((s + 4)(s + 5))$ can be expressed in the form $(3/(s + 5)) - (2/(s + 4))$ for which the inverse transform is $3e^{-5t} - 2e^{-4t}$. The method is as follows:

(i) For functions of the form $B(s)/D(s)$ where $B(s)$ is of lower degree than $D(s)$ and $D(s)$ contains no repeated factors, then

$$F(s) = \frac{A}{s - s_1} + \frac{B}{s - s_2} \cdots,$$

where $A, B, \ldots$ are given by

$$A = (s - s_1)F(s)|_{s=s_1}, \quad B = (s - s_2)F(s)|_{s=s_2}, \ldots.$$

For the example above,

$$F(s) = \frac{s + 2}{(s + 4)(s + 5)} = \frac{A}{s + 4} + \frac{B}{s + 5},$$

where

$$A = (s + 4)F(s)|_{s=-4} = \frac{s + 2}{s + 5}\bigg|_{s=-4} = -2,$$

and

$$B = (s + 5)F(s)|_{s=-5} = \frac{s + 2}{s + 4}\bigg|_{s=-5} = 3,$$

whence

$$F(s) = \frac{3}{s + 5} - \frac{2}{s + 4}.$$

Because of the nature of the method, the results are effectively obtained by suppressing the corresponding factor in the denominator and the method is sometimes called the **cover-up rule**.

(ii) If there is a repeated factor in the denominator, a double or treble pole for example, additional factors are needed. For example, the function

$$F(s) = \frac{3s + 4}{(s+2)^2(s+3)}$$

must be written as

$$\frac{A_1}{(s+2)^2} + \frac{A_2}{(s+2)} + \frac{B}{(s+3)},$$

the number of factors A_1, A_2, etc., being the same as the multiplicity of the pole (two in this case). Then, A_1 is given by

$$(s+2)^2 F(s)\big|_{s=-2} = \frac{3s+4}{s+3}\bigg|_{s=-2} = -2.$$

A_2 is given by

$$\frac{d}{ds} \frac{3s+4}{s+3}\bigg|_{s=-2} = \left[\frac{3}{s+3} - \frac{3s+4}{(s+3)^2}\right]_{s=-2} = 5.$$

The factor B is found in the usual way as

$$(s+3)F(s)\big|_{s=-3} = -5,$$

to give a complete result,

$$F(s) = \frac{5}{s+2} - \frac{2}{(s+2)^2} - \frac{5}{s+3}.$$

In this second example the corresponding function of time is readily determined as
$f(t) = \mathcal{L}^{-1}[F(s)] = 5e^{-2t} - 2te^{-2t} - 5e^{-3t}$. As previously noted, the double pole introduces the factor t into the relevant term.

A range of examples illustrate the various principles.

Example 6.12   *Deduce the natural component of the current flowing when a 0.1 µF capacitor, initially charged to 5 V, is discharged through an inductance of 36 mH and a resistance of 100 Ω in series. Repeat the calculation with the resistance set at its critical value and with R = 3 kΩ, i.e. in an overdamped condition.*

The transformed circuit is shown in Fig. 6.24 with conventional circuit symbols. From the circuit

$$0 = V_L(s) + V_R(s) + V_C(s),$$

$$0 = sLI(s) + RI(s) + \frac{I(s)}{sC} + \frac{v(0)}{s},$$

giving

$$I(s) = \frac{-v(0)/s}{R + sL + (1/sC)}$$

$$= -\frac{v(0)}{L} \frac{1}{s^2 + (sR/L) + (1/LC)}.$$

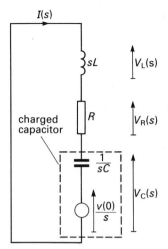

Fig. 6.24 Transformed circuit for Example 6.12

Substituting values $v(0) = 5\,\text{V}$, $R = 100\,\Omega$, $L = 36\,\text{mH}$ and $C = 0.1\,\mu\text{F}$.

$$I(s) = -\frac{139}{s^2 + 2.78 \times 10^3 s + 2.78 \times 10^8}.$$

The inverse transform may be obtained by completing the square (in the manner of Example 6.10(iii)):

$$I(s) = \frac{139}{(s + 1.39 \times 10^3)^2 + (16.6 \times 10^3)^2}.$$

Adjusting the numerator to put the expression into the standard form given in Table 6.1,

$$I(s) = -8.37 \times 10^{-3} \frac{16.6 \times 10^3}{(s + 1.39 \times 10^3) + (16.6 \times 10^3)^2}.$$

The inverse transform is then,

$$i(t) = -8.37 e^{-1.39 \times 10^3 t} \sin 16.6 \times 10^3 t \ \text{mA}.$$

A typical underdamped response is illustrated in Fig. 6.20.

The critical resistance in this circuit is $2\sqrt{(L/C)} = 1200\,\Omega$. And the expression for the current then becomes

$$I(s) = -\frac{139}{s^2 + 3.33 \times 10^4 s + 2.78 \times 10^8}$$

$$= -\frac{139}{(s + 16.6 \times 10^3)^2}.$$

The form of this expression is $1/(s + \alpha)^2$ whose inverse transform is $te^{-\alpha t}$, using the 'multiplication by t' entry in Table 6.2. Thus, $i(t) = -139 t e^{-16.6 \times 10^3 t}\,\text{mA}$. This is also illustrated in Fig. 6.20.

Finally, setting R at $3\,\text{k}\Omega$ gives

$$I(s) = -\frac{139}{s^2 + 8.33 \times 10^4 s + 2.78 \times 10^8}.$$

Completing the square

$$I(s) = -\frac{139}{(s^2 + 4.16 \times 10^4)^2 - (3.82 \times 10^4)^2}.$$

Adjusting the numerator

$$I(s) = 3.63 \times 10^{-3} \frac{3.82 \times 10^4}{(s^2 + 4.16 \times 10^4) - (3.82 \times 10^4)^2},$$

and

$$i(t) = -3.63 e^{-4.16 \times 10^4 t} \sinh 3.82 \times 10^4 t \ \text{mA}.$$

This completes the set of three responses illustrated in Fig. 6.20.

Example 6.13 *Repeat Example 6.2 (Section 6.2.4) using the Laplace-transform method.*

Referring to the transformed network in Fig. 6.25,

$$I(s) = \frac{E(s) - v(0)/s}{R + 1/sC},$$

where $E(s)$ is the transform of the forcing function which, for the

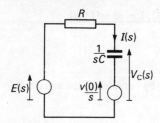

Fig. 6.25 Transformed circuit for Example 6.13

given ramp function, is $5 \times 10^6/s^2$. Thus,

$$I(s) = \frac{(5 \times 10^6/s^2) - (5/s)}{10^4 + (1/s \times 220 \times 10^{-12})}$$

$$= \frac{500}{s(s + 4.54 \times 10^5)} - \frac{5 \times 10^{-4}}{s + 4.54 \times 10^5}.$$

Reducing the first term to single-pole form:

$$I(s) = \frac{1.1 \times 10^{-3}}{s} - \frac{1.6 \times 10^{-3}}{s + 4.54 \times 10^5}.$$

Then

$$V_C(s) = \frac{I(s)}{sC} + \frac{v(0)}{s}$$

$$= \frac{5 \times 10^6}{s^2} - \frac{7.27 \times 10^6}{s(s + 4.54 \times 10^5)} + \frac{5}{s}.$$

Again arranging in single-pole form,

$$V_C(s) = \frac{5 \times 10^6}{s^2} - \frac{11}{s} + \frac{16}{s + 4.54 \times 10^5},$$

from which, using Table 6.1, the inverse transform is

$$v_C(t) = 5 \times 10^6 t - 11 + 16e^{-4.54 \times 10^5 t} \, \text{V}.$$

The result obtained in Example 6.13 is the same as that obtained in Example 6.2. It will be seen that, in this case, the work required using the Laplace method is greater than the methods of Example 6.2; although the Laplace method has advantages, it should not automatically be assumed that it is the most convenient or rapid method of solution in every case.

Example 6.14   *Determine the voltage waveform across the 10 kΩ resistor in Fig. 6.26. The voltage v_i is a 5 V pulse of 10 ms duration. The capacitor is initially uncharged.*

Fig. 6.26 Circuit for Example 6.14

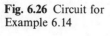

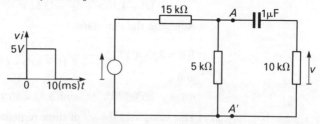

Applying the Thévenin theorem to the circuit to the left of terminals AA' gives the modified circuit shown in Fig. 6.27. The equivalent pulse amplitude, v_i', is now $5 \times (5/(5 + 15)) = 1.25$ V and the equivalent resistance is $(5 \times 15)/(5 + 15) = 3.75$ kΩ. The equivalent input pulse can be represented by a step voltage, $1.25u(t)$, to which is added a negative delayed step, $-1.25u(t - 10^{-2})$, the width of the pulse being 10^{-2} s. Thus

$$v_i' = 1.25[u(t) - u(t - 10^{-2})].$$

Its transform is (using the time-shift theorem),

$$1.25 \left[\frac{1}{s} - \frac{e^{-10^{-2}s}}{s} \right].$$

Fig. 6.27 Thévenin equivalent of the circuit in Fig. 6.26

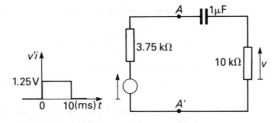

Now, using potential-divider method,

$$\mathscr{L}[v] = V(s) = \frac{10^4}{10^4 + 3.75 \times 10^3 + 1/10^{-6}s} \cdot 1.25\left[\frac{1}{s} - \frac{e^{-10^{-2}s}}{s}\right]$$

$$= \frac{1.25(1 - e^{-10^{-2}s})}{1.375s + 100} = \frac{0.91}{s + 73} - \frac{0.91e^{-10^{-2}s}}{s + 73}.$$

Taking the inverse transform from the table (and using the time-delay theorem),

$$v = 0.91e^{-73t}u(t) - 0.91\,e^{-73(t-10^{-2})}u(t - 10^{-2})\ \text{V}.$$

The waveform is shown in Fig. 6.28.

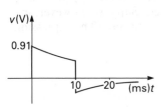

Fig. 6.28 Solution to Example 6.14

The final example provides a justification for the capacitor-voltage variation assumed in Section 2.4.3 of Chapter 2. It also illustrates the use of initial conditions when an impulsive current flows.

Example 6.15 *Determine the variation with time of the voltage across C_2 and the current in the circuit shown in Fig. 6.29. C_1 is initially charged to voltage V_0 (i.e. $v_{C_1}(0-) = V_0$) and C_2 is initially uncharged.*

The transformed circuit is shown in Fig. 6.30. The initial value of v_{C_1} is shown as $(v_{C_1}(0-))/s$, i.e. V_0/s. Applying the Kirchhoff voltage law,

$$\frac{V_0}{s} - \frac{I(s)}{sC_1} - RI(s) - \frac{I(s)}{sC_2} = 0.$$

$$\therefore\quad I(s) = \frac{\dfrac{V_0}{s}}{\dfrac{1}{sC_1} + R + \dfrac{1}{sC_2}} = \frac{\dfrac{V_0}{R}}{s + \dfrac{C_1 + C_2}{RC_1C_2}} = \frac{\dfrac{V_0}{R}}{s + \dfrac{1}{CR}},$$

where

$$C = \frac{C_1C_2}{C_1 + C_2}.$$

Taking the inverse transform:

$$i = \frac{V_0}{R}e^{-t/CR},$$

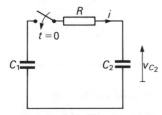

Fig. 6.29 Circuit for Example 6.15

as shown in Fig. 2.27. Also,

$$V_{C_2}(s) = \frac{I(s)}{sC_2} = \frac{\dfrac{V_0}{R}}{sC_2\left(s + \dfrac{C_1 + C_2}{RC_1C_2}\right)} = \frac{\dfrac{V_0C_1}{C_1 + C_2} \cdot \dfrac{1}{CR}}{s\left(s + \dfrac{1}{CR}\right)},$$

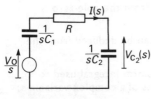

Fig. 6.30 Transformed circuit representation of Fig. 6.29

whose inverse transform is

$$v_{C_2}(t) = \frac{V_0 C_1}{C_1 + C_2}(1 - e^{-t/CR})$$

as shown in Fig. 2.27.

In Example 6.15 the initial value of the voltage C_1 was taken to be $v_{C_1}(0-)$ (i.e. V_0) and, because normally $v_C(0+) = v_C(0-)$, there were no worries about applying this at $t = 0+$ after the switch was closed. Suppose, however, in an ideal (nonpractical) situation R were zero. The expression for $I(s)$ would now become

$$\frac{\dfrac{V_0}{s}}{\dfrac{1}{sC_1} + \dfrac{1}{sC_2}} = CV_0,$$

using the previous definition of C. The inverse transform of this function is the impulse function, $CV_0\delta(t)$ and this is the function shown in Fig. 2.27(c). Also, the transform of the voltage across C_2 is $I(s)/sC_2 = (C_1 V_0)/(s(C_1 + C_2))$ whose inverse transform is a step of height $C_1/(C_1 + C_2)$ and this is consistent with the result obtained in Chapter 2 using conservation-of-charge principles. It will be seen that even when $v_C(0+) \neq v_C(0-)$ the $0-$ initial condition still gives a valid result. In this case, use of the $0+$ conditions would simply indicate that no current flows after $t = 0$ because $v_{C_1}(0+) = v_{C_2}(0+)$. This is consistent with the impulsive nature of the current flow in this idealised situation.

Key points to remember

- time response has two components, natural and forced;
- both components may be determined by solution of a differential equation deduced from the network, the forcing function and the initial conditions;
- a pole-zero diagram can be drawn by factorising a network function expressed as a function of the complex frequency s;
- forced response to exponential forcing functions (the generalised phasor) can be deduced from the pole-zero diagram;
- the nature of the natural response can be deduced from the pole-zero diagram;
- the Laplace transformation is a transform integral used to express functions of time as functions of a complex variable s;
- transforms of differential or integral relationships (with the transforms of other time functions) enable the complete time response of networks to be determined.

Further reading

Kuo, F. F., *Network Analysis and Synthesis* (2nd edn). J. Wiley 1966).
Nilsson, J. W., *Electric Circuits* (2nd edn). Addison-Wesley (1983).
O'Neil, P. V., *Advanced Engineering Mathematics.* Wadsworth
   (1983).
Riley, K. F., *Mathematical Methods for the Physical Sciences.*
   Cambridge University Press (1974).

Appendix 6A Representation of the sinusoid

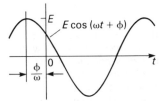

Fig. 6A.1 General sinusoidal waveform

A sinusoidally varying function of time can be represented by a trigonometric expression such as $E \cos(\omega t + \phi)$. Fig. 6A.1 shows this function plotted on a time axis. However, there are many situations in which use of this expression and the corresponding waveform diagram is cumbersome and an alternative method of presentation is preferable.

To investigate alternative forms, $E \cos(\omega t + \phi)$ is expressed in its exponential form:

$$\frac{E}{2} e^{j(\omega t + \phi)} + \frac{E}{2} e^{-j(\omega t + \phi)},$$

or, in the polar form,

$$\frac{E}{2} \underline{/\omega t + \phi} + \frac{E}{2} \underline{/-(\omega t + \phi)}.$$

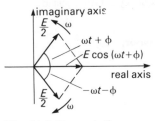

Fig. 6A.2 Two rotating phasors representing the sinusoid

Both components have constant magnitude and an angle which changes with time and can therefore be represented on an Argand diagram as **rotating phasors** (Fig. 6A.2). The two phasors rotate at the angular frequency ω, one in a clockwise direction and the other anticlockwise and the diagram demonstrates how their resultant always lies along the real axis, each having a real component

$$\mathrm{Re}\left(\frac{E}{2} e^{\pm j(\omega t + \phi)}\right) = \frac{E}{2} \cos(\omega t + \phi).\dagger$$

To illustrate, graphically, how these two (complex) phasors sum to give the (real) sinusoid, Fig. 6A.3(*a*) and (*b*) show the two components plotted three dimensionally with their resultant in Fig. 6A.3(*c*).

Although splitting the sinusoid into two components may appear to complicate the situation, it does, in fact, make a more convenient representation possible. This is because the varying-amplitude sinusoid can be represented by two constant-amplitude phasors; the amplitude variation could be considered to be an 'interference pattern' between the two components. Furthermore, since the complex components always form a conjugate pair, just one of them is sufficient to represent the sinusoid. Fig. 6A.4 shows how the positive-frequency component $E e^{j(\omega t + \phi)}$, when doubled in amplitude and projected onto the real axis, gives the same time-varying result as the summation of the pair as in Fig. 6A.2. Accepting that the

---

† To avoid having to insert a factor of $\sqrt{2}$ in all the phasor diagrams, peak rather than r.m.s. values will be used in this appendix.

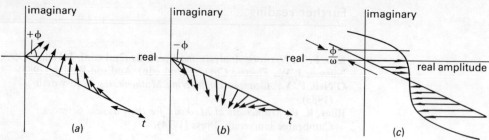

Fig. 6A.3 Pictorial representation of Fig. 6A.2

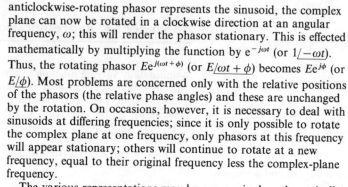

Fig. 6A.4 A single rotating phasor

anticlockwise-rotating phasor represents the sinusoid, the complex plane can now be rotated in a clockwise direction at an angular frequency, ω; this will render the phasor stationary. This is effected mathematically by multiplying the function by $e^{-j\omega t}$ (or $1/-\omega t$). Thus, the rotating phasor $Ee^{j(\omega t + \phi)}$ (or $E/\omega t + \phi$) becomes $Ee^{j\phi}$ (or E/ϕ). Most problems are concerned only with the relative positions of the phasors (the relative phase angles) and these are unchanged by the rotation. On occasions, however, it is necessary to deal with sinusoids at differing frequencies; since it is only possible to rotate the complex plane at one frequency, only phasors at this frequency will appear stationary; others will continue to rotate at a new frequency, equal to their original frequency less the complex-plane frequency.

The various representations may be summarised mathematically:

real sinusoidal function: $E\cos(\omega t + \phi)$,

complex form of function: $\dfrac{E}{2}(e^{j(\omega t + \phi)} + e^{-j(\omega t + \phi)})$

– these are the positive and negative-frequency rotating phasors;

complex form (positive ω): $Ee^{j(\omega t + \phi)}$

– this is the **positive-frequency rotating phasor**;

complex form multiplied by $e^{-j\omega t}$:

$Ee^{j(\omega t + \phi)} \times e^{-j\omega t} = Ee^{j\phi}$ (or E/ϕ)

– this is the **positive-frequency stationary phasor**.

EXERCISES 6

6.1   Given that the two energy-storage elements in the second-order *LCR* system in Section 6.1 are the inductance and the capacitance, what are the storage media in the pendulum system?

6.2   Use the Kirchhoff voltage law to write down a differential equation for the current in a series inductance-resistance circuit in response to a step-voltage input.

6.3   Derive an expression for the current in and the time constant of the circuit in Exercise 6.2 and calculate the value of the current (as a percentage of its maximum value) after time periods of 1, 5 and 10 time constants following application of the step input.

6.4   (a) Sketch your own version of the diagram in Appendix 6A (Fig. 6A.3) showing how two rotating phasors sum to give a sinusoidal function of time.

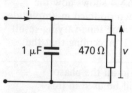

Fig. E6.1

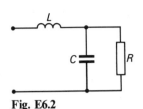

Fig. E6.2

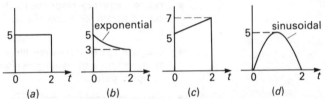

Fig. E6.3

Fig. E6.4

(b) Set up a differential equation to determine the response of the voltage v to the forcing-function current i in Fig. E6.1. Hence deduce a phasor operator relating phasor forms of v and i and use this to determine the forced response of v to the forcing functions

(i) $i = 6e^{-10^4 t}$ mA; and

(ii) $i = 6 \cos 10^4 t$ mA.

6.5 Determine the admittance network function (of s) for the network in Fig. E6.2.

6.6 Sketch the pole-zero diagram for the admittance function derived in Exercise 6.5 when $L = 10$ mH, $C = 1\,\mu$F and $R = 100\,\Omega$.

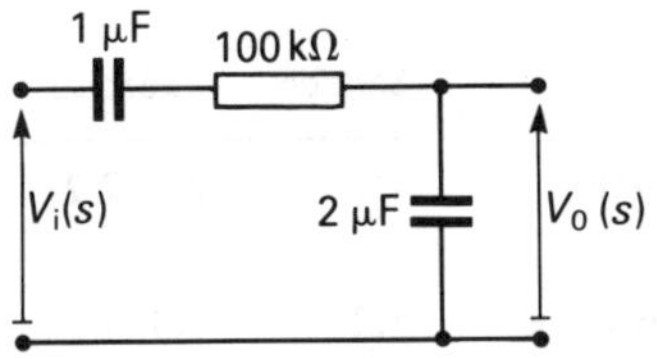

6.7 Determine the pole-zero diagram for the transfer network function $(V_o(s))/(V_i(s))$ for network shown in Fig. E6.3.

6.8 Deduce the general shape of the natural response of the network shown in Fig. E6.2 using data from Exercise 6.6. What would be the effect of lowering the value of R to $40\,\Omega$?

6.9 Working entirely from the pole-zero diagram obtained in Exercise 6.7, determine the forced component of V_o to the following forcing functions:

(i) a direct voltage of 4 V;
(ii) a real exponential decay $4e^{-6t}$ V; and
(iii) a cosinusoidal voltage $4 \cos 6t$ V.

6.10 Determine the Laplace transforms of the functions of time shown in Fig. E6.4(a), (b), (c) and (d).

6.11 Obtain an expression for the current which would flow into the network shown in Fig. E6.2 in response to a unit step voltage applied to the terminals using data from Exercise 6.6. Also determine the current flow due to a unit impulse at the terminals.

Repeat the exercise with R at $40\,\Omega$.

6.12 Determine the current response of the network in Fig. E6.2 (with the data from Exercise 6.6) to a ramp voltage having a slope of 10^3 V/s.

7 Frequency response

The principal learning objectives of this chapter are to:

		Section	Exercise
•	discuss the importance of frequency response;	1.1	7.1, 7.2
•	explain the salient features of the series-resonant circuit;	1.2	7.3
•	derive Bode diagrams for simple networks;	2.1, 2.2	7.4, 7.5
•	relate frequency response to the pole-zero diagram for networks with real poles and zeros;	3.1	7.6, 7.7
•	relate frequency response to the pole-zero diagram for networks with complex poles;	3.2, 3.3	7.8
•	evaluate the Butterworth-filter response as an example containing real and complex poles;	3.4	7.9
•	derive and apply characteristics of the parallel resonant circuit as the dual of the series circuit;	4.1, 4.2	7.10, 7.11
•	explain how the frequency response may be presented in polar form.	5	7.12

7.1 General considerations concerning CR and LCR circuits

7.1.1 General introduction

Chapter 6 investigated the response of networks and systems by determining the way in which the chosen variable changed with respect to time. Whether the signal is the output of an analogue system or the pattern of 1's and 0's at the output of a digital system, its variation with respect to time is clearly of fundamental importance. However, there are situations in which the time response to a particular forcing function is not the primary design objective. For example, when tuning a radio receiver, the circuit components are adjusted in such a way that the required station is selected, thus setting the **frequency response** of the receiver in a particular way.

Frequency response is a collective term describing the variation in the magnitude and phase angle (with respect to frequency) of the signal at a device or system output relative to conditions at the input. In the receiver example, the primary design objective is to achieve a response of a particular shape matching the spectral content of the required signal. Another example within everyday experience is the frequency response of an amplifier designed to amplify speech and music signals – an audio amplifier. In this case, it is known that the music signals contain components in the approximate frequency range 20 Hz–20 kHz and the amplifier is therefore designed to amplify components in this range, again without knowledge of the actual waveforms.

In both examples, the circuits are designed without reference to the particular forcing function which is to be used. Whilst the general nature of the time-varying waveforms may be known, the specific content of a radio broadcast or a piece of music cannot be predicted. Nevertheless, designing for a specified frequency response will produce the required time response. For example, part of a system (e.g. a filter) may be designed to provide a given frequency response with the knowledge that this implies a known time response to a specified input waveform, such as a pulse.

Finally, the Fourier-transform method to be considered in Chapter 8, enables the time response of a network to be predicted from its frequency response.

7.1.2 An example

Having introduced frequency response in a very general way, the form of the response of an elementary network is now determined using the techniques established in Chapter 4. Later work in this chapter will look at an alternative method, based on the use of poles and zeros.

The network to be considered is the simple CR network shown in Fig. 7.1. The voltages and currents on this diagram are in the phasor form. Using the potential-divider technique, the capacitor voltage

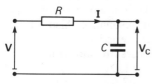

Fig. 7.1 A CR network

$$\mathbf{V_C} = \mathbf{V}/j\omega C(R + 1/j\omega C),$$

and, hence,

$$\mathbf{V_C}/\mathbf{V} = 1/(1 + j\omega CR) \text{ or } 1/(1 + j\omega \tau) \quad \text{where } \tau = CR.$$

Sketches of the magnitude and the phase angle plotted against frequency are shown in Fig. 7.2(a) and (b). The magnitude response is given by $1/\sqrt{(1 + (\omega\tau)^2)}$ and the phase response by $-\tan^{-1}\omega\tau$. In these general sketches, no scale details are given except to indicate that the response has a magnitude value of 0.707 and a phase angle of $-45°$ at the angular frequency, $\omega = 1/\tau$; this is an important frequency and further reference is made to it in Sections 7.1.3 and 7.2.2. The magnitude ratio 0.707 can alternatively be expressed in the **decibel** form as -3 dB. The decibel is a logarithmic measure of ratio and is fully described in Appendix B.

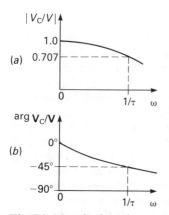

Fig. 7.2 Magnitude and phase response of the CR network

The CR circuit, whose natural and forced time responses were discussed in Section 2 of Chapter 6, is seen to have the characteristic of a simple **low-pass filter** in the frequency domain; as for the network in Fig. 5.9, this means that low-frequency sinusoidal signals would be 'passed' with little or no attenuation, whereas high-frequency components will be significantly reduced in amplitude. The response characteristic does not show a sharp transition from the low-frequency **pass band** (i.e. the frequency range $\omega = 0$ to $\omega = 1/\tau$) to the high-frequency **stop band** as may be expected of a filtering circuit but, nevertheless, it does have the essential properties of a filter.

7.1.3 The series resonant circuit

As a second example, based on the methods developed in Chapters 3 and 4, the frequency response of the **series-resonant circuit** is now considered. This circuit is also treated through the use of poles and zeros in Section 7.3.3.

The phasor impedance of the network shown in Fig. 7.3 is given by

$$\mathbf{Z} = R_s + j\omega L + 1/j\omega C,$$

and the current by:

$$\mathbf{I} = \mathbf{V}_s/(R_s + j\omega L + 1/j\omega C)$$

$$= \mathbf{V}_s/(R_s + j(\omega L - 1/\omega c)).$$

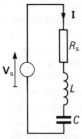

(*R_s represents the series resistance of the coil*)

Fig. 7.3 An RLC circuit

If now the sinusoidal oscillator supplying the network is set at a frequency ω_0 which makes the inductive and capacitive reactances equal in magnitude (i.e. $\omega_0 L = 1/\omega_0 C$), then $\omega_0 L - 1/\omega_0 C = 0$ and the current will have a maximum value $\mathbf{V}_s/R$. This is known as **resonance** and the frequency at which it occurs, $f_0 = 1/2\pi\sqrt{(LC)}$, the **resonant frequency**.

If, as is often the case, R_s is small (in comparison with $\omega_0 L$), the current could be relatively large in comparison with its value at frequencies well away from resonance. Also, at the resonant frequency, the circuit is purely resistive.

Typical magnitude and phase responses are shown in Fig. 7.4. As with Fig. 7.2, the only scale factor indicated is that at which the magnitude falls to 0.707 (or -3 dB) of its maximum and the phase shift is $\pm 45°$. The frequencies at which this occurs (ω_1 and ω_2 on the sketches) are known as the **half-power frequencies** and the points on the curve are the **half-power points**, because the power transferred to the networks falls to half its maximum value at these frequencies. These points and the frequencies ω_1 and ω_2 are also known as the **3 dB points** and the **3 dB frequencies** respectively.

The range of frequencies between the 3 dB frequencies is known as the **bandwidth** of the network, or, more precisely, the **3 dB bandwidth**. Bandwidth is sometimes rather loosely defined but, unless specified otherwise, is normally assumed to be bounded by either one or two 3 dB points. In the sketch in Fig. 7.2, for example, the bandwidth would normally be taken as the frequency range $\omega = 0$ to $\omega = 1/\tau$. Related to the bandwidth is the ratio of the reactance of the coil (whose magnitude is equal to the reactance of the capacitor at resonance) to its series resistance, known as the **quality factor**, or **Q factor** of the coil. Thus, the Q of coil is $\omega L/R_s$ at the general frequency ω and, at the resonance frequency, Q_0 is

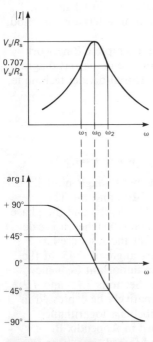

Fig. 7.4 Magnitude and phase response of the RLC circuit

$\omega_0 L/R_s$ (or $1/\omega_0 C R_s$). The particular value of the Q factor of the coil at resonance, Q_0, becomes the Q factor of the circuit at resonance.

Rearranging the expression for the current:

$$\mathbf{I} = \mathbf{V}_s/[R_s + j(\omega L - 1/\omega C)]$$
$$= \mathbf{V}_s/R_s[1 + j(\omega L/R_s - 1/\omega C R_s)]$$
$$= \mathbf{V}_s/R_s[1 + jQ_0(\omega/\omega_0 - \omega_0/\omega)].$$

At the 3 dB frequencies ω_1 and ω_2 the imaginary component in the denominator is equal to -1 and $+1$, respectively. Thus

$$Q_0(\omega_1/\omega_0 - \omega_0/\omega_1) = -1 \quad \text{and} \quad Q_0(\omega_2/\omega_0 - \omega_0/\omega_2) = +1,$$

from which $\omega_2 - \omega_1 = \omega_0/Q_0$ and the bandwidth is therefore numerically equal to the resonance frequency divided by the Q factor, i.e. bandwidth = f_0/Q.

In addition to the band-pass filtering properties of the series-resonant circuit, one of the more interesting aspects of the circuit is the fact that, although the inductive and capacitive reactances cancel in the impedance expression, voltages (which are equal in magnitude but opposite in phase) are developed across these elements. Furthermore, if the resistance is small, the current at resonance will be relatively large, making the voltage across the capacitor (which is equal to the current multiplied by the capacitive reactance) large. Typically, in a high-Q circuit, this voltage could be a hundred times the source-voltage magnitude. Fig. 7.5 shows a typical phasor diagram for a series RLC circuit in the resonant condition with $|V_C|$ and $|V_L|$ well in excess of $|V_s|$. It will be seen that the ratio $|V_C/V_s| = 1/R_s\omega_0 C = Q_0$.

The resonance effect can be exploited in the design of tuned amplifiers, which can provide a high gain at and near the resonance frequency. In other cases, resonance can be an undesirable effect; for example, in a mechanical system, a relatively small vibrating forcing function (possibly due to an engine) can result in large and dangerous vibrations in another component having a resonant frequency at or near the forcing-function frequency. There is a further discussion on resonant circuits in Section 4 of this chapter.

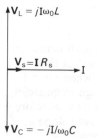

Fig. 7.5 Phasor diagram for the RLC circuit at resonance

7.2 Bode diagrams

7.2.1 Logarithmic magnitude and phase diagrams

In Section 1 of this chapter two circuits were considered and their frequency-response characteristics drawn. These are useful results in their own right but the methods did not follow a formal pattern. The purpose of this section is to introduce one component of a formal procedure known as the **Bode diagram**.

It is convenient to start with the relationship derived for the CR circuit (Fig. 7.1), namely,

$$\mathbf{V}_C/\mathbf{V} = 1/(1 + j\omega\tau) \quad \text{where } \tau = CR.$$

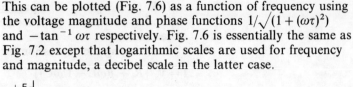

This can be plotted (Fig. 7.6) as a function of frequency using the voltage magnitude and phase functions $1/\sqrt{(1 + (\omega\tau)^2)}$ and $-\tan^{-1}\omega\tau$ respectively. Fig. 7.6 is essentially the same as Fig. 7.2 except that logarithmic scales are used for frequency and magnitude, a decibel scale in the latter case.

Fig. 7.6 Magnitude and phase responses on logarithmic scales

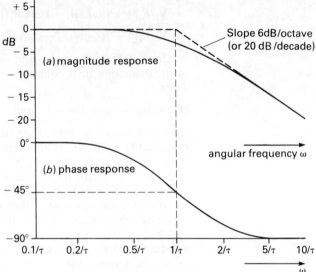

7.2.2 Straight-line approximations

Fig. 7.2 shows that the magnitude response is 3 dB below the low-frequency value and the phase angle is $-45°$ at the frequency $\omega = 1/\tau$. At low angular frequencies when $\omega\tau \ll 1$, $\sqrt{(1 + (\omega\tau)^2)} \simeq 1$ and $|V_C/V| \simeq 1$ whereas, at high frequencies, $\omega\tau \gg 1$ and $|V_C/V| \simeq 1/\omega\tau$. The response curve may therefore be approximated to two straight lines, one of zero slope at low frequencies and one of slope -6 dB per octave of frequency at high frequencies. The figure of -6 dB represents a halving of the magnitude as the frequency is doubled. Alternatively, the slope may be taken as -20 dB per decade, -20 dB being a magnitude ratio of 10:1 and a decade being a frequency ratio of 10:1.

These lines are superimposed on the response curves in Fig. 7.6 and are known as the **straight-line approximations** to the Bode diagram. Because of their nature they are also referred to as the **asymptotic responses**. They intersect at the frequency, $\omega = 1/\tau$, which is therefore known as the **break** or **corner frequency**.

Because of the logarithmic nature of the Bode diagrams, a network response which is the product of two functions may be obtained by adding the individual response curves. If the network response is a quotient of two functions, the individual curves would be subtracted. Example 7.1 illustrates this idea.

The straight-line-approximation principle may also be applied to the phase-response curves. In this case, it is a question of obtaining the best fit for the actual curves and a straight line passing through the points $\omega = 0.1/\tau$, $\omega = 1/\tau$ and $\omega = 10/\tau$, and flat beyond $\omega = 0.1/\tau$ and $\omega = 10/\tau$, may be

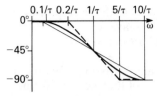

Fig. 7.7 Alternative approximations to the phase response

used. Alternatively, a straight line through $\omega = 0.2/\tau$. $1/\tau$ and $5/\tau$ may be used. As the sketch in Fig. 7.7 shows, the latter approximates to the slope of the phase characteristic at $\omega = 1/\tau$, whereas the former suggests a lesser slope. The true slope is given by $d/d\omega(\tan^{-1}\omega\tau)$ when $\omega = 1/\tau$, i.e.

$$1/\tau(1/\tau^2 + \omega^2)\big|_{\omega = 1/\tau} = \tau/2.$$

Example 7.1   *Sketch straight-line approximations to the Bode magnitude and phase diagrams for the network function,*

$10/(1 + j\omega0.2)(1 + j\omega0.5)$.

The network function consists of a constant factor, 10, and two factors each of the form $1/(1 + j\omega\tau)$. The Bode diagrams may therefore be constructed by adding the individual responses of these factors.

The factor of 10 results in a frequency-independent response of magnitude 20 dB, whilst the other two components have the general response form shown in Fig. 7.6(a) but with break frequencies given by

$$\omega_1 = \frac{1}{0.2} = 5\,\text{rad/s} \quad \text{and} \quad \omega_2 = \frac{1}{0.5} = 2\,\text{rad/s}.$$

The phase responses of the factors are thus: there is no phase shift arising from the factor of 10 and responses of the form shown in Fig. 7.6(b) (passing through $\omega = 0.1/\tau$ and $10/\tau$) for each of the other two factors have break frequencies of 5 and 2 rad/s.

The results are shown below with the unbroken line showing the resultant in each case (Fig. 7.8(a) and (b)).

Fig. 7.8 Magnitude and phase responses for Example 7.1

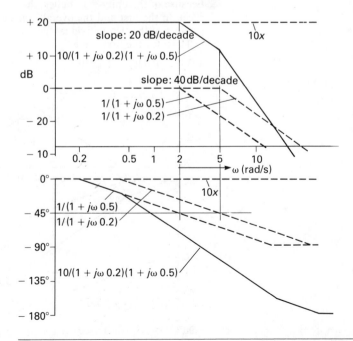

It will be seen that adding the two logarithmic responses each having magnitude slope of 6 dB/octave (or 20 dB/decade) results in a slope of 12 dB/octave (40 dB/decade).

The general discussion and the example involved factors of the form, $1/(1 + j\omega\tau)$. This is only one of four possible forms which may be encountered. These, together with the straight-line approximations, are tabulated in Fig. 7.9.

Fig. 7.9 Summary of magnitude and phase responses

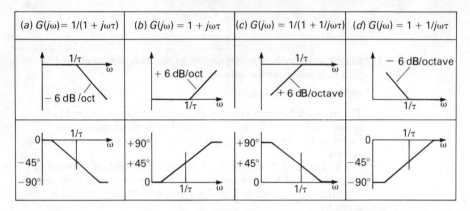

(a) $G(j\omega) = 1/(1 + j\omega\tau)$	(b) $G(j\omega) = 1 + j\omega\tau$	(c) $G(j\omega) = 1/(1 + 1/j\omega\tau)$	(d) $G(j\omega) = 1 + 1/j\omega\tau$

Example 7.2   *Sketch straight-line approximations to the Bode magnitude and phase diagrams for the circuit arrangement shown in Fig. 7.10.*

Fig. 7.10 Circuit for Example 7.2

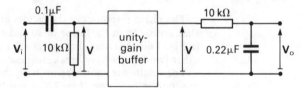

Because of the unity-gain buffer, the second CR stage has no loading effect on the first and the overall transfer function is given by the product of the two individual functions.

Thus, for the first stage,

$$V/V_i = 10^4/(10^4 + 1/j\omega 10^{-7}) = 1/(1 + 1/j\omega 10^{-3})$$

Fig. 7.11 Magnitude and phase responses for Example 7.2

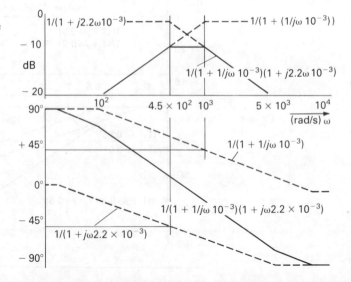

and, for the second stage,

$$V_o/V = 1/j2.2\omega \times 10^{-7}(10^4 + 1/j2.2\omega \times 10^{-7})$$
$$= 1/(1 + j2.2\omega \times 10^{-3}).$$

The overall transfer function is then

$$V_o/V_i = 1/(1 + 1/j\omega 10^{-3})(1 + j2.2\omega \times 10^{-3}).$$

The magnitude and the phase responses are given by adding the responses for the individual factors with break frequencies, $1/10^{-3} = 10^3$ rad/s and $1/2.2 \times 10^{-3} = 4.54 \times 10^2$ rad/s. These are shown in Fig. 7.11.

There is a further example of Bode-diagram plotting in the next section.

7.3 Relationship between frequency response and poles and zeros

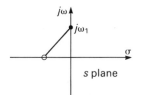

Fig. 7.12 Phasor operator for a network with a single zero

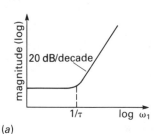

(a)

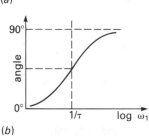

(b)

Fig. 7.13 Magnitude and phase variations as ω_1 is varied

7.3.1 Real negative poles and zeros

Because the pole and zero locations (introduced in Section 3 of Chapter 6) completely describe a network function (apart from a real scaling factor), there must be a relationship between the pole-zero pattern and the frequency response. This relationship may be demonstrated as follows.

The simple network function $H(s) = s + 1/\tau$ has a single zero at $s = -1/\tau$ but no poles. Drawing a line between the zero and a particular point on the s plane, shown as $s = j\omega_1$ (Fig. 7.12), the magnitude and the angle of the line (which is a phasor operator) is given by $s - (-1/\tau) = j\omega_1 + 1/\tau$. If now ω_1 is imagined to take on a range of values from 0 to $+\infty$ (i.e. moving vertically up the imaginary axis) the length of the line will increase, slowly at first, but then proportionately with frequency (Fig. 7.13(a)). Its angle is initially zero, but as ω_1 increases, tends towards $+90°$ (Fig. 7.13(b)).

Comparison of these curves with Fig. 7.9(b) shows them to be essentially the same. Thus the variations with respect to frequency in the length and angle of the line in the pole-zero diagram describe the magnitude and phase responses of the network represented by that diagram.

In the general case, the response is given by the network function

$$H(j\omega) = K \frac{(j\omega - z_1)(j\omega - z_2) \cdots}{(j\omega - p_1)(j\omega - p_2) \cdots},$$

where $z_1, z_2, \ldots$; $p_1, p_2, \ldots$ are, respectively, the network zeros and poles, and the overall frequency characteristics are given (on a log scale) by the summation of individual responses.

Inspection of Fig. 7.12 shows that if ω_1 has a numerical value equal to the magnitude of the value of the pole (i.e. $\omega_1 = |1/\tau|$), the magnitude of the line is $\sqrt{2} \times$ its magnitude at low frequencies and its angle is 45°. Thus, in relation to the straight-line approximations shown in Fig. 7.9(b), it may be argued that, as ω increases, passing through a value equal to the numerical value of a zero causes the slope of the magnitude characteristic to increase by 20 dB/decade as compared with its low-frequency value. Conversely, as ω falls, the characteristic slope will decrease by 20 dB/decade on passing the critical point.

The reverse is true for pole values. As ω increases past the value of the pole, the slope of the straight-line approximation decreases by 20 dB/decade or, as ω decreases, the slope increases. The following example illustrates how these results may be used.

Example 7.3   *The equivalent circuit of an amplifier is shown in Fig. 7.14. Determine the straight-line approximation to the frequency response by determining the poles and zeros of the transfer function.*

Fig. 7.14 Circuit for Example 7.3

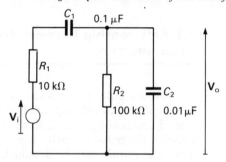

Working initially in terms of symbols and using the potential-divider method:

$$\frac{V_o(s)}{V_i(s)} = \frac{1/(1/R_2 + sC_2)}{1/(1/R_2 + sC_2) + R_1 + 1/sC_1}$$

$$= \frac{1}{1 + (R_1 + 1/sC_1)(1/R_2 + sC_2)}.$$

Rearranging and substituting values:

$$\frac{V_o(s)}{V_i(s)} = \frac{1}{1 + R_1/R_2 + sC_2R_1 + C_2/C_1 + 1/sC_1R_2}$$

$$= \frac{s/C_2R_1}{s^2 + s(1 + R_1/R_2 + C_2/C_1)/C_2R_1 + 1/C_1C_2R_1R_2}$$

$$= \frac{10^4s}{s^2 + 1.2 \times 10^4s + 10^6}$$

$$= \frac{10^4s}{(s + 84)(s + 11\,900)}.$$

There is a zero at $s = 0$ and poles at $s = -84$ and $-11\,900$, as illustrated in the pole-zero sketch (Fig. 7.15). The general shape of the response curves is as follows (Fig. 7.16(a)): the zero at $s = 0$ causes the response to increase at 6 dB/octave from zero frequency upward. At $\omega = -p_1$ (i.e. 84 rad/s) the response slope is reduced by 6 dB/octave, making it flat (independent of frequency). At $\omega = -p_2$ (11 900 rad/s) the slope again reduces by 6 dB/octave and continues thus to $\omega = \infty$.

The corresponding phase response is shown in Fig. 7.16(b) although, in contrast with the previous examples, $0.2/\tau$ and 5τ limits (see Section 7.2) are used to suit the scale of the diagram. To provide a magnitude scale, the magnitude of the response at a suitable

Fig. 7.15 Pole-zero diagram for Example 7.3

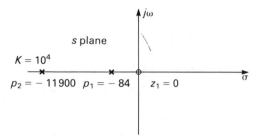

spot frequency may be determined. Suppose that a value lying between 84 rad/s and 11 900 rad/s is selected, 1000 rad/s for example. Then, subject to the approximation implicit in the use of straight-line approximations, the term $(s + 84)$ is approximately s and the term $(s + 11\,900)$ is approximately $11\,900$. Setting $s = j10^3$ rad/s then gives the magnitude of the whole expression

$$10^4 \frac{10^3}{10^3 \times 11\,900} = 0.84 \text{ or } -1.5 \text{ dB}.$$

Fig. 7.16 Magnitude and phase responses for Example 7.3

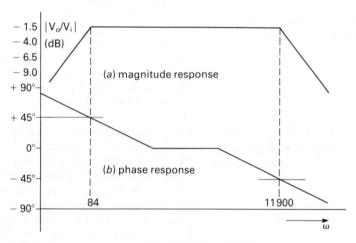

This is the value shown in Fig. 7.16. Fig. 7.17 illustrates the approximations. Although a value between 84 rad/s and 11 900 rad/s is very convenient any frequency may be used. For example, at $s = j2 \times 10^4$ (i.e. $\omega = 2 \times 10$ rad/s) which is higher than both break frequencies, $(s + 84) \simeq s$ and $(s + 11\,900) \simeq s$, resulting in a magnitude

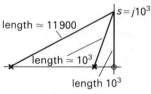

Fig. 7.17 How the magnitude is determined

$$10^4 \frac{2 \times 10^4}{2 \times 10^4 \times 2 \times 10^4} = 0.5 \text{ or } -6 \text{ dB}.$$

This agrees with the value shown in Fig. 7.16.

7.3.2 Complex poles and zeros

When, as in the previous section, the poles and zeros lie on the real (negative) axis it is an easy matter to identify the break frequencies because it is simply a matter of setting $s = jp$ (or jz) in order to set up an angle of $+45°$ with the real axis. In the more general case, the poles may be complex (although, for a practical network, they will occur in conjugate pairs) and this simple relationship will clearly not apply. However, the general principle of determining the length and angle of the phasors, and hence determining the frequency response, still applies.

Consider, as an example, the series RLC circuit discussed in Section 3.6 of Chapter 6 for which the admittance network function is

$$H(s) = 1/(R + sL + 1/sC)$$
$$= s/L(s^2 + sR/L + 1/LC).$$

Factorising (assuming that $4/LC > (R/L)^2$) gives

$$H(s) = s/L(s + \alpha - j\omega_d)(s + \alpha + j\omega_d),$$

where $\alpha = R/2L$ and is called the **damping coefficient** and $\omega_d = \sqrt{[1/LC - (R/2L)^2]}$ and is the **damped natural frequency**. ω_d can also be expressed as $\sqrt{(\omega_0^2 - \alpha^2)}$ where ω_0 is the **undamped natural frequency**. Fig. 7.18 shows the pole-zero diagram together with the three phasors, labelled $\mathbf{M_1}$, $\mathbf{M_2}$ and $\mathbf{M_3}$, which join the single zero and the two poles to a particular value of $s = j\omega_1$. The three phasors represent $s - 0$, $s - (-\alpha + j\omega_d)$ and $s - (-\alpha - j\omega_d)$, respectively, and, hence, the network function is $K(\mathbf{M_1}/\mathbf{M_2}\mathbf{M_3})$ when $s = j\omega_1$.

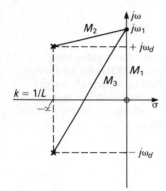

Fig. 7.18 Pole-zero diagram for the RLC circuit

This particular function will be regarded as the general second-order function and the following section investigates a technique for determining the response of a network having this network function. It is important that any technique should be easy to apply but, as may be expected, a method as straightforward as that for the first-order CR network is unlikely to be applicable.

7.3.3 The frequency response of the LCR series circuit

The pole-zero diagram shown in Fig. 7.18 is that for the LCR circuit for which $\alpha < \omega_0$ or $R < 2\sqrt{(L/C)}$. Recalling the discussion in Chapter 6, this is known as the **underdamped** condition in which the natural response is oscillatory. Also discussed were the critically and overdamped conditions and Fig. 7.19 relates these conditions to the pole-zero configuration. The first three diagrams correlate with Fig. 6.20 whilst the fourth shows the completely undamped condition in which $R = 0$. Because $\omega_d^2 + \alpha^2 = \omega_0^2$, the poles in (b), (c) and (d) lie on a semicircle of radius ω_0.

Fig. 7.19 Relationship between pole positions and damping

For the overdamped and critically damped cases the poles are real and negative and the procedure outlined in the previous section may be used. Indeed, the pole-zero diagram

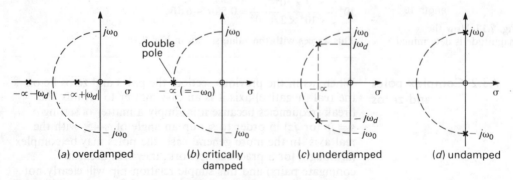

(a) overdamped   (b) critically damped   (c) underdamped   (d) undamped

In each case $\alpha = \dfrac{R}{2L};\ \omega_0^2 = \dfrac{1}{LC};\ \omega_d^2 = \dfrac{1}{LC} - \left(\dfrac{R}{2L}\right)^2 = \omega_0^2 - \alpha^2$

Fig. 7.20 Relationship between frequency response and damping

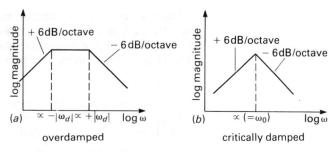

(a) overdamped

(b) critically damped

for the overdamped case has exactly the same form as the *CR* network in Example 7.3 (although typical numerical values will differ). The magnitude (only) responses are sketched in Fig. 7.20(a) and (b).

For the underdamped case, a new factor is introduced. This is the **damping ratio** ζ, defined as α/ω_0. Thus, $\alpha = \omega_0\zeta$ and $\omega_d = \omega_0\sqrt{(1-\zeta^2)}$ and denominator may be expressed in the form $s^2 + 2\zeta\omega_0 s + \omega_0^2$. Variation of this ratio from 0 to 1.0 moves a pair of complex poles from their position on the imaginary axis (for the undamped case) through the complex plane until, for $\zeta = 1$, they join (at the negative real axis) to give critical damping. If the magnitude and phase angle of the phasor product $1/M_2 M_3$ (see Fig. 7.18) is plotted for ζ values of $<0.1, 0.5$ and 1.0, the results are as shown in Fig. 7.21. The straight-line approximation to the $\zeta = 1$ case is included as a reference. For the phase response, straight-line limits between $0.2\omega_0$ and $5\omega_0$ are used. In particular, it will be noted that, although the natural frequency ω_d varies as the poles move across the plane, the resultant phase response is always 'centred' on ω_0. The magnitude response exhibits a distinct peak (at a frequency approaching ω_0 as $\zeta \rightarrow 0$) for ζ less than approximately 0.5; when ζ is 0.5, the response shape follows the reference straight-line approximation quite closely and the latter may therefore be used as a guide for ζ values between 0.5 and 1.0. ζ is also related to the Q factor through $\zeta = \alpha/\omega_0 = R/2\omega_0 L = 1/2Q_0$; thus, when $\zeta = 0.5$, $Q_0 = 1$.

Fig. 7.21 Frequency response in the underdamped case

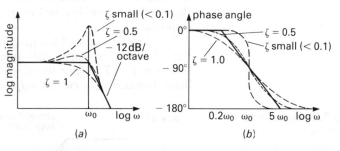

(a)

(b)

Fig. 7.22 Frequency response of a circuit with a zero at the origin

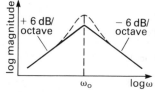

Returning to the complete network function (which also includes the zero at $s = 0$), a typical magnitude response for the *LCR* series-circuit admittance function is shown in Fig. 7.22 for $\zeta \simeq 0.4$. The effect of the additional zero (apart from changing the low-frequency response) is to centralise the peak exactly at ω_0 and this is true for all values of ζ. This response leads directly to the resonant condition, previously discussed in Section 7.2.2.

Because the network function under consideration is an admittance function the frequency-response curves represent the current response to a constant-magnitude, variable-frequency voltage forcing function, i.e.

$$I(s) = Y(s)V(s).$$

It may well be that the variable of interest is the capacitor voltage rather than the current. If so, this may be obtained by multiplying $I(s)$ by $1/sC$ so that

$$V_C(s) = I(s)/sC = Y(s)V(s)/sC.$$

Thus, a new network function, a transfer function in this case, $H(s) = V_C(s)/V(s) = Y(s)/sC$ is obtained. Dividing $Y(s)$ by sC gives,

$$H(s) = 1/LC(s + \alpha - j\omega_d)(s + \alpha + j\omega_d)$$

and the effect (as compared with the admittance function) is to remove the zero at $s = 0$ and modify K from $1/L$ to $1/LC$. With only the two poles remaining, the response shape will be that shown in Fig. 7.21, originally introduced to show the effect of various damping ratios. In this case, the voltage maximum occurs at a frequency lower than ω_0 (and increasingly so as ζ increases from zero) in contrast with the current maximum which always occurs exactly at ω_0. If the magnitude of the network function is differentiated with respect to ω, the maximum can be shown to occur at a frequency, $\omega_0\sqrt{(1 - 2\zeta^2)}$.

7.3.4 The Butterworth response

The **Butterworth** or **maximally flat** response is a filter characteristic which provides a useful example combining both real and complex poles. It is one of a number of standard filter responses and for unity low-frequency gain is defined by the magnitude-response function:

$$|H(j\omega)| = 1/\sqrt{(1 + \omega^{2n})}.$$

The function is not defined in terms of phase (although the network does, of course, have a particular phase response), the network being designed to provide a particular magnitude response.

The general shape of the magnitude response depends on the value of n, typical straight-line approximations being shown in Fig. 7.23. For this low-pass filter configuration, the break frequency (or **cut-off** frequency in filter terminology) is

Fig. 7.23 Butterworth response

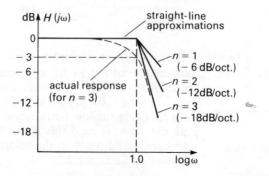

normalised to 1 (for all n), although this can be scaled to any required value. Not shown in Fig. 7.23 is the fact that, for all values of n, the characteristics are always 3 dB down at $\omega = 1$; this is because $|H(j\omega)| = 1/\sqrt{(1 + 1^{2n})} = 1/\sqrt{2}$ for all n.

In spite of having only the magnitude characteristic from which to work, it can be shown (Kuo, 1966) the pole-zero diagram consists of n poles displaced around a unit-radius semicircle as shown in Fig. 7.24. There are no finite zeros.

Fig. 7.24 Pole positions for Butterworth responses

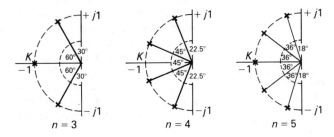

The pole positions are related to a network function which, for $n = 3$, for example, is:

$$H(s) = \frac{K}{(s + 1)(s + 0.5 + j0.866)(s + 0.5 - j0.866)}$$

$$= \frac{K}{(s^3 + 2s^2 + 2s + 1)}.$$

The coefficients of the Butterworth polynomial (the denominator of the network function) for $n = 1$ to $n = 8$ are listed in Kuo (1966).

The immediate aim of this chapter is to relate the pole positions to the frequency response and this is simply done by adding the logarithmic responses due to each pole or pair of poles. For $n = 3$ there is a single real pole at $s = -1$ and a conjugate pair at $s = -0.5 \pm j0.866$. In the latter case $\zeta = \alpha/\omega_0 = 0.5/1 = 0.5$. Fig. 7.25(a) shows the component responses determined in accordance with the procedures outlined in the previous two sections. Fig. 7.25(b) shows the sum of the components. In both cases, the straight-line approximations and the true response curves are shown.

The complete response illustrates why the Butterworth response is also known as the maximally flat response. The magnitude remains constant at 0 dB almost up to the cut-off frequency.

Fig. 7.25 Butterworth response (a) component parts (b) overall

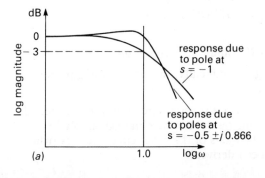

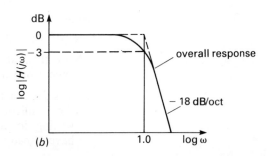

7.4 The parallel resonant circuit

7.4.1 Series-parallel equivalence

In parallel resonant circuit in Fig. 7.26(*a*), L_s and R_s represent the inductive and resistive properties of a practical coil. Although R_s could include an 'external' resistance, it is normally the resistance of the coil alone and, for a high-Q coil, is therefore relatively small.

In contrast with the series circuit, the resonance effect is observed in the voltage variation (with respect to frequency) when a constant-magnitude, variable-frequency current flows into the circuit terminals. The network function of interest is therefore the impedance function, a typical variation of which is plotted in Fig. 7.26(*b*). Neither the maxima of the magnitude response nor the zero-phase shift condition occur at ω_0 although, for low ζ values (high Q values) they can often be assumed to coincide with ω_0.

Fig. 7.26 Parallel resonant circuit: two circuit representations and their response

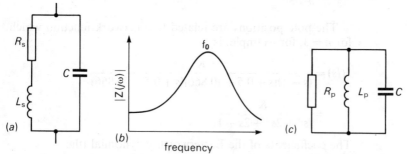

For a detailed analysis of the parallel-resonant circuit, the parallel-network configuration shown in Fig. 7.26(*c*) may be used. If the three circuit elements are regarded as three separate components, the circuit is not practical. However, if R_p (or part of it) and L_p are taken to be the equivalent parallel representation of a practical coil (which must have some resistance associated with it) the circuit is practical, although R_p and L_p become frequency dependent circuit-element values, as shown below. Thus, any frequency-response curves drawn on the basis of constant values would not be strictly valid.

The frequency dependence of R_p and L_p is apparent if the admittance of the parallel circuit is equated to the reciprocal of the impedance of the series circuit at a frequency ω:

$$1/R_p - j/\omega L_p = 1/(R_s + j\omega L_s)$$

$$= (R_s - j\omega L_s)/(R_s^2 + (\omega L_s)^2).$$

Hence,

$$R_p = (R_s^2 + (\omega L_s)^2)/R_s \quad \text{and} \quad L_p = (R_s^2 + (\omega L_s)^2)/\omega^2 L_s.$$

Notwithstanding this difficulty, the circuit configuration is convenient because:

(i) it is the exact dual of the series circuit and, therefore, all the parallel-circuit results can be obtained simply by writing down the duals of the series-circuit results (which have already been derived);

(ii) if, as is often the case, there is an additional resistance shunting the circuit (Fig. 7.27(a)), its effect can very readily be taken into account by combining the two resistive elements in parallel. Thus, in Fig. 7.27(b), $R'_p = R_p R/(R_p + R)$.

Fig. 7.27 The effect of an additional parallel resistor

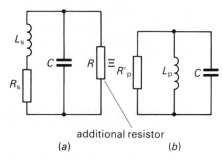

additional resistor

(a)   (b)

7.4.2 Properties of the parallel resonant circuit

In order to take advantage of the convenience afforded by this circuit and at the same time avoid possible errors from the frequency dependence of R_p and L_p, analysis should be based either on a single operating frequency or on a small range of operating frequencies, over which ω may be regarded as nominally constant. As an example of the former situation, the zero-phase-angle resonant frequency for the parallel circuit may be obtained (by duality) from the series-circuit case as

$$\omega_{p0}^2 = 1/CL_p,$$

or, in terms of series-circuit elements,

$$\omega_{p0}^2 = \omega_{p0}^2 L_s / C(R_s^2 + (\omega_{p0} L_s)^2).$$

Rearranging,

$$\omega_{p0}^2 = 1/L_s C - R_s^2/L_s^2 \text{ or } \omega_0^2(1 - 4\zeta^2).$$

If the assumption is made that the Q factor of the circuit is high (ζ is small), the resonance peak becomes quite sharp and the different frequencies given by the differing definitions of resonant frequency (i.e. ω_0, zero-phase or maximum-magnitude) and their associated 3 dB frequencies are all so close to ω_0 that the approximation $\omega_{p0} \simeq \omega_0$ may be made and a whole set of approximate, but nevertheless very useful, results follows:

Initially, for the high-Q assumption ($\omega L_s \gg R_s$),

$$L_p \simeq \omega^2 L_s^2 / \omega^2 L_s$$

$$= L_s,$$

i.e. the inductance value is the same ($= L$, say),

$$R_p \simeq \omega^2 L_s^2 / R_s \text{ or } Q\omega L \text{ or } Q^2 R_s.$$

Then, applying duality to the series-circuit results, substituting the approximate expressions for L_p and R_p and putting $\omega = \omega_0$,

resonant frequency $\omega_0^2 = 1/LC$;

3 dB bandwidth $2\alpha_p = G_p/C = R_s/\omega_0^2 L^2 Q_0 = \omega_0/Q_0$ or $2\zeta\omega_0$

(or f_0/Q_0 if frequency is expressed in hertz);

circuit impedance at resonance $Z_d = Q_0\omega_0 L$ or L/CR_s.

The last result follows because, at resonance, the impedance of the parallel combination of L and C is infinite and therefore the total impedance is simply R_p, or its equivalents at the resonant frequency, $Q_0\omega_0 L$ or L/CR_s. Z_d is known as the **dynamic impedance**.

7.5 Polar plotting of frequency responses

In previous sections separate magnitude and phase-angle methods of display have been used. In particular, the use of the logarithmic scales and the straight-line approximations have led to some useful approximate methods.

There is, however, an alternative method of displaying the magnitude and phase response of networks in which points are plotted on **polar graph** paper. Their distance from the origin represents their magnitude and their angular position indicates the phase angle. The frequency scale then appears as a series of indicated points on the graph.

Table 7.1 shows the calculated values of $H(j\omega)$ at key values of ω for the network function,

$H(j\omega) = 10/(1 + j\omega 0.2)(1 + j\omega 0.5)$, from Example 7.1. The values are plotted in Fig. 7.28. Frequency responses drawn in this form are often known as **Nyquist diagrams** because they were used by H. Nyquist as a means of establishing the stability of systems; they are used in this way in Chapter 14. They are also known as **locus diagrams** because the graph traces out the locus of the tip of the phasor (plotted in polar form) as frequency is varied. Detailed investigations of locus diagrams are not presented but there are techniques by which composite diagrams for network functions (such as that drawn in Fig. 7.28) may be developed from basic diagrams

Table 7.1. *Values for H(jω)*

ω (rad/s)	H(jω)
0	$10/\underline{0^\circ}$
1	$8.77/\underline{-38^\circ}$
2	$6.57/\underline{-67^\circ}$
5	$2.63/\underline{-113^\circ}$
10	$0.88/\underline{-142^\circ}$
100	$0.01/\underline{-176^\circ}$

Fig. 7.28 Polar diagram derived from Table 7.1

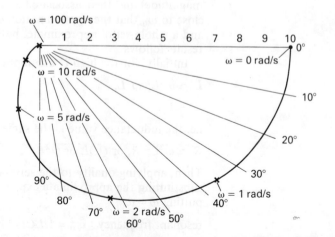

for component parts of the transfer function. To illustrate this technique briefly, the graph shown in Fig. 7.28 may be formed by multiplying together the two component phasors shown in Fig. 7.29(a) and (b) and the factor 10. A typical phasor for a given frequency $\omega = \omega_1$ is shown. The locus of the tip of this phasor can be shown to be a unity radius semicircle for each of the components.

Fig. 7.29 Locus diagrams for the function in Example 7.1

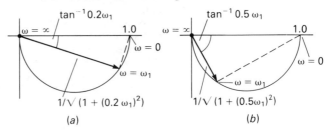

(a)   (b)

Key points to remember

- in certain applications frequency response is of greater relevance than time response but the two are related;
- the LCR series circuit can exhibit a resonance effect;
- frequency response can be displayed on a Bode diagram with logarithmic scales;
- frequency response is related to the pole-zero diagram which governs break frequencies and slopes;
- the Butterworth circuit has a regular pole distribution and provides a maximally flat filter response;
- the parallel LCR circuit can be analysed using the parallel equivalent representation of the coil;
- frequency responses may be presented as a polar diagram.

Further reading

Kuo, F. F., *Network Analysis and Synthesis* (2nd edn). J. Wiley (1966).
Nilsson, J. W., *Electric Circuits* (2nd edn). Addison-Wesley (1986).
Van Valkenburg, M. E. and Kinariwala, B. K., *Linear Electronics.* Prentice-Hall (1983).

EXERCISES 7

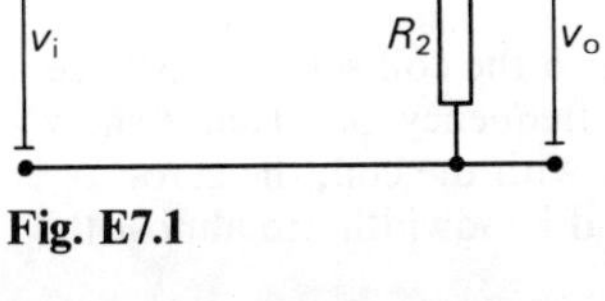

Fig. E7.1

7.1 Determine the function $V_o(j\omega)/V_i(j\omega)$ for the network shown in Fig. E7.1 in terms of R_1, R_2 and C. Hence sketch the general shapes of the frequency response graphs indicating the main features if $R_1 = 2\,k\Omega$, $R_2 = 1\,k\Omega$ and $C = 0.1\,\mu F$.

7.2 Repeat Exercise 7.1 but interchange the series combination of

R_1 and C with R_2, i.e. take the output across the series combination of R_1 and C.

7.3 A series circuit comprises a resistance of 25 Ω, an inductance of 40 mH and a capacitance of 0.1 μF. Sketch a graph showing the variation in current with frequency when a variable-frequency, constant magnitude 10 V source is connected across the circuit.

Mark the resonant frequency and 3 dB bandwidth on the graph.

Also calculate the voltage across the capacitor at resonance and show that its magnitude is equal to the supply voltage multiplied by Q.

What will be the effect of doubling the resistance?

7.4 Sketch straight-line approximations to the Bode magnitude and phase diagrams for the function

$$\frac{j\omega 100}{(50 + j\omega)(1 + j\omega 0.1)}.$$

7.5 Draw straight-line approximations to the Bode magnitude and phase diagrams for the two networks described in Exercises 7.1 and 7.2.

7.6 Draw pole-zero diagrams for the networks in Exercises 7.1 and 7.2 and deduce the approximations to the Bode magnitude diagrams for comparison with the results of Exercise 7.5.

7.7 Derive the transfer function $V_o(s)/V_i(s)$ for the circuit shown in Fig. E7.2 and hence obtain values for the pole(s) and zero(s) of the function.

Fig. E7.2

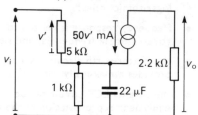

Sketch a pole-zero diagram and deduce the straight-line approximation to the Bode magnitude response indicating break frequencies and a magnitude scale.

7.8 Explain the term damping ratio and relate it to the Q factor in a series-resonant circuit. A series RLC circuit has $L = 40\ \mu H$ and $C = 10\ nF$.

Sketch frequency-response curves and corresponding pole-zero diagrams for the current when constant voltage is applied and

(i) $Q_0 = 0.5$;
(ii) $Q_0 = 1.0$; and
(iii) $Q_0 = 10$.

7.9 Working from the geometry of the pole-zero diagram for an $n = 4$ Butterworth filter (Fig. 7.24) calculate the damping coefficient α and hence the damping ratio ζ for each of the two pairs of poles.

Hence sketch component responses to show, within the limits of sketching tolerances, that the overall response is maximally flat.

7.10 Determine the parallel equivalents to the coil series resistance and inductance in Exercise 7.3 (at frequency ω_0). Hence show that, with the capacitor in parallel with the coil, the zero-phase-angle resonant frequency and bandwidth are almost the same as for the series circuit, but the impedance at resonance is Q_0^2 times that of the series circuit.

7.11 The circuit in Fig. E7.3 represents a tuned amplifier in which a voltage-dependent current source drives a current through a parallel tuned circuit to provide an output voltage whose variation with frequency follows the general tuned-circuit response shape.

Fig. E7.3

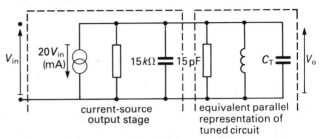

current-source output stage   equivalent parallel representation of tuned circuit

If the maximum value of $|V_o/V_{in}|$ is to be 120 at a centre frequency of 465 kHz and the bandwidth is to be 9 kHz, determine the value of the tuning capacitance C_T and the inductance and Q factor of the coil.

7.12 Sketch a polar graph of the function given in Exercise 7.4.

Section B Signals

8 Fourier series and transform

The principal learning objectives of this chapter are to:

	Section	Exercise
• explain the general principles of the Fourier series;	2.1	
• determine the coefficients of the Fourier series;	2.2	8.1, 8.2
• display the Fourier coefficients on a spectral diagram;	2.3	8.3
• develop the exponential or phasor form of the Fourier series;	2.4, 2.5	8.4
• apply the phasor form to the determination of the spectral content of a pulse waveform;	2.6	8.5
• investigate the response of linear circuits to non-sinusoidal forcing functions;	3	8.6, 8.7, 8.8
• discuss the general properties of the Fourier transform;	4.1	8.9
• develop the Fourier integral and its inverse;	4.2	
• derive a range of basic transforms;	4.3	8.10
• apply the Fourier transform to determine the time response of a system with known frequency response;	5.1	8.11
• discuss the ideal phase and magnitude responses of networks;	5.2	8.12, 8.13
• deduce the time response of a bandlimited ideal channel;	5.3	
• appreciate general bandwidth/rise time relationships.	5.4	

8.1 Introduction

This chapter introduces the concept of the Fourier series whereby a periodic non-sinusoidal signal is represented by a series of discrete sinusoidal components known as harmonics. This principle is then adapted to the non-periodic case and the concept of a continuous function of frequency, the Fourier transform, is introduced. Thus, whereas in Chapter 6 the Laplace transform was used only as a tool for the determination of the time response of networks, in the Fourier case the emphasis is on the transform itself as a description of the frequency content (or spectral content) of signals. Also demonstrated, with the help of expressions developed in Chapter 7 for the frequency response of networks, is the use of the Fourier transform to determine the time response of networks whose frequency response is known.

The chapter concludes with a discussion on general aspects of time-frequency response relationships.

8.2 Fourier analysis of non-sinusoidal waveforms

8.2.1 The Fourier series

In the discussion on the importance of sinusoids in Chapter 4 it is noted that a periodic non-sinusoidal function, such as a square or triangular waveform, can be synthesised from a number of sinusoidal components at harmonically related frequencies, including, in general, a direct (d.c.) component. The principle can be demonstrated graphically: presuming the results to be obtained in Example 8.1, the four terms,

$$(V/2) + (2V/\pi) \cos \omega_0 t - (2V/3\pi) \cos 3\omega_0 t + (2V/5\pi) \cos 5\omega_0 t,$$

may be added to give an approximation to a square wave, as demonstrated in Fig. 8.1. Stated in general terms, a periodic function $f(t)$ can be written as,

$$f(t) = a_0 + a_1 \cos \omega_0 t + a_2 \cos 2\omega_0 t + \cdots$$
$$+ b_1 \sin \omega_0 t + b_2 \sin 2\omega_0 t + \cdots,$$

or

$$a_0 + \sum_{n=1}^{\infty} a_n \cos n\omega_0 t + \sum_{n=1}^{\infty} b_n \sin n\omega_0 t,$$

where $\omega_0 = 2\pi/T$ (T is the period) and is known as the **fundamental frequency**. The other components are called **harmonics**, second when $n = 2$, third when $n = 3$, etc.

There are certain sufficiency conditions for the validity of the Fourier series known as the **Dirichlet conditions**. Briefly,

Fig. 8.1 Harmonic content of a square wave

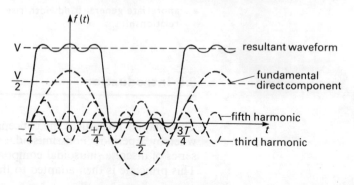

these are that if, over a period, $\int |f(t)|\, dt < \infty$ and $f(t)$ has a finite number of discontinuities and maxima and minima, the series converges to a point of continuity or to $(f(t+0-)+f(t+0+))/2$ at a discontinuity, i.e., in the latter case, half-way between the limits of the discontinuity.

In particular cases, some of the coefficients of the series may be zero. For example, in the four terms of the series for the square waveform shown in Fig. 8.1, all the b coefficients and the even-numbered a coefficients are zero. Alternatively, if the time origin were advanced by a quarter-period, the first four terms would become

$$f(t) = (V/2) + (2V/\pi)\sin\omega_0 t + (2V/3\pi)\sin 3\omega_0 t$$
$$+ (2V/5\pi)\sin 5\omega_0 t,$$

in which case all of the a coefficients (except a_0) and the even-numbered b coefficients are zero.

8.2.2 Evaluation of coefficients

The series coefficients a_0, a_n and b_n may be evaluated for a function $f(t)$ as follows.

The value of the integral, $\int_{-T/2}^{T/2}\cos m\omega_0 t \cos n\omega_0 t\, dt$ (where $\omega_0 = 2\pi/T$), is always zero except when $n = m$, in which case its value is $T/2$. Thus, if the series,

$$f(t) = a_0 + a_1\cos\omega_0 t + a_2\cos 2\omega_0 t + a_3\cos 3\omega_0 t + \cdots,$$

is multiplied by a factor $\cos n\omega_0 t$ and integrated over the period T, setting n to any particular value (say, 3) will 'pick out' the $n = 3$ term, i.e. $a_3\cos 3\omega_0 t$. The other terms in the series will not contribute to the value of the integral. Thus,

$$\int_{-T/2}^{T/2} f(t)\cos n\omega_0 t\, dt = a_n T/2,$$

and, hence,

$$a_n = 2/T \int_{-T/2}^{T/2} f(t)\cos n\omega_0 t\, dt.$$

By a similar argument

$$b_n = 2/T \int_{-T/2}^{T/2} f(t)\sin n\omega_0 t\, dt.$$

The direct component a_0 (which is the mean value) is given by

$$\int_{-T/2}^{T/2} f(t)\cos 0\, dt = a_0 T$$

or

$$a_0 = 1/T \int_{-T/2}^{T/2} f(t)\, dt.$$

The multiplying factor $\cos n\omega_0 t$ (or $\sin n\omega_0 t$), with n taking on the integral values $0,1,2,3,\ldots$ in turn, may be thought of as a frequency 'scan' in which each term in the series is considered in turn and an output, proportional to its amplitude, generated.

To illustrate these relationships, the following example determines the series for the square wave.

Example 8.1 *Determine the Fourier series for the waveform shown in Fig. 8.2.*

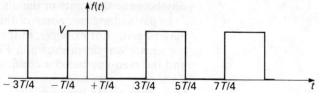

Fig. 8.2 Waveform for Example 8.1

Over the time period $-T/2 < t < +T/2$ the square waveform is defined by,

$$f(t) = V \quad -T/4 < t < +T/4,$$

and

$$f(t) = 0 \quad -T/2 < t < -T/4 \text{ and } T/4 < t < T/2.$$

Therefore

$$a_0 = 1/T \int_{-T/4}^{+T/4} V \, dt = V/2,$$

$$a_n = 2/T \int_{-T/4}^{+T/4} V \cos n\omega_0 \, dt$$

$$= 2V/n\omega_0 T [\sin n\omega_0 t]_{-T/4}^{+T/4}.$$

Substituting 2π for $\omega_0 T$ gives

$$a_n = \frac{2V}{n\pi} \sin \frac{n\pi}{2},$$

and

$$b_n = 2/T \int_{-T/4}^{+T/4} V \sin n\omega_0 t \, dt = 2V/n\omega_0 T [-\cos n\omega_0 t]_{-T/4}^{+T/4}.$$

Substituting 2π for $\omega_0 T$ gives

$$b_n = \frac{V}{n\pi} \left(-\cos \frac{n\pi}{2} + \cos \frac{n\pi}{2} \right), \quad \text{which is always zero.}$$

Substituting integral values for n results in a_n taking on the values, $2V/\pi, 0, -2V/3\pi, 0, 2V/5\pi, \ldots$, the series becoming

$$f(t) = (V/2) + (2V/\pi) \cos \omega_0 t - (2V/3\pi) \cos 3\omega_0 t$$
$$+ (2V/5\pi) \cos 5\omega_0 t + \cdots .$$

It will be seen that the even harmonics (second, fourth, etc.) are zero; this is a characteristic of a square wave shape, as discussed in Section 8.2.6.

8.2.3 The spectral diagram

It is convenient to display the terms of the Fourier series graphically. The method usually adopted is to draw a frequency scale on the horizontal axis with an amplitude scale on the vertical axis, as illustrated in Fig. 8.3. These diagrams are known as **line-spectrum diagrams** or **spectral diagrams**, the term **spectrum** being used to describe the frequency content of any time-varying signal, whether periodic or not. For the square wave in Example 8.1 the amplitude spectrum is shown in Fig. 8.3.

Fig. 8.3 Spectral content of a square wave (magnitude only)

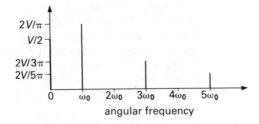

8.2.4 The exponential or phasor form of the Fourier series

An alternative form of the Fourier series is the more compact **exponential** or **phasor form**, which follows from the general procedure described in Chapter 6 for the sinusoidal signal. As discussed in Appendix 6A, the general sinusoidal waveform may be replaced by two rotating phasors and, expressed in this form, the nth term in the Fourier series becomes:

$$a_n \cos n\omega_0 t + b_n \sin n\omega_0 t$$
$$= a_n(e^{jn\omega_0 t} + e^{-jn\omega_0 t})/2 - jb_n(e^{jn\omega_0 t} - e^{-jn\omega_0 t})/2$$
$$= ((a_n - jb_n)e^{jn\omega_0 t})/2 + ((a_n + jb_n)e^{-jn\omega_0 t})/2$$
$$= C_n e^{jn\omega_0 t} + C_{-n}e^{-jn\omega_0 t},$$

where

$$C_n = (a_n - jb_n)/2 \quad \text{and} \quad C_{-n} = C_n^* = (a_n + jb_n)/2,$$

C_{-n} (or C_n^*) being the complex conjugate of C_n.

Fig. 8.4 shows typical sinusoidal and cosinusoidal functions with their alternative rotating-phasor representation. A more compact form of the Fourier series is now possible because positive values of n can be used for the anticlockwise phasors with negative values for the clockwise components. Thus, $f(t)$ can be expressed in the form,

$$f(t) = \sum_{n=-\infty}^{+\infty} C_n e^{jn\omega_0 t}.$$

Fig. 8.4 Relating trigonometric and phasor forms of the Fourier series

This is a complete statement of the Fourier series, including the direct component.

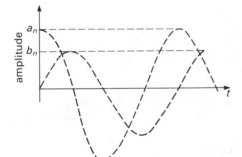

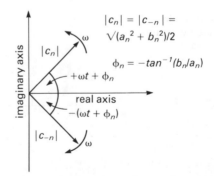

To determine C_n, a procedure similar to that used to determine a_n and b_n may be followed. There, it was argued that if the function $f(t)$ were multiplied by $\cos n\omega_0 t$ and $\sin n\omega_0 t$ (respectively) and then integrated, the values of a_n and b_n could be found. The procedure 'picked out' the required term from the rest of the series. The equivalent procedure in the phasor form is to multiply $f(t)$ by a rotating phasor $e^{-jn\omega_0 t}$ which, at differing speeds of rotation corresponding to integral values of n from $-\infty$ to $+\infty$, will render successive component phasors of $f(t)$ stationary. Then, taking a particular term, $\mathbf{C}_m e^{jm\omega_0 t}$, and multiplying it by a phasor $e^{-jn\omega_0 t}$ rotating at the same speed (i.e. $n = m$) and integrating the result over the period $-T/2$ to $+T/2$ gives

$$\int_{-T/2}^{+T/2} \mathbf{C}_m e^{jm\omega_0 t} e^{-jn\omega_0 t}\, dt = \int_{-T/2}^{+T/2} \mathbf{C}_m\, dt = \mathbf{C}_m T.$$

Thus, integrating a phasor which has been rendered stationary yields its magnitude. If, on the other hand, $m \neq n$ so that the product of the selected term and the rotating phasor yields another rotating phasor (at angular velocity $(m - n)\omega_0$) the value of the integral will be zero, i.e.

$$\int_{-T/2}^{+T/2} \mathbf{C}_m e^{j(m-n)\omega_0 t}\, dt = 0 \quad \text{for integral values of } (m - n).$$

In general, therefore, the complex coefficient $\mathbf{C}_n$ is given by,

$$\mathbf{C}_n = 1/T \int_{-T/2}^{+T/2} f(t) e^{-jn\omega_0 t}\, dt.$$

The value of $\mathbf{C}_n$ when $n = 0$ will be seen to be $1/T \int_{-T/2}^{+T/2} f(t)\, dt$, which is the mean value of $f(t)$ and equal to the direct component, a_0, in the trigonometric form. Thus, the summation $\sum_{n=-\infty}^{+\infty} \mathbf{C}_n e^{jn\omega_0 t}$, which includes an $n = 0$ term, includes the direct component of $f(t)$.

The phasor values of $\mathbf{C}_n$ may be displayed on a spectral diagram in much the same way as for the trigonometric form except that, in this case, n takes on positive and negative values. Fig. 8.5 shows the diagrams for the waveform previously analysed in Example 8.1.

Fig. 8.5 Magnitude and phase spectral diagrams for the square wave

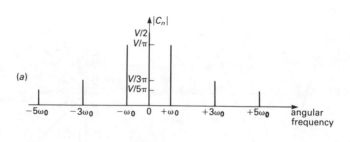

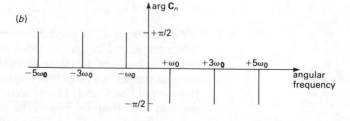

Reworking Example 8.1 using the phasor (exponential) form, but with the time origin shifted $T/4$ to the left

$$\mathbf{C}_n = 1/T \int_{-T/2}^{+T/2} f(t) e^{-jn\omega_0 t}\, dt$$

$$= 1/T \int_0^{+T/2} V e^{-jn\omega_0 t}\, dt$$

$$= V/-jn\omega_0 T(e^{-jn\omega_0 T/2} - e^0)$$

$$= jV/2\pi n(e^{-jn\pi} - 1).$$

Substituting $n = \cdots -3, -2, -1, 0, +1, +2, +3, \ldots$, etc., yields values of the complex coefficient $\mathbf{C}_n$ of $jV/3\pi, 0, jV/\pi, V/2,†\ -jV/\pi, 0, -jV/3\pi, \ldots$ resulting in the amplitude and phase spectral diagrams shown in Fig. 8.5(a) and (b) respectively. The function of time $f(t)$ is given by reinserting the rotating unit phasor $e^{jn\omega_0 t}$. Thus,

$$f(t) = \cdots + (jV/3\pi)e^{-j3\omega_0 t} + (jV/\pi)e^{-j\omega_0 t} + (V/2)e^0$$
$$- (jV/\pi)e^{j\omega_0 t} - (jV/3\pi)e^{j3\omega_0 t} \cdots,$$

which is the same result as that quoted at the end of Section 8.2.1.

Fig. 8.6 shows sets of phasors (up to the ninth harmonic in order to obtain reasonable accuracy) at three successive instants around the time at which the voltage rises from 0 to V. The magnitudes of the resultants are indicated on the diagrams.

8.2.5 Notes on the phasor form of the Fourier series

As mentioned in the discussion on phasor representation of the single sinusoid in Chapter 6, it is common practice to express even a final result in the phasor form, it being understood that the phasor represents a sinusoidal function of time. Such is the case when the Fourier series is expressed in terms of the complex quantity $\mathbf{C}_n$ without reinserting the rotating phasor $e^{jn\omega_0 t}$.

It will also be seen that the form of the Fourier series now considered effectively yields the two-phasor representation with positive and negative values for n (as discussed in Appendix 6A) and that the amplitudes in Fig. 8.5(a) are half those in Fig. 8.3, except when $n = 0$. As Appendix 6A shows, the 'negative-frequency' components in Fig. 8.5 arise naturally in the two-phasor representation, both components (which are complex conjugates) being necessary in order that their sum should yield the real sinusoidal (or cosinusoidal) function of time, just as $\cos \omega t$ is represented by $\frac{1}{2}e^{j\omega t}$ and $\frac{1}{2}e^{-j\omega t}$.

A similar situation occurs with the 'standing wave' on a transmission line (see Chapter 5) in which components exhibiting positive and negative phase rotations (with respect to distance in this case) must exist in order to produce the standing-wave amplitude variations along the line.

---

† In order to determine the direct component (where $n = 0$) it is necessary to use the relationship, $(e^{j\theta} - 1)/j\theta \to 1$ as $\theta \to 0$.

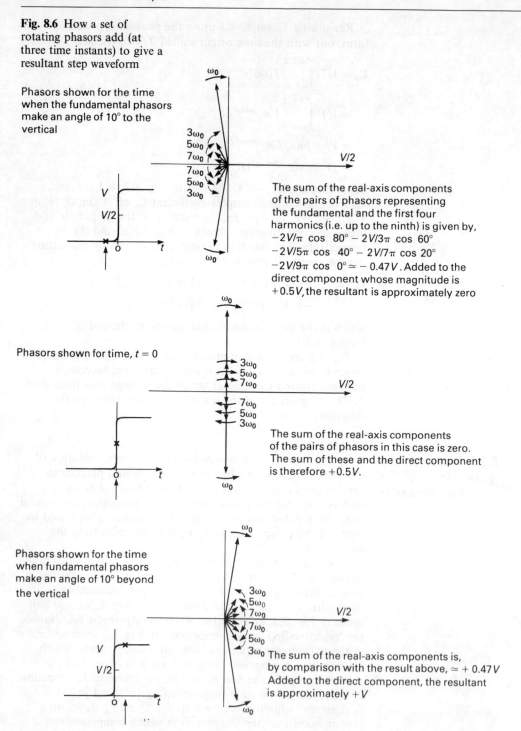

Fig. 8.6 How a set of rotating phasors add (at three time instants) to give a resultant step waveform

Phasors shown for the time when the fundamental phasors make an angle of 10° to the vertical

The sum of the real-axis components of the pairs of phasors representing the fundamental and the first four harmonics (i.e. up to the ninth) is given by, $-2V/\pi \cos 80° - 2V/3\pi \cos 60°$ $-2V/5\pi \cos 40° - 2V/7\pi \cos 20°$ $-2V/9\pi \cos 0° \simeq -0.47V$. Added to the direct component whose magnitude is $+0.5V$, the resultant is approximately zero

Phasors shown for time, $t = 0$

The sum of the real-axis components of the pairs of phasors in this case is zero. The sum of these and the direct component is therefore $+0.5V$.

Phasors shown for the time when fundamental phasors make an angle of 10° beyond the vertical

The sum of the real-axis components is, by comparison with the result above, $\simeq +0.47V$ Added to the direct component, the resultant is approximately $+V$

8.2.6 Spectral content of rectangular pulse waveform

The pulse waveform is probably the most important function to be analysed because the result is widely applicable in its own right and it may be conveniently used to demonstrate the extension of the Fourier series to the Fourier integral; the latter aspect is discussed in Section 8.4.

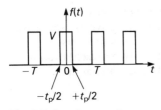

Fig. 8.7 A pulse waveform

The waveform to be analysed is shown in Fig. 8.7. It is a periodic pulse waveform of period, T, and pulse width, t_p.

Over one period, the function may be described by,

$$f(t) = V \quad \text{for } -t_p/2 < t < t_p/2,$$

$$f(t) = 0 \quad \text{for } -T/2 < t < -t_p/2 \text{ and } +t_p/2 < t < T/2.$$

$$\therefore \quad C_n = 1/T \int_{-t_p/2}^{+t_p/2} V e^{-jn\omega_0 t} \, dt$$

$$= jV \frac{e^{-jn\omega_0 t_p/2} - e^{jn\omega_0 t_p/2}}{n\omega_0 T}.$$

With some rearrangement, this expression becomes

$$V \frac{t_p}{T} \cdot \frac{e^{jn\omega_0 t_p/2} - e^{-jn\omega_0 t_p/2}}{j2n\omega_0 t_p/2},$$

which, through $\sin \theta = (e^{j\theta} - e^{-j\theta})/j2$, can be written as

$$\mathbf{C}_n = V \frac{t_p}{T} \cdot \frac{\sin x}{x} \quad \text{where } x = n\omega_0 t_p/2 \text{ or } n\pi t_p/T.$$

Use of the normalised amplitude variable, x, simplifies interpretation of the expression but, in using a symbol normally associated with a continuous variable, it should be borne in mind that $n\omega_0 t_p/2$ is discrete, taking on discrete values in accordance with integer values for n. As before, in order to restore the time variable, the factor $e^{jn\omega_0 t}$ must be reinserted to give

$$f(t) = \sum_{n=-\infty}^{\infty} Vt_p/T \cdot \frac{\sin x}{x} e^{jn\omega_0 t}.$$

Various methods of illustrating the spectral content are shown in Fig. 8.8, each of which makes use of the general $(\sin x)/x$ form of $\mathbf{C}_n$. In Fig. 8.8(a) the magnitude and phase angle of the complex phasor are shown on separate diagrams.

Fig. 8.8 Spectral content of a pulse

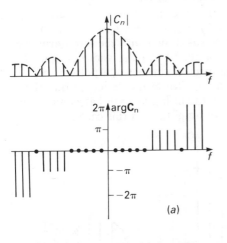

(a)

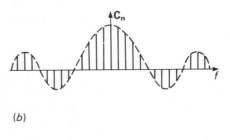

(b)

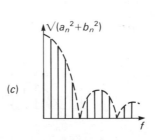

(c)

In such cases, where the phase angles have only two possible values differing by 180°, the alternative positive-and-negative representation, shown in Fig. 8.8(*b*), is sometimes used. Another possibility is the magnitude-only representation in Fig. 8.8(*c*). Here, $\sqrt{(a_n^2 + b_n^2)}$ is plotted against ω in accordance with the function,

$$f(t) = Vt_p/T + 2\frac{Vt_p}{T}\sum_{n=1}^{\infty}\left|\sin x/x\right|.$$

In this 'single-sided' representation all components except the direct component are doubled in magnitude compared with the previous diagrams.

The spectral lines on the amplitude diagrams will be seen to be bounded by a dotted line. This is known as an **envelope** and it is useful to be able to describe this spectral envelope mathematically. To do this x is regarded as a continuous variable, defined for all values of ω (including, of course, $\omega = n\omega_0$) so that, for Fig. 8.8(*b*), the envelope is described by $f_e(\omega) = (Vt_p/T)\sin x/x$ and for Fig. 8.8(*c*) by $(2Vt_p/T)|\sin x/x|$. In both cases, the envelope has its maximum value at $x = 0$ (i.e. $\omega = 0$) because $\sin x \to x$ (x in radians) as $x \to 0$.

In following the $\sin x/x$ function (where x is a linear function of frequency), the envelope becomes zero at certain frequencies and, if a harmonic frequency coincides with one of these frequencies, the amplitude will be zero. In the sketches in Fig. 8.8 these zeros or nulls are shown coincident with the 5th, 10th, 15th, ..., etc. harmonics.

In the special case of the square-wave function, zeros coincide with the even harmonics, the square wave being a particular case of this more general treatment. Fig. 8.9 shows the amplitude spectrum for a square wave and should be compared with Fig. 8.3.

In the general case, the position of the envelope zeros is given by those frequencies at which $\sin x/x = 0$. Provided x is not zero, $\sin x = 0$ when $\sin x/x = 0$, i.e. when $x = \pm\pi, \pm 2\pi, \ldots$. Writing x as $\omega t_p/2$, the continuous variable ω replacing the discrete variable $n\omega_0$, gives $\omega t_p/2 = \pm\pi, \pm 2\pi, \ldots$ so that the zero positions are given by $\omega = \pm 2\pi/t_p, \pm 4\pi/t_p, \ldots$ or $f = \pm 1/t_p, \pm 2/t_p, \ldots$. For example, whereas Fig. 8.8 was drawn with the fifth harmonic at zero (implying a ratio of period to pulse width of exactly 5.0), Fig. 8.10 shows the spectral content of a pulse whose width is slightly less than one-fifth of the period so that the envelope zero lies between the fifth and sixth harmonics; none of the harmonics have zero amplitude in this case.

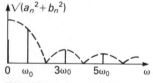

Fig. 8.9 Special case of a square wave

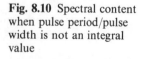

Fig. 8.10 Spectral content when pulse period/pulse width is not an integral value

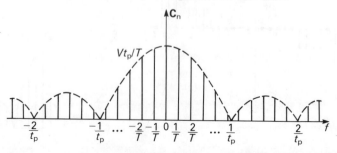

Summarising, the general form of the spectral content of the pulse waveform consists of harmonics of amplitude $(Vt_p/T) \sin x/x$ spaced at frequencies given by 1/period and contained within an envelope having zeros at frequencies given by 1/pulsewidth. The maximum amplitude of the envelope (for the double-sided spectrum shown in Fig. 8.10) is (pulse height × pulse width)/period.

8.3 Behaviour of linear circuits with periodic non-sinusoidal inputs

In this section the results of Section 8.2 are used with the circuit-analysis techniques developed in Chapters 3 and 4 to predict the time-response function of linear RLC circuits to periodic non-sinusoidal forcing functions. For example, the approximate shape of the voltage waveform appearing across the capacitor in a series CR circuit in response to a rectangular-pulse input waveform is determined.

The technique is based on the superposition principle by which the response of a network to each frequency component of the periodic forcing function is determined individually and the resultant response obtained by summing the component responses. As with other analysis techniques the network must be linear in order to apply this method. Also, the method yields only the steady-state forced response to the periodic forcing function. The procedure is illustrated by an example in which it is assumed the Fourier components of the forcing function are already known.

Example 8.2   *A voltage waveform, with a period of 1 ms, consists of a fundamental component and a second harmonic, whose amplitude is 40% of that of the fundamental (Fig. 8.11). If this voltage is applied across a series CR network having $C = 0.22\ \mu F$ and $R = 1\ k\Omega$ determine the percentage second harmonic in the capacitor-voltage waveform and sketch the waveform.*

Fig. 8.11 Summation of fundamental and second harmonic (Example 8.2)

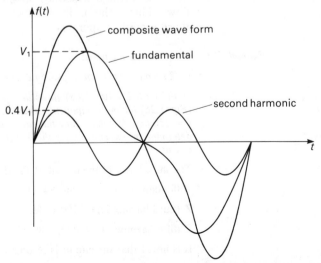

Magnitude of reactance of the capacitor at the fundamental frequency $(1\,\text{kHz}) = 1/2\pi \times 10^3 \times 0.22 \times 10^{-6} = 723\,\Omega$.

Magnitude of reactance at second-harmonic frequency $= 362\,\Omega$.

Using the phasor technique (and potential-divider method)

$$V_C(\text{fundamental}) = -j723V_1\underline{/0^\circ}/(1000 - j723)$$

$$= 0.586V_1\underline{/-54^\circ}\ \text{V}$$

and

$$V_C(\text{second harmonic}) = -j362 \times 0.4V_1\underline{/0^\circ}/(1000 - j362)$$

$$= 0.136V_1\underline{/-70^\circ}\ \text{V}$$

(in each case, $V_1\underline{/0^\circ}$ is the fundamental source voltage). From these results the percentage second-harmonic amplitude is $(0.136/0.586) \times 100\% = 23.2\%$. Translating these phasor quantities into functions of time, the composite capacitor waveform is given by

$$v_C(t) = 0.586V_1 \sin(\omega t - 54^\circ) + 0.136V_1 \sin(2\omega t - 70^\circ)\ \text{V}.$$

Waveforms are sketched in Fig. 8.12. It will be noted that the angle (-70°) in the second-harmonic case relates to the second-harmonic period, i.e. a given angle on a 'second-harmonic scale' corresponds to half the time that the same angle would do on the 'fundamental-scale'.

Fig. 8.12 Summation after phase and magnitude changes (Example 8.2)

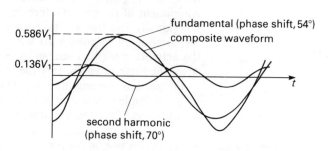

Following the same basic technique as Example 8.2 above, the following example illustrates the effect of resonance in a network through which a non-sinusoidal periodic current flows. This is the basis on which the frequency-selective or **tuned amplifier** operates.

Example 8.3 *A square-wave current,*

$$i = 2 \sin \omega t + \tfrac{2}{3} \sin 3\omega t + \tfrac{2}{5} \sin 5\omega t + \cdots \text{mA}$$

(with $\omega = 8.2 \times 10^6$ rad/s) flows in a parallel-resonant circuit (Fig. 7.26) having component values, $L_s = 5\,\mu H$, $R_s = 4\,\Omega$ and $C = 330\,pF$. Assuming that the values do not vary with frequency, determine an expression for the waveform of the voltage across the circuit.

The impedance of the circuit at the three frequencies is:

$\mathbf{Z}$ (fundamental) $=$ $46\underline{/84^\circ}\,\Omega$,

$\mathbf{Z}$ (third harmonic) $= 3790\underline{/0^\circ}\,\Omega$,

$\mathbf{Z}$ (fifth harmonic) $=$ $115\underline{/-89^\circ}\,\Omega$.

It is noted that the circuit is resonant at the third-harmonic frequency. The voltage is then given by,

$$v = 0.092 \sin(\omega t + 84°) + 2.52 \sin 3\omega t$$
$$+ 0.046 \sin(\omega t - 89°) \, \text{V}.$$

Without even sketching this waveform, it is easy to see that the components of voltage at the fundamental and fifth-harmonic frequencies (92 mV and 46 mV respectively) are negligible in comparison with the 2.52 V at the third-harmonic frequency. It is in this way that a tuned amplifier is able, in effect, to select components at (or near) the resonance frequency whilst rejecting others.

To complement these examples, the following analysis determines the voltage waveform across the capacitor in a series CR network when a periodic square-wave voltage is applied to its input terminals. In Chapter 6 a direct solution of the differential equation, with substitution of the appropriate initial conditions, gave the characteristic capacitor charging curve (Fig. 6.5) in response to a step-input voltage. For a square-wave voltage input the 'charge-discharge' voltage will eventually settle to the steady-state waveform shown in Fig. 8.13.

Fig. 8.13 Steady-state output from a CR network with square-wave input

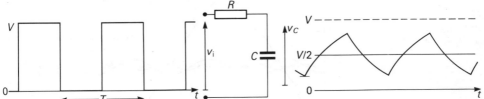

The problem is now tackled by expressing the input waveform as a set of Fourier components, determining the network response due to each and obtaining the complete response by adding all the component responses. The procedure is illustrated by an example.

Using the phasor (exponential) form of the Fourier series, the coefficients for the square wave are (from Section 8.2.4),

$$\mathbf{C}_n = \cdots jV/5\pi, 0, jV/3\pi, 0, jV/\pi, V/2, -jV/\pi,$$
$$-jV/3\pi, -jV/5\pi \cdots.$$

Using the potential-divider technique in Fig. 8.13,

$$\mathbf{V}_C = (\mathbf{V}_i/j\omega C)/(R + 1/j\omega C)$$
$$= \mathbf{V}_i/(1 + j\omega\tau),$$

where $\tau = CR$ and is assumed to be $0.4T$ in this case. The response phasors at $\omega = n\omega_0$, $\mathbf{C}_n/(1 + jn\omega_0\tau)$, are given by substituting $\omega_0\tau = 2\pi\tau/T = 2.51$ and, for successive values of n, their values are:

$$\cdots 0.025\underline{/175°}, 0, 0.07\underline{/172°}, 0, 0.589\underline{/158°}, 2.5,$$
$$0.589\underline{/-158°}, 0.07\underline{/-172°}, 0, 0.025\underline{/-175°} \cdots.$$

Multiplying each term by $e^{jn\omega_0 t}$, with n taking on the relevant value, restores the phasors to their time-varying form:

$$v_C(t) = 2.5 + 1.178 \cos(\omega_0 t - 158°)$$
$$+ 0.14 \cos(3\omega_0 t - 172) + 0.05 \cos(5\omega_0 t - 175°) \cdots.$$

These components are sketched in Fig. 8.14 which shows that
the resultant approximates to the output waveform in
Fig. 8.13. With the addition of the seventh- and the ninth-
harmonic components, this waveform would become quite a
good approximation to the true charge–discharge
characteristic.

Fig. 8.14 Harmonic
components added to give
the approximate output in
Fig. 8.13

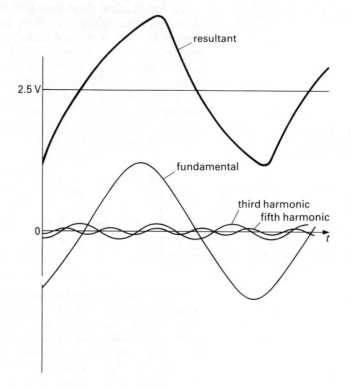

The essence of the technique is as follows:

(i) Resolve the input-waveform, $f(t)$, into its Fourier
     components: in the phasor form, the nth component,

$$C_n = \frac{1}{T} \int_{-T/2}^{+T/2} f(t) e^{-jn\omega_0 t} \, dt.$$

(ii) Determine the network function $H(jn\omega_0)$ at each harmonic
     frequency, $n\omega_0$. In the above example,
     $H(jn\omega_0) = 1/(1 + jn\omega_0 \tau)$.

(iii) Determine the network response (in phasor form) to
      each harmonic component of $f(t)$. This is given by
      $R(jn\omega_0) = C_n H(jn\omega_0)$, for the nth harmonic.

(iv) Reinsert $e^{jn\omega_0 t}$ to restore the phasor rotation and express
     the response, $r(t)$, as a summation of real functions of
     time.

8.4 Fourier integral and transform

8.4.1 Introduction

The method by which the capacitor-voltage variation was determined in the previous section is not a particularly convenient one; nor is the result expressed in a particularly convenient form. Nevertheless, it does contain most of the basic procedures of the **time-to-frequency transformation** technique although, as explained below, it is not a true 'transform' in the generally accepted sense of the term.

Essentially, the function of time is multiplied by a series of rotating phasors, $e^{-jn\omega_0 t}$, and integrated over one period so that, if the function contains a component at the frequency $n\omega_0$, its amplitude and phase are evaluated in complex form by the integration process. The function of time is now represented by a series of complex numbers, one for each discrete-frequency component in $f(t)$. To determine the time response each complex component is then multiplied by the complex network function at that frequency and finally, to restore the time variable, each result is multiplied by the oppositely rotating phasor, $e^{jn\omega_0 t}$. The summation of all these components is the required time function. The (stationary) phasor analysis for the single sinusoid in Chapter 4 is a special case of this procedure in which there is one frequency component only, i.e. $n = +1$ only. However, the purpose of this section is to extend the argument in the other direction so that, instead of dealing with a series of discrete complex amplitudes, the function of time is expressed as a continuous (complex) function of frequency. This is the true **transform**.

8.4.2 The Fourier transform and its inverse

In Section 8.2.6 it was shown that the periodic pulse waveform has a spectral content whose amplitude can be described by the function $(Vt_p/T)(\sin x/x)$. Various methods for displaying the content were shown in Fig. 8.8.

Because the harmonic spacing is the reciprocal of the period, the longer the period, the closer the spacing. Fig. 8.15 shows part of the spectral content for a pulse of width $2\,\mu s$ and period $60\,\mu s$. It is not difficult to imagine (but it is difficult to draw!) the harmonics when the period is increased to 60 ms; there would be approximately 30 000 spectral lines between zero frequency and the first zero of the envelope. As the period tends to infinity, the spectral-line spacing tends to zero, resulting, in the limit, in a **continuous spectrum**. The

Fig. 8.15 Spectral content of pulse with very long period

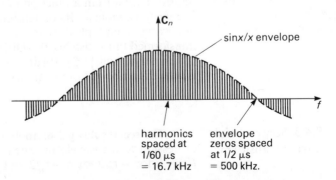

harmonics
spaced at
$1/60\,\mu s$
$= 16.7$ kHz

envelope
zeros spaced
at $1/2\,\mu s$
$= 500$ kHz.

amplitude and phase of the 'components' of this continuous spectrum are still specified by the $\sin x/x$ envelope and the continuous function of frequency is therefore proportional to $\sin x/x$, where x is now a continuous function of frequency. Although a pulse is used as an example, the general principle applies to the general function $f(t)$ and the discrete-frequency Fourier coefficient

$$C_n = \frac{1}{T} \int_{-T/2}^{+T/2} f(t) e^{-jn\omega_0 t} \, dt$$

becomes the continuous-frequency **Fourier integral**

$$F(\omega) = \int_{-\infty}^{+\infty} f(t) e^{-j\omega t} \, dt.$$

The limits have become $\pm\infty$, and as each harmonic component becomes indistinguishable from the next, the continuous variable ω replaces $n\omega_0$. The factor $1/T$ in C_n tends to zero as $T \to \infty$ (as the spectral content of a pulse would become smaller as the pulses become less frequent) and in defining $F(\omega)$ an additional factor T is effectively introduced to compensate for this loss of amplitude. The **inverse Fourier integral**, which corresponds with the discrete-frequency relationship $f(t) = \sum_{n=-\infty}^{\infty} C_n e^{jn\omega_0 t}$, therefore effectively contains a factor $1/T$ which, as $T \to \infty$, tends to $d\omega/2\pi$. Thus, with ω replacing $n\omega_0$ and the discrete summation replaced by the continuous integral, the inverse integral is given by,

$$f(t) = \frac{1}{2\pi} \int_{-\infty}^{+\infty} F(\omega) e^{j\omega t} \, d\omega.$$

$F(\omega)$ and $f(t)$ are thus related in the form of a Fourier-transform pair $f(t) \Leftrightarrow F(\omega)$, where $F(\omega) = \mathscr{F}[f(t)]$.

In terms of the rotating-phasor concept (discussed in relation to the Fourier series in Section 8.2.4), $F(\omega)$ is given by multiplying the function of time by a continuously-variable-speed rotating phasor $e^{-j\omega t}$: this contrasts with the discrete-speed phasor $e^{-jn\omega_0 t}$ used to evaluate C_n. Thus, whereas any component of a periodic function at a harmonic frequency $n\omega_0$ may be evaluated by the expression for C_n, in the present case components at *every* frequency ω are evaluated, yielding a continuous magnitude and phase spectrum: this is the **Fourier transform**. It is, essentially, a transformation from a function of the time variable t to the frequency variable ω. Its dimensions are those of the original time variable multiplied by time. Not all functions can be transformed but satisfying the Dirichlet conditions in any finite interval and $\int_{-\infty}^{+\infty} |f(t)| \, dt < \infty$ are sufficient conditions for the existence of Fourier transforms.

8.4.3 Some useful Fourier transforms

(i) **The rectangular pulse:** applying the Fourier-transform expression to the waveform shown in Fig. 8.16(a), for which $f(t) = V$ for $-t_p/2 < t < +t_p/2$ and $f(t) = 0$ for all other

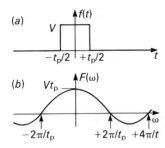

Fig. 8.16 A pulse and its transform

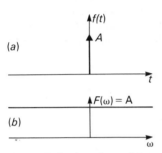

Fig. 8.17 An impulse and its transform

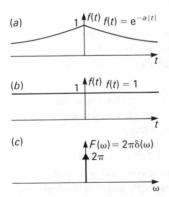

Fig. 8.18 A constant level and its transform

values of t

$$F(\omega) = \int_{-t_p/2}^{+t_p/2} V e^{-j\omega t}\, dt$$

$$= \frac{V}{j\omega}(e^{j\omega t_p/2} - e^{-j\omega t_p/2}).$$

Rearranging,

$$F(\omega) = V t_p \frac{e^{j\omega t_p/2} - e^{-j\omega t_p/2}}{j2\omega t_p/2}$$

$$= V t_p \sin x / x, \quad \text{where } x = \omega t_p/2.$$

This is illustrated in Fig. 8.16(b).

(ii) **The impulse:** a special case of the rectangular pulse occurs when $t_p \to 0$: x also tends to 0, $\sin x/x \to 1$ and $F(\omega) \to V t_p$. In effect, the Fourier transform becomes a constant whose value is equal to the area under the pulse. As discussed in Chapter 9 (Section 9.1.1), the pulse described here is an impulse of strength $V t_p$ and, hence, the Fourier transform of the general impulse, $f(t) = A\delta(t)$, is given by $F(\omega) = A$. Fig. 8.17 shows the time and frequency-domain representations of the impulse. Formally, the transform of $f(t) = A\delta t$ is given by

$$F(\omega) = \int_{-\infty}^{+\infty} A\delta(t)e^{-j\omega t}\, dt = A,$$

or, using a notation similar to that used for the Laplace transform,

$$\mathcal{F}[\delta(t)] = 1 \quad \text{and} \quad \mathcal{F}^{-1}[1] = \delta(t).$$

(iii) **Unit-amplitude constant:** this function does not satisfy the condition $\int_{-\infty}^{+\infty} |f(t)|\, dt < \infty$. However, the transform of $f(t)$ in Fig. 8.18(a) can be found and, if a is subsequently allowed to tend to zero, the transform of the d.c. level can be determined:

$$F(\omega) = \int_{-\infty}^{0} e^{at}e^{-j\omega t}\, dt + \int_{0}^{+\infty} e^{-at}e^{-j\omega t}\, dt$$

$$= 1/(a - j\omega) + 1/(a + j\omega) = 2a/(a^2 + \omega^2).$$

As $a \to 0$, $F(\omega)$ is zero except when $\omega = 0$ where, by L'Hospital's rule,

$$F(\omega) = \lim_{a \to 0} 2/2a = \infty.$$

Thus, the transform is an impulse whose strength (the area of the impulse) may be obtained by integrating $F(\omega)$ over the frequency range. Thus,

$$\int_{-\infty}^{+\infty} F(\omega)\, d\omega = \int_{-\infty}^{+\infty} 2a/(a^2 + \omega^2)\, d\omega = 2\pi,$$

and this is the strength of the impulse function shown in Fig. 8.18(c).

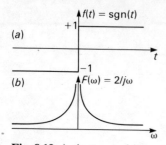

Fig. 8.19 A signum and its transform

(iv) **The signum function:** this is illustrated in Fig. 8.19(a) and defined as

$sgn(t) = +1$ for $t > 0$,

$sgn(t) = 0$ when $t = 0$,

$sgn(t) = -1$ for $t < 0$.

The shape is that of Fig. 8.18(b) but with $f(t)$ inverted for $t < 0$. Thus, using the previous result,

$$F(\omega) = \lim_{a \to 0} (1/(a + j\omega) - 1/(a - j\omega)) = 2/j\omega.$$

There is no impulse in this case.

(v) **The unit step:** adding the two functions of time shown in Figs. 8.18(b) and 8.19(a), and dividing by 2, results in the unit step in Fig. 8.20(a). The transform (Fig. 8.20(b)) is then half the sum of the transforms of the individual time functions giving,

$$F(\omega) = \tfrac{1}{2}(2/j\omega + 2\pi\delta(\omega)) = 1/j\omega + \pi\delta(\omega).$$

This is the transform of the unit step.

Fig. 8.20 A unit step and its transform

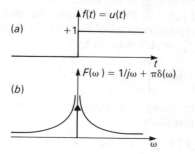

8.4.4 Properties of the transform

As with the Laplace transform there are a number of properties which facilitate the transformation from the time domain to the frequency domain and vice versa. A short list of three follows.

(i) **Linearity:** the transform is linear in the sense that the Fourier transform of the scaled sum of two functions of time is the scaled sum of the transforms. Thus,

$$\mathscr{F}[K_1 f_1(t) + K_2 f_2(t)] = K_1\mathscr{F}[f_1(t)] + K_2\mathscr{F}[f_2(t)].$$

(ii) **The modulation theorem:** this states that a signal multiplied by a unit phasor rotating with angular velocity ω_1 shifts the entire frequency spectrum by an amount $(-\omega_1)$. Thus, if $\mathscr{F}[f(t)] = F(\omega)$ then

$$\mathscr{F}[f(t)e^{j\omega_1 t}] = F(\omega - \omega_1).$$

An application of this theorem lies in determining the transform of a cosine wave. If a d.c. level is converted into a cosine wave by multiplying by $(e^{j\omega_1 t} + e^{-j\omega_1 t})/2 (= \cos \omega_1 t)$. Then, $F(\omega) = 2\pi(\tfrac{1}{2}\delta(\omega - \omega_1) + \tfrac{1}{2}\delta(\omega + \omega_1))$ and the transform will be seen to consist of two impulse functions at frequencies $\pm\omega_1$, as illustrated in Fig. 8.21.

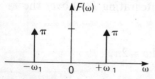

Fig. 8.21 Transform of a cosine wave

(iii) **The time-translation or delay theorem:** this states that if $\mathscr{F}[f(t)] = F(\omega)$, then

$$\mathscr{F}[f(t-a)] = e^{-j\omega a}F(\omega),$$

i.e. a signal delayed in time by a is subject to a phase shift $-\omega a$ in the frequency domain, a topic to be discussed further in Section 8.5 of this chapter.

Example 8.4

Show that the same transform results if the pulse shown in Fig. 8.16 is delayed by time $t_p/2$ as compared with the summation of the two step functions shown in Fig. 8.22.

The transform of the pulse in Fig. 8.16 is

$$F(\omega) = (Vt_p \sin \omega t_p/2)/\omega t_p/2.$$

Delaying the pulse by time $t_p/2$ introduces a factor $e^{-j\omega t_p/2}$ into the transform which then becomes:

$$Vt_p \frac{\sin \omega t_p/2}{\omega t_p/2} e^{-j\omega t_p/2}.$$

This reduces to

$$(V/j\omega)(1 - e^{-j\omega t_p}).$$

Now considering the pulse as the sum of the two steps, the negative step being delayed by time t_p,

$$F(\omega) = V(\pi\delta(\omega) + 1/j\omega) - V(\pi\delta(\omega) + 1/j\omega)e^{-j\omega t_p}$$

$$= \pi\delta(\omega)V(1 - e^{-j\omega t_p}) + (V/j\omega)(1 - e^{-j\omega t_p}).$$

The first term is always zero because $\delta(\omega)$ is zero for all values of ω except when $\omega = 0$ (because it is an impulse function) and, when $\omega = 0$, $(1 - e^{-j\omega t_p}) = 0$. Therefore, $F(\omega) = (V/j\omega)(1 - e^{-j\omega t_p})$, as before.

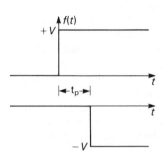

Fig. 8.22 A pulse resolved into two step functions

8.5 Time and frequency response relationships

8.5.1 Use of the Fourier transform in determining time response

In Examples 8.2 and 8.3, each component of the Fourier series (expressed in phasor form) was multiplied by the network function (of $j\omega$) at the relevant harmonic frequency to give the series of component responses, also in phasor form. The method is summarised at the end of Section 8.3.

The principle also applies in the continuous-spectrum case and can be expressed in the form.

$$R(\omega) = H(\omega)F(\omega),$$

where $F(\omega)$ is the Fourier transform of the forcing function, $H(\omega)$ (or $H(j\omega)$)† is the network function and $R(\omega)$ is the Fourier transform of the response. The response as a function of time can be obtained by taking the inverse transform

---

† The use of $F(\omega)$ for the Fourier transform is common practice but it now presents a problem in as much as, for consistency, the network function is now written $H(\omega)$ where previously $H(j\omega)$ has been used. Care should be exercised when changing from $H(s)$ to $H(\omega)$ to ensure that the substitution $s = j\omega$ is made.

of $R(\omega)$,

$$r(t) = \mathscr{F}^{-1}[R(\omega)]$$
$$= \mathscr{F}^{-1}[H(\omega)F(\omega)].$$

This is essentially the same procedure as used in Chapter 6 to determine time response using the Laplace-transform,

$$r(t) = \mathscr{L}^{-1}[H(s)F(s)].$$

Returning to the $r(t) = \mathscr{F}^{-1}[H(\omega)F(\omega)]$ relationship, the network function expressed in terms of frequency, $j\omega$, is the same as that which yielded the magnitude and phase-response characteristics (i.e. the frequency response) in Chapter 7. Thus, the time response can be predicted from frequency response information. For example, the effect on the waveshape of a pulse can be predicted when the bandwidth of a filter through which it is passed is altered. This topic is briefly explored in the next section, but the following example illustrates the general principle. The frequency-response characteristic used is that already developed (Chapter 7) for the CR network and, therefore, as a check, the time response should be the familiar exponential charge and discharge shape.

Example 8.5   *Using the Fourier transform of a rectangular pulse (Example 8.4), determine the output-voltage $v_o(t)$ for the network having the frequency response shown in Fig. 8.23.*

Fig. 8.23 Network and input waveform for Example 8.5

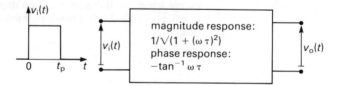

The transform of the input waveform is $(V/j\omega)(1 - e^{-j\omega t_p})$ from Example 8.4. The phase and magnitude functions shown in Fig. 8.23 are those which correspond to the network function $1/(1 + j\omega\tau)$. The transformed response is then the product of the input-waveform transform and network function:

$$V_o(\omega) = \frac{V(1 - e^{-j\omega t_p})}{j\omega(1 + j\omega\tau)}.$$

The time response $v_o(t)$ is the inverse transform of this function. As with the Laplace method no attempt is made to determine v_o as a function of time using the inversion integral; instead, the function is broken down into component parts each of which is recognised as a standard form. In this case,

$$V_o(\omega) = (V(1 - e^{-j\omega t_p})/j\omega) - (V(1 - e^{-j\omega t_p})/(1/\tau + j\omega)),$$

from which,

$$v_o(t) = \left(\frac{V}{2}\operatorname{sgn}(t) - \frac{V}{2}\operatorname{sgn}(t - t_p)\right) - (Ve^{-t/\tau}u(t))$$

$$+ (Ve^{-(t - t_p)/\tau}u(t - t_p)).$$

This result is illustrated in Fig. 8.24.

Fig. 8.24 Solution to
Example 8.5

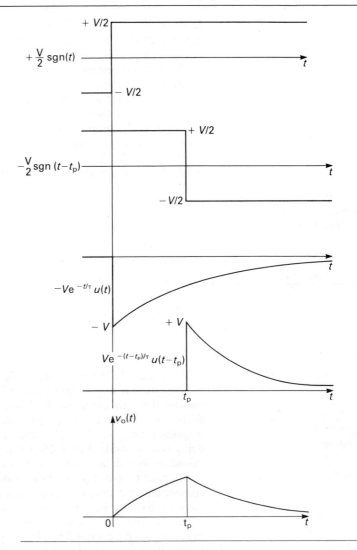

8.5.2 Ideal network phase and magnitude characteristics

In this example, the time response has been determined without knowledge of the components of the network; even though it was a network which has been described previously, only frequency-response information was used. The principle is used in a more complex example in Section 8.5.3 for which the following section contains preparatory work.

If it is assumed that the objective is to transmit a signal through a linear network without distortion, it is desirable that the network should have two particular properties:

(i) that its attenuation (or gain) should be constant or zero with respect to frequency over the entire frequency band occupied by the signal, and

(ii) that the phase shift through the network should be proportional to frequency over the relevant band (or that it should be constant at $n\pi$, where n may be any positive or negative integer, including zero).

In discussing these conditions it is assumed that the network is terminated in a specific way, for example, by its characteristic impedance.

The two properties are shown graphically in Fig. 8.25(a). To appreciate their significance, it is convenient to think in terms of a square wave (for example) resolved into its Fourier components, as shown in Fig. 8.1. Provided the attenuation is constant, each component will be subject to the same magnitude change, maintaining its proper relative proportions. If differential magnitude changes do occur (as in Example 8.2, for example), **amplitude distortion** of the signal results.

Fig. 8.25 Ideal phase and magnitude characteristics and time delay

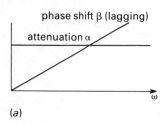

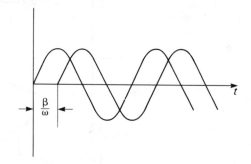

(a)

The effect of a network phase lag β at an angular frequency ω is to cause a sinusoidal signal to be delayed in time on passing through the network. This is known as the **phase delay** and is given by the phase shift divided by the angular frequency, i.e. β/ω. With β in rad and ω in rad/s, the phase delay is in seconds. Fig. 8.25(b) shows two equal-amplitude sinusoids, one delayed in time β/ω with respect to the other.

In order to avoid **phase-delay distortion** each Fourier component of a non-sinusoidal signal must be subject to the same time delay, i.e. they must remain 'in step' with each other. This means that a third-harmonic component, for example, must be shifted in phase by three times the angle by which the fundamental is shifted. Thus, the slope of β/ω graph must remain constant and it must pass through the origin. Special cases arise when the phase shift is constant at $\pm\pi$, $\pm 2\pi$ rad, etc. In these cases each component is either inverted or unchanged in phase and there is no distortion even though the β/ω graph does not pass through the origin. The resultant waveforms in Examples 8.2 and 8.3 and in the case study in Section 8.3 may all be regarded as examples of composite amplitude and phase distortion resulting from the two conditions not being met.

Another form of delay in networks is **group delay**, being the time delay experienced by the resultant effect of groups of sinusoids, usually contained within a narrow band of frequencies. In Chapter 10, for example, the envelope variations occurring in an a.m. signal may be seen as an example of such a resultant effect. Group delay can be shown to be given by the slope of the phase/frequency characteristic, i.e. $d\beta/d\omega$. Group-delay distortion can occur when the phase-frequency characteristic is non-linear over the frequency range of interest, causing the resultants of groups of sinusoids at differing frequencies to be delayed by differing times.

8.5.3 Time response of a band limited transmission channel

The objective is to determine the response to a rectangular pulse of a network having the ideal phase characteristic previously described but with a low-pass magnitude function which cuts off sharply at a frequency B (Hz). Fig. 8.26 shows the characteristics in its double-sided form. The Fourier transform of the input signal is (from Section 8.4.3)

$$V(e^{+jt_p\omega/2} - e^{-jt_p\omega/2})/j\omega.$$

Fig. 8.26 Band-limited channel response

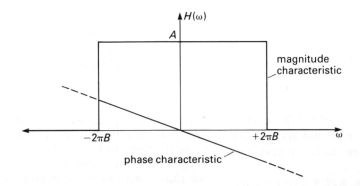

The network function is $Ae^{-jt_d\omega}$ for $-2\pi B < \omega < +2\pi B$ and is zero for all other frequencies. The Fourier transform of the output signal is then the product of these two expressions:

$$R(\omega) = -jAV(e^{j(t_p/2 - t_d)\omega} - e^{-j(t_p/2 + t_d)\omega})/\omega \quad \text{for } -2\pi B < \omega < +2\pi B.$$

The inverse Fourier transform of this function is

$$= \frac{1}{2\pi} \int_{-\infty}^{+\infty} R(\omega)e^{j\omega t}\, d\omega$$

$$= \frac{-jAV}{2\pi} \int_{-2\pi B}^{+2\pi B} \left[e^{j\omega(t - t_d + t_p/2)} - e^{j\omega(t - t_d - t_p/2)}\right] d\omega.$$

Evaluation of this integral can be shown to be given by

$$r(t) = V/\pi[\text{Si}(2\pi B(t - t_d + t_p/2) - \text{Si}(2\pi B(t - t_d - t_p/2))],$$

where the Si function is the **sine integral function** given by the relationship $\text{Si}(x) = \int_0^x \sin x/x \, dx$. Fig. 8.27 shows the $\sin x/x$ and $\text{Si}(x)$ functions.

The summation of the two Si functions, relative to the input-pulse shape, is shown in Fig. 8.28 for typical filter bandwidths equal to the reciprocal of the pulse width and five times this value. The shape of the waveform is discussed in the next section but the implied appearance of an output in advance of the input pulse cannot occur in a real system. This underlines the assumption of independent magnitude and phase characteristics for the analysis. Notwithstanding this limitation, the results obtained are useful first-order guides to the effect of low-pass filtering a pulse waveform.

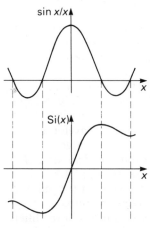

Fig. 8.27 $\sin x/x$ and $\text{Si}(x)$ functions

Fig. 8.28 Input pulse and output pulse for assumed channel response

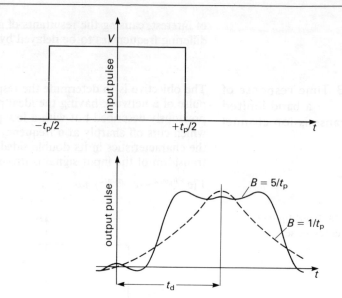

8.5.4 Bandwidth, risetime and general-response relationships

Fig. 8.29 Rise time and tilt for a CR network

Before discussing the waveforms in Fig. 8.28 it is of interest to discuss the bandwidth/risetime relationship for the *CR* network shown in Fig. 8.29(*a*). In this diagram it is assumed that the filter time constant τ has a value such that the output waveform rises to a value in excess of 90% of the input-pulse amplitude during the pulse-width period t_p.

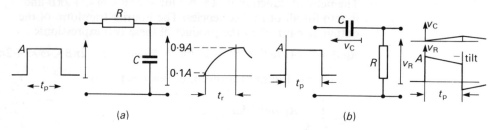

(*a*)   (*b*)

The **risetime** t_r of the output waveform may be defined as the time period during which the voltage rises from 10% to 90% of the pulse amplitude. Evaluating t_r from the charge equation $v_o = A(1 - e^{-t/\tau})$ gives t_r as 2.2τ. The filter bandwidth B is also related to τ (Chapter 7) by $2\pi B = 1/\tau$ (B is in hertz) and, therefore, the rise time is related to bandwidth by $t_r = 2.2\tau = 0.35/B$.

An associated concept is that of the tilt or sag on an output pulse from a *CR* high-pass-filter network. Fig. 8.29(*b*) shows such a network whose time constant is long in comparison with the pulse width. The output-waveform is obtained by subtracting the capacitor-voltage charge waveform from the input waveform. From the definition of time constant, the initial slope of the waveform is A/τ and, assuming that the waveform is linear throughout the pulse period t_p, the tilt is At_p/τ. As a percentage, the tilt is $100t_p/\tau$%. Alternatively, if τ is expressed in terms of the filter cut-off frequency, f_c through $\tau = 1/2\pi f_c$, the percentage tilt is $100t_p/\tau = 200\pi t_p f_c$%.

Returning to Fig. 8.28, which shows the idealised response of the phase-linear low-pass filter. The rise time for the $2\pi B \gg 1/t_p$ waveform can be shown to be approximately $0.5/B$ based on a zero-to-maximum criterion and approximately $0.35/B$ on a 10% to 90% criterion. Thus, for the wideband condition, the bandwidth required is determined by the specified rise time.

Another interesting feature of the idealised response is its oscillatory nature, arising from the $\sin x/x$ form of the response. Without carrying out a detailed analysis, it will be seen that, because in this case $x = 2\pi B(t - t_d - t_p/2)$, the frequency of the oscillation is numerically equal to the filter cut-off frequency. Also apparent from the expression for x is the inherent delay introduced by the filter. As may be expected, this is t_d where, as previously defined, t_d is the slope of the filter's phase characteristic.

Key points to remember

- a periodic, non-sinusoidal function can be resolved into a series of harmonically related sinusoidal components;

- the series can be expressed as a summation of sinusoids or in the exponential (phasor) form $\mathbf{C}_n = 1/T \int_{-T/2}^{+T/2} f(t) e^{-jn\omega_0 t} \, dt$;

- the components can be displayed on a spectral diagram;

- the spectral content of a pulse can be expressed in $\sin x/x$ form;

- circuits with non-sinusoidal forcing functions can be analysed by treating each harmonic separately and summing component responses;

- the spectral content of a single pulse can be used to introduce the concept of a continuous spectrum and the Fourier transform;

- the Fourier transform can be used to deduce the time response of a network or system whose frequency response is known;

- a network has phase delay given by β/ω and group delay $d\beta/d\omega$;

- bandwidth and output rise-time (with a pulse input) can be related for a given network.

Further reading

Glazier, E. V. D. and Brown, J., *Telecommunications.* Chapman and Hall (1974).

Neff, H. P., *Continuous and Discrete Linear Systems.* Harper and Row (1984).

Nilsson, J. W., *Electric Circuits* (2nd edn). Addison-Wesley (1983).

Van Valkenburg, M. E. and Kinariwala, B. K., *Linear Electronics.* Prentice-Hall (1983).

EXERCISES   8

8.1   The amount of work in determining Fourier-series coefficients can be reduced by recognising various forms of symmetry. Table E8.1 summarises these conditions, indicating in general which coefficients may exist in each case.

Table E8.1. *Waveform symmetry*

Symmetry	a_0	a_n	b_n
Even $f(t) = f(-t)$	yes	yes	no
Odd $f(t) = -f(-t)$	no	no	yes
Half-wave	no	yes	yes
$f(t) = -f(t - (T/2))$		(n odd only)	(n odd only)

By determining the first few terms in the Fourier series for the function shown in Fig. E8.1 with the time origin at:

(i) $t = t_1$, and
(ii) $t = t_2$,

using the method in Section 8.2.2, check whether the data in Table E8.1 are satisfied in these cases.

8.2   Determine the first four Fourier coefficients of the full-wave rectified sinusoid shown in Fig. E8.2.

8.3   Illustrate the result of Exercise 8.2 on a spectral diagram.

8.4   Determine the first four Fourier coefficients in the exponential (phasor) form of the waveform shown in Fig. E8.2 using the expression for C_n developed in Section 8.2.4. Draw a double-sided spectral diagram and compare it with the answer to Exercise 8.3.

8.5   Determine the magnitude of the first eight Fourier coefficients for the periodic voltage waveform shown in Fig. E8.3 and sketch a spectral diagram. Use results of Section 8.2.6.

8.6   The network shown in Fig. E8.4 has a frequency response exhibiting a band-pass characteristic: determine the ratio $V_o(jn\omega_0)/V_i(jn\omega_0)$ for $n = 1$, 3 and 5 (i.e. fundamental, third and fifth-harmonic frequencies) when the input waveform has a period which makes the third-harmonic frequency equal to $1/2\pi CR$.

8.7   By summing the responses due to individual Fourier components, determine the approximate time response of a CR network (as in Fig. 8.13) if it has a 20 ms time constant and the input waveform is that in Fig. E8.2.

8.8   Explain why the voltage output from a single-transistor tuned amplifier may be sinusoidal even though the transistor collector (or drain) current is not sinusoidal.
What might be deduced concerning the frequency range occupied by an input signal if it is to be amplified without distortion.

8.9   Redraw the spectral content (first eight components) if the pulse width in Exercise 8.5 is changed from 0.8 μs to 8 ns. What relevance has this result to the Fourier transform of the impulse (Section 8.4.3)?

8.10   (i) Determine the Fourier transform of the function

$$f(t) = te^{-\alpha t}u(t).$$

(ii) Prove the delay theorem in Section 8.4.4.
(iii) Show that if $\mathscr{F}[f(t)] = F(\omega)$,

$$\mathscr{F}[df(t)/dt] = j\omega F(\omega).$$

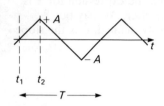

Fig. E8.1

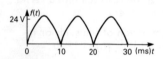

Fig. E8.2

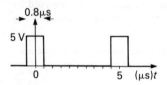

Fig. E8.3

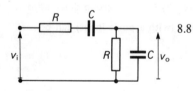

Fig. E8.4

8.11 A network has a frequency response given by

$$H(j\omega) = j\omega\tau/(1 + j\omega\tau).$$

If the input pulse from Example 8.5 is applied to the network input, determine the Fourier transform of the output signal. By determining the Fourier transform of the function $e^{-t/\tau}u(t)$, determine the output signal as a function of time.

8.12 A network has a linear phase response with slope of 0.1 rad/kHz and a constant attenuation of 10 dB over a certain frequency range. Sketch the output pulse which would result if a 5 V, 1 ms pulse were fed into the input. Assume that the response remains linear over the frequency range occupied by all significant harmonics of the pulse.

8.13 A rectangular waveguide has a phase coefficient given by

$$\beta = \sqrt{\left(\left(\frac{\omega}{c}\right)^2 - \left(\frac{\pi}{a}\right)^2\right)} \, \text{rad/m} \quad \text{where } c = 3 \times 10^8 \, \text{m/s}.$$

Determine the phase and group velocities (i.e. the reciprocals of the phase and group delays) for a guide for which $a = 22.86$ mm at a frequency of 8 GHz.

9 Impulse response and sampling

The principal learning objectives of this chapter are to:

	Section	Exercise
• define the impulse function;	1.1	
• determine the circuit response to a near impulsive forcing function;	1.1	9.1
• apply Laplace and Fourier-transform methods to determine impulse response;	1.2	9.2
• discuss convolution as the time-domain equivalent of the frequency-domain product;	2.1	9.3
• evaluate convolution integral in simple examples;	2.1	9.4
• apply the convolution theorem;	2.2	9.5
• apply convolution to determination of time response using an impulse technique;	2.3	9.6, 9.7
• compare analogue and digital systems;	3.1	
• explain the process of analogue multiplexing;	3.2	
• discuss the need for sampling and determine sampling rate;	3.3	9.8
• deduce the spectral content of sampled signals;	3.4	9.9
• explain how aliasing can arise;	3.5	9.9
• discuss the origins and meaning of the z transform;	4.1	
• determine the z transform of simple functions;	4.1	9.10
• deduce the z-transfer function through the impulse response;	4.2	9.11
• derive difference equations and determine sampled output in simple cases.	4.3	9.12

9.1 Impulse response of networks

9.1.1 The impulse function

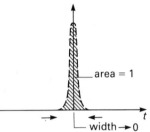

Fig. 9.1 Representation of a unit impulse

Fig. 9.2 Response of a CR network to an impulse

The impulse function $\delta(t)$ was introduced in Chapter 2 and in Section 4.3 of Chapter 8 where it was shown that the Fourier transform of an impulse at time $t = 0$ is a constant equal in amplitude to the strength of the impulse. The same result applies for the Laplace transform.

The unit impulse function may be described mathematically as follows:

$$\int_{-\infty}^{+\infty} \delta(t)\,\mathrm{d}t = 1 \quad \text{and} \quad \delta(t) = 0 \text{ for } t \neq 0.$$

These statements describe a pulse waveform whose width tends towards zero but whose area remains at unit value (Fig. 9.1). For this to be possible, the **height** of the pulse (as opposed to the **magnitude**, or **strength** which is the area of the pulse) must tend towards infinity. In practice, any pulse whose width is very short in comparison with the time constant(s) or the natural periods of the network under consideration behaves as an impulse. For example, Fig. 9.2 shows a $10\,\mu s$ pulse applied to a network having a time constant of $10^4 \times 10^{-7} = 1\,\text{ms}$. The response (Fig. 9.2(c))

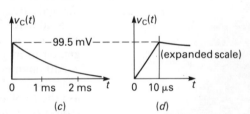

(a) (b) (c) (d)

shows a very short charging period during which v_C rises only to about $100\,\text{mV}$ (as compared with the $10\,\text{V}$ input-pulse height) followed by the relatively slow discharge back to zero voltage. Viewed on the timescale of Fig. 9.2(c), the capacitor voltage appears to change its value almost instantaneously. In practice (as discussed in Chapter 2), v_C cannot change instantaneously in this practical system and this is confirmed by the expanded timescale in Fig. 9.2(d).

The theoretical impulse response (to an idealised impulse) is derived in the next section. In this case, the capacitor voltage does exhibit an instantaneous change but this is in response to a non-practical, infinite-height, zero-width pulse. Nevertheless, near-ideal impulsive forces and responses are not unusual in everyday experience; the blow of a hammer on a nail is impulsive and the nail does appear to change its position instantaneously.

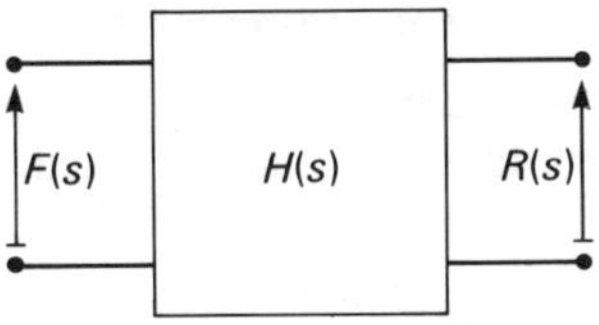

9.1.2 Determination of impulse response using Fourier or Laplace transforms

Fig. 9.3 Relating $R(s)$ to $F(s)$

It has been established in previous chapters that the zero-state response function (of s or $j\omega$) is given by the product of the forcing function $F(s)$ and the network function, $H(s)$,

$$R(s) = H(s)F(s).$$

Fig. 9.3 illustrates this relationship. Because the transform

$F(s)$ (or $F(\omega)$) of the unit impulsive forcing function is unity, the transform of the zero-state impulse-response function is simply the network function $H(s)$. Thus, the impulse response of a network $h(t)$ may be determined by finding the inverse transform of the network function. This is illustrated by Example 9.1.

Example 9.1   *Determine the response of the network shown in Fig. 9.2(b) to unit impulse at $t = 0$.*

As previously established,

$H(s) = 1/(1 + s\tau)$

where $\tau = 10^4 \times 10^{-7} = 10^{-3}$ s. Therefore, the impulse response is given by

$h(t) = \mathscr{L}^{-1}[1/(1 + s10^{-3})] = 10^3 e^{-10^3 t} u(t)$

(using the Laplace-transform table in Table 6.1).

The expression obtained in Example 9.1 is an idealised version of Fig. 9.2(c) (i.e. with an instantaneous rise in v_C at $t = 0$) except that the amplitude at $t = 0$ is 10^3 V instead of the 99.5 mV shown in Fig. 9.2. The reason for the large amplitude difference lies in the size of the impulse. The calculation assumes that the idealised impulse has unit value (i.e. unit area) as compared with an area of $10 \times 10 \times 10^{-6} = 10^{-4}$ V–s for the pulse shown in Fig. 9.2(a). Thus, the 'ideal' result can be expected to be a factor of 10^4 greater in magnitude than that for Fig. 9.2(c).

Although either Fourier or Laplace transforms could have been used in Example 9.1, it is generally more convenient to use the Laplace transform because of its greater generality. However, in principle, the results also apply for the Fourier transform and the following statements summarise the relationships:

$\mathscr{L}[h(t)] = H(s);$ the Laplace transform of the response to unit impulse is the network function of s.

$\mathscr{F}[h(t)] = H(\omega);$ the Fourier transform of the response to unit impulse (i.e. the spectral content of the impulse response) is the network function of ω, i.e. the network frequency response.†

In either case the alternative form, that the impulse response is the inverse transform of the network function, may be used. Thus $h(t)$ is given by $\mathscr{L}^{-1}[H(s)]$.

9.2 Convolution

9.2.1 The convolution integral

The opening statement in the previous section was $R(s) = H(s)F(s)$. The relationship states that the zero-state response is the product of the network and the forcing functions and is a form of relationship which has arisen quite

---

† See footnote on page 189.

naturally through the analysis techniques in Chapter 6. For example, current response is the product of a voltage forcing function and an admittance network function,

$$I(s) = Y(s)V(s),$$

or, in terms of an impedance function,

$$I(s) = V(s)/Z(s).$$

This is just the form which may be intuitively expected from earlier work on resistive networks.

For resistive networks, the product (or quotient) form holds in both time and frequency domains. However, when the network or system contains energy-storage elements the frequency-domain relationship still holds but there is no such straightforward relationship in the time domain. The purpose of this subsection, therefore, is to investigate a general form of a relationship valid in the time domain when the product or quotient form applies in the frequency domain.

To meet this requirement, the **convolution integral** is proposed. The result of convolving two functions $f_1(t)$ and $f_2(t)$ together is

$$f_1(t) * f_2(t) = \int_0^t f_1(t - \tau)f_2(\tau)\,d\tau,$$

or

$$f_2(t) * f_1(t) = \int_0^t f_1(\tau)f_2(t - \tau)\,d\tau,$$

where τ is a dummy variable and the star notation indicates the convolution of one function with another. To demonstrate the convolution process Fig. 9.4 shows a step function convolved with a decaying exponential. Also shown is the result $r(t)$ which will be seen to have the form of an

Fig. 9.4 Convolution of two time functions

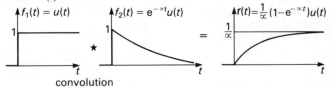

convolution

exponential 'charging' curve. Although the form of the result may not be immediately apparent it can be justified by evaluating the convolution integrals as follows:

$$r(t) = f_1(t) * f_2(t),$$

where $f_1(t) = u(t)$ and $f_2(t) = e^{-\alpha t}u(t)$. Using the convolution integral:

$$r(t) = \int_0^t f_1(t - \tau)f_2(\tau)\,d\tau$$

$$= \int_0^t u(t - \tau)e^{-\alpha \tau}u(\tau)\,d\tau$$

$$= \int_0^t e^{-\alpha \tau}\,d\tau$$

$$= \frac{1}{\alpha}(1 - e^{-\alpha t}),$$

and, using the alternative form:

$$r(t) = \int_0^t f_1(\tau) f_2(t - \tau)\, d\tau$$

$$= \int_0^t u(\tau) e^{-\alpha(t - \tau)} u(t - \tau)\, d\tau$$

$$= \int_0^t e^{-\alpha(t - \tau)}\, d\tau$$

$$= \frac{1}{\alpha}(1 - e^{-\alpha t}).$$

Fig. 9.5 The convolution process

To supplement these derivations, Fig. 9.5 presents a graphical interpretation of the steps in the integration process.

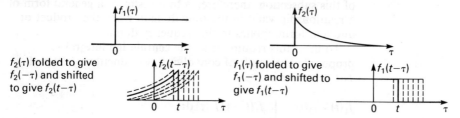

$f_2(\tau)$ folded to give $f_2(-\tau)$ and shifted to give $f_2(t-\tau)$

$f_1(\tau)$ folded to give $f_1(-\tau)$ and shifted to give $f_1(t-\tau)$

In each case, the full line shows waveforms for a particular value of t; other values for t are denoted by dotted lines

$f_2(t-\tau)$ multiplied by $f_1(\tau)$

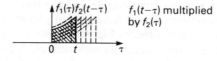

$f_1(t-\tau)$ multiplied by $f_2(\tau)$

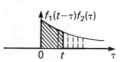

The shaded area in both graphs is the integral of the product at $\tau = t$. Plotting values as t varies gives $f(t)$ as $\int_0^t f_1(\tau) f_2(t-\tau)\, d\tau$ or $\int_0^t f_1(t - \tau) f_2(\tau)\, d\tau$

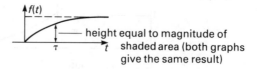

height equal to magnitude of shaded area (both graphs give the same result)

9.2.2 The convolution theorem

The convolution process was initially proposed as the time-domain equivalent of the frequency-domain product. Thus, it is no coincidence that the convolution of a step function and a decaying exponential (the latter being considered to be the impulse response of a series CR network) is the characteristic capacitor charging curve. Fig. 9.6 illustrates the relationship in the time domain (above the network) and in the frequency domain (below the network). The expressions differ only from those in Fig. 9.4 in the amplitude scales. Use is made of the fact that the impulse response $h(t)$ is the time-domain equivalent of the network function $H(s)$, i.e. $h(t) = \mathcal{L}^{-1}[H(s)]$.

The formal relationship between the time- and frequency-domain forms is given by the **convolution theorem** which states that if $f_1(t)$ and $f_2(t)$ have Laplace transforms $F_1(s)$ and $F_2(s)$, the transform of the convolution of $f_1(t)$ and $f_2(t)$ is the

Fig. 9.6 Convolution of a time function and an impulse response

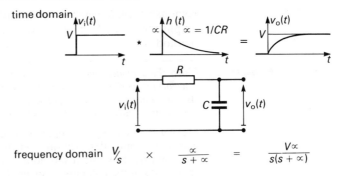

product of $F_1(s)$ and $F_2(s)$. Thus

$$\mathcal{L}[f_1(t) * f_2(t)] = F_1(s)F_2(s),$$

or

$$\mathcal{L}^{-1}[F_1(s)F_2(s)] = f_1(t) * f_2(t).$$

9.2.3 Convolution and impulses

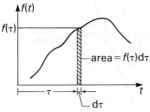

Fig. 9.7 A function divided into small strips

An alternative view of the convolution integral is to regard it as the summation of a train of weighted impulses. In Fig. 9.7 the function $f(t)$ is regarded as being composed of narrow strips, each of width $d\tau$ and height $f(\tau)$. Because each strip is narrow and has area $f(\tau)\,d\tau$, the resultant network response can be considered to be the summation of a sequence of impulse responses $h(t - \tau)$, each weighted by a factor $f(\tau)\,d\tau$, giving an overall response function,

$$r(t) = \int_0^t h(t - \tau)f(\tau)\,d\tau.$$

This process assumes, of course, that the network is linear and that superposition applies. This is identical in form to the convolution integral discussed above, and opens up the possibility of a discrete-time technique for calculating the time response of networks by repeatedly summing a series of progressively delayed standard functions (i.e. impulse

Fig. 9.8 Response determined by summation of impulse responses

(a) The forcing function (a step function) is represented by a set of discrete impulses of weight $f(\tau)\,d\tau$. In this case all have equal weights.

(b) The weighted impulse response for $t = \tau$ (in full line). Dotted lines indicated responses for other values of τ.

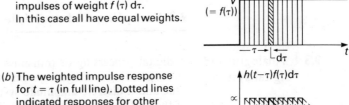

(c) Output waveform as the sum of the impulse responses in (b). (not to scale). Note that, unlike the previous illustration, the output waveform is the sum of the ordinates *not* the cumulative area under the graph.

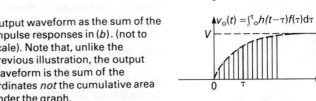

responses), each weighted in accordance with the changing amplitude of the forcing function. Fig. 9.8 summarises the method.

Example 9.2 *Using the graphical method outlined in Fig. 9.8, determine the output waveform $v_o(t)$ if $v_i(t)$ is a sinusoidal waveform of period 16 time units. Assume that the impulse response of the CR network is a decaying exponential whose amplitude halves every 2 time units.*

Fig. 9.9 shows a sequence of impulse-response functions whose maximum amplitudes vary sinusoidally in accordance with the input function $v_i(t)$. The output waveform is obtained by summing the amplitudes of these impulse-response functions.

Fig. 9.9 Solution to Example 9.2

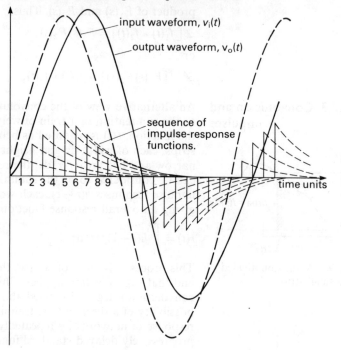

9.3 Sampling and multiplexing

9.3.1 Analogue and digital systems

A digital processing or transmission system differs from the corresponding analogue system in that it is both a **discrete-time** and a **discrete-amplitude** system. The discrete-time nature of the system is considered initially.

In an analogue system (Fig. 9.10(a)), the input signal exists and may be specified at any and every instant in time; the signal is **continuous** in time. The output signal is also continuous in time and is related to the input signal in a particular way; in Fig. 9.10(a), for example, by a constant gain factor.

In the digital case (Fig. 9.10(b)), the processing or transmission system deals with a sequence of 'numbers' presented to the system at (usually) regular time intervals and

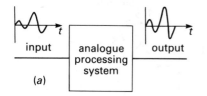

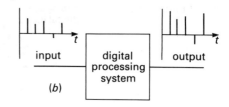

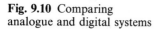

Fig. 9.10 Comparing analogue and digital systems

The height of the ordinates represents the magnitude of the numbers.

the data is **discrete** in time. The system output will also be discrete in time, the value of the output being related to the input by the functional characteristics of the system. A constant scaling factor is shown in this case also.

Whilst all digital systems are discrete-time systems, not all discrete-time systems are digital. In a digital system, the signal-amplitude levels are also discrete. Thus, whereas in the analogue system the signal level may take on any one of an infinite number of values (within a specified range), the digital signal may only take on one of a limited number of discrete values. For example, in a 4-bit binary digital system, only 2^4 ($=16$) different signal levels would be permissible. This would be equivalent to an analogue system, having a signal-voltage range of 0–1.5 V, allowing the voltage to assume only one of 16 discrete values, $0, 0.1, 0.2, 0.3, \ldots, 1.5$ V; a level of, say, 0.26 V would not be permissible. The allocation of discrete signal levels is known as **quantisation** of the signal and the levels themselves, **quantisation levels**. In general, the number of levels in a digital system is given by raising the system base (see Chapter 16) to the power of the number of digits. For an 8-bit system, the number of levels is $2^8 = 256$, or, for a 3-digit octal system, the number of levels is $8^3 = 512$. The magnitude of the 'gap' between levels, the quantisation interval, is the maximum signal range divided by the number of levels less one (see Example 9.3).

The assumption is normally made that a digital system is one which operates with binary numbers and, for example, the accepted meaning of the term analogue-to-digital converter (ADC) is an analogue to binary-digital converter; the device commonly known as a digital-to-analogue converter (DAC) is more properly a binary-digital to quantised-analogue converter but the distinction between continuous-amplitude and multi-level discrete signals is rarely made in this context.

9.3.2 Multiplexing

Discrete-time systems can deal with more than one input signal at a time by means of a technique known as **time-division-multiplexing**, usually referred to simply as **multiplexing** in the context of digital systems. In this technique, a number of signals are sampled in sequence, as shown schematically in Fig. 9.11, and the samples passed sequentially through the processing/transmission system. At the system output, the signals are demultiplexed back onto the respective output lines. The input multiplexer and the

Fig. 9.11 Multiplexing

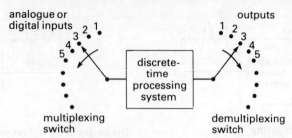

analogue or digital inputs

outputs

discrete-time processing system

multiplexing switch

demultiplexing switch

output demultiplexer are, of course, synchronised with due allowance being made for delays introduced by the system. In this way it is possible to transmit or process signals or data from a number of different sources using a single transmission or processing system. Both analogue and digital multiplexers are used, handling analogue and digital information respectively; the devices discussed in this chapter are **analogue multiplexers**.

9.3.3 Sampling

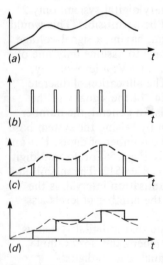

Fig. 9.12 Sampled waveforms

Because the digital system employs signals which are discrete in time, it is necessary to **sample** a continuous-time analogue signal in order to prepare it for digital processing. Fig. 9.12(a) shows a continuous analogue signal; (b) is a sampling waveform; and (c) is the sampled signal obtained by multiplying the analogue signal by the sampling waveform. Fig. 9.12(d) shows an alternative sampled signal in which a **sample-and-hold** circuit has been used; in this case, the sample amplitude has been held constant until the next sample is taken. Ideally, the sampling process should translate all the information contained in the continuous-time analogue signal into the discrete-time samples. On first sight it may appear that this can never be achieved but, provided that the sampling rate (i.e. the number of samples per second) exceeds twice the frequency of the highest-frequency sinusoid in the analogue signal, the sampled signal does, in fact, contain all the information and the original signal may be recovered from it without distortion. For example, if a speech signal, having a maximum frequency component of 3.3 kHz, is sampled at a rate in excess of 6600 samples per second, all components of the speech signal can be recovered. The required sampling rate is embodied in the **sampling theorem** which may be stated in the form: 'A signal having no spectral components above a frequency B, is completely described by a series of discrete-time samples of its amplitude taken at uniform time intervals not exceeding $1/2B$. The theorem can be extended to non-uniform sampling intervals but this aspect is not considered here. There is further discussion on sampling rate in the following sections.

Example 9.3 *A time-division-multiplexed monitoring system checks the temperature at 20 points in an industrial system. Each electrical input to the system is derived from a linear temperature transducer operating over the range 0–100 °C. If the data bit rate is 120 bits/s and each transducer output is sampled once every second, determine the maximum quantisation error in degrees centigrade.*

Number of samples per second = 20   (20 monitor points),

number of bits per sample $\quad = \dfrac{120}{20} = 6$.

As explained in Section 9.3.2, the maximum input signal range is $(2^n - 1)$ quantisation intervals (where n is the number of bits), the temperature interval is $100/63 = 1.59\,°\text{C}$ and maximum error is half the quantisation interval, $0.795\,°\text{C}$.

9.3.4 The spectral content of sampled signals

The spectral content may be determined by a procedure similar to that used to determine the spectral content of the output of the balanced modulator or mixer in Chapter 15. Fig. 9.13 shows an arrangement in which a sampling circuit produces a sampled output from a sinusoidal input signal. It is assumed that the sampling waveform is a periodic unipolar pulse waveform whose pulse width is small compared with its period. The output is proportional to the product of the input signal and the sampling waveform. But, following the method used in Chapter 15, the product of two sinusoids gives sum- and difference-frequency components and, therefore, the effect of the sampling is to produce sum- and difference-frequency components between the input signal and the harmonic components of the sampling waveform.

Fig. 9.13 Operation of a sampling unit

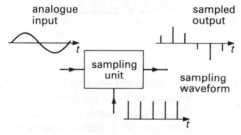

Chapter 8 explained how the harmonic components may be determined. There it was shown that the spectral content of a waveform of period T and pulsewidth t_p has the general $(\sin x)/x$ form shown in Fig. 9.14(b). In this case, with the pulsewidth very much less than the period, the first spectral zero occurs at a relatively high frequency giving the spectral content shown in Fig. 9.14(c) with the first few components at almost the same amplitude $2t_p/T$. In sampling-waveform terminology the reciprocal of the pulse period $1/T$ becomes the sampling frequency f_s and, combining the two concepts, sampling a sinusoidal signal of frequency f_i results in the sum- and difference-frequency components shown in Fig. 9.15(a). In particular, the d.c. component of the sampling waveform results in the 'sum'-frequency component at the signal-input frequency f_i. It is assumed in this diagram that f_i is less than half f_s and that the sampling pulsewidth is small.

Fig. 9.15(b) shows the sum and difference-frequency components resulting from the usual situation in which the spectral content of the sampling signal is spread over the band of frequencies, 0–B.

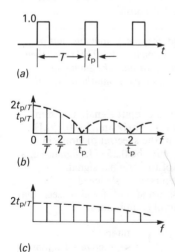

Fig. 9.14 Spectral content of a pulse waveform

The diagrams show that, despite sampling, the sampled signals contain all the information in the original signal (in the frequency band, 0–B). Furthermore, the signal may be

Fig. 9.15 Spectral content of sampled signals

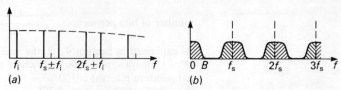

(a) (b)

reconstructed by passing the sampled signal through a low-pass filter. Fig. 9.16(a) shows a filter characteristic which would reject all the higher-order components but pass the required information; also, provided that the sampling frequency is well in excess of 2B, the reconstruction filter need not have an unrealistically sharp cut-off characteristic.

The effect of having too low a sampling rate can be seen in Fig. 9.16(b) and (c). (b) shows the sampling rate just equal to twice the signal bandwidth B, and (c) shows the effect of f_s being less than twice B. In (b) recovery of the sampled signal by low-pass filtering is theoretically possible, but in (c) this cannot be done.

Fig. 9.16 Information recovery by filtering and effect of sampling frequency

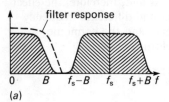 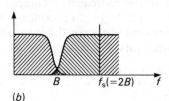 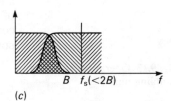

(a) (b) (c)

9.3.5 Aliasing   The spectrum overlap shown in Fig. 9.16(c) is known as **aliasing** and can be demonstrated in both frequency and time domains, as Example 9.4 shows. The term 'aliasing' arises from the effect, demonstrated by this example, by which the reconstructed signal can appear at the output at a frequency which differs from that of the original signal.

Example 9.4   *Show diagrammatically in both time and frequency domains that a sinusoidal signal of frequency 0.75 kHz, sampled at 1.0 kHz and then passed through a low-pass filter cutting off at half the sampling frequency will yield a new sinusoid at a frequency one-third that of the original signal.*

Fig. 9.17 shows the sampling points on the input signal. The sum- and difference-frequency components at 0.75 kHz and 1 ± 0.75 kHz ($= 0.25$ kHz and 1.75 kHz) are shown in the spectral diagram in Fig. 9.17(b). Low-pass filtering passes only the 0.25 kHz signal, i.e. a sinusoid at one-third of the frequency of the original signal. Returning to Fig. 9.17(a), the output sinusoid is sketched on the same scale as that used for the input sinusoid and it will be seen that the waveform is consistent with the sample amplitudes.

Fig. 9.17 Aliasing effect in Example 9.4

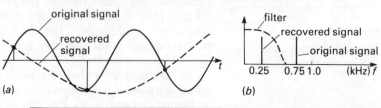

(a) (b)

A low-pass filter placed immediately in front of the sampling unit to ensure that no frequency components in excess of half the sampling frequency (i.e. $> f_s/2$) enter the sampling unit, is known as an **antialiasing filter**.

9.3.6 Sample and hold circuits

There are many applications in which it is desirable to hold an analogue signal at a constant level for a specified period following a sample; for example, it may be desirable to hold the sample amplitude constant during an analogue-to-digital conversion process. A capacitor can be used as the basic 'holding' device because it can store charge for a relatively long period. Fig. 9.18(a) shows a possible basic arrangement using two buffer stages, a switch and a capacitor. The input buffer has a low output impedance and, therefore, the switch-capacitor arrangement is fed from a low-impedance analogue source. In this condition, closing the switch will cause the capacitor voltage to follow any input-signal variations which may occur. Provided that the output buffer has a high input impedance, on opening the switch there will (ideally) be no discharge path for the capacitor and it will remain charged at the particular analogue-input voltage value which existed at the instant the switch was opened. The analogue input will have been sampled and held.

Fig. 9.18 Sample-and-hold operation

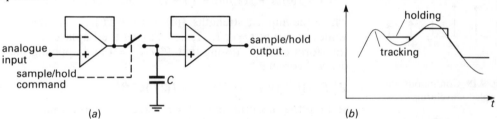

(a)   (b)

The essential action of the sample-and-hold circuit is illustrated in Fig. 9.18(b) from which it will be seen that it is basically a **tracking** and holding action; however, the taking of samples is inherent in the operation of the device. As may be expected, there are a number of factors which result in the operation of the circuit falling short of the ideal.

9.4 Introduction to the z transform

9.4.1 The nature of the z transform

As Laplace and Fourier transforms may be used in the analysis of continuous-time signals, so the z transform may be used in the analysis of discrete-time systems. The z transform of a function comprising, for example, a sequence of values given by

$$f(n) = 1, 3, 5, 7, \ldots$$

may be written in the form

$$F(z) = 1 + 3z^{-1} + 5z^{-2} + 7z^{-3} + \cdots,$$

where the coefficients of the series are the sequence values and the variable z^{-1} signifies a delay of one 'step' in the sequence. The notation $F(z)$ means 'function of z' in the same way as $F(s)$ signifies 'function of s'.

Example 9.5   *Determine the z transform of the sequence $1, -2, 4, -8, \ldots$ and express it in closed form if possible.*

$$F(z) = 1 - 2z^{-1} + 4z^{-2} - 8z^{-3} + \cdots ,$$

or, in closed form,

$$F(z) = (1 + 2z^{-1})^{-1}.$$

Note: the correctness of the closed form may be checked by expanding by means of the binomial theorem.

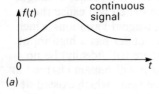

(a)

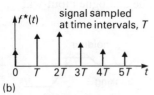

(b)

Fig. 9.19 Continuous and sampled waveforms

In the context of the earlier sections of this chapter, the sequence of values may be amplitudes of a sequence of narrow pulses resulting from sampling a continuous-time wave form. Fig. 9.19(a) shows the continuous waveform with impulsive samples (denoted by $f^*(t)$) in Fig. 9.19(b). $f^*(t)$ can therefore be expressed as an impulse train $\delta(t) + \delta(t - T) + \delta(t - 2T) + \cdots$ whose strength is modulated by $f(t)$, i.e.

$$f^*(t) = f(0)\delta t + f(T)\delta(t - T) + f(2T)\delta(t - 2T) + \cdots ,$$

where the impulse strengths $f(0), f(T), f(2T), \ldots$ are the values of $f(t)$ at $t = 0, T, 2T, \ldots$. Taking the Laplace transform of $f^*(t)$, noting that $\mathcal{L}[\delta(t)] = 1$ and applying the delay theorem,

$$\mathcal{L}[f^*(t)] = f(0) + f(T)e^{-sT} + f(2T)e^{-2sT} + \cdots .$$

Making the substitution $e^{-sT} = z^{-1}$ (i.e. z^{-1} represents a delay of one sampling period) gives the **unilateral z transform**

$$F(z) = f(0) + f(T)z^{-1} + f(2T)z^{-2} + \cdots$$

$$= \sum_{n=0}^{+\infty} f(nT)z^{-n}.$$

This function has the same general form as that used above to describe the discrete sequence in which z^{-1} represents a single-step delay and the coefficients of the series represent sample amplitudes.

Example 9.6   *Determine the z transform of sampled data obtained from the time function, $f(t) = \exp(-at)$ for $t \geqslant 0$.*

The function and its sampled form are shown in Fig. 9.20. As compared with Fig. 9.19, the x axis has been changed to show the discrete-time variable nT where n represents the

Fig. 9.20 Sample sequence for Example 9.6

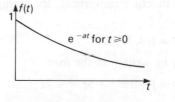

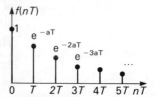

sample number. Thus, $f(nT) = e^{-anT}$. Using the definition established above,

$$F(z) = \sum_{n=0}^{\infty} f(nT)z^{-n}$$

$$= 1 + e^{-aT}z^{-1} + e^{-2aT}z^{-2} + \cdots.$$

This is the required result but the series may be obtained in closed form using standard series summation techniques. Thus,

$$F(z) = 1/(1 - e^{-aT}z^{-1}).$$

That these expressions are the same may be checked by means of the binomial expansion of $(1 - e^{-aT}z^{-1})^{-1}$.

Transforms for the sampled unit impulse (unit sample) and sampled unit step functions may be derived as follows:

(i) Sampled unit impulse: in this case, $f(nT)$ is zero for all values of n except $n = 0$. Thus,

$$F(z) = \sum_{n=0}^{\infty} f(nT)z^{-n}$$

$$= f(0)z^0 \quad \text{when } n = 0$$

$$= 1.$$

(ii) Sampled unit step:

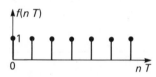

$$F(z) = \sum_{n=0}^{\infty} f(nT)z^{-n}$$

$$= 1 + z^{-1} + z^{-2} + \cdots.$$

Fig. 9.21 Unit sample and unit-sample sequence

In the closed form,

$$F(z) = 1/(1 - z^{-1}).$$

Fig. 9.21 shows $f(nT)$ for the two functions.

9.4.2 The z transfer function

As for Laplace and Fourier transforms, there exists the general forcing/response-function relationship,

response function of $z =$ (network function of z)

$$\times \text{(forcing function of } z).$$

Also, because the transform of a unit impulse is unity, the z transform of the impulse response is the same as the z transform of the network function, i.e.

$$R(z) = H(z) \quad \text{when } F(z) = 1.$$

Thus, if for example the impulse response of a system were found to be that shown in Fig. 9.20, it could be inferred that its network function is $1/(1 - e^{-aT}z^{-1})$, and the response to any other forcing function, $F(z)$, could be predicted from the relationship,

$$R(z) = F(z)/(1 - e^{-aT}z^{-1}).$$

The amplitude of the discrete-time response can be

determined from the coefficients of the series expansion of $R(z)$ as shown in the following example:

Example 9.7

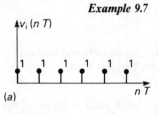

(a)

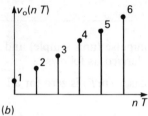

(b)

Fig. 9.22 Input and output samples for Example 9.7

Determine the output amplitudes from a discrete-time integrator to which a sampled unit step function is applied.

Fig. 9.22(a) shows the input signal, for which $V_i(z) = 1/(1 - z^{-1})$. The network function $H(z)$ is given by the sampled unit-impulse response which, for an integrator, is a sampled unit step. Thus, in this particular example, $H(z)$ is the same as $V_i(z)$, i.e. $1/(1 - z^{-1})$

$$V_o(z) = H(z)V_i(z),$$

and therefore

$$V_o(z) = 1/(1 - z^{-1})^2.$$

Expanded by means of the binomial theorem,

$$V_o(z) = 1 + 2z^{-1} + 3z^{-2} + 4z^{-3} + \cdots.$$

The amplitude of the output samples is therefore, $1, 2, 3, 4, \ldots$. As may be expected, integrating a series of unit samples results in a linearly increasing output.

Building on the few examples introduced in the course of the discussion, a short table of z transforms (with the Laplace transforms of the corresponding continuous-time functions) is given in Table 9.1.

Table 9.1. z transforms

	$f(t)$ $(t \geqslant 0)$	$F(s) = \mathcal{L}[f(t)]$	$F(z) = \mathcal{Z}[f(nT)]$
Impulse	$\delta(t)$	1	1
Delayed impulse	$\delta(t - T)$	e^{-sT}	z^{-1}
Impulse train	$i(t)$	$1/(1 - e^{-sT})$	$1/(1 - z^{-1})$
Step	$u(t)$	$1/s$	$1/(1 - z^{-1})$
Exponential decay	$e^{-\alpha t}$	$1/(s + \alpha)$	$1/(1 - e^{-\alpha T}z^{-1})$
Ramp	t	$1/s^2$	$z^{-1}T/(1 - z^{-1})^2$
Sinusoid	$\sin \omega t$	$\omega/(s^2 + \omega^2)$	$z^{-1} \sin \omega T/(1 - 2z^{-1} \cos \omega T + z^{-2})$

9.4.3 The use of difference equations

It may be apparent from the solution to Example 9.7 that use of a more complex network or input function could result in a very tedious expansion into the open-form series. An alternative method, and one which can be readily implemented by software on a digital computer, involves use of **difference equations**.

It has been noted that, as defined, $z^{-1} = e^{-sT}$ and therefore it represents a delay of one sampling period in the time domain. If, now, the expression in Example 9.7, is written in the form,

$$V_o(z) = H(z)V_i(z)$$

$$= V_i(z)/(1 - z^{-1}),$$

and both sides are multiplied by $1 - z^{-1}$,

$$(1 - z^{-1})V_o(z) = V_i(z),$$

or

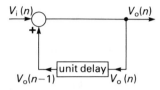

Fig. 9.23 Implementing a difference equation

$$V_o(z) = V_i(z) + z^{-1}V_o(z),$$

the expression can be interpreted in the time domain as follows: the present output is equal to the present input to which is added the output delayed by one sampling period: Fig. 9.23 shows the block diagram of an arrangement by which the expression may be implemented. Following through the difference equation (as a computer would do) gives the following time-domain result.

	Previous output +	current input	= current output
$n = 0$	0 +	1 =	1
$n = 1$	1 +	1 =	2
$n = 3$	2 +	1 =	3
$n = 4$	3 +	1 =	4, etc.

Example 9.8   *Use the difference-equation method to determine the successive outputs from a discrete-time system whose unit-impulse response sample amplitudes lie on the curve $0.25(1 - e^{-4t})u(t)$. The input is a unit-amplitude sequence at 0.25 s intervals.*

The z transform of the network may be deduced from Table 9.1. Thus,

$$H(z) = \tfrac{1}{4}(1/(1 - z^{-1}) - 1/(1 - e^{-4T}z^{-1})).$$

The z transform of the output signal is now given by

$$V_o(z) = H(z)V_i(z)$$
$$= \tfrac{1}{4}(1/(1 - z^{-1}) - 1/(1 - e^{-4T}z^{-1}))V_i(z).$$

Substituting $T = 0.25$, and hence $e^{-4T} = 0.368$, and rearranging,

$$V_o(z)(1 - z^{-1})(1 - 0.368z^{-1}) = 0.158z^{-1}V_i(z).$$
$$\therefore \quad V_o(z) = 0.158z^{-1}V_i(z) + 1.368z^{-1}V_o(z) - 0.368z^{-2}V_o(z).$$

Interpreting z^{-1} as unit time delay, the discrete-time domain equivalent of this expression may be written as

$$V_o(nT) = 0.158V_i((n-1)T) + 1.368V_o((n-1)T) - 0.368V_o((n-2)T),$$

where n indicates current conditions, $n - 1$ the previous state, etc.

For the unit-amplitude input, $V_i(nT) = 1$ for all values of n and therefore,

for $n = 0$, $V_0(0) = 0$;

for $n = 1$, $V_0(1) = 0.158$;

for $n = 2$, $V_0(2) = 0.158 + 1.368 \times 0.158 = 0.374$;

for $n = 3$, $V_0(3) = 0.158 + 1.368 \times 0.374 - 0.368 \times 0.158 = 0.611$;

for $n = 4$, $V_0(4) = 0.158 + 1.368 \times 0.611 - 0.368 \times 0.374 = 0.856$;

Key points to remember

- the impulse function is given by $\int_{-\infty}^{+\infty} \delta(t)\,dt = 1$ and $\delta(t) = 0$ for $t \neq 0$;

- the time response to unit impulse input is the inverse Laplace transform of the network function;

- the Fourier transform of the response to unit impulse input is the network frequency response;

- the convolution of two functions of time is given by $f_1(t) * f_2(t) = \int_0^t f_1(t-\tau) f_2(\tau)\,d\tau$;

- $\mathscr{L} f_1(t) * f_2(t) = F_1(s) F_2(s)$;

- the response to an arbitrary input function can be determined by resolving it into a series of 'impulses';

- multiplexing enables a number of signals to be handled by a single processing or transmission system;

- sampling converts a continuous-time signal into a discrete-time function;

- sampling should take place at time intervals of not more than $1/2B$; failure to do this causes aliasing;

- the z transform can be used to describe discrete-time signals;

- the z-transfer function of a system is the z transform of the discrete-time response to unit impulse input;

- a difference equation can be deduced from the z-transfer function enabling a discrete-time system output to be computed recursively.

Further reading

Banks, S. P., *Control Systems Engineering.* Prentice-Hall (1986).

Gabel, R. A. and Roberts, R. A., *Signals and Linear System* (3rd edn). J. Wiley (1987).

Neff, H. P., *Continuous and Discrete Linear Systems.* Harper and Row (1984).

EXERCISES 9

9.1   Use the transfer network function in Exercise 6.7 to determine the voltage response across the $2\,\mu\text{F}$ capacitor when the input is a unit impulse. Hence determine the approximate form of the response when the input is a 5 V pulse of 5 ms duration.

9.2   The impulse response of a network is given by $h(t) = 4e^{-10^4 t} - 4e^{-2 \times 10^4 t}$ for $t \geq 0$. Determine the network function and hence determine the response to a unit-step input.

9.3   The frequency response (magnitude only) of a filter may be determined by feeding into it a pulse waveform having a relatively long period and a very short pulse width and observing the output on a spectrum analyser. Explain the basis of the method and sketch a typical output display which might be obtained when testing a low-pass filter.

By reference to Section 2.6 in Chapter 8, explain how the display shape would be modified if the pulse width were approximately the same as the reciprocal of the filter cut-off frequency.

9.4   Obtain the step response in Exercise 9.2 by convolving the step input and the impulse response. Sketch the various steps in the style of Fig. 9.5.

Show that the same result is obtained by convolving the impulse response with the step input.

9.5   Show that the relationship

$$\mathscr{L}[f_1(t) * f_2(t)] = F_1(s) F_2(s)$$

holds in the case where $f_1(t) = t$ and $f_2(t) = u(t)$ by comparing the transform of their convolution with the product of the separate transforms of $f_1(t)$ and $f_2(t)$.

9.6   Determine the general shape of the step response in Exercise 9.2 by regarding the unit-step input as a series of impulses (as in Fig. 9.8) and summing the impulse responses.

9.7   Use the result of Exercise 9.1 to determine the approximate response of the circuit in Exercise 6.7 to a 5 V pulse of 40 ms duration by regarding the pulse as the summation of eight 5 ms pulses.

9.8   Forty-eight signals each bandlimited to 3.3 kHz are to be transmitted by means of multiplexed samples converted into binary form. If the quantisation interval is not to exceed 20 mV for signals in the range 0 to $+5$ V determine the minimum data rate in bits per second.

9.9   Sketch the spectral content of a 1 kHz sinusoidal signal sampled, as shown in Fig. 9.13, with very narrow sampling pulses 4000 times per second. Indicate the component frequencies.

Resketch the spectral content (with the original sampling rate) if the sampling-pulse width is increased to 100 μs.

9.10   Determine the z transform corresponding to the ramp function shown in Table 9.1.

9.11   A discrete-time circuit element having a z-transfer function $1/(1 - z^{-1})$ has a sampled ramp signal (with a slope of 4 and a sampling period of 0.5) applied to its input. Determine the z transform of the output signal, and by expanding with the help of the binomial theorem, deduce the amplitude of the first four output samples.

9.12   Form a difference equation for the circuit element in Exercise 9.11 and hence determine the output due to the specified ramp-voltage input.

Check the result with that obtained in Exercise 9.11.

9.13   A system has a z-transfer function

$$\frac{z^{-1}(1 - e^{-\alpha T})}{1 - z^{-1} e^{-\alpha T}}, \quad \text{where } \alpha \text{ and } T \text{ are constants.}$$

Use the difference-equation method to determine the output (as a sequence of values) in response to a sampled step input with $\alpha T = 0.4$.

<u>10</u> Modulation

The principal learning objectives of this chapter are to:

	Section	Exercise
● appreciate the need for modulation;	1.1	
● state methods of representing signals;	1.2	
● deduce an expression for an amplitude-modulated (a.m.) signal;	2.1	10.1
● analyse an a.m. signal;	2.2	10.2
● explain the phasor diagram and calculate power relationships for an a.m. signal;	2.3, 2.4	10.3
● describe the single-sideband (s.s.b.) and double-sideband suppressed-carrier (d.s.b.) a.m. signals;	3.1–3.3	10.4
● compare s.s.b. and d.s.b. signals;	3.4	10.5
● deduce an expression for a frequency-modulated (f.m.) signal;	4.1	10.6
● analyse an f.m. signal with reference to spectral content, bandwidth and power relationships;	4.2–4.5	10.7, 10.8
● determine an expression for a phase-modulated signal;	4.6	
● compare phase and frequency modulated signals;	4.7	10.9
● describe the pulse-modulation techniques known as pulse-amplitude, pulse-width, pulse-position and pulse-code modulation;	5.1–5.7	10.10
● describe the keying techniques, known as amplitude, frequency and phase-shift keying and estimate their spectral content;	6.1–6.4	10.11
● explain frequency-division multiplexing.	7	

10.1 Introduction

10.1.1 Reasons for modulation

Modulation is an important process in signal-transmission systems whereby the information or data to be transmitted modifies or varies an aspect of a **carrier** signal, usually a higher-frequency sinusoid.

The reasons for using modulation may be one or more of the following:

(i) Transmission systems impose constraints on the signals they will accept. For example, the frequency response of a telephone channel is designed for speech transmission and is not suitable for data. However, if the data is modulated onto a carrier, the signal can be matched to the channel.

(ii) The nature of the modulation process is such that it permits the transmission of more than one signal over a single transmission channel, and enables any given signal to be reselected at the receiving terminal. An obvious example is the transmission of a large number of radio signals over a single channel (space) any one of which may be selected by tuning a receiver.

(iii) Partly in order to meet the needs arising from (ii) above and partly arising from performance requirements, many of the components in a signal-transmission system are designed to operate over a limited fractional frequency range, i.e. the ratio of the bandwidth to the centre frequency is small. Signals having the same properties may be formed by the modulation process.

(iv) The fourth reason is less obvious but nevertheless important. Modulation allows conditions to be established in which a transmitted signal may be less influenced by noise and interference, albeit at the expense of increased bandwidth. Two examples are the superior performance of frequency modulation over amplitude modulation for broadcasting and the use of pulse-code modulation for the transmission of speech. These aspects are discussed in Chapter 11.
This chapter describes and analyses a number of different modulation techniques including amplitude modulation (a.m.), frequency modulation (f.m.) and phase modulation as well as some of their derivatives. Also considered are the keying techniques used for digital-data transmission.

10.1.2 Signal representation

An appreciation of the various methods of signal representation is a prerequisite to a proper understanding of modulation. Waveform, spectral and phasor-diagram representations of the signals are used. These forms of representation are described in some detail in Appendix 6A and in Section 2 of Chapter 8 but, by way of summary, Fig. 10.1(*a*), (*b*), (*c*) and (*d*) show, respectively, waveform, spectral and phasor diagrams, the latter in rotating and stationary forms.

Fig. 10.1 Various representations of a sinusoid

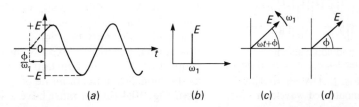

(*a*)   (*b*)   (*c*)   (*d*)

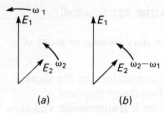

(a)   (b)

Fig. 10.2 Rotating phasors for sinusoids at differing frequencies

An extension of these principles is the representation of two or more sinusoids of differing frequencies on one phasor diagram. Fig. 10.2(a) shows two phasors of arbitrary amplitudes, E_1 and E_2, and frequencies ω_1 and ω_2. If, following previously established practice, the reference frame is rotated backwards (clockwise) either phasor (but not both) could be made stationary. For example, in Fig. 10.2(b) the reference frame is rotated with angular velocity ω_1 rendering phasor 1 stationary but leaving phasor 2 rotating at angular velocity $\omega_2 - \omega_1$, which is assumed to be positive. If ω_2 were less than ω_1, the arrow rotation could be shown in the opposite direction or it could remain as shown but be annotated $\omega_1 - \omega_2$.

10.2 Amplitude modulation

10.2.1 The nature of the modulated signal

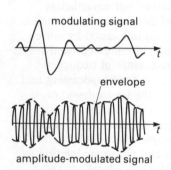

Fig. 10.3 Amplitude modulation

In this modulation technique the amplitude of a **carrier wave** is caused to vary in accordance with the information to be transmitted, the **modulating** or **baseband signal**. Normally, the carrier is a sinusoid having a frequency considerably higher than that of the modulating signal. For example, medium-waveband transmissions use carrier frequencies of the order of megahertz to transmit speech and music signals having bandwidths of the order of kilohertz.

The amplitude of the carrier varies proportionately with the amplitude of the modulating signal, causing the **envelope** of the carrier to vary in sympathy with the modulating signal, as shown in Fig. 10.3 by the dashed line. It is emphasised that the envelope is not an independent waveform but simply a boundary within which the peak excursions of the carrier are enclosed. Nevertheless, it can be described mathematically.

To obtain a mathematical expression for the modulated signal, it is assumed that the modulating signal is sinusoidal and represented by $E_m \cos \omega_m t$. The unmodulated carrier is represented by $E_c \sin \omega_c t$. The nature of the modulation process is such that the carrier amplitude is changed from its unmodulated peak value E_c to $E_c + k_a E_m \cos \omega_m t$. This expression will be seen to contain a component proportional to the modulating signal, k_a being a constant for the amplitude-modulating circuit. The complete expression for the amplitude-modulated signal then becomes,

$$(E_c + k_a E_m \cos \omega_m t) \sin \omega_c t.$$

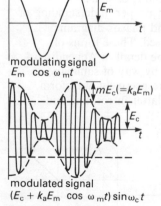

modulated signal
$(E_c + k_a E_m \cos \omega_m t) \sin \omega_c t$

Fig. 10.4 A sinusoidally-modulated waveform

The baseband and modulated-signal waveforms are shown in Fig. 10.4. Although the peak amplitude of the modulating signal E_m is an independent variable, the peak envelope amplitude $k_a E_m$ only has significance in relation to E_c. Thus, it is normal practice to express the envelope amplitude as a proportion of E_c, the constant of proportionality being known as the **modulation depth** m, i.e. $k_a E_m = m E_c$. It will be apparent from Fig. 10.4 that m must have a value between 0 and 1 or, as a percentage, 0 and 100%. The constant k_a $(= mE_c/E_m)$ is effectively the envelope variation per unit amplitude variation of modulating-signal variation. Using m, the expression for the amplitude-modulated carrier becomes

$$E_c(1 + m \cos \omega_m t) \sin \omega_c t.$$

10.2.2 Analysis of the amplitude-modulated signal

Expansion of the expression for the a.m. signal gives

$$E_c \sin \omega_c t + mE_c \cos \omega_m t \sin \omega_c t.$$

The modulated signal will be seen to consist of the unmodulated carrier, $E_c \sin \omega_c t$ plus the product term $mE_c \cos \omega_m t \sin \omega_c t$, a product term being a characteristic of modulated signals. If the product term is expanded, two sinusoids result:

$$\frac{mE_c}{2} [\sin(\omega_c + \omega_m)t + \sin(\omega_c - \omega_m)t].$$

These components at the sum and difference frequencies between the carrier and modulating-signal frequencies, are known as **sidefrequencies** and are shown, together with the carrier-frequency component, in the spectral diagram in Fig. 10.5(*a*). In particular, it will be seen that although the envelope varies at the modulating-signal frequency the modulated signal contains no component at that frequency.

Because each frequency component of a non-sinusoidal modulating signal produces a pair of sidefrequencies, a band of components at the modulating-signal frequency (for example, the baseband signal in the frequency range 0–*B* shown in Fig. 10.5(*b*)) would, when modulated, result in a pair of **sidebands**, upper and lower sidebands being shown in Fig. 10.5(*c*). In effect, the baseband signal is translated upward in the frequency spectrum and is duplicated in the process.

Fig. 10.5 Baseband and transmission-band signals

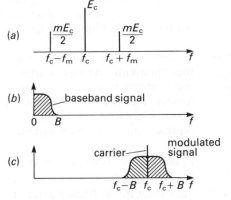

Example 10.1   *A signal generator with an a.m. facility requires a 10 V peak modulating-signal input to produce 100% modulation depth. Draw the waveform and spectral diagrams when the baseband signal is a 4 V (peak) sinusoid at 2 kHz and the radio frequency (r.f.) output level is set at 100 mV (peak) at a frequency of 1 MHz. How would the diagrams change if the input signal were changed to a square wave of 4 V peak amplitude?*

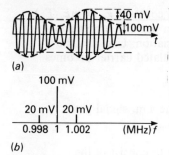

(a)

(b)

Fig. 10.6 Sinusoidal-modulation waveform and spectral diagram for Example 10.1

Fig. 10.7 Square-wave modulation waveform and spectral diagram for Example 10.1

The waveform diagram is shown in Fig. 10.6. The modulation depth is 0.4 (or 40%) because a 10 V modulating signal results in 100% modulation and only 4 V is applied in this case. (The value of k_a is 10 mV/V.) With $m = 0.4$, the sidefrequency amplitudes are $0.4 \times 100/2 = 20$ mV. The waveshape for the square-wave modulated signal follows quite readily (Fig. 10.7(a)), but to determine its spectral content some knowledge of the spectral content of the square-wave signal is required. Using the results from Chapter 8, the harmonic content of a 4 V square wave is as shown in Fig. 10.7(b). Because a sinusoidal envelope variation of a given amplitude produces two sidefrequency components each of half the amplitude, each component shown in Fig. 10.7(b) results in a pair of sidefrequencies amplitude scaled by a factor of $k_a/2$, i.e. 5 mV/V. The resulting spectral content is shown in Fig. 10.7(c).

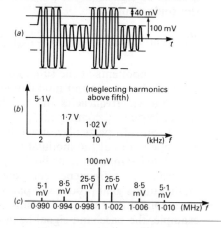

Example 10.1 emphasises the nature of modulation as a frequency-translation process. For amplitude modulation, there is a linear translation of the baseband signal upward in frequency resulting, in this case, in upper and lower sidebands located about the carrier frequency. This form of amplitude modulation is known as **double-sideband amplitude modulation** (with carrier), abbreviated to the initial letters a.m.

10.2.3 Phasor diagram for amplitude-modulated signal

Difficulties can arise in visualising how a varying-amplitude (but apparently constant-frequency) a.m. signal contains three constant-amplitude components, none of which is at the frequency of the variation, and the phasor representation provides a useful link between the time and frequency-domain representations. Three components,

$$E_c \sin \omega_c t, \quad \frac{mE_c}{2} \sin(\omega_c + \omega_m)t \quad \text{and} \quad \frac{mE_c}{2} \sin(\omega_c - \omega_m)t,$$

are shown in the phasor diagram in Fig. 10.8(a) in which, in accordance with Section 10.1.2, the reference plane is assumed to be rotated clockwise at ω_c rad/s making the carrier phasor stationary but leaving the sidefrequency phasors rotating at velocities $\pm\omega_m$ rad/s. Fig. 10.8(b) shows typical sidefrequency-phasor positions as time proceeds from which it will be seen that the resultant of the sidefrequency phasors is always either in phase or in antiphase with the carrier-frequency phasor.

The result is a varying-amplitude signal as shown in the waveform diagram in Fig. 10.8(c).

Fig. 10.8 Phasor diagrams for an a.m. waveform

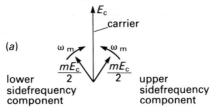

(a)

lower
sidefrequency
component

upper
sidefrequency
component

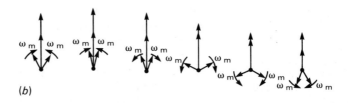

(b)

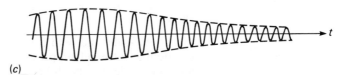

(c)

10.2.4 Power relationships in an amplitude-modulated signal

As is the case for any non-sinusoidal waveform, the power dissipation in a resistive circuit element may be determined by summing the powers due to the individual sinusoidal components. For sinusoidal modulation (and noting that E_c is a peak value), the total power in a resistor R is therefore:

$$E_c^2/2R + (mE_c/2)^2/2R + (mE_c/2)^2/2R = E_c^2/2R(1 + m^2/2)$$
$$= P_c(1 + m^2/2),$$

where P_c is the power due to the unmodulated carrier. It is emphasised that this formula applies only in the particular case of sinusoidal modulation and cannot, for example, be used for square-wave modulation. Nevertheless the sum of the individual-component powers can be used in any case. Since, in general, power is (r.m.s. voltage)^2/resistance, the r.m.s. value of the modulated waveform is given by the square root of the sum of the squares of the individual-component r.m.s. values.

Example 10.2

Calculate the power dissipation in a 50 Ω resistor by an a.m. signal modulated by the sinusoidal and square-wave baseband signals in Example 10.1. Neglect square-wave harmonics above the fifth.

Power due to the carrier $= 0.1^2/2 \times 50 = 10^{-4}$ W.

For sinusoidal modulation,

power due to each sidefrequency $= (20 \times 10^{-3})^2/2 \times 50$
$$= 4 \times 10^{-6} \text{ W}.$$

Therefore,

total power $= (100 + 4 + 4) \times 10^{-6} = 108 \ \mu$W.

For squarewave modulation,

carrier power $= 10^{-4}$ W,   as before.

Sideband power $=[2(25.5 \times 10^{-3})^2 + 2(8.5 \times 10^{-3})^2$

$$+ 2(5.1 \times 10^{-3})^2]/2 \times 50$$

$$= 15 \times 10^{-6} \text{ W}.$$

Therefore,

total power $= 115\,\mu$W.

10.3 Suppressed-carrier and single-sideband amplitude modulation

10.3.1 General discussion

In the form of modulation described in Section 10.2, the baseband signal is translated up in the frequency band to give a double-sideband modulated signal with carrier.

Three variants are illustrated in Fig. 10.9 in which are shown:

(a) double-sideband with carrier (a.m.);
(b) double-sideband suppressed carrier (d.s.b.); and
(c) single-sideband (s.s.b.) amplitude modulation, suppressed carrier implied.

In fact, all three forms of the amplitude-modulated signal are used in various systems. Their merits are discussed in Section 10.3.4 but, initially, d.s.b. and s.s.b. are considered in greater detail.

Fig. 10.9 Different forms of amplitude modulation

(a)

f_c-B f_c f_c+B f

(b)

f_c-B f_c f_c+B f

(c)

f_c f_c+B f

10.3.2 Double-sideband suppressed-carrier amplitude modulation (d.s.b.)

This form of modulation is the same as a.m. but with the component at carrier frequency missing. However, to generate this form of modulation it is not necessary to generate a.m. and then remove the carrier because devices such as the balanced modulator (Chapter 15) generate d.s.b. signals directly. In effect, they are sum- and difference-frequency component generators.

As described in Chapter 15, sum- and difference-frequency components around harmonics of the carrier frequency may also be generated (Fig. 10.10(b)) and filtering may be used to

Fig. 10.10 Output from a balanced modulator

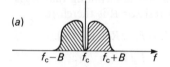

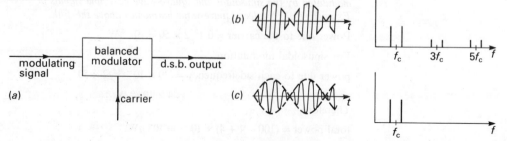

(a) modulating signal — balanced modulator — d.s.b. output

carrier

(b)

(c)

f_c $3f_c$ $5f_c$ f

f_c f

remove these (Fig. 10.10(*c*)) to produce d.s.b. In effect, the balanced modulator and filter combine to form an ideal multiplier so that, if the modulating signal is $E_m \cos \omega_m t$ and the carrier signal is $E_c \sin \omega_c t$, the system output will be

$$kE_m E_c \cos \omega_m t \sin \omega_c t$$

(where k is a constant for the modulator), giving the double-sideband suppressed-carrier signal as,

$$\frac{k}{2} E_m E_c [\sin(\omega_c + \omega_m)t + \sin(\omega_c - \omega_m)t].$$

Because the basis of modulation is the impression of a modulating signal on a carrier, it may be thought that its removal (or non-generation as in this case) would have a disastrous effect on the modulation process. This is not the case, however, since as this section has shown, it is only the component at the carrier frequency that is removed; there is no loss in or change to the content of the sidebands in which the transmitted information is contained.

10.3.3 Single-sideband amplitude modulation (s.s.b.)

Fig. 10.11 shows waveform and spectral diagrams for an s.s.b. signal with the d.s.b. signal redrawn for reference. In the diagram, the lower sidefrequency has been removed although, in principle, either may be removed. The removal of the sidefrequency may be effected by a filter having a well-defined response and the sinusoidally modulated s.s.b. waveform is then simply another sinusoid at a frequency $f_c + f_m$ (or $f_c - f_m$ for lower sidefrequency). Single-sideband modulation is therefore a linear translation of the baseband signal up to the transmission band. Demodulation would be the reverse procedure. For example, if a speech signal in the frequency range 0.3–3.3 kHz were modulated onto a 100 kHz carrier, the transmitted signal would lie in the frequency range 100.3–103.3 kHz if the upper sideband were transmitted. For the lower sideband the frequency range would be 96.7–99.7 kHz.

Fig. 10.11 Double- and single-sideband modulation

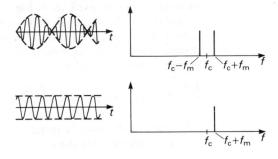

10.3.4 Comparison of the different forms of amplitude modulation

In choosing a transmission technique for broadcasting (for example) s.s.b. would appear to be the most attractive of the three systems, requiring the smallest transmission bandwidth and not wasting power in the carrier-frequency component. However, in spite of its simplicity in the frequency domain, it is less convenient to generate than either a.m. or d.s.b., requiring the generation of a suppressed-carrier signal followed by a critical filter to eliminate one of the sidebands. An alternative method could use a phase-cancellation method on one of the sidebands.

Simplicity of equipment favours a.m. in the modulation process and the same is true for the demodulation process; in fact, not only are s.s.b. receivers more complex than a.m. receivers but, in a broadcasting system, there are many more receivers than transmitters. Thus, some reference must be made to demodulating techniques in order to make a reasoned comparison between the two systems. The a.m. signal can be demodulated by recovering the envelope variation because this is proportional to the baseband signal. The recovery can be achieved very simply by means of a circuit known as a **diode detector** or **envelope detector**. Fig. 10.12 shows a simplified circuit and gives an indication of the way in which it operates. The process is one of rectification and smoothing, the diode making the output waveform unidirectional and the $C-R$ combination effecting the smoothing. For the sake of clarity, only a few carrier cycles are shown over the span of the envelope variation considered. Typically, there are of the order of 1000 carrier cycles during this period so that the carrier ripple on the output is much smaller than that shown. Essentially, the output waveform 'follows' the envelope variation and thereby reproduces the modulating signal after removal of the direct component. Thus, the a.m. signal can be demodulated simply, cheaply and reliably.

Fig. 10.12 Operation of a diode detector

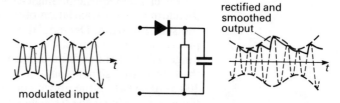

modulated input

rectified and smoothed output

In order to demodulate an s.s.b. signal a balanced modulator can be used, as in Fig. 10.13. A sinusoidally modulated s.s.b. signal, $E_s \sin(\omega_c + \omega_m)t$, and a reinserted carrier, $E_c \sin \omega_c t$, are fed into the modulator to produce a product term $(E_s \sin(\omega_c + \omega_m)t)(E_c \sin \omega_c t)$. Expanding, the output is proportional to

$$\frac{E_s E_c}{2} \cos(2\omega_c + \omega_m)t \quad \text{and} \quad \frac{E_s E_c}{2} \cos \omega_m t.$$

Filtering out the sum-frequency component leaves the required difference-frequency component,

$$\frac{E_s E_c}{2} \cos \omega_m t.$$

This is proportional to the original modulating signal.

The demodulation concept is quite straightforward but there is a hidden difficulty: if there is a frequency error in the reinserted carrier, this will be translated onto the output signal. Specifically, if the reinserted carrier is $E_c \sin(\omega_c + \delta\omega)t$,

Fig. 10.13 Demodulation with balanced modulator and filter

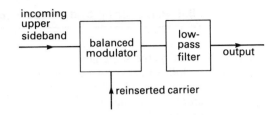

the output will be $(E_s E_c/2)\cos(\omega_m - \delta\omega)t$. This frequency error in the demodulated signal can result in an unpleasant form of distortion and, as a general rule, the reinserted-carrier frequency must be held at the frequency of the transmitter carrier within quite close limits. How close these limits are depends on the nature of the transmission but, typically, a few hertz would be of the right order for speech. Whatever the tolerable error, the main point is that a relatively high-stability oscillator will be required to effectively demodulate an s.s.b. signal as compared with the a.m. demodulator which requires no reinserted-carrier oscillator at all.

The demodulation of a d.s.b. signal may also be accomplished by means of a balanced modulator. The circuit is the same as for s.s.b. (Fig. 10.13) except that the d.s.b. signal replaces the s.s.b. input. Thus, if the received signal is $E_s(\sin(\omega_c + \omega_m)t + \sin(\omega_c - \omega_m)t)$ and the reinserted carrier is $E_c \sin \omega_c t$, the output will contain components

$$\frac{E_s E_c}{2}\left[\cos \omega_m t - \cos(2\omega_c + \omega_m)t + \cos(-\omega_m)t - \cos(2\omega_c - \omega_m)t\right].$$

The second and fourth components may be filtered out by the low-pass filter, leaving the first and third terms which combine to give $E_s E_c \cos \omega_m t$ which is proportional to the original modulating signal. If, however, there is a frequency error $\delta\omega$ in the reinserted carrier, the error will be transferred to the output (as in the s.s.b. case) but, after filtering the remaining first and third terms would now be,

$$\frac{E_s E_c}{2} \cos(\omega_m - \delta\omega)t \quad \text{and} \quad \frac{E_s E_c}{2} \cos(-\omega_m - \delta\omega)t.$$

Combining these two terms gives an expression,

$$E_s E_c \cos \delta\omega t \cos \omega_m t,$$

which is the required baseband signal multiplied by a term $\cos \delta\omega t$. The effect would be a periodic fade in amplitude at twice the error frequency which, for any signal, is intolerable. Furthermore, a constant phase error would effectively 'freeze' the amplitude of the demodulated signal at its normal amplitude multiplied by a factor $\cos \phi$, where ϕ is the phase error. Thus, unless the reinserted carrier in a d.s.b. system is locked in phase and frequency to a carrier-reference signal, the output signal will be virtually unusable. Nevertheless, d.s.b. systems are used (with synchronised reinserted carriers) in certain applications, notably as a component part of stereo f.m. and colour t.v. signals.

10.4 Frequency and phase modulation

10.4.1 Frequency modulation

Initially, the same general procedure as in the a.m. case may be followed, except that the frequency of the modulated carrier is modified from f_c to $f_c + k_f E_m \cos \omega_m t$ instead of the amplitude being changed from E_c to $E_c + k_a E_m \cos \omega_m t$. k_f is a constant for the modulator (normally in kHz/V) and determines the magnitude of the carrier-frequency variation per unit amplitude variation of the modulating signal. The peak value of this frequency variation is known as the **deviation**, Δf, i.e. $\Delta f = k_f E_m$, so that the instantaneous frequency of the f.m. signal becomes

$$f_c + \Delta f \cos \omega_m t.$$

Following the a.m. procedure, it might be expected that this modified frequency would be substituted into the unmodulated carrier expression, $E_c \sin \omega_c t$. However, this would be incorrect since it ignores the fact that the frequency is itself a function of time; the correct procedure is to determine an expression for the phase angle $\theta = \int \omega \, dt$ or $2\pi \int f \, dt$. The instantaneous phase angle of the modulated carrier θ is then given by:

$$\theta = 2\pi \int_0^t (f_c + \Delta f \cos \omega_m t) \, dt$$

$$= 2\pi f_c t + \frac{2\pi \Delta f}{\omega_m} \sin \omega_m t$$

$$= \omega_c t + \frac{\Delta f}{f_m} \sin \omega_m t.$$

Substituting this value into $E_c \sin \theta$ and writing m_f in place of $\Delta f / f_m$ gives the expression for the frequency-modulated signal as

$$E_c \sin(\omega_c t + m_f \sin \omega_m t),$$

where m_f is the **frequency-modulation index**, given by the ratio,

$$\frac{\text{frequency deviation } \Delta f}{\text{modulating-signal frequency } f_m}.$$

10.4.2 Analysis of the frequency-modulated signal

If the expression for the f.m. signal is expanded:

$$E_c \sin(\omega_c t + m_f \sin \omega_m t)$$

$$= E_c[\sin \omega_c t \cos(m_f \sin \omega_m t) + \cos \omega_c t \sin(m_f \sin \omega_m t)].$$

The expressions, $\cos(m_f \sin \omega_m t)$ and $\sin(m_f \sin \omega_m t)$ are not products but are cosines of sines and sines of sines whose expansions involve a class of functions known as **Bessel functions**. The expansion of $\cos(m_f \sin \omega_m t)$ is:

$$J_0(m_f) + 2J_2(m_f) \cos 2\omega_m t + 2J_4(m_f) \cos 4\omega_m t + \cdots,$$

and the expansion of $\sin(m_f \sin \omega_m t)$ is:

$$2J_1(m_f) \sin \omega_m t + 2J_3(m_f) \sin 3\omega_m t + \cdots,$$

where the coefficients $J_0(m_f)$, $J_1(m_f)$, etc., are Bessel functions of the first kind. The general function, $J_r(m_f)$ of order r and argument m_f, may be determined from the general expression,

$$J_r(m_f) = \sum_{k=0}^{\infty} \frac{(-1)^k (m_f/2)^{(r+2k)}}{k!\,(k+r)!}.$$

Usually, however, either graphs or tables will be used. Graphs are shown in Fig. 10.14 and an abbreviated table is given in Table 10.1. More comprehensive tables are readily available.

Fig. 10.14 Bessel functions

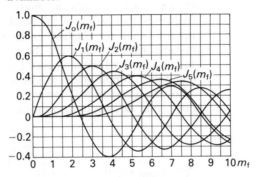

Table 10.1. *Bessel functions (values <0.01 not shown)*

m_f	$J_0(m_f)$	$J_1(m_f)$	$J_2(m_f)$	$J_3(m_f)$	$J_4(m_f)$	$J_5(m_f)$	$J_6(m_f)$	$J_7(m_f)$	$J_8(m_f)$
0	1.00	–	–	–	–	–	–	–	–
0.2	0.99	0.10	–	–	–	–	–	–	–
0.5	0.94	0.24	0.03	–	–	–	–	–	–
1.0	0.77	0.44	0.11	0.02	–	–	–	–	–
1.5	0.51	0.56	0.23	0.06	0.01	–	–	–	–
2.0	0.22	0.58	0.35	0.13	0.03	–	–	–	–
2.5	−0.05	0.50	0.45	0.22	0.07	0.02	–	–	–
3.0	−0.26	0.34	0.49	0.31	0.13	0.04	0.01	–	–
4.0	−0.40	−0.07	0.36	0.43	0.28	0.13	0.05	0.02	–
5.0	−0.18	−0.33	0.05	0.36	0.39	0.26	0.13	0.05	0.02

Returning to the expression,

$$E_c\left[\sin \omega_c t \cos(m_f \sin \omega_m t) + \cos \omega_c t \sin(m_f \sin \omega_m t)\right],$$

and substituting the Bessel-series expansions gives sum- and difference-frequency components between ω_c and ω_m, $2\omega_m$, $3\omega_m$, ..., and, hence, the final expression for the frequency-modulated signal becomes

$E_c J_0(m_f) \sin \omega_c t$ (modulated carrier-frequency component)

$\quad + E_c J_1(m_f) \sin(\omega_c + \omega_m)t - E_c J_1(m_f) \sin(\omega_c - \omega_m)t$

(first pair of sidefrequencies)

$\quad\quad + E_c J_2(m_f) \sin(\omega_c + 2\omega_m)t + E_c J_2(m_f) \sin(\omega_c - 2\omega_m)t$

$\quad\quad \vdots$ (second pair of sidefrequencies).

The f.m. signal will be seen to contain a carrier-frequency component together with an infinite number of pairs of sidefrequency components symmetrically disposed (with frequency spacing f_m) either side of the carrier-frequency component. The amplitudes of carrier and side-frequency components are determined by the appropriate Bessel functions which themselves are determined by the value of the modulation index m_f. A typical spectral diagram is shown in Fig. 10.15. Because the various component amplitudes are a function of m_f $(= \Delta f / f_m)$, they can only be determined from a knowledge of the deviation and the baseband-signal frequency. The spectral content of an f.m. signal is thus a much more complex function of the modulation index than in the a.m. case in which the modulated spectrum is simply a frequency translation of the baseband signal. However, as a general trend, the sidefrequencies become smaller as they become more distant from the carrier-frequency component. In contrast with the a.m. case the carrier-frequency component amplitude is a function of the modulation index. Also, the linear translation in frequency does not apply to the f.m. signal and superposition cannot be applied.

Fig. 10.15 A typical f.m. spectral diagram

amplitudes of the spectral components for a unit-amplitude f.m. wave

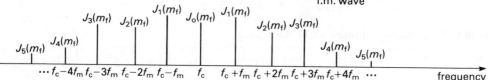

Example 10.3   *Determine the spectral content and draw a spectral diagram for an f.m. signal having an unmodulated carrier frequency of 90.0 MHz and amplitude 100 mV, sinusoidally modulated by a 2 V (peak), 10 kHz signal if the modulator constant is 12.5 kHz/V.*

The frequency deviation is proportional to the amplitude of the baseband signal; since this is 2 V, the deviation is $2 \times 12.5 = 25$ kHz which means that the modulated signal will vary sinusoidally between the limits, 89.975 MHz and 90.025 MHz, 10 000 times per second. To determine the spectral content, the modulation index m_f is determined using $\Delta f / f_m = 25/10 = 2.5$. Inspection of the table of Bessel functions gives

$$J_0(m_f) = -0.05; \quad J_1(m_f) = 0.50; \quad J_2(m_f) = 0.45;$$
$$J_3(m_f) = 0.22; \quad J_4(m_f) = 0.07; \quad J_5(m_f) = 0.02.$$

Because the unmodulated carrier amplitude is 100 mV, the figures are multiplied by 100 mV to give the spectral content shown in Fig. 10.16. The minus sign is neglected because only magnitudes are plotted.

Fig. 10.16 Spectral diagram for Example 10.3

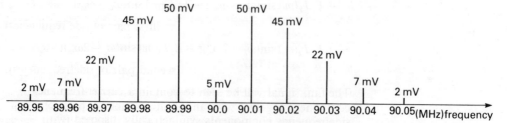

10.4.3 Power relationships in a frequency-modulated signal

Since there is, ideally, no amplitude variation in a frequency-modulated signal, the mean power due to a modulated signal is exactly the same as that due to the unmodulated signal $E_c^2/2R$. If, for any reason, it were required to determine the power due to, say, the carrier-frequency component alone or to a limited number of sidefrequencies, the power due to individual components may be summed in a similar way to that used in the a.m. case.

10.4.4 Bandwidth of a frequency-modulated signal

Because the Bessel series is infinite, the bandwidth is theoretically infinite. However, a practical limit may be set in a number of ways, two of which are discussed below.

(i) The bandwidth to include those sidefrequencies whose amplitudes are equal to or greater than 1% of the unmodulated carrier. For example, if $f_m = 10\,\text{kHz}$ and $\Delta f = 30\,\text{kHz}$, $m_f = 3$ and there are six pairs of sidefrequencies whose amplitudes exceed 1% of the unmodulated-carrier amplitude, the bandwidth is then 12 times the sidefrequency spacing $= 120\,\text{kHz}$. In general, this method gives the bandwidth as $f_m \times$ number of sidefrequency components with amplitude $\geqslant 0.01 E_c$.

(ii) The bandwidth to include those sidefrequencies (and the modulated carrier) whose amplitudes are such that the total power due to them is equal to or greater than 98% of the power due to the unmodulated carrier. As a rule-of-thumb, the approximate term $2(\Delta f + f_m)$ correlates with this criterion over a wide range of m_f without the need for tables or graphs as required in (i). If $f_m = 10\,\text{kHz}$ and $\Delta f = 30\,\text{kHz}$, this expression gives a bandwidth of 80 kHz. That the two methods give different results serves to emphasise that they are arbitrary and independent methods.

For the extreme cases where m_f is small (typically less than 0.2) or large (greater than 50) the approximations $2f_m$ and $2\Delta f$ respectively, may be used for bandwidth calculations. In the former case, there are effectively only two sidefrequencies (one pair) in the spectrum; this condition is sometimes referred to as the **narrow-band** condition in which the number of sidefrequencies, and hence the bandwidth, is the same as for a.m. This condition exists when the deviation is small compared with the modulating-signal frequency. When the deviation is large, the term **wideband** f.m. is sometimes used.

10.4.5 Phasor diagram for a frequency-modulated signal

When the a.m. phasor diagram was drawn the sidefrequencies were shown equally displaced in phase on either side of the carrier (Fig. 10.8). This is necessary in order to produce the amplitude variations without any change in phase. The f.m. phasor diagram can be expected to differ, and inspection of the final expression shows that it does. The even-order sidefrequency terms (i.e. J_2, J_4, etc.) bear the same phase relationships to the carrier-frequency component as in the a.m. case (Fig. 10.17(a)), whereas the odd-order sidefrequency terms (i.e. J_1, J_3, etc.) have a resultant which is in quadrature with the carrier (Fig. 10.17(b)), as indicated by the minus sign preceding the $E_c J_1(m_f) \sin(\omega_c - \omega_m)t$ term. The following

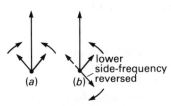

Fig. 10.17 A.M. and f.m. phasor diagrams

example shows how a series of phasors sum to give an f.m. signal.

Example 10.4   *Draw a series of phasor diagrams and a corresponding low-carrier-frequency waveform diagram for an f.m. signal for which the modulation index $m_f = 1.0$. Use the Bessel-function values from Table 10.1 but neglect the J_3 coefficient which is too small to show on the diagram.*

From Table 10.1, $J_0(1.0) = 0.77$; $J_1(1.0) = 0.44$; $J_2(1.0) = 0.11$. Phasors based on these values are drawn in Fig. 10.18 together with their resultant (shown by the dashed line).

Notes: Fig. 10.18 shows that the frequency has a maximum value (i.e. largest positive deviation) when the rate of change of phase angle is positive and at a maximum (at t_2). As the phasor turns (at t_4), the rate of change of phase is zero and the frequency is the nominal carrier frequency. At time t_6, the frequency deviation has its maximum negative value and the frequency is at its lowest. It may also be noted that the maximum phase deviation is, as may be judged from the diagram, equal to 1 rad, numerically the same as the modulation index. This is discussed in the next section.

Fig. 10.18 Relating phasor and waveform diagrams

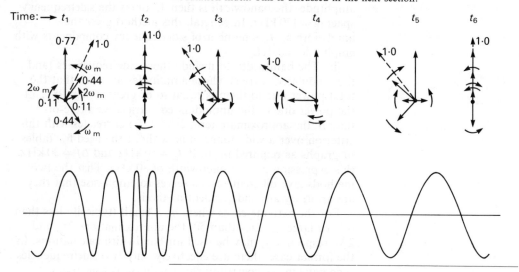

10.4.6 Phase modulation

The third parameter in the unmodulated carrier expression, $E_c \sin(\omega_c t + \phi)$ is the phase angle ϕ. If it is made variable, dependent on a baseband signal $E_m \sin \omega_m t$ such that $\phi = k_p E_m \sin \omega_m t$, where k_p is a constant (in rad/V), the phase-modulated signal can be written as

$$E_c \sin(\omega_c t + k_p E_m \sin \omega_m t).$$

Further, if the peak phase variation $k_p E_m$ is expressed as the **phase deviation** $\Delta\phi$, the phase-modulated signal becomes

$$E_c \sin(\omega_c t + \Delta\phi \sin \omega_m t).$$

If in this phase-modulated signal a **modulation index** m_{ph} is defined as the phase deviation, the expression for the modulated signal becomes identical to that for the f.m. signal (but with m_{ph} replacing m_f and a baseband signal $E_m \sin \omega_m t$ rather than $E_m \cos \omega_m t$) and the analysis may follow the same procedure.

10.4.7 Comparison of phase and frequency modulation

It has been deduced that the analysis of phase and frequency-modulated signals may follow the same path once the respective expressions, $E_c \sin(\omega_c t + \Delta\phi \sin \omega_m t)$ and $E_c \sin(\omega_c t + (\Delta f/f_m) \sin \omega_m t)$ are established. Evidently, if f.m. and ph.m. signals were generated such that $\Delta\phi = \Delta f/f_m$ (or $\Delta f = f_m \Delta\phi$), they would be identical. However, if the modulating frequency, f_m, were varied the signals would differ because the frequency-modulation index $m_f = \Delta f/f_m = k_f E_m/f_m$ varies inversely with f_m, whereas the phase-modulation index $m_{ph} = \Delta\phi = k_p E_m$ is independent of f_m. Both are directly dependent on the modulating-signal amplitude E_m, changes in which therefore affect each signal equally.

The phase-frequency relationships $\theta = \int \omega \, dt$ and $\omega = d\theta/dt$ suggest the possibility of using the arrangements shown in Fig. 10.19: preceding a phase modulator by an integrator is one method of generating frequency-modulated signals.

Fig. 10.19 Phase- and frequency-modulation relationships

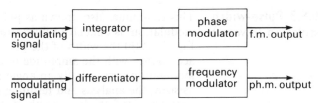

10.5 Pulse modulation

10.5.1 Introduction

There are a number of pulse-modulation techniques including pulse-amplitude, pulse-position, pulse-width and pulse-code modulation. The first three can be considered to be the counterparts of amplitude and angle modulation but with a pulse waveform as carrier rather than a sinusoid. Because pulse modulation is effectively a discrete-time system, a continuous-time modulating signal must be sampled before it can be transmitted. Sampling rates and the need for bandlimiting the signal are discussed in Chapter 9 and are not further considered here except to note that in the following work it is assumed that the signals are adequately bandlimited and are sampled at an appropriate rate. The discrete-time nature of the signals also permits the use of time-division multiplexing.

10.5.2 Pulse-amplitude modulation (p.a.m.)

As shown in Fig. 10.20(a) the amplitude of the sequence of pulses varies in accordance with the sample amplitudes. Whether the pulse amplitude varies in direct proportion to the sample amplitudes depends on the demands of the particular system. There are situations in which a non-linear relationship may be deliberately used; an example is the companding process described in the next chapter. Also described in Chapter 9 is the spectral content of the p.a.m. signal, Fig. 9.16 showing the content for a typical signal. It also shows how the baseband signal can be recovered by low-pass filtering.

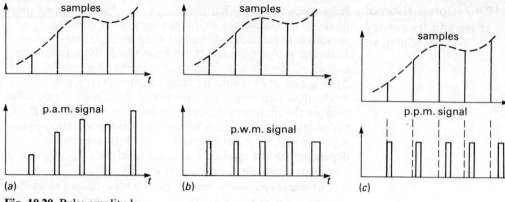

Fig. 10.20 Pulse-amplitude, pulse-width and pulse-position modulation

10.5.3 Pulse-width modulation (p.w.m.)

This technique, also known as pulse-duration or pulse-length modulation, is difficult to illustrate accurately, but in Fig. 10.20(*b*) the width of the pulse is shown varying in accordance with the amplitude of the samples. Pulse-width modulation is essentially an angle-modulation technique and, as such, the analysis and resulting spectral content are quite complex. Also, the bandwidth of the modulated signal will, in general, be wider than for the p.a.m. signal and notwithstanding the requirements of the sampling theorem, the sampling rate may need to be in excess of three times the base bandwidth to facilitate low-pass filter recovery.

The original baseband signal may be recovered by low-pass filtering because the width of the modulated pulses varies with the modulating signal and hence the average value of waveform (the area of the pulse divided by the period) contains the modulating-signal information as in p.a.m.

10.5.4 Pulse-position modulation (p.p.m.)

In the form of p.w.m. shown in Fig. 10.20(*b*) the falling edges of the pulses are modulated by the sample amplitude. However, it is possible to transmit the information simply by transmitting 'timing pulses' to correspond with the modulated edge of the p.w.m. pulse.

Fig. 10.20(*c*) illustrates the p.p.m. signal. Low-pass filtering would not recover the original baseband signal directly in this case but conversion to p.a.m. would allow recovery. It will also be seen that the p.p.m. signal is not self-clocking as are the p.a.m. and p.w.m. signals.

10.5.5 Pulse-code modulation (p.c.m.)

In this pulse-modulation technique, the sample amplitudes are encoded into binary form, being quantised in the process. The stages in the generation of the p.c.m. signal are thus sampling and encoding (which implies quantisation) and these aspects are fully discussed in Chapter 9. Fig. 10.21 summarises the process for a 4-bit system in which linear quantisation (i.e. equal quantisation steps) is used. The use of non-linear quantisation is discussed in the following chapter. After encoding, it is necessary to add synchronising information to suit the system in which the technique is used.

Fig. 10.21 Principle of pulse-code modulation

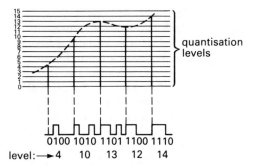

quantisation levels

0100 1010 1101 1100 1110
level:→4   10   13   12   14

10.6 Digital modulation: amplitude, phase and frequency-shift keying

10.6.1 General discussion

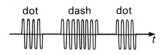

dot   dash   dot

Fig. 10.22 Morse code signalling waveform

The term 'keying' originates in the use of a key to transmit signals such as Morse code. A typical on–off keyed carrier is shown in Fig. 10.22, in which a dot is represented by a short-duration tone and a dash by a longer-duration tone: the signal comprises a series of 'marks' and 'spaces', the space indicating a 'no-signalling state'. This is a suitable format for the transmission of data intended for aural reception but for reception by machine it is possible to economise by using the 'off' condition to represent one level of a binary signal with the presence of the tone representing the other level. Also, equal element and code lengths facilitate machine operation.

10.6.2 Amplitude-shift keying

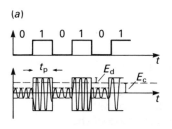

(a)

0   1   0   1   0   1

t_p E_d
            E_c

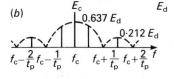

(b) E_c E_d
        0.637 E_d
                    0.212 E_d

$f_c - \frac{2}{t_p}$ $f_c - \frac{1}{t_p}$ f_c $f_c + \frac{1}{t_p}$ $f_c + \frac{2}{t_p}$

Fig. 10.23 Amplitude-shift keying (a) waveform (b) spectral content

On–off keying is a particular form of amplitude-shift keying (a.s.k.) in which the 'off' amplitude is zero: a general form of a.s.k. waveform is illustrated in Fig. 10.23(a). In the diagram, the two-level digital baseband signal or **keying waveform** is represented by a string of alternate 0's and 1's. Equally relevant terms are 'high' and 'low' or, 'on' and 'off'.

For the assumed keying waveform, the a.s.k. signal is an amplitude-modulated (a.m.) signal with a square modulating waveform. As such, its spectral content may be determined in the same way as in Example 10.1; there, the spectral content of the modulated waveform was obtained by frequency-translating the square-wave baseband signal up to the carrier frequency. Fig. 10.23(b) shows the spectral diagram for the general case of a carrier waveform of amplitude E_c modulated such that the peak envelope variation is E_d. The carrier frequency is f_c and t_p is the duration of the shortest element of the data signal (normally one bit), i.e. for the square-waveform data signal t_p is one-half of the period. For a waveform of the type which may be expected in normal operating conditions, a minimum base bandwidth is $1/2t_p$ (i.e. up to half the first envelope zero of the sin x/x spectrum) and hence the corresponding transmission bandwidth is $1/t_p$. For the particular baseband signal shown in Fig. 10.23, only the fundamental would be included if the bandwidth were limited to $1/t_p$. However, the bandwidth is specified to suit a general baseband signal and not just the square wave assumed in this case.

10.6.3 Frequency-shift keying

Fig. 10.24(a) shows a square-wave-modulated f.s.k. signal in which frequency f_1 represents the 1 level and frequency f_0 the 0 level. It is essentially a frequency-modulated signal and the sidefrequency amplitudes are governed by Bessel functions. However, when the two component frequencies are widely spaced, a guide to the general form of the spectral content may be obtained by considering the f.s.k. signal to be two linearly superimposed a.m. signals, as demonstrated in Fig. 10.24(b) and (c) for an assumed square-wave baseband signal. However, f.m. is not a linear modulation system and the results are only a guide, see Stremler (1982). Assuming a spectral content of this form and using the same criteria as for the a.s.k. case, a practical bandwidth could be taken as $f_0 - f_1 + 1/t_p$. This is in agreement with the 'rule-of-thumb' bandwidth used for the sinusoidally modulated f.m. signal $2\Delta f + 2f_m$ (Section 10.4.4) because $f_0 - f_1$ is twice the deviation and $1/t_p$ is twice the effective base bandwidth.

Fig. 10.24 Frequency-shift keying (a)–(c) waveforms (d) spectral content

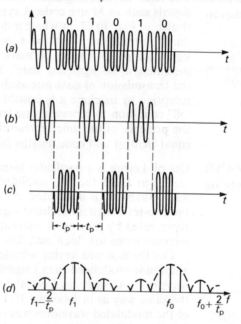

10.6.4 Phase-shift keying (p.s.k.)

A number of forms of p.s.k. are used, the form considered here being that in which the phase of the carrier is either 'normal' or shifted through 180° according to whether the baseband signal is a 1 or a 0. Fig. 10.25(a) shows the modulated signal with the corresponding square-wave baseband signal. As for the f.s.k. case, the spectral content in the general case should be determined by the appropriate Bessel functions but, for the particular situation shown in Fig. 10.25(a), d.s.b. theory may be used because the modulated waveform is just that which would be obtained if a bipolar square-wave modulating signal were applied to a balanced modulator. The arrangement is shown in Fig. 10.25(b). The spectral content is that of the d.s.b. signal with sidebands but no carrier. An approximate bandwidth of $1/t_p$ may therefore be used as in the a.s.k. case. Comparing

Fig. 10.25 Phase-shift keying (*a*) waveforms (*b*) modulator and spectral content

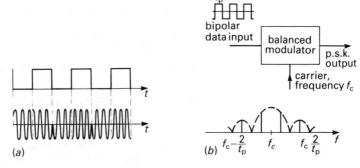

(*a*)

(*b*)

the three methods, the bandwidth of the f.s.k. signal exceeds that of the a.s.k. and p.s.k. signals by the value of the frequency shift.

Devices used at the interface between data lines and transmission media, and which implement the modulation–demodulation process, are known as **modems**.

10.7 Frequency-division multiplexing

As mentioned in Chapter 9, the term 'multiplexing' is normally used, in the context of digital systems, to mean time-division multiplexing. However, there is also a technique known as **frequency-division multiplexing** (f.d.m.) by which signals may be simultaneously transmitted over the same channel, by allocating each a non-overlapping slot in the frequency spectrum.

Fig. 10.26 shows a number of upper-sideband s.s.b. signals whose distribution over the frequency band is effected by using differing carrier frequencies f_{c_1}, f_{c_2}, etc. Typically, 12 speech signals could be modulated onto carriers spaced 4 kHz apart and the whole group (now having a bandwidth of 48 kHz) then treated as a single composite signal for transmission to a distant point. The receiving equipment would select the required signal by means of appropriate filters. This form of signal selection by filtering is precisely that which occurs when tuning a radio receiver, although, in that case, the modulation is normally a.m. (on the medium waveband) or f.m. on the very-high-frequency (v.h.f.) band. The same technique applies equally to a group of lower-sideband signals.

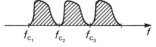

Fig. 10.26 Frequency-division multiplexing

Key points to remember

- modulation is often necessary to ensure signal/transmission-medium compatibility, permit multiplexing and allow noise/bandwidth trading;

- amplitude modulation generates two sidebands in the frequency spectrum;

- a phasor diagram can be used to relate time and frequency-domain representations of a modulated signal;
- power in a modulated signal is the sum of the powers due to each component;
- within certain limitations, signal transmission can take place without the carrier and without one of the sidebands;
- frequency modulation generates sidebands whose component amplitudes are determined by Bessel functions and linear superposition does not apply;
- a pulse train can be modulated in amplitude, width and position to produce discrete-time modulated signals;
- pulse-code modulation involves the generation of binary signals from samples of a continuous signal;
- the keying methods known as amplitude-shift, frequency-shift and phase-shift keying can be used to transmit digital signals;
- frequency-division multiplexing permits more than one signal to be transmitted over a single channel.

Further reading

Carlson, A. B., *Communication Systems.* McGraw-Hill (1974).
Stanley, W., *Electronic Communications Systems.* Reston (1982).
Stremler, F., *Introduction to Communications Systems* (2nd edn). Addison-Wesley (1982).
Young, P. H., *Electronic Communication Techniques.* C. Merrill (1985).

EXERCISES 10

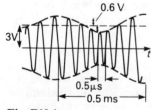

Fig. E10.1

10.1   A sinusoidally modulated a.m. signal has the waveform shown in Fig. E10.1. Deduce an expression for the modulated waveform stating the modulation index.

10.2   Sketch the spectral diagram for the waveform shown in Fig. E10.1.
Also, use the result of Exercise 8.1 to sketch the spectral diagram if the envelope variation has the waveshape shown in Fig. E8.1 (Chapter 8 exercises) but the amplitude and period values are as in Fig. E10.1.

10.3   Show that when the square-wave modulated current waveform shown in Fig. E10.2 flows in a 100 Ω resistor the power dissipation is twice that of the unmodulated carrier

(i) by calculating the power due to individual spectral components; and
(ii) working from first principles.

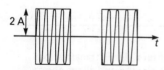

Fig. E10.2

10.4   Fig. E10.3 shows an arrangement for transmitting two direct voltages over a channel. Draw waveforms at modulator and summer outputs for different direct-voltage amplitude inputs. Also sketch a block diagram of a circuit which could be used to recover the two voltage levels.

Fig. E10.3

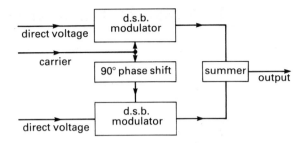

10.5 A 1 kHz tone is transmitted using

(i) s.s.b., and
(ii) d.s.b. (suppressed carrier),

on a 10 MHz carrier. If the locally generated carrier at the receiver has a frequency error of 1 part in 10^6, describe, in each case, the output which would be heard on the receiver loudspeaker.

10.6 An unmodulated carrier $E_c \sin \omega_c t$ is to be frequency modulated such that its instantaneous angular frequency is changed from ω_c to $(\omega_c + \Delta\omega \sin \omega_m t)$, dependent upon a sinusoidal modulating signal at frequency ω_m. Explain why the modulated carrier is *not* given by $E_c \sin(\omega_c + \Delta\omega \sin \omega_m t)t$.

10.7 Sketch the spectral content at the output of an f.m. signal generator with carrier frequency and amplitude set to 10.7 MHz and 1.2 V and modulating-signal frequency and amplitude at 10 kHz and 5 V respectively. The modulator constant is 10 kHz/V.
Estimate the bandwidth by two methods, and make new estimates for half the modulating-signal amplitude.

10.8 One method of calibrating a deviation-meter on an f.m. signal generator is the 'Bessel-zero' method. In this method the condition at which one of the spectral components becomes zero is detected on a spectrum analyser. Use Fig. 10.14 to estimate the percentage calibration error if, when indicating a deviation of 75 kHz, a modulating-signal frequency of 14 kHz is required to bring the carrier-frequency component to zero. Assume that the meter is not grossly inaccurate.

10.9 Two receivers, one designed to receive frequency-modulated signals and the other phase-modulated signals, each receive a frequency-modulated test transmission. What would be the effect on each receiver if

(i) the test-tone amplitude were doubled;
(ii) the test-tone frequency were doubled.

10.10 Two signals $v_1 = 3 \sin 10^4 t$ V and $v_2 = 2 \sin 10^5 t$ V are to be transmitted over a multiplexed p.a.m. channel. Assuming the signals are sampled alternately, determine the minimum sampling frequency and the maximum pulse amplitude assuming only positive pulse amplitudes are used. Assume that the modulator constant is unity.
What would be the data rate (in bits per second) if the p.a.m. signal is now converted into a binary code such that the quantisation interval is not less than 25 mV?

10.11 A phase-shift keying system uses $0°$ and $180°$ as the two phase values. Assuming 2 V peak amplitude, sketch the waveform and spectral diagrams when a 1.8 kHz sinusoidal carrier is modulated by a 200 Hz square wave.

11 Noise in transmission systems

The principal learning objectives of this chapter are to:

	Section	Exercise
• describe the general characteristics of white noise;	1	
• explain how noise may be represented by an effective (r.m.s.) value;	2.1, 2.2	11.1
• explain how the probability density function can be used to quantify noise;	2.3	11.2
• determine signal-to-noise ratio (S/N);	3.1	11.3
• discuss various interpretations of noise figure;	3.2	11.4
• explain noise temperature;	3.3	11.5
• evaluate the overall-noise performance of cascaded systems;	4	11.6, 11.7
• derive error-rate figures for threshold detectors in the presence of noise;	5	11.8
• deduce the effect of quantisation in discrete-amplitude systems;	6.1	11.9
• distinguish between the performance of a.m. and f.m. receivers in the presence of a small interfering signal.	6.2	11.10

11.1 Introduction

Noise may be defined in a general way as any unwanted signal in a circuit or system. This general definition includes not only the inescapable random 'background' signals (for example, the hiss which may be heard in a loudspeaker during quiet passages in a radio transmission) but also unwanted interference signals generated by the system itself. However, this chapter is primarily concerned with the naturally occurring internal random-noise signals and with their effect on the operation of that system.

Two principal forms of internal noise can be identified. These are **thermal noise** (also known as Johnson noise) arising from the random motion of electrons in a conductor and **shot noise** (or device noise) resulting from random variations in the

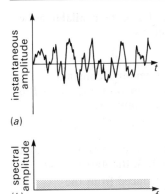

(a)

(b)

Fig. 11.1 Noise in time and frequency domains

flow of charge carriers across, for example, a p–n junction. Each is described in more detail in the following subsections but it may be noted at this stage that each appears in the time domain as a random voltage or current variation (Fig. 11.1(*a*)) and in the frequency domain as a uniformly distributed spectrum (Fig. 11.1(*b*)). Because of this spectral distribution, they are known as **white noise**, by analogy with white light which has a uniform spectral distribution over a range of frequencies.

Both representations of the noise signal are used in determining its effect on system performance. When dealing with an analogue subsystem (such as an amplifier with a limited bandwidth), the spectral model is used to determine the total noise power contained within the frequency band of interest. As described in Section 11.3, this value may then be compared with the signal power to calculate the **signal-to-noise ratio** (*S*/*N*). When dealing with a digital subsystem, in which the noise may affect the decision on whether a particular signal level represents a 1 state or a 0 state, the time-domain model may be used to determine the probability of the noise signal reaching a sufficiently high level to affect that decision. As described in Section 11.5, this may be done by means of a probability density graph which, for thermal and shot noise, has a **Gaussian** or **normal** distribution. For this reason, **Gaussian noise** is an alternative term.

11.2 Quantifying noise signals

11.2.1 The nature of the quantity

Because of the random way in which its amplitude varies, it is not possible to describe the instantaneous value of a noise signal in the same way as, for example, a sinusoid may be described by the term, *E* sin *ωt*. However, just as a sinusoid may be quantified by its effective or r.m.s. value, noise may also be so described. When this is done, it is possible to use the r.m.s. value directly in system-performance calculations as, for example, the r.m.s. value of the sinusoid may be used to determine its heating effect. If, in other circumstances, information on the instantaneous value is needed, a statistical method may then be used to predict the probability of the instantaneous amplitude exceeding the r.m.s. value (or any value proportionately related to it).

11.2.2 R.M.S. values of white (Gaussian) noise

Because white noise is uniformly distributed over the frequency band, its spectral power density is uniform and, hence, its mean-square value will be proportional to the frequency band of interest. This is because, as defined in Chapter 4, the mean-square value (i.e. the r.m.s. value squared) is proportional to power. Furthermore, because thermal noise arises from the temperature-dependent random motion of electrons in conductors, the noise power which is transferred from a 'noisy' resistor (or resistive source) into a matched load is found to be proportional to both absolute temperature and system bandwidth. Thus, the **available noise power** from a resistive source is given by

$$N_a = kTB,$$

where k is a constant, known as Boltzmann's constant ($= 1.38 \times 10^{-23}$ J/K), T is absolute temperature (K) and B is the system bandwidth (Hz). If 'room' temperature is conveniently taken as $17\,^{\circ}$C (290 K) the product kT is 4×10^{-21} W/Hz.

With power kTB transferred from source resistance R to a matched load of resistance R (Fig. 11.2), the mean-square open-circuit noise e.m.f. $\overline{e_n^2}$ may be deduced from the expression $N_a = kTB = \overline{i_n^2}R$ where $\overline{i_n^2}$ is the mean-square noise current. But $\overline{i_n^2}R = \overline{e_n^2}R/(2R)^2$ from which $\overline{e_n^2} = 4kTBR$.

The mean-square value is seen to be proportional to the resistance value and this also applies to networks whose output resistance is R. In effect, even though the source network may consist of a number of resistive elements, the noise e.m.f. is determined only by the Thévenin-equivalent resistance at the output terminals, assuming all elements are at the same temperature. This raises an interesting situation in which a source, feeding a matched load through a matched cable (or attenuator), transfers noise power kTB into the cable and the cable transfers the same power into the load. The signal power from the source will, however, be reduced by cable losses (or the attenuation of the attenuator) so that there is a reduction in the ratio of signal power to noise power on passing through the system. This aspect is considered in the next section.

When dealing with systems fed from devices or networks having a resistive source impedance, thermal noise is used in the calculations. However, when circuits (such as amplifiers) employ semiconductor devices, other forms of noise must be taken into account. One of the principal forms is *shot noise*, arising in thermionic and semiconductor-junction devices as a result of small random variations in the flow of charge carriers.

In this chapter, which is principally aimed towards a transmission-systems-overview treatment of noise, the various effects resulting in the generation of noise within amplifiers, etc., are lumped together into a composite figure of merit known as the noise figure, defined in the next section. It is simply noted here that at a p–n junction, for example, shot noise may be quantified by the expression,

$$\overline{i_n^2} = 2qIB,$$

where $\overline{i_n^2}$ is the mean-square noise current, q is electronic charge, I is the quiescent current and B is the system bandwidth. It will be seen that for both forms of white noise the noise power is proportional to the system bandwidth.

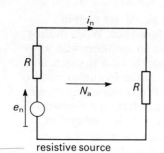

resistive source

Fig. 11.2 Noise power transferred to a matched load

11.2.3 Probability density function

If a number of instantaneous values of the noise signal shown in Fig. 11.1 were taken and plotted on a graph showing frequency of occurrence against amplitude, a distribution of the form shown in Fig. 11.3(a) would be obtained. This is a **Gaussian** or **normal** distribution.

In addition to the shape of the distribution, two figures quantify the samples. These are the **mean value**, given by dividing the sum of the sample values by the number of samples, and the **standard deviation** given by the square root of the mean of the squares of the differences between the sample amplitudes and the mean value. When the mean value is zero, standard deviation and the root of the mean of the sample amplitudes squared (i.e. the r.m.s. value) have the same significance.

If a very large number of instantaneous values are taken the curve becomes continuous and is described by a **probability density function (p.d.f.)**,

$$F(e_n) = e^{-e_n^2/2\sigma^2}/\sigma\sqrt{(2\pi)}.$$

This is plotted in Fig. 11.3(b) in terms of the standard deviation σ which, because the mean value is zero, is also the r.m.s. value. The p.d.f. will be seen to have a maximum value of $0.399/\sigma$, with values of $0.24/\sigma$ and $0.054/\sigma$, at $e_n = \pm\sigma$ and $\pm 2\sigma$.

The probability of the instantaneous value lying within a certain range of values is given by the area under the curve. For example, the shaded area in Fig. 11.3(b) is the probability of e_n exceeding $+2\sigma$ (i.e. twice the r.m.s. value). Tables are available listing these areas but typical values are 0.683 for e_n to lie between $-\sigma$ and $+\sigma$, 0.997 for e_n to lie between -3σ and $+3\sigma$ and 0.0014 for e_n to exceed $+3\sigma$. Application of these results is given in Section 11.5.

Fig. 11.3 Gaussian distributions

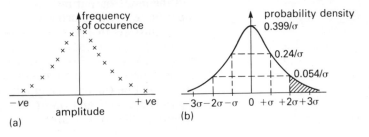

(a)

(b)

11.3 Signal-to-noise ratio, noise figure and noise temperature

11.3.1 Signal-to-noise ratio (S/N)

The absolute value of the noise voltage or power in a system is, by itself, of lesser importance. It is the ratio of the signal power to the noise power or **signal-to-noise ratio** (S/N) that is of greater significance. For example, if the speech level from a radio receiver is almost inaudible, it is a simple matter to include an additional audio amplifier, but because the noise level is also increased, it may be of little benefit. Furthermore, not only will the amplifier amplify whatever noise exists at its input, but it will generate additional noise itself and thus reduce the S/N.

The performance of amplifier stages is discussed in the next section: here, S/N is simply defined as the signal power at a particular point in a system divided by the noise power at that point. Normally, it is expressed in decibels. For example, a matched resistive load fed from a 50 Ω signal source having 100 mV (r.m.s.) open-circuit e.m.f. would dissipate a power of $(100 \times 10^{-3}/2)^2 50 = 50\,\mu W$. If the source temperature were 290 K and the system bandwidth were 5 MHz, the noise power transferred to the load would be $kTB = 1.38 \times 10^{-23} \times 290 \times 5 \times 10^6 = 2 \times 10^{-14}\,W$ and the S/N would be $50 \times 10^{-6}/2 \times 10^{-14} = 2.5 \times 10^9$ (or $10 \log 2.5 \times 10^9 = 94\,dB$). In this example, and in the following discussion, it is assumed throughout that each stage of the system is matched to the previous stage and to the following stage. This does not imply that the noise generated by a given stage in a system has a minimum value in this condition but it does specify a unique operating condition that affords simpler calculations. However, in mismatched conditions the S/N would remain the same because the same mismatch factor would apply equally to the signal and to the noise.

11.3.2 Noise figure

The **noise figure** of a system or part of a system may be defined as the input S/N divided by the output S/N when the input noise power is the available power with the source at room temperature, denoted T_0 (290 K). It may be noted that the general definition, input S/N divided by output S/N, is insufficient because the noise power added by a stage or system is a fixed quantity (in specified operating conditions) and the input–output ratio is only defined uniquely when the input noise power is defined.

To illustrate this point, suppose that the noise power generated by a device is N. The total noise-power output will be $N + GN_i$ where G is the stage gain and N_i is the noise-power input. If S_i is the signal-power input, the signal-power output will be GS_i and the input and output S/N will then be, respectively, S_i/N_i and $GS_i/(GN_i + N)$. Using the general definition, the noise figure is

$$(S_i/N_i) \times (GN_i + N)/GS_i = 1 + N/GN_i,$$

which is clearly a function of N_i. To regularise the definition, G and N_i are uniquely specified as the available power gain G_a and the available input noise power N_a $(= kT_0B)$ to give $F = 1 + N/G_a kT_0B = 1 + N/G_a N_a$.

A useful variation on the $1 + N/G_a N_a$ noise figure expression is obtained by expressing N as an equivalent input noise power, i.e. the noise which, if applied to the input of a noise-free stage, would cause N to appear at the output. This equivalent input noise would have a value $N_{ei} = N/G_a$ and the noise-figure expression would become

$$F = 1 + N_{ei}/N_a.$$

Thus, $N_{ei} = (F - 1)N_a$ and the total effective noise input is $N_a + (F - 1)N_a = FN_a$. This relationship is illustrated in Fig. 11.4.

Fig. 11.4 Illustrating equivalent noise input and a noiseless stage

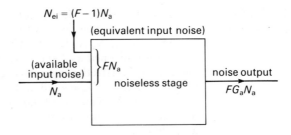

$N_{ei} = (F-1)N_a$

(equivalent input noise)

(available input noise)

N_a

FN_a

noiseless stage

noise output

FG_aN_a

Two further variants on the noise-figure definitions are as follows: F is the actual noise-power output divided by the noise-power output if the amplifier were noise free, the input noise power being N_a in each case. In terms of the symbols used above, F is then given by $(N + G_aN_a)/G_aN_a$ which will be seen to be $1 + N/G_aN_a$, as before. Alternatively, F is the output S/N if the amplifier were noise free divided by actual output S/N. This can be written as G_aS_i/G_aN_a divided by $G_aS_i/(G_aN_a + N)$, again the same as $1 + N/G_aN_a$.

Example 11.1 *An amplifier, having a gain of 20 dB and a bandwidth of 100 kHz under matched conditions, has a noise figure of 6 dB. Assuming that the source temperature is that for which the noise figure is defined (i.e. 290 K), determine the available input noise power, the equivalent input noise power and the total output noise power. What percentage of the output noise power is generated by the amplifier itself?*

The available noise N_a is given by

$kT_0B = 1.38 \times 10^{-23} \times 290 \times 10^5 = 4 \times 10^{-16}$ W.

The noise figure is 4 (6 dB) and, hence, the equivalent input noise N_{ei} is

$(4-1)4 \times 10^{-16} = 1.2 \times 10^{-15}$ W.

The total output noise power is

$(N_a + N_{ei})G_a$ (or FG_aN_a) $= 1.6 \times 10^{-15} \times 100$ W

$= 1.6 \times 10^{-13}$ W.

The percentage power generated by the amplifier is

$N_{ei}/(N_{ei} + N_a) \times 100\%$ (or $(F-1)/F \times 100\%) = 75\%$.

It is important to appreciate that noise figure is defined and measured on the basis of a standard source temperature T_0, i.e. $N_a = kT_0B$. If the source is at a different temperature T_s the noise figure remains the same (as defined) but the output S/N is no longer given by $(S/N)_o = (S/N)_i/F$ where $N_i = kT_0B$.

The new noise-power input will now be kT_sB and the equivalent input noise generated by the amplifier $(F-1)kT_0B$ (as before) giving a new $(S/N)_o = G_aS_i/G_akB(T_s + (F-1)T_0)$. With a new $(S/N)_i = S_i/kT_sB$, the relationship becomes

$(S/N)_o = (S/N)_i[T_s/(T_s + (F-1)T_0)]$.

In the particular case when $T_s = T_0$, this reduces to $(S/N)_o = (S/N)_i/F$, as before.

11.3.3 Noise temperature

In Fig. 11.4, the equivalent input noise representing the noise generated by the stage itself is shown as $N_{ei} = (F - 1)N_a$. In the same way as N_a is given by kT_0B, where T_0 is the source temperature (defined as 290 K), N_{ei} can be written as kT_eB where T_e is the **effective input noise temperature** of the amplifier. Because $N_{ei} = kT_eB$ and $(F - 1)kT_0B$, $T_e = (F - 1)T_0$, or $F = 1 + T_e/T_0$. Thus, the total noise output may be expressed as the summation of GkT_0B and GkT_eB, i.e. $GkB(T_0 + T_e)$.

The use of noise temperature is particularly convenient when dealing with low-noise systems where small differences in noise figures, say 1.15 and 1.10, are reflected as larger differences in equivalent temperature, viz. 44 K and 29 K, respectively. A noiseless device has a noise figure of 1.0 and a temperature of 0 K.

An associated concept which relates to external rather than internal noise is that of the effective noise temperature of an aerial. This may be defined by the relationship, available power from aerial $= kT_aB$ where T_a is the effective aerial temperature. In this case, the effective temperature represents external noise picked up by the aerial and, in general, is a function of the noise signals existing in the space towards which the aerial is directed.

11.4 Noise in cascaded analogue systems

If a system consists of a series of cascaded stages (Fig. 11.5), each stage may be expected to add some noise so that the overall S/N will gradually deteriorate on passing through the system. If the stages are amplifiers, the signal level may well increase significantly from input to output, but the noise level will increase even more. The extent of the worsening of the S/N can be determined by deriving an expression for the overall effective temperature and noise figure for a cascaded system.

Fig. 11.5 shows three representative stages in a system, which, for the purpose of this discussion, is assumed to be matched throughout. The total noise-power output from the three stages is given by the sum of the source-noise power multiplied by the three amplifier gains and the equivalent input-noise powers multiplied by the gain of the amplifier(s) which follows. Having established that the source noise power is kT_sB and that the equivalent input-noise power is kT_eB, the total noise-power output is then given by

$$N_o = G_1G_2G_3k(T_s + T_{e_1})B + G_2G_3kT_{e_2}B + G_3kT_{e_3}B.$$

Fig. 11.5 A cascaded system

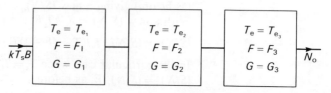

$T_e = T_{e_1}$	$T_e = T_{e_2}$	$T_e = T_{e_3}$
$F = F_1$	$F = F_2$	$F = F_3$
$G = G_1$	$G = G_2$	$G - G_3$

kT_sB →

→ N_o

If the overall equivalent input-noise temperature is T_e, N_o is also given by $G_1G_2G_3k(T_s + T_e)B$ and, equating the two expressions for N_o,

$$T_s + T_e = T_s + T_{e_1} + T_{e_2}/G_1 + T_{e_3}/G_1G_2,$$

and, hence,

$$T_e = T_{e_1} + \frac{T_{e_2}}{G_1} + \frac{T_{e_3}}{G_1G_2}.$$

In terms of noise figures, using the general relationship $T_e = (F - 1)T_0$,

$$(F - 1)T_0 = (F_1 - 1)T_0 + (F_2 - 1)T_0/G_1 + (F_3 - 1)T_0/G_1G_2,$$

or,

$$F = F_1 + \frac{F_2 - 1}{G_1} + \frac{F_3 - 1}{G_1G_2}.$$

For m stages, the mth term would be $T_{e_m}/G_1G_2 \cdots G_{m-1}$ (for T_e) and $(F_m - 1)/G_1G_2 \cdots G_{m-1}$ for F.

Example 11.2 *Determine the overall noise figure for a system (Fig. 11.5) having $F_1 = 3\,dB$, $F_2 = 7\,dB$ and $F_3 = 6\,dB$ and $G_1 = 10\,dB$, $G_2 = 20\,dB$ (G_3 is not needed).*

Using the expressions derived above (after converting the decibel values into ratios)

$$F = 2 + \frac{5 - 1}{10} + \frac{4 - 1}{10 \times 100} = 2.403 \text{ or } 3.81\,\text{dB}.$$

The form of the expression and the calculation in Example 11.2 both draw attention to the importance of G_1 and F_1 (i.e. the properties of the first stage) in a system. If G_1 is large, F is approximately equal to F_1 and the overall noise figure is approximately that of the first stage. This may be expected because, in the first stage, the noise input is the available noise and the noise output, by definition, is G_1F_1 times that noise. If G_1 is large, the noise input to the second stage will be very much in excess of the equivalent input noise of that stage, i.e. $(F_2 - 1)N_a$, so that the noise added by the stage itself has less significance. As the noise level builds up through the system, the relatively small amounts of noise power added have less and less effect on the overall performance.

Further insight into the signal and noise relationships in a system may be gained by calculating signal and noise levels for a cascaded system such as that having the figures detailed in Example 11.2. Typical signal and noise-power levels are shown in Fig. 11.6; the assumed values give an input S/N of 54 dB. The method used is to split the input-noise power into two components at each stage. One component is the available-noise power of 40 pW and the other is the balance. In calculating the noise output from each stage, the former is multiplied by the gain *and* the noise figure whereas the latter is multiplied by the gain alone, a procedure following directly from the noise-figure definition. The cumulative output-noise power of $96.12G_3$ nW, when divided into the signal output power of $10G_3$ mW, gives an output S/N of 50.17 dB, making an overall S/N degradation of $53.98 - 50.17 = 3.81$ dB. This is exactly the same figure as that obtained in Example 11.2; this method however, although based on the same principles as the equivalent-input noise method, does follow a different procedure (and one which is very cumbersome to express in terms of symbols).

Fig. 11.6 Signal and noise levels at various stages in a cascaded system

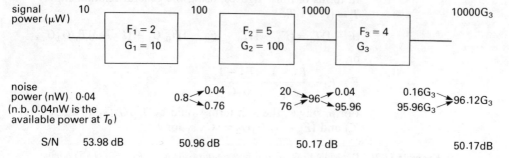

| signal power (μW) | 10 | | 100 | | 10000 | | $10000G_3$ |

| $F_1 = 2$ | $F_2 = 5$ | $F_3 = 4$ |
| $G_1 = 10$ | $G_2 = 100$ | G_3 |

noise power (nW) 0.04
(n.b. 0.04nW is the available power at T_0)

0.8 ⟨0.04 / 0.76⟩   20 ⟨76⟩ →96⟨0.04 / 95.96⟩   0.16G_3 ⟨95.96G_3⟩ →96.12G_3

S/N   53.98 dB   50.96 dB   50.17 dB   50.17dB

An interesting consequence of the predominant effect of the first stage in a cascaded system is that the order of connection of the stages affects the overall noise figure, although the signal level is not affected. An example occurs in the domestic television receiving system in which the first stage is normally the cable from the aerial to the receiver. A cable is the least suitable first stage because, as established in Section 11.2.2, the noise input and output powers are the same whereas the signal-power level falls by the value of the attenuation. In effect, the noise figure is numerically equal to the attenuation (assuming, as is usual, that the cable temperature is T_0) and the 'gain' is equal to the reciprocal of the attenuation. To illustrate the point, suppose the three stages specified in Example 11.2 were preceded by a cable having a 6 dB ($4\times$) loss. Then $F_c = 4$ and $G_c = \frac{1}{4}$ and the overall noise factor is now given by

$$F = 4 + \frac{2-1}{\frac{1}{4}} + \frac{5-1}{\frac{1}{4} \times 10} + \frac{4-1}{\frac{1}{4} \times 10 \times 100}$$

$$= 4 + 4 + 1.6 + 0.012 = 9.612 \text{ or } 9.83 \text{ dB}.$$

This is 6 dB worse than the previous figure. However, suppose that the first amplifier stage were placed immediately next to the aerial, the main cable run being between this and the next amplifier stage. The new noise figure would be

$$F = 2 + \frac{4-1}{10} + \frac{5-1}{10 \times \frac{1}{4}} + \frac{4-1}{10 \times \frac{1}{4} \times 100}$$

$$= 2 + 0.3 + 1.6 + 0.012 = 3.912 \text{ or } 5.92 \text{ dB}.$$

This represents a 4 dB improvement over the overall noise figure calculated above, and the general principle that the first stage should have as low a noise figure and as high a gain as possible is demonstrated.

11.5 Noise in digital systems

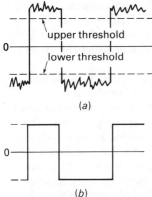

0 ——— upper threshold

lower threshold

(a)

0 ———

(b)

Fig. 11.7 The effect of threshold levels on a noisy signal

A source of noise at the interface between analogue and digital systems is the quantisation noise or error introduced in Chapter 9. There is further discussion on this aspect in the next section of this chapter, the primary aim of this section being consideration of the effect of adding white noise to the pulse waveforms used in digital systems.

In the analogue case it was the composite effect of the noise (e.g. the hiss in the loudspeaker) over the relevant band of frequencies which was of interest. In the digital system, the situation is entirely different. Even though a waveform may have substantial noise added to it (Fig. 11.7(*a*)), if this noise fails to exceed the respective threshold levels the recovery device will effectively regenerate a perfect waveform (Fig. 11.7(*b*)).

Apparently, the digital system could be arranged to be entirely immune to signal-level fluctuations due to added noise. However, this is not the case because the amplitude of the noise signal, being a random effect, *could* exceed any given threshold value (as a freak wave could exceed the height of a sea wall). Naturally, the greater the height of the threshold (the sea wall), the lower the probability of it being overcome.

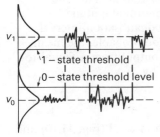

V_1 ——— 1 – state threshold

0 – state threshold level

V_0 ———

Fig. 11.8 Threshold levels related to the Gaussian distribution

The problem may be approached by regarding the signal amplitudes, V_1 for the 1 level and V_0 for the 0 level, as mean amplitudes about which the actual signal levels vary (Fig. 11.8). Against these instantaneous-signal variations are shown the Gaussian distribution graphs previously drawn in Fig. 11.3(*b*) but, in this case, constructed with vertical amplitude scales. The diagram also shows the 1 and 0 threshold levels which, when projected onto the p.d.f. curves enable the probabilities of the instantaneous noise-signal levels exceeding the respective thresholds to be determined. As described in Section 11.2.3, these probabilities are given by the shaded areas under the curves. The following example illustrates how such calculations could be made.

Example 11.3

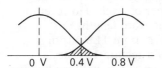

0 V   0.4 V   0.8 V

Fig. 11.9 Solution to Example 11.3

Following transmission, the voltage levels in a stream of binary data are 0.8 V (representing 1) and 0 V (representing 0), each level having a zero-mean-value noise signal of amplitude 100 mV r.m.s. superimposed on it. Determine the probability of error in detecting the message if a single threshold level is set at 0.4 V and 1's and 0's are equiprobable in the message.

In this example, the r.m.s. value $\sigma = 0.1\,\text{V}$ and with the threshold at 0.4 V, the probability of an error in the 0-level is given by the shaded area above 4σ (Fig. 11.9). From statistical tables, this area (for $e_n \geqslant 4\sigma$) is 0.000 03. In this case, the area under the 1-level curve is the same and hence the combined probability of errors in reading 0's and 1's is

$$0.5 \times 0.000\,03 + 0.5 \times 0.000\,03 = 0.000\,03$$

or on average three errors in one hundred thousand bits.

11.6 Noise reduction methods

11.6.1 Quantisation noise and companding

It was established in Chapter 9 that the quantisation process, which inevitably occurs during analogue-to-digital conversion, leads to an uncertainty or error in the digital signal of up to $\pm\frac{1}{2}$ quantisation interval. It was also established that increasing the word length by one bit halved that error. Thus, quantisation noise may be reduced by increasing the system word length.

In a digital processing system, an increase in the word length may require more hardware and possibly more complex software. For example, if in an 8-bit microprocessor-based system the quantisation error was too great with the 256 levels offered by an 8-bit word it would be necessary to increase the word length, which may then have to be handled in two stages, e.g. eight bits followed by two bits. This would complicate the program and require more memory locations (which, it is assumed, would also only hold eight bits each). Additionally, for a digital transmission system, greater channel bandwidth would be required if the 10-bit words were to be transmitted at the same word speed as the 8-bit words.

Inasmuch as the signal level before quantisation is continuous, in the range $\pm\frac{1}{2}$ quantisation interval, the quantisation noise would have a uniform amplitude distribution within the range of the quantisation interval. Thus, assuming that all levels are equiprobable, the mean-square value of the analogue noise output from a digital-to-analogue converter would be given by

$$\frac{1}{d}\int_{-d/2}^{+d/2} v_q^2 \, dv_q = \frac{d^2}{12},$$

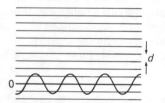

Fig. 11.10 A small-amplitude signal variation

where d represents one quantisation interval (Fig. 11.10) and v_q is the quantisation-error voltage.

The actual signal-to-noise ratio at the analogue output will depend upon the amplitude of the signal level at that point. Because the mean-square noise amplitude is the same at all quantisation levels (assuming that these are equally spaced), at very low signal levels the S/N will be very low. Fig. 11.10 shows a bipolar sinusoidal signal variation not exceeding $3d$. In this case, the mean-square signal would be $(3d/2\sqrt{2})^2$ and the S/N would be $(9d^2/8) \times (12/d^2) = \frac{108}{8}$ or 11.3 dB. For a large signal variation of, say, $255d$ (for an 8-bit word) the S/N would be $((255d)^2/8) \times (12/d^2)$ or approximately 50 dB.

One method of achieving a reasonably high S/N at low signal levels is to increase the number of levels. However, as noted above, this would increase the word length. For example, to increase the low-level S/N from 11.3 dB to, say, 35 dB in the previous example, would require 16 times as many quantisation levels, requiring an additional four bits in each word. This is consistent with the general rule that each additional bit improves the S/N by 6 dB.

In digital transmission systems where a wide dynamic signal range is involved (e.g. for speech transmission),

companding can be used to improve the S/N at low signal levels at the expense of that at high signal levels without significantly increasing the number of levels required. In this technique, the signal is non-linearly compressed in amplitude before encoding. A typical compression characteristic is shown in Fig. 11.11. Passing the signal through this compressor before quantisation effectively allocates more levels to the low-level signal compared with the high-level signal. After digital-to-analogue conversion at the receiving end of the transmission channel the signal is passed through a reverse-characteristic expandor to restore it to its proper proportions.

Fig. 11.11 Compression characteristic

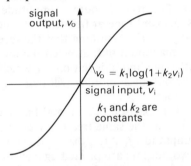

signal output, v_o

$v_o = k_1 \log(1 + k_2 v_i)$

signal input, v_i

k_1 and k_2 are constants

11.6.2 Noise reduction in frequency-modulated systems

Chapter 10 described the principles of amplitude-modulation (a.m.) and frequency-modulation (f.m.) systems. In this section it is shown that under certain circumstances and in the presence of a given noise level at the receiver input the S/N at the output of an f.m. receiver may be better than that at corresponding a.m. receiver output. The analysis, which is intended only to demonstrate the principle rather than obtain detailed S/N-improvement figures, is based on the effect of a small interfering signal in the presence of an unmodulated carrier (Fig. 11.12(a)). In an extended analysis, the interfering signal can be regarded as one element of a noise signal distributed over the frequency band. It is assumed that the amplitude E_x is very much smaller than E_c.

Fig. 11.12(b) is a phasor diagram showing the two signals and their resultant E_r. Signal E_x is rotating at angular velocity ω_x relative to the carrier and provided $E_x \ll E_c$, the resultant amplitude variation is approximately sinusoidal with time. The objective of the analysis is to determine the effect at the respective receiver outputs when this resultant signal is applied to their inputs.

The a.m. receiver will respond only to amplitude variations and, because the peak amplitude variation is $\pm E_x$, the a.m. receiver output will be an approximate sinusoid of frequency f_x and amplitude (E_x/E_c) of the maximum output assuming, for the purpose of this analysis, that maximum output occurs when the input amplitude variation is $\pm E_c$ (i.e. 100% modulation depth).

The f.m. receiver will respond to instantaneous frequency variations in the resultant signal. The nature of the variation is not immediately obvious from the phasor diagram but may be derived from the phase variation which is also

E_c (unmodulated carrier)

(interfering signal)

$|E_x$

$f_c \longleftarrow f_x \longrightarrow f_c + f_x \qquad f$

(a)

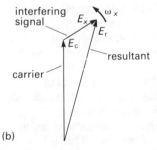

interfering signal $\quad E_x \quad \omega_x$

E_r

E_c

resultant

carrier

(b)

Fig. 11.12 A small interfering signal added to a larger sinusoid

approximately sinusoidal and of peak amplitude approximately equal to the ratio of the two components E_x/E_c. The phase variations may therefore be expressed by

$$\theta = (E_x/E_c)\sin\omega_x t,$$

and the corresponding frequency variation can be deduced as

$$\omega = d\theta/dt = (\omega_x E_x/E_c)\cos\omega_x t,$$

or

$$f = \omega/2\pi = (f_x E_x/E_c)\cos\omega_x t.$$

This is a sinusoidal variation of peak amplitude $f_x E_x/E_c$ and the f.m. receiver-output amplitude will therefore be a sinusoidal tone at frequency f_x and of amplitude proportional to $f_x E_x/E_c$. Assuming that the receiver is designed to provide its maximum output when the input-signal deviation is Δf_{max} (the maximum deviation for which the system is designed), the output amplitude will be $(f_x E_x/\Delta f_{max} E_c)$ of the maximum output.

Comparison of a.m. and f.m. receiver-outputs shows them to be at the same frequency but with the f.m.-output amplitude $f_x/\Delta f_{max}$ that of the a.m.-output amplitude. The two outputs are plotted against frequency in Fig. 11.13(a) and (b) for, respectively, Δf_{max} greater than B (the maximum base bandwidth) and Δf_{max} less than B.

Fig. 11.13 Relative outputs of a.m. and f.m. receivers

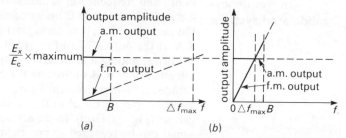

(a)   (b)

The two interesting features of the f.m.-receiver output amplitude are that: (i) it is proportional to f_x so that the farther the interfering signal is from the carrier, the greater the output noise amplitude, and (ii) by selecting the system maximum deviation so that it is much larger than the maximum baseband frequency, the output amplitude can be made much smaller than the a.m.-output. To illustrate these points, if B is 15 kHz and Δf_{max} is 75 kHz, the amplitude of the noise output of the f.m. system never exceeds 20 % of the a.m. output and, at the lower baseband frequencies, is considerably less. Further analysis is necessary to determine noise power output.

Not only is the f.m. output less than in the a.m. case provided $\Delta f_{max} > B$ but by **pre-emphasising** the high baseband frequencies relative to the lower frequencies before modulation and **de-emphasising** them after demodulation, a further improvement in overall S/N is possible. This is because, on de-emphasis, the high-frequency components of the noise output are reduced. The high-frequency components of the signal are, of course, also reduced but the combined effect of the pre- and de-emphasis maintains the proper proportions.

Key points to remember

- white noise has a uniform spectral distribution;
- noise may be quantified by its r.m.s. value and the probability of the instantaneous value exceeding a specified limit;
- noise figure and effective temperature are measures of the noise introduced by a system;
- the overall noise temperature in a cascaded system is given by $T_{e1} + T_{e2}/G_1 + T_{e3}/G_1 G_2$;
- probability of error in a threshold-detector system may be determined from statistical tables;
- effect of noise at low signal levels in a quantised-amplitude system may be reduced by non-linear quantisation;
- noise in a frequency-modulated system may be reduced by increasing deviation and hence bandwidth.

Further reading

Buckingham, M. J., *Noise in Electronic Devices and Systems*. Ellis-Horwood (1983).
Carlson, A. B., *Communication Systems*. McGraw-Hill (1974).
Stanley, W., *Electronic Communication Systems*. Reston (1982).

EXERCISES 11

11.1   A 600 Ω resistive source is connected to a system having a bandwidth of 5 MHz. Determine the r.m.s. noise voltage appearing at the input terminals at a temperature of 290 K if the system input impedance is very high. What system input impedance would cause maximum noise power to be transferred into the system, and calculate the value of that power.

11.2   Sketch an approximate probability density function $F(e_n)$, in accordance with the expression given in Section 11.2.3, by calculating values at $e_n = \sigma$, 2σ and 3σ.
Make the sketch on squared paper and hence, *estimate* the probability of a white-noise signal exceeding twice its r.m.s. value.

11.3   If in Exercise 11.1 the signal source open-circuit e.m.f. is 10 mV (r.m.s.) determine the signal-to-noise ratio (S/N) at the system input terminals in the matched case.
Recalculate the S/N if the system input impedance is reduced to half its matched value.

11.4   (*a*) In the block diagram shown in Fig. E11.1, the noise power input of 5 fW is the available power from a

Fig. E11.1

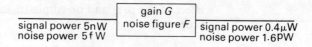

signal power 5nW
noise power 5fW

gain *G*
noise figure *F*

signal power 0.4μW
noise power 1.6PW

matched source at standard temperature. Calculate the
gain and noise figure for the system showing that the
same result for *F* is obtained using the noise-figure
definitions (using the symbols from Section 3.2)

(i) $F = (S/N)_i/(S/N)_o$;

(ii) $F = N_o/GN_i$;

(iii) $F = (S/N)'_o/(S/N)_o$

where $(S/N)'_o$ is the output signal-to-noise ratio if the
system were noise free.
(b) What will be the output signal-to-noise ratio if the input
noise is increased to 25 fW?

11.5   What is the effective input noise temperature of the system in
Exercise 11.4(a) above? Does the value change with the
additional input power in 11.4(b)?

11.6   The signal-to-noise ratio at the output of a domestic
television receiver is to be improved by using a preamplifier
which can be positioned either between the aerial down lead
and the receiver or between the aerial and the down lead.
Using the following data:

receiver noise figure   6 dB;
down-lead power loss   4 dB;
preamplifier gain   20 dB;
preamplifier noise figure   3 dB;

and assuming that the system is matched throughout,
calculate the improvement in receiver-output signal-to-noise
ratio in each case compared with not using the preamplifier.
Which is the more effective position for the preamplifier?

11.7   A receiving system comprises an aerial and a receiver
connected by 12 metres of coaxial cable. Use the following
data to determine the necessary aerial e.m.f. to provide a
signal-to-noise ratio of 50 dB at the receiver output assuming
the whole system is matched to the 75 Ω aerial impedance:

receiver noise figure   4 dB;
aerial effective noise temperature   290 K;
receiver bandwidth   5 MHz;
cable attenuation coefficient   0.5 dB/m.

11.8   A threshold detector in a two-level system is set to detect
signals above 4.6 V for the high state and below 0.38 V for
the low state. If a zero-mean-value 0.1 V r.m.s. noise signal
having a normal distribution is superimposed on nominal
signal levels of +5 V (representing the high state) and 0 V
(representing the low state) determine the probable error rate
if low and high states are equiprobable.

Note: statistical tables are required for this exercise.

11.9   Determine the quantisation signal-to-noise ratio at the output
of a 10 bit analogue-to-digital converter if a sinusoidal input
signal extends over the maximum converter range. How can
the ratio be improved for small signal levels?

11.10 It is required to compare the performance of a.m. and f.m.
receivers in the presence of an interfering signal. The a.m.
receiver uses an envelope detector (Chapter 10) and produces

the same maximum output power when the depth of modulation is 100% as the f.m. receiver does when the f.m. input signal deviation is 4 kHz. Determine the ratio of their output powers when both receivers are tuned to the same carrier signal to which an interfering signal, differing in frequency from the carrier by 3 kHz and at one-tenth of its amplitude, is added.

What would be the effect if the deviation in the f.m. case were increased to 40 kHz?

Section C Devices

12 Semiconductor devices: characteristics and models

The principal learning objectives of this chapter are to:

	Section	Exercise
• state the general properties of semiconductor materials;	1.1	
• explain differing operating conditions for semiconductor devices;	2.1, 2.2	12.1
• describe the characteristics of the junction diode;	3.1, 3.2	12.1
• analyse simple circuits containing diodes by a graphical method;	4.1	12.2
• apply small and large-signal models of the diode;	4.2, 4.3	12.3
• determine the components of voltage and current using a power-series model;	4.4	12.4
• recognise that diodes have capacitance;	4.5	12.5
• state the behaviour of the Zener diode;	4.6	12.6
• explain the essential action of the bipolar junction transistor and determine its currents;	5.1–5.4	12.7
• describe the shape of the transistor characteristics;	5.5–5.7	
• compare graphical methods and the use of a large-signal model in determining transistor behaviour;	6.1–6.4	12.8, 12.9
• discuss the use of small-signal bipolar-transistor models;	7.1, 7.2 and Appendices	
• apply the small-signal models;	7.3	12,10, 12.11
• describe the field-effect principle and the characteristics of the junction field-effect transistor;	8.1–8.3	12.12
• describe the principle and characteristics of the metal-oxide-semiconductor field-effect transistor;	8.4, 8.5	
• apply a graphical method and circuit models to the junction field-effect transistor.	9.1, 9.2	12.13

12.1 Semiconductor materials

12.1.1 Intrinsic and extrinsic materials

The study of electronic devices at the present time is primarily concerned with the study of the movement of charge within solid materials. In earlier days, emphasis was placed on charge movement in a gas or in a vacuum, the basic electronic amplifying and switching device then being the **vacuum tube** or **valve**. Whilst the study of charge movement in vacuum or in gases is, of course, still of importance (for the cathode-ray tube used in video monitors and oscilloscopes, for example), virtually all amplifying and switching devices are now formed from solid materials, mostly based on the element silicon.

The property of silicon which makes it suitable for use in electronic circuits is an atomic structure in which the outermost electrons, the **valence** electrons, form **covalent bonds** between neighbouring atoms, notionally shown in two-dimensional form in Fig. 12.1. The valence electrons are closely tied to the parent atoms with a degree of bonding dependent upon the temperature of the material. Consequently, at low temperatures there are virtually no free electrons which may contribute to conduction and the material may be described as an insulator.

Fig. 12.1 The effect of adding impurities to atoms with different numbers of valence electrons

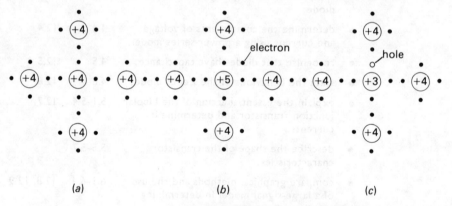

(a)   (b)   (c)

At normal (room) temperatures, a few electrons acquire sufficient energy to break from the bond structure and, in response to an applied potential, a small current will flow, but the material is still substantially an insulator. Because the current increases with the temperature, the material's resistance decreases and it is said to have a negative temperature coefficient of resistance.

Notwithstanding the behavioural properties of the pure semiconductor material (also called **intrinsic** semiconductor material), the important aspect from the microelectronic viewpoint is the ability to modify the conducting properties of the material in a controlled manner. The process is called **doping** and consists of introducing a small amount of material having a different number of valence electrons into the silicon. This is done in two ways: a doping material with five valence electrons (a pentavalent material) permits four bonds to be formed with four surrounding silicon atoms but leaves a fifth electron surplus to the bonding requirements, as represented in Fig. 12.1(*b*). This is a 'free' electron and is available for conduction, the conductivity being controlled by the proportion of pentavalent atoms introduced. The proportion is typically of the order of 1 in 10^8 but, as implied, may be deliberately varied in order to effect the required microelectronic action. Material to which a pentavalent impurity is added is called **n-type semiconductor** material because of the free negatively charged electrons. The other form of doping involves introducing a **trivalent** impurity (three valence electrons). In this case only three covalent bonds can be completed and what is called a **hole** appears in the material structure which, because the material as a whole remains electrically neutral, effectively has a positive charge equal in magnitude to that of the electrons: this is represented in Fig. 12.1(*c*). Furthermore, because a neighbouring electron can fill a hole and thereby leave a new hole, the hole is effectively mobile and behaves as an independent positive-charge carrier. Material doped in this way is called **p-type semiconductor** material.

The difference in the charge flow mechanism in n- and p-type materials manifests itself in differing mobilities (Section 8.2 in Chapter 1) for electrons and holes. For silicon these are, respectively, $\mu_n = 0.13$ in m^2/V-s and $\mu_p = 0.03 \, m^2/V$-s at 300 K. The general term **extrinsic semiconductor** is used to describe the doped material.

12.2 Operating conditions

12.2.1 D.C., large-signal and small-signal operation

The semiconductor devices described in this chapter are all non-linear in the sense that, in general, the current flow between a particular pair of terminals is not proportional to the voltage across them. Fig. 12.2 shows a typical non-linear characteristic which illustrates three identifiable operating modes known as **bias**, **large-signal** and **small-signal operating conditions**. The current i_B and the voltage v_B are intended to represent typical variables.

Fig. 12.2 Bias, large-signal and small-signal operation

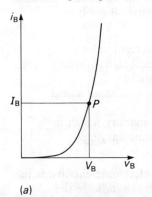

(a)

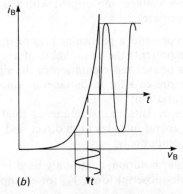

(b)

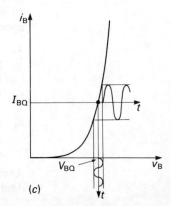

(c)

In Fig. 12.2(*a*), the point *P* represents a specific operating point on the characteristic for which the particular value of v_B (denoted V_B) corresponds to a unique value of current I_B. It is also known as a d.c. operating point. For this non-linear characteristic, the ratio of v_B to i_B is not constant but may be determined either graphically (from the characteristic), from an equation representing the characteristic or from a circuit model. These options are discussed in Section 12.4.

In Fig. 12.2(*b*) a **large-signal** variation in v_B, assumed sinusoidal, results in a corresponding large-signal variation in i_B. These variations are illustrated by the commonly used practice of setting up time axes on the characteristic against the v_B and i_B axes. The current variation is non-sinusoidal as a result of the non-linearity of the curve. Again, specific values may be determined graphically, from an equation or from a model. Often the large-signal variation will start at the origin and may then be referred to as the **total-signal** variation.

Fig. 12.2(*c*) shows the **small-signal** operating condition. Here, a small-amplitude variation (assumed sinusoidal) takes place either side of suitable bias values which in this context are known as **quiescent** values, denoted by V_{BQ} and I_{BQ}. Normally, it is implicitly assumed that there is a linear relationship between the variables in the small-signal case. In other words, doubling the amplitude of the voltage variation will double the amplitude of the current variation, implying that the characteristic is linear over the operating range. The question may well arise in a borderline case whether a given signal should be regarded as a 'small signal', with the consequent implication of linearity, or whether it is a 'large signal'. The answer depends on the context: in virtually all situations the characteristics of a real device will exhibit some non-linearity and a decision must be based on whether a small-signal representation will introduce sufficiently large errors to invalidate the results obtained.

12.2.2 Notation   Previously, lower-case symbols have been used to denote the instantaneous values of time-varying quantities with upper-case symbols for direct (d.c.), r.m.s., phasor and transformed quantities. When dealing with circuits involving combined direct and time-varying quantities, a more exacting notation is required. In the following summary, the variable is assumed to be a voltage, subscripted with the letter B (or b as appropriate):

V_B represents a particular bias or quiescent value;
V_b represents the r.m.s. value of a small-signal variation (or a phasor representation of the signal);
v_b represents the instantaneous value of a small-signal variation;
v_B represents an instantaneous **total quantity** which in general includes both direct and time-varying components.

Another notation, commonly used in electronic circuits, is the double-subscript form, V_{BB} for example, to indicate the magnitude of a d.c. supply voltage connected, in this example, to terminal *B* of the device. In many cases, there will be a passive component between the supply and the terminal but the notation is still used.

12.3 The junction diode

The previous section has outlined how two types of semiconductor material result from doping the intrinsic material; furthermore, the possibility of controlling the impurity concentration (and hence conductivity) has been noted. Using these materials it is possible to manufacture a whole range of microelectronic devices, the first of which to be considered is the junction diode in which adjacent sections of p- and n-type material are arranged to form a **p–n junction**.

12.3.1 The p–n junction diode

With p- and n-type materials on opposite sides of the junction there is a diffusion of charge carriers into the opposing region, holes to the n-type and electrons into the p-type material. This leaves a **depletion region** or **transition region** across the junction. As illustrated in Fig. 12.3, the absence of the mobile charge carriers leaves the fixed ions which, in the p-type material, have a net negative charge and, in the n-type material, a net positive charge. Following the principle established in Chapter 1, the charge sets up an electric field and, hence, a potential difference. The potential difference sets up a drift-current flow and, without an externally applied voltage, equilibrium is established with the drift current balanced by the current due to the diffusion process.

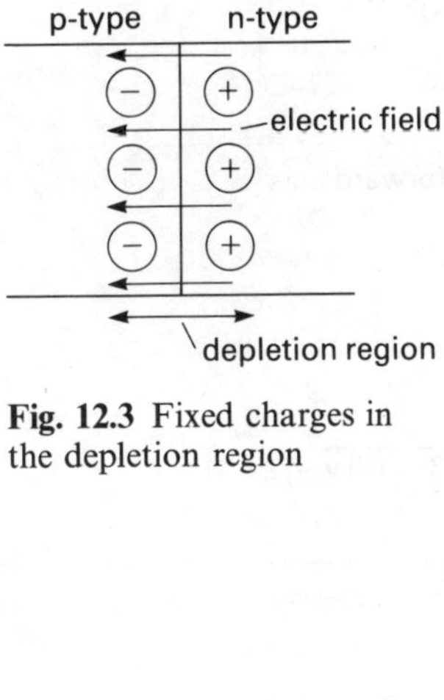

On applying an external voltage the balance is upset and a current will flow in the circuit so formed. A **forward bias**, with the p-type material positive with respect to the n type, results in a relatively large current flow associated with a narrowing of the depletion region. A **reverse bias** on the other hand widens the depletion region and only a very small current flows. It is this property which accounted for the use of the term 'valve' for the thermionic device, diode originally being used adjectivally to signify a two-electrode device.

An expression for the current flow in the junction diode may be deduced from the magnitudes of the carrier densities at the edge of the depletion region. These vary exponentially with the applied voltage so that the total current flow is given by the **diode equation**

$$i = I_s(e^{v/V_T} - 1),$$

where *i* is the current flow; *v* is the bias voltage; I_s is a constant dependent on the doping concentration, the material and temperature; and V_T is a temperature-dependent factor. At room temperature V_T is 25 mV being given by kT/q where *k* is Boltzmann's constant ($= 1.38 \times 10^{-23}$ J/K), *T* is absolute temperature ($= 290$ K at room temperature) and *q* is the charge on the electron ($= 1.6 \times 10^{-19}$ C).

Fig. 12.3 Fixed charges in the depletion region

12.3.2 Diode characteristics

It is implicit in the statement of the diode equation that it applies for both forward and reverse-bias conditions. The reason for the markedly differing characteristics in the two cases may be appreciated by setting v at quite modest positive and negative values. For example, when $v = 0.1\,\text{V}$ (or greater) e^{v/V_T} is much greater than unity and when $v = -0.1\,\text{V}$ (or is more negative) e^{v/V_T} is much less than unity. Thus, for the forward-bias condition, $i \simeq I_s e^{v/V_T}$ and for the reverse-bias condition, $i \simeq -I_s$. It is for this reason that I_s is known as the **reverse saturation current**, being independent of the magnitude of the reverse-bias voltage once this has become more negative than about $-0.1\,\text{V}$.

Fig. 12.4 shows typical characteristics for silicon and germanium devices. Because the reverse current is normally so much smaller than the forward current, different scales have been used. A better approximation to a real diode characteristic is given by introducing a factor η into the equation

$$i = I_s(e^{v/\eta V_T} - 1).$$

η is normally taken to be about unity for germanium diodes and silicon diodes at high current levels and approximately 1.5 to 2.0 for silicon diodes at rated current levels.

Fig. 12.4 Diode characteristics

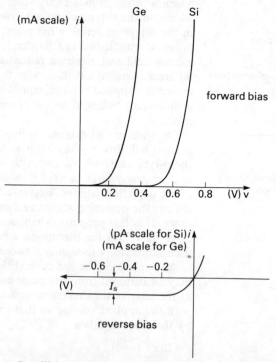

It will be seen that the forward-bias curves exhibit a **threshold** or **cut-in** point, V_γ, at about 0.2 V for germanium and about 0.7 V for silicon. This effect is entirely consistent with the exponential dependence of i upon v, the differences between the threshold values being determined by greatly differing values for I_s for the two materials and the different values of η.

Example 12.1 Use the diode equation to determine values for diode current when a forward-bias voltage is applied:

(i) for a germanium diode for which $I_s = 1\,\mu A$;
(ii) for a silicon diode for which $I_s = 1\,nA$;
(iii) for a silicon diode for which $I_s = 1\,nA$ and $\eta = 2$.

In all cases the reverse current is assumed to be the respective value of I_s. Forward-biased current values are drawn up in Table 12.1. Fig. 12.5 illustrates the forward-bias values.

Table 12.1. *Current values for Example 12.1*

Forward-bias voltage (V)	Current (mA)		
	Ge	Si (n = 1)	Si (n = 2)
0.1	55×10^{-3}	55×10^{-6}	7.4×10^{-6}
0.2	3.0	3.0×10^{-3}	55×10^{-6}
0.3	163	0.16	0.4×10^{-3}
0.4	–	8.89	3.0×10^{-3}
0.5	–	485	22×10^{-3}
0.6	–	–	0.16
0.7	–	–	1.20
0.8	–	–	8.89

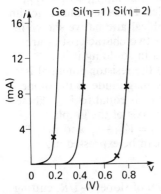

Fig. 12.5 Solution to Example 12.1

The reverse saturation current is strongly temperature dependent, an approximate guide for silicon and germanium devices being a doubling of I_s for a 10 °C temperature rise at around room temperature. Also, the total current i is related to the applied voltage through the temperature-dependent V_T and I_s and it is therefore possible to relate i, v and temperature. In the particular case when i is constant, it is found that v changes with temperature at an approximate rate of $-2\,mV/°C$ at 300 K.

12.4 The p–n junction diode as a circuit element

12.4.1 Graphical analysis

The characteristic equation for the junction diode describes an essentially non-linear device in which the current does not vary proportionately with the voltage across it. Nevertheless, it is resistive in the sense that, as stated, the diode equation contains no capacitive or inductive elements. Section 12.4 describes a capacitive component but this is neglected in the present analysis.

To investigate possible approaches to the circuit representation of the diode, a series diode and resistor are considered. Fig. 12.6 illustrates the arrangement and introduces the circuit symbol for the diode. The arrow head indicates the direction in which current would flow if the diode were forward biased and the bar indicates that only a small leakage current would flow in the opposite direction. To determine the magnitude of the circuit current and the voltages v_D and v_R when a constant voltage V_{DD} is maintained

Fig. 12.6 Voltage across a diode and resistor in series

across the circuit elements by an external source, a possible approach is to write down equations for the devices:

$$i = I_s(e^{v_D/V_T} - 1) \quad \text{for the diode}$$

and

$$v_R = Ri \qquad\qquad \text{for the resistor.}$$

These, together with the voltage relationship $v_D + v_R = V_{DD}$, may be solved for the three variables. However, this is not an attractive proposition and the graphical alternative shown in Fig. 12.7 is generally preferred. The two characteristics are plotted on a single pair of axes, and in so doing it is acknowledged that (as in Fig. 12.6) the resistor potential is raised above the datum level by the magnitude of the diode voltage and that the sum of v_R and v_D is equal to V_{DD}. These conditions are translated onto the x axis of the graph.

The resistor voltage is given by $v_R = V_{DD} - v_D$ and $v_R = Ri$ and, therefore, the resistor current can be expressed as,

$$i = v_R/R = -v_D/R + V_{DD}/R.$$

This is the equation of a straight line of slope, $-1/R$, cutting the i axis at V_{DD}/R and the v axis (when $i = 0$) at $v_D = V_{DD}$. It is known as a **load line**, the point of intersection with the diode characteristic being the operating point Q. Although normally drawn in this way, the order of circuit connection has no bearing on the construction of the diagram and the inset of Fig. 12.7 is an equally valid construction.

Load-line methods are useful in providing a picture of the operating point (as well as the effect of variations either side of that point) in relation to the complete characteristic of the device and some useful results may be obtained. However, they become increasingly difficult to handle as the circuit becomes more complex and the amount of information they are able to yield without difficulty can be limited. Frequently, the use of diode circuit models is a more convenient method and these are discussed in the following subsections.

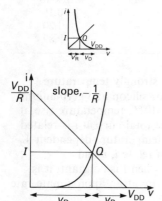

Fig. 12.7 Load-line construction, with alternative form in inset

12.4.2 Small-signal model of the diode

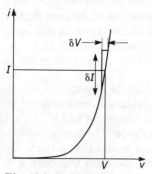

Fig. 12.8 Small-signal variations superimposed on diode characteristic

In many applications it is only necessary to determine the ratio of small changes in diode current in response to small changes in voltage. Fig. 12.8 shows a small change in current δI resulting from a small change in voltage δV about a previously established voltage V. It will be seen that the ratio of δI to δV is the slope of the characteristic over the operating region, it being implicit that the slope is constant over this range. Taking the diode voltage–current characteristic to be given by: $i \simeq I_s e^{v/\eta V_T}$ where v is a forward-bias voltage,

$$di/dv = \frac{I_s}{\eta V_T} e^{v/\eta V_T} = i/\eta V_T.$$

This is the slope of the characteristic whose reciprocal is the **slope resistance** r_d, given by

$$r_d = dv/di = \eta V_T/i.$$

Substituting values at a temperature of 290 K, $V_T = 25\,\mathrm{mV}$ and with $\eta = 2$, $r_d = 50/I\,\Omega$, where I is a particular value of i (see Fig. 12.8) and is expressed in milliamperes.

12.4.3 A piecewise-linear large-signal model

If it is required to determine the approximate behaviour of a diode across which there are relatively large voltage excursions from the origin (of the order of half a volt, for example), the piecewise linear model may be used. The technique combines aspects of the graphical and the small-signal methods, the diode characteristic being represented by straight-line approximations to the actual characteristic. Fig. 12.9(a) shows a possible piecewise linearisation. For voltages up to the threshold level, the current is assumed to be zero; beyond, it is assumed to increase linearly. The slope of the linear section is given by the slope resistance at the centre of the range of current over which the device is to be operated; if the range is not precisely known, an estimate may be made as in Example 12.2. Coarser approximations are shown in Fig. 12.9(b) and (c). In (b), the slope resistance is assumed to be zero and this may be used where the diode is connected in series with a resistor whose resistance is very much greater than the slope resistance. In (c), the crudest representation, the diode is shown as an ideal rectifier, behaving as a short circuit in the forward-biased condition and an open circuit in the reverse direction. It is this circuit representation which is sometimes implied by the term, **ideal diode**: this may be used in situations where the circuit voltages are well in excess of the threshold voltage.

The three linearisations in Fig. 12.9 suggest the possibility of representing the diode by means of combinations of linear circuit elements as shown in Fig. 12.10(a), (b) and (c). These correspond to Fig. 12.9(a), (b) and (c). The ideal diode is shown as an unshaded version of the circuit symbol previously used for the real device. If relevant, the reverse saturation current can be shown as a constant-current source of magnitude I_s.

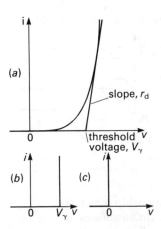

Fig. 12.9 Linear representations of a diode characteristic

Fig. 12.10 Diode models

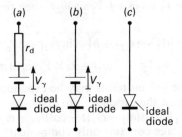

(a)   (b)   (c)

Example 12.2   *Sketch the diode-voltage, resistor-voltage and circuit-current waveforms for the circuit shown in Fig. 12.11 when v_{in} is a sinusoid of 2 V peak amplitude. Assume*

(i) the model in Fig. 12.10(c), and
(ii) the model in Fig. 12.10(a) with $V_\gamma = 0.7\,V$ and an appropriate value for r_d.

(i) With zero voltage drop across the diode for all current values, the full input voltage will appear across the load resistor during

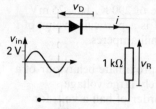

Fig. 12.11 Circuit for Example 12.2

Fig. 12.12 Solution for Example 12.2

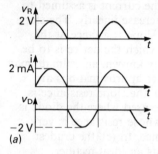

(a)

positive half-cycles of the input. During negative half-cycles, the diode has infinite resistance and no current flows, the input voltage appearing across the diode itself. The waveforms are shown in Fig. 12.12(a).

(ii) The equivalent circuit is shown in Fig. 12.12(b). The value of the diode slope resistance, r_d, is shown as $50\,\Omega$ on the basis of an estimated mean operating current of about $1\,mA$ and in accordance with the discussion in Section 12.4.2. In the forward-biased case (v_{in} positive), the voltage appearing across the load resistor is now $(v_{in} - 0.7)\,V$, giving a peak current of $(2.0 - 0.7)/1050 = 1.24\,mA$ and a peak voltage across the load resistor of $1.24\,V$. As shown in Fig. 12.12(c), the diode does not conduct until v_{in} exceeds $0.7\,V$. When v_{in} is instantaneously less positive than $0.7\,V$, negligible current flows and the entire input voltage appears across the diode.

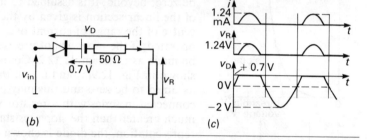

(b)

(c)

12.4.4 A power-series model

The non-linear voltage–current relationship which the junction diode possesses is, in most circumstances, a disadvantage. However, there are applications where the non-linearity can be used to advantage, for example, to generate harmonics or sum and difference-frequency components. The way in which this may come about may be explained by expressing the diode voltage–current relationship (around a suitable operating point) by the power series:

$$i = bv + cv^2 + dv^3 + \cdots,$$

where b, c and d are constants. If, for example, the voltage were the sum of two sinusoidal voltages, $v = V_1 \sin \omega_1 t + V_2 \sin \omega_2 t$, then the current would be given by,

$$i = bV_1 \sin \omega_1 t + bV_2 \sin \omega_2 t + cV_1^2 \sin^2 \omega_1 t$$
$$+ cV_2^2 \sin^2 \omega_2 t + 2cV_1 V_2 \sin \omega_1 t \sin \omega_2 t + \cdots.$$

The $\sin^2 \omega t$ terms may be expanded to give $(1 - \cos 2\omega t)/2$ whilst the product term gives $cV_1 V_2(\cos(\omega_1 - \omega_2)t - \cos(\omega_1 + \omega_2)t)$ and thus, although the voltage contains only components at frequencies ω_1 and ω_2, the current contains components at frequencies, ω_1, ω_2, $(\omega_1 - \omega_2)$, $(\omega_1 + \omega_2)$, $2\omega_1$, and $2\omega_2$. Had the dv^3 term been included in the expansion, many more frequency components would have appeared in the current expression (at frequencies, $3\omega_1$, $3\omega_2$, $2\omega_1 \pm \omega_2$, etc.), and so on for higher powers in the series. In order to make use of the frequency components generated by the non-linearity, it is normally necessary to use a frequency-selective network to pick out the required component. For example, for use as a **harmonic**

generator (for which only a single sinusoidal voltage is required), the frequency selective network would be a high-Q tuned circuit, tuned to the required harmonic frequency. For use as a **frequency changer** or **mixer**, the tuned circuit may be set so as to select the difference-frequency component between the two input signals at frequencies ω_1 and ω_2. If on the other hand it were required to linearly process a signal containing two or more frequency components, any circuit elements having a non-linear characteristic would introduce unwanted frequency components, resulting in a particular form of distortion known as **intermodulation distortion**.

12.4.5 Diode capacitances

When dealing with high-frequency signals it may become necessary to take diode capacitances into account. These are the **transition** or **junction capacitance** C_j associated with the charges in the depletion region, and the **diffusion capacitance** C_d, associated with the charges outside the region. The former predominates under reverse-bias conditions. The transition capacitance can be estimated from the width of the depletion region shown as $l_n + l_p$ in Fig. 12.13. For a small increase in the reverse-bias voltage the lengths l_p and l_n would increase by small amounts δl_n and δl_p. The incremental charges contained in the incremental lengths are separated by width $l \ (= l_n + l_p)$ because the region expands at its outer edges and it is therefore possible to define an incremental capacitance $\delta q / \delta v$ as

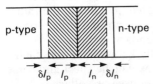

Fig. 12.13 Depletion-region capacitance

$$\frac{\varepsilon \times \text{cross-sectional area } A}{\text{width } l},$$

just as for the parallel-plate capacitor in Chapter 1. Thus, $C_j = \varepsilon A / l$ where A is the cross-sectional area of the depletion region seen from the side in Fig. 12.13. Analysis shows the width to be approximately proportional to the square root of the total junction voltage and the capacitance is therefore inversely proportional to the square root of this voltage; it is this non-linear relationship between the charge and the potential difference that makes it necessary to work in terms of $\delta q / \delta v$ rather than simply q/v to determine the capacitance.

As with the non-linearity in the diode's voltage–current characteristic, the presence of the junction capacitance is generally unhelpful and unwanted. However, there is an application in the **variable-capacitance diode**, manufactured to exploit the dependence of capacitance on (reverse) bias voltage. In a typical application, the diode is connected in parallel with the main tuning capacitance of an inductance–capacitance oscillator in order that bias variations across it shall alter its capacitance and, hence, the oscillator's operating frequency. Except for small changes, neither the bias-capacitance nor the capacitance-frequency relationships are linear.

12.4.6 Reverse-bias breakdown

Very high-value electric fields can exist within the narrow depletion region and these can lead to a breakdown of the diode in which the current increases very rapidly for only a very small voltage change. Two breakdown mechanisms have been identified and these are known as the **avalanche** and **Zener** effects; neither is irreversible in the sense that the device will behave quite normally once the biasing condition causing breakdown is removed. Damage may, however, result from a secondary cause, such as overheating when a large current flows.

The avalanche effect is a cumulative effect in which a fast-moving carrier, accelerated by a large electric field across the depletion region, dislodges an electron from a covalent bond. Given an electric field of the order of 10^7 V/m, the effect becomes cumulative, resulting in a very large increase in reverse-bias current for a very small increase in voltage.

The Zener effect occurs at even higher field intensities where electrons may be removed from their covalent bonds simply by the force of the field: it is not due to collisions as in the avalanche effect. Zener breakdown may occur before avalanche breakdown in devices which have a very narrow depletion region (i.e. are very heavily doped), producing intense electric fields of the order of 5×10^7 V/m at relatively low bias voltages. The Zener effect predominates in the thin transition region because the carriers do not have time to produce a significant number of secondary carriers.

All breakdown diodes are generally known as **Zener diodes** even though some operate with the avalanche effect and some with the Zener effect. They are widely used as voltage-reference devices as illustrated in Chapter 13.

12.5 The bipolar transistor: operating principles and characteristics

12.5.1 The component parts of the transistor

The principles of the p–n junction introduced in Section 12.3 are used as the basis for a discussion of the operating principles of the bipolar transistor. Fig. 12.14 shows an **n–p–n bipolar junction transistor** (BJT) manufactured by the **planar** process in which a lightly doped section of n-type material (the residue of which subsequently forms the *collector*) has a controlled amount of p-type impurity diffused into it to form a predominantly p-type region known as the **base**. A mask is used to control the distribution. After remasking, there is a further diffusion of n-type impurity to form a highly doped n-type region known as the **emitter**. The result of these impurity diffusions is shown (but not to scale) in the diagram together with an insulating layer of silicon dioxide and the contacts to each of the three regions. Although reference is made principally to this n–p–n device in this chapter, p–n–p-type transistors are also manufactured.

12.5.2 Essential transistor operation

It will be appreciated from Fig. 12.14 that the transistor is basically a two-junction device and, in normal operation, the emitter-base junction is forward biased and the collector-base junction reversed biased. Fig. 12.15 shows the important components of current flow: electrons are injected from the

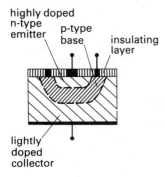

highly doped
n-type
emitter   p-type
base   insulating
layer

lightly
doped
collector

Fig. 12.14 Bipolar transistor construction

Fig. 12.15 Essential bipolar transistor operation

heavily doped emitter into the base as a result of the forward bias. The base region is relatively thin so that, once in the base, nearly all the electrons diffuse across it and across the reverse-biased collector-base junction and thence to the collector contact. A very small proportion combine with holes in the base (typically of the order of 1%) so that there is a small current flow in the base lead to supply this recombination. In effect, there is a substantial current flowing in the emitter lead (say, 1 mA), most of which appears at the collector terminal (say, 0.99 mA) with the remainder (0.01 mA) flowing in the base lead. Because the ratio of the current in the collector to that in the base remains substantially constant over a range of operating conditions (being determined by the construction of the transistor), it is, evidently, possible to control a relatively large collector current by means of relatively small base-current variations. Moreover, by inserting a resistor in the collector lead, the collector-current variations would cause relatively large voltage variations across it, again controlled by the small base-current changes.

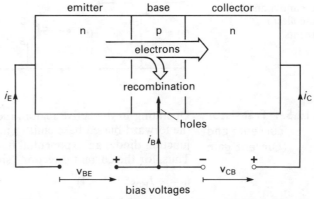

Because the current flow in the forward-biased emitter-base junction is, in turn, dependent on the bias voltage, this may be regarded as the controlling factor, small changes in emitter-base voltage causing significant collector-current changes and hence voltage changes across a resistor in the collector lead. Whether base current or base-emitter voltage are regarded as independent variables, the resulting collector-current changes are virtually independent of the collector-base voltage; it is only necessary to hold the collector-base junction in a reverse-biased condition.

12.5.3 Operating modes

The previous section referred to the transistor operated with the base-emitter junction forward biased and the collector-base junction reverse biased. This is one of four possible operating regions summarised in Fig. 12.16 as the **active**, **saturation**, **cut-off** and **reverse-active** regions according to bias conditions at the junctions. It is to the active region to which most discussion refers because this is the normal operating region for linear operation. Nevertheless, operation in other regions does occur.

Allied to the operating region is the connection mode of

Fig. 12.16 Operating regions for bipolar transistors

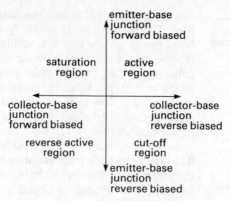

the transistor. Three modes are possible for this three-terminal device and these are referred to as the **common-base**, **common-emitter** and **common-collector** modes as illustrated in Fig. 12.17(*a*), (*b*) and (*c*) respectively. The diagrams also illustrate the circuit symbol for the n–p–n device. The emitter arrow head is reversed for the p–n–p transistor.

Fig. 12.17 Common-base, common-emitter and common-collector arrangements

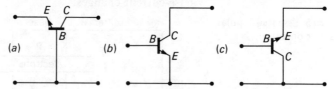

12.5.4 Transistor currents and current gain

Operating in the active region, the current flowing towards the forward-biased base-emitter junction is (as for the junction diode) an exponential function of the bias voltage. Thus, for the current directions shown in Fig. 12.15,

$$i_E = -I_{E0}(e^{v_{BE}/V_T} - 1)$$

$$\simeq -I_{E0}e^{v_{BE}/V_T},$$

where v_{BE} is the base-emitter voltage, V_T is as defined for the diode (Section 3.1) and I_{E0} is the reverse saturation current with the collector open circuited ($i_C = 0$).

As described in Section 12.5.2, most of the emitter current passes on through the base into the collector. The proportion reaching the collector terminal is quantified by the **common-base short-circuit current gain** α so that, for the current direction shown in Fig. 12.15,

$$i_C = -\alpha i_E.$$

Because the collector-base junction is reverse biased there is, in addition to $-\alpha i_E$, a small reverse saturation current I_{C0} resulting in

$$i_C = -\alpha i_E + I_{C0}.$$

The transistor is often operated in the common-emitter mode and it is convenient to define a **common-emitter short-circuit current gain**, β, relating base and collector currents:

$$i_C = -\alpha i_E + I_{C0}.$$

But, in Fig. 12.15,

$$i_E = -(i_C + i_B).$$

$$\therefore \quad i_C = \alpha(i_C + i_B) + I_{C0}.$$

Rearranging,

$$i_C = \frac{\alpha}{1-\alpha} i_B + \frac{I_{C0}}{1-\alpha}$$

$$= \beta i_B + (\beta + 1)I_{C0} \quad \text{where } \beta = \alpha/(1-\alpha).$$

Values for α and β vary from transistor to transistor, with operating conditions and with temperature. Typical values for α lie in the range 0.95 to 0.998 with corresponding β values varying from 20 to 500. It will be seen that, although the range of values for α may seem rather small, the corresponding range for β is very significant. The variation of α and β with temperature and operating conditions is dependent on several factors; a fuller discussion is provided in the references to further reading.

12.5.5 Base-width modulation or Early effect

The previous section has presented a simplified view of the various currents flowing in the bipolar transistor from which a general impression of the behaviour of an actual device may be formed. A number of assumptions are implied in the analysis, including uniform cross-sectional areas, abrupt junctions and neglect of potential drops across the bulk p and n regions. However, there is one second-order effect, which although not immediately apparent, does have a direct bearing on the shape of the characteristics. This is the **base-width modulation** effect.

It was previously assumed that variations in the collector-base potential had no effect on the transistor currents provided that the junction was reverse biased. However, bias variations have the effect of varying the width of the depletion region; an increase in collector-base voltage increases the collector-base depletion width and thus reduces the effective width of the base. The effect on the transistor's characteristics is described in the following sections.

12.5.6 Common-base characteristics

Fig. 12.18(a) shows the circuit configuration with relevant voltages and currents. Fig. 12.18(b) illustrates the input characteristic for a typical silicon device with its exponentially increasing current flow across the forward-biased junction and, as discussed above, a second-order dependence on the collector-base voltage. Fig. 12.18(c) shows a set of output

Fig. 12.18 Common-base arrangement with input and output characteristics

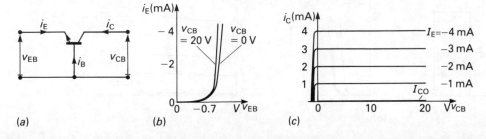

(a)

(b)

(c)

characteristics. The collector-current is virtually independent of v_{CB} as indicated by the almost horizontal characteristics; the base-width modulation effect is barely perceptible on this scale.

Reducing v_{CB} to zero has negligible effect on the collector current: in fact, to reduce the collector current to zero, the collector-base junction must be slightly forward biased, taking the transistor into the saturation region. The reverse saturation I_{C0} is also shown on the characteristics but, again, the magnitude for the silicon transistor is such that it can barely be seen on this scale.

12.5.7 The common-emitter characteristics

Since the base and emitter currents remain in approximately fixed proportion, the common-emitter input characteristic (Fig. 12.19(b)) has the same general shape as that for the common-base mode, although the current scale is much reduced. Increasing the collector-emitter voltage shifts the characteristic slightly to the right because the base-width modulation effect has the effect of reducing the base current for a given value of base-emitter voltage. There is a marked change in the $v_{CE} = 0$ characteristic where the transistor is operated in the saturation region, as explained below.

The output characteristics are also similar to those for the common-base mode but with two significant differences. The first is due to the base-width modulation effect which causes the characteristics to have a more pronounced positive slope: because narrowing the base width causes an increase in i_E (for a given value of v_{BE}) and reduces i_B for a given value of i_E, the fixed-i_B characteristics show a significant increase in i_E, and hence i_C, with increasing v_{CE}. In effect, the small increase in α results in a significant increase in β. The second major difference is the general shift to the right with the transistor entering the saturation region for positive values of v_{CE}. From Fig. 12.19(a) v_{CE} is the sum of v_{BE} and v_{CB}, and since v_{BE} remains nominally constant for a given value of i_B or i_C (Fig. 12.19(b)), the characteristics plotted for variations of v_{CE} resemble those for variations of v_{CB} but shifted to the right by the value of v_{BE}. Thus, for the n–p–n transistor, the saturation region occurs for low positive values of v_{CE} and the start of the saturation region is considered to occur at the knee of the characteristics; typically, $v_{CE_{sat}}$ is taken to be about 0.2 V for silicon and about 0.1 V for germanium, although, as the characteristics show, the values vary with collector current.

Fig. 12.19 Common-emitter arrangement with input and output characteristics

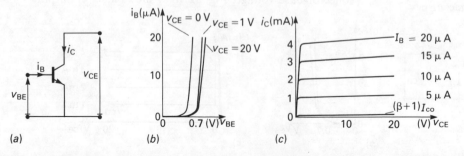

(a)

(b)

(c)

For v_{CE} values to the left of $v_{CE_{sat}}$ in Fig. 12.19(c) any increase in base current does not cause any increase in the collector current and this explains why the term 'saturated' is used.

12.6 Biasing the bipolar transistor

12.6.1 Graphical methods and models

This section is concerned with establishing bipolar-transistor operating conditions with direct (non-time-varying) currents and voltages at the three terminals. The setting up of these conditions may be an end in itself or it may be a prerequisite to operating the transistor in the small-signal mode. In either case, the procedure is essentially the same.

As for the p–n junction diode, three options are available; solution of equations representing the behaviour of the transistor and the associated passive components, a graphical approach using the device's characteristics and the use of circuit models with the circuit-analysis techniques developed in previous chapters. The solution of equations is not a very attractive proposition but the graphical and model approaches can realistically be implemented and these are included even though the graphical method has its limitations. The object, therefore, is to employ manufacturers' data in the form of characteristic curves or circuit-model parameters in order to establish specified operating conditions.

12.6.2 A total-quantity or large-signal model

This subsection presents a circuit model of the transistor which, if it were to replace the transistor terminal for terminal within a wider circuit, would cause substantially the same total currents and voltages to exist in the remaining circuit elements. The degree to which this is true depends, in general, on the complexity of the model, but that shown should provide sufficient accuracy for the majority of applications. Indeed, there is virtue in employing a simple model because it permits a more intuitive appreciation of the behaviour of circuits. Because the model applies for total quantities, in the absence of a time-varying component it can be used for direct (bias) quantities alone; used in this way it is also referred to as a d.c. model.

Using the current-transfer ratios α and β the alternative models shown in Fig. 12.20 may be deduced. In Fig. 12.20(a), the emitter current is regarded as the independent variable and therefore the circuit is suited to the common-base mode of connection whereas in Fig. 12.20(b) the base current is the independent variable and the circuit is suited to the common-emitter mode.

Both models are approximate, ignoring second-order effects such as reverse currents and base-width modulation. More complex models, although more difficult to apply, may be necessary in situations where second-order effects are important.

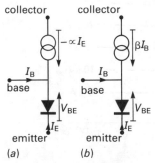

Fig. 12.20 Alternative bipolar transistor models

12.6.3 Modelling and graphical methods compared

This section discusses the way in which suitable bias currents and voltages can be established in a simple common-emitter circuit operating from a single d.c. power-supply unit. The behaviour of the circuit is examined through a circuit model and by using a set of characteristics. The circuit arrangement is shown in Fig. 12.21(*a*) and the corresponding circuit model in Fig. 12.21(*b*). With V_{BE} given as 0.65 V in this case the base voltage is 0.65 V above earth and the base current is then $(10 - 0.65)/10^6 = 9.35\,\mu A$. With $\beta = 200$ the collector current will be $200 \times 9.35 \times 10^{-6} = 1.87$ mA. With this current flowing in the 2.2 kΩ load resistor, the potential drop across it will be $2.2 \times 1.87 = 4.1$ V. Subtracting this from the supply voltage of 10 V, makes the collector voltage 5.9 V with respect to earth (ground).

Fig. 12.21 Use of a transistor model

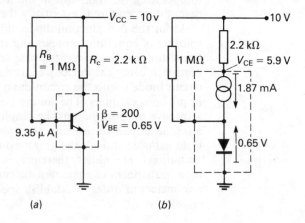

(a) (b)

The graphical method involves locating the operating points on the common-emitter input and output characteristics (shown in Fig. 12.22(*a*) and (*b*) respectively) which, within the limits of drawing accuracy, are consistent with the numerical data given for the circuit model. The graphical construction used in Fig. 12.22 is the load-line method previously used in Section 12.4.1 to predict the operating conditions for a diode-resistor combination. In fact, Fig. 12.22(*a*) is almost identical to Fig. 12.7 and it is therefore

Fig. 12.22 Load-line construction on transistor characteristics

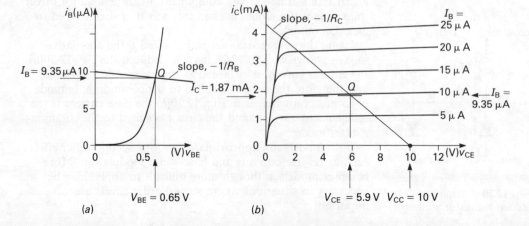

(a) (b)

simply noted here that the slope of the load line in Fig. 12.22(a) is $-1/R_B$ and that in Fig. 12.22(b) is $-1/R_C$. The lines are drawn between the point $V_{CC} = 10$ V on the voltage axis and the points V_{CC}/R_B ($= 10\,\mu$A) and V_{CC}/R_C ($= 4.5$ mA) on the respective current axes.

It is common practice to draw only the output-characteristic load line because, as assumed for the circuit model, under normal operating conditions the base-emitter voltage is substantially independent of i_B and the base current can be calculated with a reasonable degree of accuracy using the model technique.

Although it provides detailed information on large-signal operation, the graphical approach has limitations as a general method of transistor-circuit analysis. Not least is the need to have a full set of transistor characteristics available. Even if this is the case, the set will normally comprise typical characteristics, representing the behaviour of the 'average' transistor of a given type; variations from one device to another can be inconvenient to accommodate. Another problem is dealing with circuit configurations other than the standard form shown in Fig. 12.21. Example 12.3 illustrates a circuit which differs from this standard form and which is probably more easily handled using a circuit model.

12.6.4 Two examples of transistor biasing

Both examples refer to a circuit configuration differing from the basic common-emitter arrangement in Fig. 12.21. In Example 12.3, an additional resistor is added in the emitter lead and the problem is to determine currents and voltages for given component values. In Example 12.4 only the emitter resistor is used, resulting in a common-collector or **emitter-follower** arrangement; in this case the object is to determine the component values starting with the emitter voltage and current. In the second example, the model is not explicitly drawn but, as in normal practice, its properties are used in the calculation.

Example 12.3

Use a total-quantity model to determine the direct voltages and currents in the circuit shown in Fig. 12.23(a).

Fig. 12.23 Circuit and circuit model for Example 12.3

The model is shown in Fig. 12.23(b). If the base-earth potential is V_B, the voltage across R_E is $V_B - 0.65$ V and, because

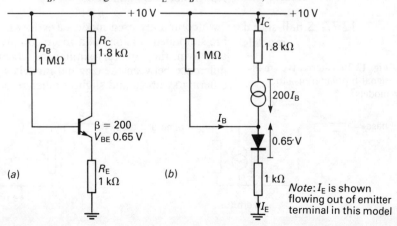

I_E ($\simeq I_C = 200 I_B$) flows through this resistor, this voltage is also $R_E I_C = 1 \times 10^3 \times 200 I_B$. Hence $V_B - 0.65 = 2 \times 10^5 \times I_B$. But, V_B and I_B are also related through $10 - V_B = 10^6 I_B$ (because $R_B = 1\,\text{M}\Omega$) and, solving the equations, $I_B = 7.8\,\mu\text{A}$ and $V_B = 2.2\,\text{V}$. Thus, the collector current $I_C = 200 \times 7.8 \times 10^{-6} = 1.5\,\text{mA}$, the voltage across $R_C = 1.8 \times 1.56 = 2.8\,\text{V}$ and the transistor collector-emitter voltage $V_{CE} = 10 - 2.8 - 2.2 = 5.0\,\text{V}$.

Example 12.4

For the circuit in Fig. 12.24 determine the resistance values required to set the emitter-earth voltage at 5 V when the collector current is nominally 2 mA and $\beta = 200$. Use preferred values.

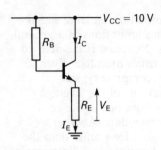

Fig. 12.24 Circuit for Example 12.4

Because the voltage across R_E and the current through it are specified, $R_E = 5/(2 \times 10^{-3}) = 2.5\,\text{k}\Omega$. The nearest preferred value is $2.7\,\text{k}\Omega$. Because $200 I_B$ is to be 2 mA, $I_B = 10\,\mu\text{A}$ and this current flows in R_B. The voltage across R_B is $10 - 0.65 - 5 = 4.35\,\text{V}$ and hence $R_B = 4.35/10 \times 10^{-6} = 0.435\,\text{M}\Omega$. The nearest preferred value is $470\,\text{k}\Omega$.

Rechecking the voltages and the currents with the preferred values:

$$I_B = (10 - 0.65 - V_E)/470 \times 10^3 \quad \text{and} \quad V_E = 200 \times 2.7 \times 10^3 I_B.$$

Solving, $I_B = 9.3\,\mu\text{A}$ and $V_E = 5.0\,\text{V}$. The collector current is now $200 \times 9.3 \times 10^{-6} = 1.85\,\text{mA}$ (or $5.0/2.7 = 1.85\,\text{mA}$) which is within 10% of the design figure.

12.7 Small-signal operation

12.7.1 Introduction

Small-signal operation refers to small, usually sinusoidal, signal variations either side of a quiescent point as illustrated in Fig. 12.2(c). As discussed in that section, linearity is implicit in the small-signal assumption.

Comments similar to those made concerning complexity of the total-quantity model apply here also. A simple model is often adequate, certainly for an initial investigation, and has the virtue of ease of both application and understanding. This section is therefore concerned primarily with simplified small-signal models, the full models being described in Appendices 12A and 12B.

12.7.2 Small-signal models

Fig. 12.25 Alternative small-signal bipolar transistor models

Two commonly used models are drawn in Fig. 12.25. Both are simplified versions of a more comprehensive model and, as drawn, they are very similar in appearance; it is the difference between the original models which account for the differing symbols and slightly different configurations.

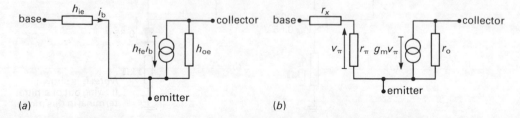

(a)   (b)

In Appendix 12A, the **hybrid-parameter model** treats the transistor as a two-port network and a given set of parameters is a snap shot of the terminal behaviour of the device in given operating conditions and, by definition, the parameters are measurable at the terminals. This does not preclude the possibility of the parameters varying with operating conditions and indeed they do vary with bias conditions, temperature and with frequency. For example, at high frequencies the hybrid parameters may be complex, taking account of the reactive elements in the circuit. The simplified model is shown in Fig. 12.25(a).

In contrast, the **transconductance model** uses a voltage-dependent current source $g_m v_\pi$, where g_m is the **transconductance** of the transistor. It has its roots in the **hybrid-π model** used to describe the high-frequency behaviour of the transistor and drawn in Appendix 12B. The model is built up through a consideration of the physical properties of the device rather than through the two-port network concept associated with the hybrid parameters. The simplified model is shown in Fig. 12.25(b).

Both models represent the same device and there is equivalence between them. Relationships are quoted in Appendix 12B but, subject to the further simplification in Fig. 12.25, the following may be used.

$$h_{ie} = r_x + r_\pi, \quad h_{fe} = g_m r_\pi \quad \text{and} \quad h_{oe} = 1/r_o.$$

Furthermore, with r_x neglected (and it is significantly smaller than r_π) the models become identical with

$$h_{ie} = r_\pi, \quad h_{fe} = g_m h_{ie} \quad \text{and} \quad h_{oe} = 1/r_o.$$

A parameter often used in association with these parameters is r_e, given by dv_{BE}/di_E. This is the slope of the v_{BE}/i_E characteristic, and following the same procedure as that used in Section 12.4.2, is approximately $25/I_E\,\Omega$ (I_E is a specific value of the emitter current in mA) at a temperature of 290 K. Furthermore, with $i_C \simeq i_E$ and with $g_m \simeq di_C/dv_{BE}$, $g_m = 1/r_e = 40 I_E$ mS, with I_E in mA. Finally, with $h_{fe} = g_m r_\pi$, $r_\pi \simeq h_{fe} r_e$. To illustrate these relationships, a transistor having $h_{fe} = 200$ and with an emitter bias current of 2 mA, would have $r_e = 12.5\,\Omega$, $g_m = 80$ mS and $r_\pi \simeq h_{ie} = 2.5$ kΩ.

12.7.3 Applications of the models

In order to apply the models, the transistor is replaced by the model and all other circuit components by their small-signal equivalent values. In particular, the d.c. power-supply unit is replaced by a short circuit on the basis that its source resistance is very small in comparison with other circuit impedances and that the small-signal component of voltage at its terminals is therefore negligible: the procedures are illustrated in the following example.

Example 12.5   *Determine the small-signal voltage gain and input and output impedances of the circuit shown in Fig. 12.26(a) using the simplified hybrid-parameter equivalent circuit and taking $h_{ie} = 2.7\,k\Omega$, $h_{fe} = 200$ and $h_{oe} = 0$.*

The equivalent circuit is shown in Fig. 12.26(b) with a Thévenin-

Fig. 12.26 Circuit and small-signal model for Example 12.5

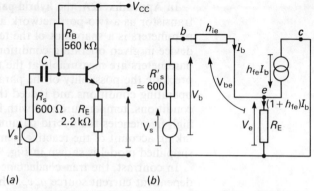

(a) (b)

equivalent source replacing V_s, R_s and R_B. It is assumed that the capacitor has negligible reactance at the operating frequency. Using the Kirchhoff voltage law, $V_b = h_{ie}I_b + R_E(1 + h_{fe})I_b$, and, since $V_e = R_E(1 + h_{fe})I_b$, the voltage gain,

$$\frac{V_e}{V_b} = \frac{R_E(1 + h_{fe})}{h_{ie} + R_E(1 + h_{fe})}.$$

Substituting values, the voltage gain is $+0.994$. The $+$ sign indicates that the emitter and the base-emitter voltages are in phase.

The input impedance at the base, V_b/I_b, is $h_{ie} + R_E(1 + h_{fe})$. Substituting values, the input impedance is $445\,\text{k}\Omega$. If R_B is included, the input impedance falls to $445 \times 560/(445 + 560) = 248\,\text{k}\Omega$.

The output impedance between emitter and earth is the ratio of the open-circuit voltage (i.e. V_e for the circuit as shown) and the current which would flow in a short circuit placed across the emitter terminal and earth. Since the value of V_{be} will be different in these two conditions, it is necessary to express both in terms of V_s': for the circuit as drawn,

$$V_s' = I_b(R_s' + h_{ie} + R_E(1 + h_{fe}))$$

from which, substituting values, $I_b = V_s'/446 \times 10^3$. But, $V_e = V_s' - I_b(h_{ie} + R_s')$ and hence $V_e = 0.993V_s'$. In the short-circuit condition, $I_b = V_s'/(R_s' + h_{ie})$ and hence the short-circuit current is

$$V_s'(1 + h_{fe})/(R_s' + h_{ie}).$$

Substituting values, $I_{sc} = 6.09 \times 10^{-2}V_s'$. The output impedance is then

$$V_e/I_{sc} = 0.993V_s'/6.09 \times 10^{-2}V_s' = 16.3\,\Omega.$$

Example 12.6 *Determine values for the bias currents and voltages in the circuit shown in Fig. 12.27 and then use a transconductance model to obtain an approximate value for the small-signal voltage gain. Assume that under the operating conditions $r_x \ll r_\pi \ll 1\,\text{M}\Omega$ and $r_o \gg 2.2\,\text{k}\Omega$.*

Fig. 12.27 Circuit and small-signal model for Example 12.6

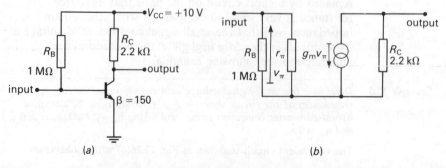

(a) (b)

To determine the bias values, assume $V_{BE} = 0.7$ V. Then, base bias current is $(10 - 0.7)/1 \times 10^6 = 9.3\ \mu\text{A}$, and the collector bias current is $9.3 \times 10^{-6} \times 150 = 1.40$ mA. The small-signal transconductance is then given by $40 \times 1.40 = 56$ mS.

The small-signal model is shown in Fig. 12.27(b). In this model the input voltage is also v_π and the output voltage is $-g_m v_\pi R_C$ or $-123v_\pi$, resulting in a voltage gain of -123.

12.8 Field-effect transistors: principles and characteristics

12.8.1 The field-effect principle

The output characteristics of the field-effect transistor (FET) bear some resemblance to those of the bipolar transistor but the operating principles differ significantly. In a simplistic view of the FET it may be considered as a device in which a current flow along a channel of semiconductor material is controlled by applying an electric field across the channel (Fig. 12.28). Current control is effected by varying the potential difference across a p–n junction. This controls the width of the depletion region and, because current flow is proportional to the cross-sectional area of the region, also the magnitude of the current. The relationship between voltage and current is not linear.

In the arrangement shown in Fig. 12.29(a) a p-type silicon substrate has an n-type channel set into it. Into the channel is set a heavily doped p-type **gate** (indicated p$^+$). Connections are made at the ends of the n channel and these are known as the **source** and **drain**. This forms the basis of the **junction field-effect transistor** (JFET) and the next section develops this theme further to outline the operational behaviour of this device. However, particularly with respect to integrated-circuit manufacture, the **metal-oxide-semiconductor transistor** (MOSFET) is of great importance and the JFET discussion is therefore followed by a consideration of the various forms of MOSFET.

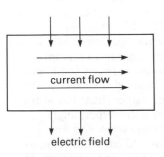

Fig. 12.28 Essential field-effect action

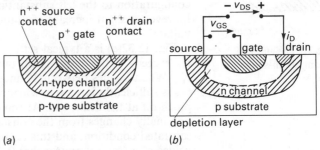

Fig. 12.29 JFET arrangement and the effect of a small bias voltage

12.8.2 JFET operating principle for small drain-source voltages

The polarities of the externally applied voltages for the n-channel JFET are shown in Fig. 12.29(b). It will be seen that the drain is held positive and the gate negative with respect to the source and, in this section, it is assumed that the variation in potential along the length of the channel is small in comparison with the gate-source voltage, i.e. there is a

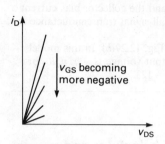

Fig. 12.30 Drain
voltage–current
characteristic for small
drain-source voltages

12.8.3 JFET operation for larger drain-source voltages

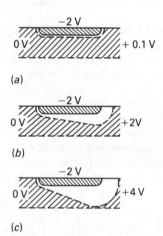

Fig. 12.31 The effect of
increasing drain-source
voltage

substantially uniform reverse-bias voltage along the length of
the channel. Subject to this assumption, application of the
positive potential to the drain causes electrons to flow from
source to drain and there is a linear relationship between the
drain current and the drain-source voltage. The constant of
proportionality is the channel resistance whose value is
controlled by the gate-source voltage. Typical characteristics
are shown in Fig. 12.30. Because the junction is reverse
biased, the gate current is very small, negligibly so for most
applications. Because the doping concentration in the gate is
much higher than that of the channel, the depletion layer can
be assumed to be almost entirely in the channel rather than
in the gate region. Then, as v_{GS} is made increasingly negative
a point will be reached where the depletion layer extends
right across the channel and the drain current is reduced to
zero. The device is then said to be **pinched-off** and the value
of v_{GS} at which this occurs is the **pinch-off voltage** V_p.

As v_{DS} is increased, the situation is modified by the fact that
the reverse-bias voltage is no longer uniform over the length
of the channel. For example, Fig. 12.31(a)–(c) shows a
progressive increase in drain-source voltage from a low value
such as that described in the previous section to a point
where there is an appreciable unbalance between conditions
at the source and drain ends of the channel. Effectively, the
reverse bias at the drain end is much larger than that at the
source and the depletion-layer width is correspondingly
greater. Pinch-off therefore occurs at the drain end first. It
might be expected that the current would cut off as soon as
the channel pinches off at any point along its length but this
cannot occur because the very existence of the varying-width
channel to the left of the drain means that there must be a
potential gradient along its length and current must continue
to flow. What does happen is that the current no longer
increases with increasing drain-source voltage and the output
characteristic (Fig. 12.32) enters a saturation condition. As
v_{DS} is further increased virtually all the additional potential is
dropped across the pinched-off tip of the channel leaving the
configuration to the left substantially unchanged. There is,
however, a slight increase of drain current with drain-source
voltage.

Fig. 12.32(a) is a typical set of output characteristics. When
v_{GS} exceeds V_p the device is cut off irrespective of the value of
v_{DS}. When v_{GS} lies between V_p and 0, a point is reached where
v_{DS} is sufficiently large (i.e. when $v_{DS} + V_p = v_{GS}$) to cause
pinch-off at the drain end. At this point the characteristic
nominally changes from the constant-resistance to the
saturated condition, and this occurs at progressively higher
values of v_{DS} as v_{GS} approaches 0. The dashed line shows the
locus of the nominal transition points and is therefore the
locus of $v_{DS} = v_{GS} - V_p$.

Fig. 12.32(b) is a **transfer characteristic**, showing how the
drain current varies with gate-source voltage for a given value
of drain-source voltage: a drain-source voltage in the
saturation region is used. The two characteristics are not

Fig. 12.32 Output and transfer characteristics for a JFET

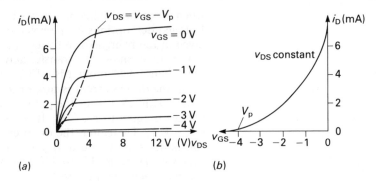

(a)

(b)

independent, the information for the transfer characteristic being obtained from the output characteristics, but the former is a more convenient way to illustrate the drain current's dependence on drain-source voltage. Experimental results suggest that a relationship of the form,

$$i_D = I_{DSS}(1 - v_{GS}/V_p)^2,$$

where I_{DSS} is the drain current when v_{GS} is zero, provides a good approximation to the actual behaviour of the device. It will be seen that the i_D/v_{GS} relationship is not linear.

Because the input current to the gate is negligible for most purposes, an input characteristic is not usually drawn.

12.8.4 The metal oxide semiconductor field effect transistor (MOSFET)

Whilst the JFET is available as a discrete component, by far the greatest application of field-effect devices is the MOSFET in integrated form. As explained in Section 4 of Chapter 13, the basic MOS inverter is used in a wide range of integrated circuit logic-switching devices.

The basic arrangement of what is known as an **enhancement-mode** n-channel device (referred to as NMOS) is shown in Fig. 12.33. It will be seen to comprise a p-type substrate into which are set two heavily doped n-type wells to which source and drain contacts are made. The gate (metal or polycrystalline silicon) is insulated from the rest of the structure by a layer of silicon dioxide. The name is derived from the metal-oxide-semiconductor construction. Although the NMOS device is shown, PMOS devices are also possible.

Fig. 12.33 Arrangement of an n-channel enhancement-mode MOSFET

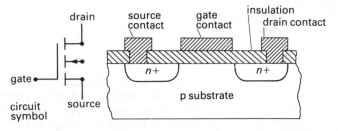

Application of a positive (for the NMOS device) gate-source voltage with v_{DS} zero results in an induced layer of negative charge in the substrate between source and drain. Increasing v_{GS} above a **threshold voltage** (V_{th}) will cause the layer to invert (i.e. become a predominantly n channel within the p substrate) thus permitting current flow to take place when a potential difference exists between drain and source. Detailed descriptions of the behaviour of the MOSFET are given in the references to further reading.

Fig. 12.34 shows the transfer and output characteristics for the enhancement-mode MOSFET (n-channel). For low values of v_{DS} the drain current is proportional to $2(v_{GS} - V_{th})v_{DS} - v_{DS}^2$; at the point at which the drain-source voltage is equal to $v_{GS} - V_{th}$, this expression reduces to v_{DS}^2 or $(v_{GS} - V_{th})^2$. Thereafter, the drain current remains substantially constant, proportional to $(v_{GS} - V_{th})^2$. Threshold-voltage values in the range 1 V to 3 V may be expected depending on the manufacturing process.

Fig. 12.34 Enhancement-mode MOSFET characteristics

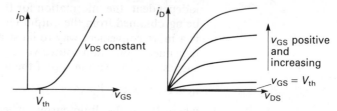

As well as the p- and n-channel enhancement MOSFET there are **depletion-mode** types. The n-channel version is shown in Fig. 12.35(*a*). It has a lightly doped n-channel formed between the drain and source wells, as a result of which there is a drain-source current flow (with an applied drain-source voltage) with no gate-source bias voltage applied. When such a bias is applied (with the gate negative with respect to source) there is an induced positive charge in the channel which depletes the charge carriers and reduces the current. If a positive gate-source voltage is applied, the channel conductivity is enhanced and the current increases. Transfer and output characteristics are shown in Fig. 12.35(*b*) and (*c*).

Fig. 12.35 Depletion-mode MOSFET and characteristics

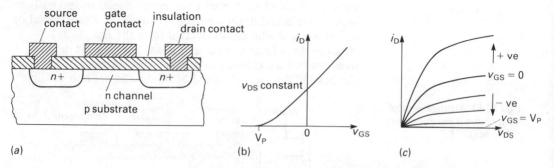

Because the gates are insulated in all MOSFET types, they have an extremely high input resistance of the order of $10^{12}\ \Omega$. Because the leakage is negligible, static charge may build up to such an extent as to damage the device. MOS devices therefore have a built-in diode protection but should nevertheless only be stored and handled in some form of conducting carrier.

12.8.5 Power MOSFET

In the standard form of construction the MOSFET is unsuitable for handling large currents with high breakdown

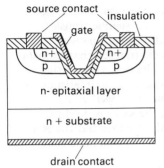

Fig. 12.36 VMOS construction

voltages. One technique for achieving these conditions is the **vertical MOSFET** (VMOS) method.

The VMOS transistor is characterised by a construction (Fig. 12.36) which allows current to flow vertically from drain to source. Control is exercised through induced channels in the p-type body adjacent to the sides of the notch. As the gate is made positive, a relatively low-resistance n-type conducting path exists from drain to source. The VMOS configuration is one of a number of power-MOSFET types designed to handle currents of the order of amperes with breakdown voltages of a few hundred volts.

12.9 Operation of the junction field effect transistor

12.9.1 Graphical methods and a model

Fig. 12.37(a) and (b) shows load lines constructed on typical common-source JFET characteristics in a way corresponding to those for the bipolar transistor in Fig. 12.22. The circuit arrangement to which these load lines relate is shown in Fig. 12.37(c).

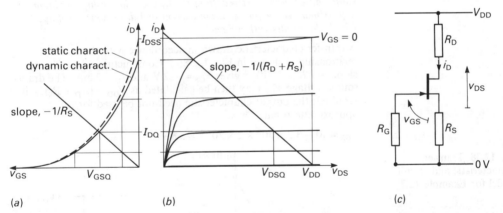

(a)   (b)   (c)

Fig. 12.37 Load lines and circuit for a JFET

In this case biasing is achieved by inserting a resistor into the source lead such that, as the source current flows, the source is taken above earth potential (by, say, $+2\,\text{V}$). However, the gate is tied to earth through the resistor R_G which, although having a large value, does not have a significant direct-voltage drop across it because only a minute current flows in the gate circuit. Thus, the gate potential is negative with respect to that of the source (for the n-channel device shown) and the transistor is correctly biased. The load line for the biasing component R_S is therefore drawn on the transfer characteristic rather than on the input characteristic as was the case for the bipolar transistor.

The transfer characteristic itself differs slightly from that shown in Fig. 12.32 which was drawn for a fixed value of drain-source voltage and is sometimes called a **static** characteristic. In the present case, it is evident from Fig. 12.32 that as the drain-source voltage varies so does the drain current and this has a second-order effect on the transfer characteristic, which is then called the **dynamic** transfer characteristic. In Fig. 12.37, the output load line was therefore drawn first and the dynamic transfer characteristic was plotted from this information. The difference in the values obtained using static and dynamic characteristics will usually be quite small and the former may well give a sufficiently accurate result. Strictly, the same procedure should have been followed in the bipolar case but the effect of moderate changes in v_{CE} on the input characteristic is very small.

The same comparative arguments concerning graphical and model techniques apply in principle to the JFET as much as to the bipolar transistor. In the JFET case a very simple model may be adequate, taking the form of a voltage controlled current source whose value is given by the relationship in Section 12.8.3

$$i_D = I_{DSS}(1 - v_{GS}/V_p)^2,$$

with symbols as defined in that section.

Example 12.7   *A JFET having $I_{DSS} = 8\,mA$ and $V_p = -4\,V$ is connected as shown in Fig. 12.37(c) with $R_D = 2.2\,k\Omega$, $R_S = 1\,k\Omega$ and $V_{DD} = 10\,V$. Use a static characteristic derived from the i_D/v_{GS} relationship to obtain an approximate value for the drain current and drain-source voltage. Check the results with a model.*

A transfer characteristic drawn in accordance with the stated relationship is shown in Fig. 12.38(a). Constructing a load line of slope $-1/R_S = -10^{-3}$ gives $V_{GS} = -2\,V$ and $I_D = 2\,mA$. The drain-source voltage V_{DS} may then be calculated as $V_{DD} - (R_D + R_S)I_D$ if required; the output characteristic need not be used for this approximate result. Thus,

$$V_{DS} = 10 - 3.2 \times 10^3 \times 2 \times 10^{-3} = 3.6\,V.$$

Fig. 12.38 Transfer characteristic and circuit model for Example 12.7

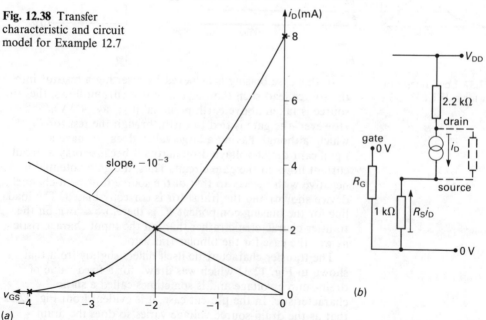

The model is shown in Fig. 12.38(*b*). The gate-source voltage is given by $-10^3 I_D$ where $I_D = 8 \times 10^{-3}(1 - (-10^3 I_D)/(-4))^2$. One solution to this quadratic equation is $I_D = 2\,\text{mA}$, consistent with the graphical result.

Because of the essential non-linearity of the model, the solution still involves the solution of an equation. Furthermore, to take account of the variation of i_D with v_{DS} would be even more complex, requiring use of the resistance shown dotted in Fig. 12.38(*b*). This would effect an increase in drain current as drain-source voltage increases. A typical value might be of the order of 50 kΩ, resulting in an increase of 0.2 mA for a 10 V increase in v_{DS}.

12.9.2 A small-signal model for the junction field-effect transistor

A simple transconductance model is adequate for many low-frequency applications. The common-source circuit is shown in Fig. 12.39(*a*). Because only a very small current flows into the gate, the gate terminal is shown simply as a reference point on the diagram. The current-source $g_m v_{gs}$ is shunted by r_d representing the drain output resistance. Expressions for g_m and r_d are given by writing down an expression for the small-signal drain current

$$i_d = g_m v_{gs} + \frac{1}{r_d} v_{ds}.$$

Thus

$$g_m = \left. \frac{i_d}{v_{gs}} \right|_{v_{ds}=0},$$

and

$$r_d = \left. \frac{v_{ds}}{i_d} \right|_{v_{gs}=0}.$$

Fig. 12.39 Small-signal JFET model for low- and high-frequency operation

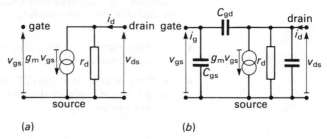

(*a*)   (*b*)

These small-signal parameters vary with the operating point on the characteristics. For example, working in terms of total values

$$g_m = \frac{di_D}{dv_{GS}},$$

where (from Section 12.8.3)

$$i_D = I_{DSS}(1 - v_{GS}/V_p)^2,$$

and therefore

$$g_m = -\frac{2 I_{DSS}}{V_p}(1 - v_{GS}/V_p).$$

This expression indicates the dependence of g_m on the gate-source voltage v_{GS}.

At high frequencies capacitance must be taken into account and the model shown in Fig. 12.39(*b*) can be used.

Key points to remember

- pure semiconductor material (e.g. silicon) is doped to produce p-type and n-type semiconductor materials;

- the junction diode comprises adjacent sections of p- and n-type material and has a current flow exponentially dependent on bias voltage;

- the exponential characteristic gives the diode rectifying properties enabling it to be used as a half-wave rectifier;

- special reverse-biased diodes can be used as variable capacitances and as voltage-reference devices;

- the bipolar transistor is a three-terminal device and behaves as a current-controlled current source;

- straightforward bias-circuit problems can be analysed either by means of a simplified circuit model or by drawing a load line on characteristics;

- the small-signal behaviour of the transistor can be predicted using a two-port network representation with hybrid parameters or using a transconductance model;

- the field-effect transistor is a three-terminal device which behaves as a voltage-controlled current source;

- junction and MOS-type field effect transistors exist, the latter in depletion and enhancement-mode forms; VMOS power types are also available;

- graphical methods or simplified circuit models can be used to solve FET bias-circuit problems;

- small-signal analysis of the FET can be done at low frequencies using a simple model in the form of a voltage-controlled current source.

Further reading

Chirlain, P. M., *Analysis and Design of Integrated Electronic Circuits.* Harper and Row (1982).

Holt, C. A., *Electronic Circuits: Digital and Analog.* J. Wiley (1978).

Millman, J., *Microelectronics: Digital and Analog Circuits and Systems.* McGraw-Hill (1979).

Seidman, A. H., *Integrated Circuit Applications Handbook.* J. Wiley (1983).

Seymour, J., *Electronic Devices and Components.* Pitman (1981).

Appendix 12A The hybrid-parameter model of the bipolar transistor

The hybrid-parameter defining equations as developed in Chapter 4 are:

$$V_1 = h_{11}I_1 + h_{12}V_2,$$

and

$$I_2 = h_{21}I_1 + h_{22}V_2.$$

When related to the transistor in the common-emitter connection mode (Fig. 12.17(*b*)), these become,

$$V_{be} = h_{ie}I_b + h_{re}V_{ce},$$

and

$$I_c = h_{fe}I_b + h_{oe}V_{ce}.$$

The transistor and its hybrid-parameter model are shown in Fig. 12A.1. From these equations, open-circuit and short-circuit definitions for the parameters can be deduced using the same procedures as in Chapter 4:

$$h_{ie} = \left.\frac{V_{be}}{I_b}\right|_{V_{ce}=0} ; \quad h_{re} = \left.\frac{V_{be}}{V_{ce}}\right|_{I_b=0},$$

$$h_{fe} = \left.\frac{I_c}{I_b}\right|_{V_{ce}=0} ; \quad h_{oe} = \left.\frac{I_c}{V_{ce}}\right|_{I_b=0}.$$

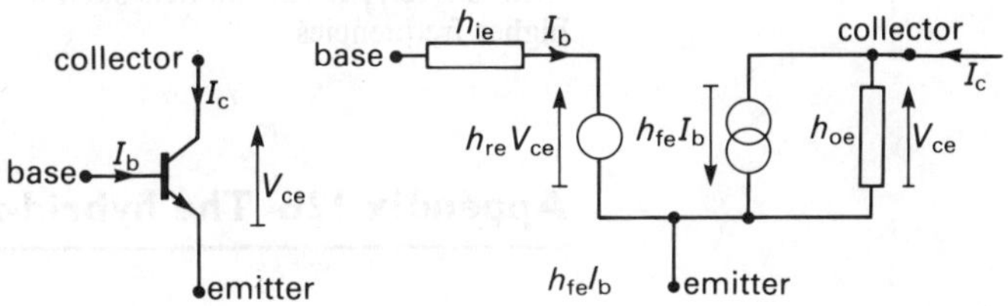

Fig. 12A.1 Hybrid-parameter model of a bipolar transistor

In this case the voltages and currents involved are not total values but are small-signal variations about a quiescent operating point, such as shown in Fig. 12.2(*c*). The notation for the variables is that representing r.m.s., phasor or transformed values of a small-signal variation. The statement that, for example, $V_{ce} = 0$ means that there is no small-signal variation of the collector-emitter voltage. It does not preclude the possibility of a bias component, V_{CE} (which, indeed, will normally exist). Thus, an alternative form for h_{ie} could be:

$$\left.\frac{V_{be}}{I_b}\right|_{v_{CE}\,\text{const}}.$$

Lower-case symbols may also be used for the variables. These represent instantaneous values of a small-signal variation and can be used to demonstrate relationships between the parameters and the characteristics. For example, the h_{ie} parameter is given by

$$h_{ie} = \left.\frac{v_{be}}{i_b}\right|_{v_{CE}\,\text{const}}$$

and is the slope of the $i_B - v_{BE}$ characteristic for a fixed value of v_{CE}.

Fig. 12A.2 summarises the relationships between the common-emitter input and output characteristics and the four hybrid parameters.

Fig. 12A.2 Hybrid parameters related to input and output characteristics

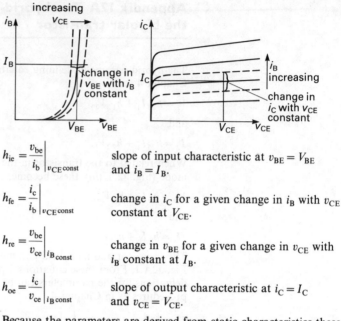

$$h_{ie} = \left.\frac{v_{be}}{i_b}\right|_{v_{CE}\,const}$$ slope of input characteristic at $v_{BE} = V_{BE}$ and $i_B = I_B$.

$$h_{fe} = \left.\frac{i_c}{i_b}\right|_{v_{CE}\,const}$$ change in i_C for a given change in i_B with v_{CE} constant at V_{CE}.

$$h_{re} = \left.\frac{v_{be}}{v_{ce}}\right|_{i_B\,const}$$ change in v_{BE} for a given change in v_{CE} with i_B constant at I_B.

$$h_{oe} = \left.\frac{i_c}{v_{ce}}\right|_{i_B\,const}$$ slope of output characteristic at $i_C = I_C$ and $v_{CE} = V_{CE}$.

Because the parameters are derived from static characteristics these are necessarily the values at low frequencies where any effects which may cause phase differences between the quantities are negligible. However, at higher frequencies such effects may not be negligible and the parameters (in phasor form) would become complex. Alternatively, circuit models such as the hybrid-π may be used at higher frequencies.

Appendix 12B The hybrid-π small-signal model

It is possible to approach the formation of a circuit model through consideration of its physical properties. The model so formed is the **hybrid-π model** shown in Fig. 12B.1. Shown dotted (but not discussed in this appendix) are two capacitances to account for the transistor's behaviour at high frequencies.

Fig. 12B.1 Hybrid-π model of a bipolar transistor

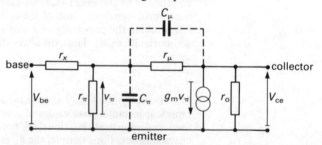

Holt, for example (see references), derives equivalent relationships between the low-frequency hybrid-parameter and hybrid-π models. Subject to reasonable practical approximations, these equivalents are,

$$h_{ie} = r_x + r_\pi, \quad h_{fe} = g_m r_\pi,$$
$$h_{re} = r_\pi / r_\mu, \quad h_{oe} = 1/r_o + g_m r_\pi / r_\mu.$$

In general low-frequency analysis, r_π and g_m are the most important elements of the hybrid-π model and a reasonable approximation to the performance of a transistor may be obtained with a knowledge of the value of these elements, together with that for the small-signal short-circuit current gain, h_{fe}, or β_0 as its low-frequency value is sometimes known in this context.

EXERCISES 12

12.1   Sketch the voltage–current characteristic at a temperature of 290 K over a suitable voltage range for a p–n junction diode having a reverse saturation current of 100 pA and for which η may be taken as 1.6. Hence sketch the current waveform which would result from an alternating voltage $0.8 \sin \omega t$ V maintained across the diode.
What might be expected if the quoted voltage is an open-circuit e.m.f. and the source impedance is relatively high.

12.2   Using the characteristic drawn for Exercise 12.1, determine the diode and resistor voltages and the current when a 5 V d.c. source having negligible source resistance is connected to the diode in series with a 800 Ω resistor. Calculate the power dissipated by the diode.
Also sketch resistor voltage and current waveforms if a 2 V peak sinusoidal voltage were superimposed on the 5 V d.c. source.

12.3   (a) For the circuit shown in Fig. E12.1, determine the output voltage waveform when v_1 is a 5 V (peak) sinusoidal voltage. Assume the diode model shown in Fig. 12.9(b) with $V_\gamma = 0.7$ V.
(b) If v_1 is now changed to a biased small-signal voltage given by $(2 + 0.1 \sin \omega t)$ V, determine the small-signal output voltage component of v_o. Take η for the diode to be 2.0 and use the model in Fig. 12.9(a).

Fig. E12.1

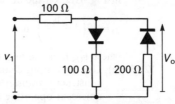

12.4   Assuming that the voltage–current characteristic of a junction diode can be approximated to the square-law characteristic $i = 3 \times 10^{-3} v^2$ over the relevant operating range, determine the magnitudes of the sum-and-difference frequency components of the current when voltage $v = (20 \sin \omega_1 t + 30 \sin \omega_2 t)$ mV is applied. Assume that the voltage is suitably biased.

12.5   A reverse-biased variable-capacitance diode has a capacitance C given by $60/\sqrt{(V)}$, where V is the magnitude of the reverse-biased voltage. If connected in parallel with an inductor L to form a parallel-tuned LC circuit (whose resonant frequency may be taken to be $1/2\pi\sqrt{(LC)}$) determine the percentage deviation in resonant frequency as a result of applying a biased small-signal voltage $(9 + 0.5 \sin \omega t)$ V across the diode.

12.6   In the circuit shown in Fig. E12.2, the Zener diode maintains an approximately constant voltage of 6 V across the load resistor R_L provided its current does not fall below 5 mA.

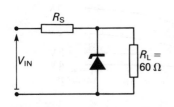

Fig. E12.2

If the diode power is not to exceed 300 mW, what range of values of R_s would maintain circuit operation with the input voltage V_{IN} varying over the range 24 V to 30 V.

Hint: work with the 'worst case' conditions, i.e. either minimum input voltage and minimum Zener current or maximum input voltage and the Zener power rating.

12.7 The magnitude of the emitter and collector currents in an n–p–n bipolar transistor are found to be 6.39 mA and 6.35 mA respectively. Assuming a value of 10 nA for I_{CO} (see Section 12.5.4) determine α and β for the transistor.

12.8 For the set of output characteristics shown in Fig. 12.19(c) and for the circuit shown in Fig. 12.21(a) make a graphical estimate of the quiescent collector current and collector emitter voltage when $R_C = 3.3 \text{ k}\Omega$ and $I_B = 10 \text{ }\mu\text{A}$. Sketch a graph showing variation in v_{CE} with i_B (i_B on the x axis) as i_B is varied over the range 0–20 μA.

12.9 Use a circuit model to determine values for R_B and R_C in Fig. E12.3 in order that V_{CE} shall be 5.6 V when $I_C = 2 \text{ mA}$. Take β to be 200.

12.10 A small-signal common-emitter amplifier in the form shown in Fig. 12.21(a) uses a transistor with hybrid parameters $h_{ie} = 2.94 \text{ k}\Omega$, $h_{fe} = 220$ and $h_{oe} = 25 \text{ }\mu\text{S}$. Draw an equivalent circuit for a collector load resistance of 2.2 kΩ and estimate the ratio of small-signal collector-emitter voltage to base-emitter voltage. Assume that R_B has negligible effect on the small-signal performance.

12.11 The circuit shown in Fig. E12.4 is used to generate nominally equal amplitude and antiphase signals v_{o_1} and v_{o_2}. Biasing components are not shown. Given that the direct component of collector current is 2 mA, determine the parameter r_e and, taking $r_x = 100 \text{ }\Omega$, r_o infinite and $h_{fe} = 200$, draw a small-signal transconductance model for the transistor. Hence determine and sketch the waveforms for v_{o_1} and v_{o_2} when $v_i = 2 \sin \omega t$ V.

12.12 Determine the current, i_D, flowing in the JFET circuit shown in Fig. E12.5 if the device characteristic is given by

$$i_D = 12\left(1 + \frac{v_{GS}}{4}\right)^2 \text{ mA},$$

where v_{GS} must be negative and in the range 0 to -4 V.

12.13 (a) Use the output characteristics in Fig. E12.6(b) to construct a transfer characteristic and hence determine the quiescent operating conditions for the n-channel JFET circuit shown in Fig. E12.6(a).

(b) Use the characteristics to estimate the small-signal parameters g_m and r_d at the quiescent operating point.

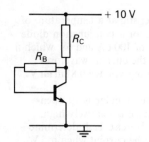

Fig. E12.3

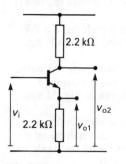

Fig. E12.4

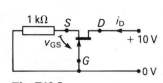

Fig. E12.5

Fig. E12.6

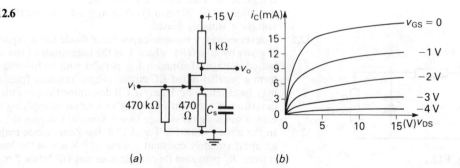

(a)   (b)

(c) Determine the small-signal voltage gain v_o/v_i of the circuit in Fig. E12.6(a) using the parameters determined in (b). Assume that the capacitor C_s has negligible reactance at the operating frequency and that the small-signal source-to-earth potential difference is negligible.

13 Semiconductor devices: circuits and applications

The principal learning objectives of this chapter are to:

	Section	Exercise
• analyse a number of bipolar-transistor subcircuits including:		
(i) biasing circuits;	1.2	13.1–13.3
(ii) differential amplifier;	1.3	13.4
(iii) level shifting circuit;	1.4	13.5
(iv) Darlington circuit;	1.5	13.6
• calculate power relationships in transistors;	2.1, 2.2	13.7
• describe transistor power-output stages;	2.3	
• explain the principles of rectification and smoothing;	3.1, 3.2	13.8
• analyse a simple regulator circuit using Zener diode;	3.3	13.9
• explain the operation of a simple transistor regulator;	3.3	
• explain the principle of the switching regulator;	3.4	
• solve problems using a thyristor;	3.5	13.10
• describe a basic TTL logic gate;	4.1	
• discuss operational aspects of TTL logic;	4.2	13.11
• explain the principles of I^2L logic;	4.3	
• state the principal features of ECL logic;	4.4	
• describe the implementation of gates in MOS and CMOS logic.	4.5–4.7	

13.1 Bipolar transistor subcircuits

13.1.1 Introduction

This section discusses a collection of transistor subcircuits, each of which may be used as part of a larger circuit. Analysis is kept to a minimum although the techniques of bias and small-signal analysis described in the preceding chapter are used where appropriate. One such subcircuit has, in fact, already been introduced in order to illustrate circuit-model analysis; this was the emitter follower (Examples 12.4

and 12.5) which, from the analyses, will be seen to have almost unity gain, high input impedance and low output impedance and thus functions as a buffer stage.

13.1.2 Current sources, current mirrors and transistor biasing

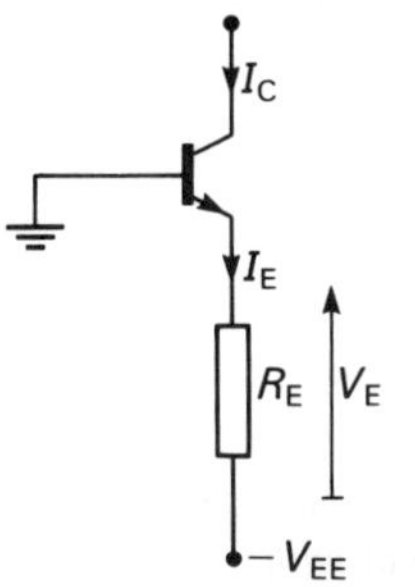

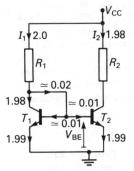

Fig. 13.1 A simple current source

As shown in Fig. 13.1 the current source (or constant-current source) in its simplest form consists of an earthed-base transistor with emitter load. With $V_{BE} \simeq 0.7$ V, and substantially constant, V_E is fixed at $V_{EE} - 0.7$, and hence the current I_E at $(V_{EE} - 0.7)/R_E$. The current flow in the circuit is therefore substantially independent of the potential on the collector provided that it remains positive. For a fixed value of V_{EE}, the circuit effectively draws a constant current.

From a small-signal viewpoint, collector-voltage changes result in very small changes in collector current and the circuit behaves as a high-value resistor. Thus, a large resistance value can be provided without the associated large direct-voltage drops which would necessitate large supply voltages. It also has advantages in integrated-circuit construction because a high-value resistor would require a relatively large chip area, more than that needed for the transistor/resistor combination. It is emphasised that, unlike a real resistor, the current source has differing total and small-signal (slope) resistance values. For example, with $+6$ V at the collector, the current may be 4 mA. Increasing the collector voltage to $+8$ V may increase the current by, say, 40 μA giving an effective *total* resistance change from 1.5 kΩ to approximately 2 kΩ, but an effective slope resistance to the changing voltage of $(8-6)/4 \times 10^{-5} = 50$ kΩ. A direct current of 4 mA would result in a 200 V potential difference across an actual 50 kΩ resistor.

A basic **current mirror** or current **repeater** is shown in Fig. 13.2. Its function is to control the current in T_2. Because the base-emitter voltages of T_1 and T_2 are the same, and assuming that the transistors are matched, almost the same current flows in both transistors. Thus, the controlled current I_2 is determined by I_1, where I_1 is given by $(V_{CC} - V_{BE})/R_1$. Assuming that, for example, I_1 is 2 mA and that each transistor has $\beta = 200$, the current values are as shown (in mA) in Fig. 13.2. The figures confirm a result which may be obtained by analysis, namely the T_2 collector current is $\beta I_1/(\beta + 2)$. For β as low as 40, I_2 is still within 5% of I_1 so that the current in T_2 is determined primarily by V_{CC} and R_1 and not by the individual transistor current gains (provided that they are the same).

The current-mirror circuit may be used as a biasing circuit for transistor T_2. It contrasts with the simple biasing circuit in Fig. 12.21 in which the collector current varies directly with the value of β for the transistor. Because there can be a wide variation in the value of β, even for transistors of a given type, a circuit whose performance depends on those values is of limited application. The current-mirror biasing arrangement is also well suited to integrated-circuit manufacture methods where matched transistors can be relatively easily fabricated and where it is desirable to avoid large resistance values because of the large chip area required.

Fig. 13.2 A current mirror

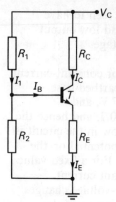

Fig. 13.3 A transistor biasing arrangement

In discrete-transistor circuitry, where transistor matching is more difficult to achieve and the resistance-value restriction does not apply, the circuit in Fig. 13.3 may be used. A measure of independence of the β value of the transistor is achieved by ensuring that the current drain through R_1 and R_2 is substantially greater than the base current. The base potential will then remain approximately independent of I_B and, hence, so will the emitter potential. The collector current will then be approximately equal to the emitter potential divided by R_E.

Example 13.1   *For the circuit shown in Fig. 13.3 determine the collector current if $R_1 = 68\ k\Omega$, $R_2 = 27\ k\Omega$, $R_C = 1.8\ k\Omega$, $R_E = 1\ k\Omega$ and with $V_{CC} = +10\ V$*

(i) $\beta = 100$; and
(ii) $\beta = 200$.

Repeat the exercise for the circuit in Fig. 13.2 with $R_1 = 4.7\ k\Omega$ and $V_{CC} = +10\ V$. Assume T_1 and T_2 are matched.

Assume that $I_E = I_C$ and that $V_{BE} = 0.65$ V. The Kirchhoff voltage law applied to the circuit then gives,

$$27(I_1 - I_B) + 68I_1 = 10 \quad \text{(through } R_1 \text{ and } R_2\text{)},$$

$$1.0I_E + 0.65 + 68I_1 = 10 \quad \text{(through } R_1, T \text{ and } R_E\text{)}.$$

Then, for part (i), solving with $I_E \simeq I_C = 100I_B$ ($\beta = 100$) gives $I_C = 1.84$ mA and, for part (ii) with $I_C = 200I_B$ ($\beta = 200$), $I_C = 2$ mA. It will be seen that a 100% increase in β results in only a 9% increase in collector current I_C. For the current–mirror circuit in Fig. 13.2, $I_1 = (10 - 0.65)/4.7 \times 10^3 = 1.99$ mA for both values of β. Using the stated result, $I_2 = \beta I_1/(\beta + 2)$, for $\beta = 100$, $I_2 = 1.95$ mA and for $\beta = 200$, $I_2 = 1.97$ mA. In this case a 100% increase in β increases I by only 1% although the result does assume matched transistors.

If the current–mirror circuit is required to generate small values of current, the value of R_1 will increase and will become inconveniently large for integrated-circuit manufacture. In such cases, an additional resistor added in T_2 emitter lead will change the balance of the circuit and permit small currents in T_2 without unreasonably large values of R_1.

13.1.3 The differential amplifier

Whilst introductory considerations of the transistor tend to lead towards a simple common-emitter amplifier with a single input terminal, a large number of applications of the bipolar transistor are in the form of a **differential amplifier**. This has two input terminals arranged so that the output signal is proportional (ideally) to the difference between the two input signals. It is implicit that the same signal at both input terminals results in zero output.

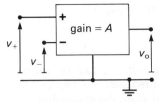

Fig. 13.4 Block diagram of a differential amplifier

Fig. 13.5 Differential amplifier circuit and small-signal model

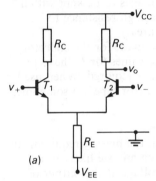

As shown in Fig. 13.4, the output due to an input v_+ at the **non-inverting input** terminal (indicated +) is Av_+ whereas that due to the input v_- at the **inverting input** terminal (indicated $-$) is Av_- so that the net output is $A(v_+ - v_-)$. It may be used as a single-ended amplifier, in either inverting or non-inverting modes provided that the other input terminal is earthed. The differential amplifier stage is widely used in the operational-amplifier circuit described in Chapter 14.

The basic common-emitter differential circuit is shown in Fig. 13.5(a). In the analysis which follows it is assumed that both halves of the circuit are identical: this is a situation realistically achieved in integrated-circuit manufacture. The relationships are derived from the transconductance model shown in Fig. 13.5(b).

Setting v_- to zero and applying the Kirchhoff voltage law to the right-hand side of the circuit (with the single dash indicating the $v_- = 0$ condition) and assuming $g_m r_\pi \gg 1$

$$0 = v'_{\pi_2} + g_m R_E(v'_{\pi_1} + v'_{\pi_2}),$$

from which

$$v'_{\pi_1} = -(1 + g_m R_E)v'_{\pi_2}/g_m R_E.$$

Applying the voltage law to the left-hand side of the circuit,

$$v_+ = v'_{\pi_1} + g_m R_E(v'_{\pi_1} + v'_{\pi_2}).$$

Substituting for v'_{π_1} (and rearranging) gives,

$$v'_{\pi_2} = -\frac{g_m R_E}{1 + 2g_m R_E} v_+.$$

But, $v'_o = -g_m R_C v'_{\pi_2}$ and, substituting for v'_{π_2},

$$v'_o = \frac{g_m^2 R_E R_C}{1 + 2g_m R_E} v_+.$$

Now setting v_+ to zero and following a corresponding procedure (with the double dash indicating the $v_+ = 0$ condition)

$$v''_{\pi_2} = -(1 + g_m R_E)v''_{\pi_1}/g_m R_E$$

and

$$v''_{\pi_2} = \frac{g_m R_E}{1 + 2g_m R_E} v_-.$$

But, $v_o'' = -g_m R_C v_{\pi_2}''$ and, substituting for v_{π_1}''

$$v_o'' = -\frac{g_m R_C(1 + g_m R_E)}{1 + 2g_m R_E} v_-.$$

The ratio v_o'/v_+ is the non-inverting gain, A_+ and the ratio v_o''/v_- is the inverting gain, A_-. As discussed in Chapter 14, these are ideally equal but it is clear from the expressions that this is only true when $g_m R_E \gg 1$. With g_m of the order of 20 mS (for collector bias currents of approximately 0.5 mA) and R_E at approximately about 50 kΩ (assuming that a current source is used in the emitter), the product is 1000.

A variation on the basic circuit uses a current source in the emitter circuit. This has the effect of increasing the effective resistance of R_E (and hence the common-mode rejection) whilst still permitting d.c. supply voltages to be kept within reasonable bounds. It also permits a high resistance to be provided on a relatively small chip area.

Similar arrangements may also be made for the collector resistors for the same reasons. Large values for R_C have the effect of providing a high gain if this is required. When used in this way, circuits of the current–mirror type are sometimes called **active loads**.

13.1.4 Level shifting

Unless special precautions are taken, the biasing requirements of the various stages in a transistor circuit are likely to be such that the direct component of voltage at the output of one stage will not be compatible with the input of the next stage. One way around this problem is to include **coupling capacitors** as series elements linking the stages. Whilst they do isolate the direct components they also introduce a break in the amplifier frequency response. In order that the effect of the break be minimised, relatively large capacitances are normally used. The effect is illustrated in Example 7.3 (Chapter 7) where the 0.1 μF capacitor introduces a zero at the origin and a pole at $s = -84$, corresponding to a break frequency of 13.4 Hz.

In many applications a low-frequency zero and pole renders the circuit ineffective; it is frequently necessary to have a response which is flat down to zero frequency in order to handle low-frequency signals without distortion. The operational amplifiers described in Chapter 14 are examples of high-gain direct-coupled amplifiers. When direct coupling is required and there is incompatibility of bias levels, a **level shifting** circuit may be appropriate.

Fig. 13.6 is a level shifting circuit which permits the matching of different direct-voltage levels without affecting small-signal changes. It also provides high-input and low-output impedances, thus combining buffering facilities with a level shift. The circuit is basically an emitter follower (and thus has nominally unity small-signal gain) whose emitter-load resistor is the current source formed by R_2 and T_2. The direct-voltage output is set by adjusting R_1, across which the potential difference is the current-source current multiplied by R_1. The small-signal output is not significantly attenuated

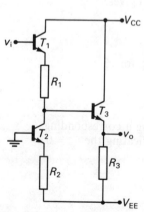

Fig. 13.6 Level-shifting circuit

because of the high resistance of the current source to signal variations. T_3 and R_3 form a low output impedance emitter-follower circuit.

13.1.5 The Darlington circuit

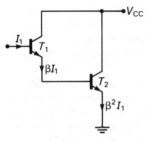

Fig. 13.7 Darlington pair

This comprises two transistors connected as shown in Fig. 13.7, available as a single package or as part of an integrated circuit. Because T_1 emitter current $(= \beta I_1)$ forms the base current of T_2, T_2 emitter current is approximately $\beta^2 I_1$. This assumes that β is the same for each transistor even though they are operating at greatly differing current levels. Thus the circuit provides a very high current gain, or, if connected as an emitter follower (with a load in T_2 emitter circuit), exhibits an input impedance a factor h_{fe} higher than the single transistor.

13.2 Power relationships and power output stages

13.2.1 Transistor-power dissipation

Fig. 13.8 Reference directions for a bipolar transistor

Although not previously considered, transistor power dissipation is a vital consideration in determining operating conditions. There is a positive power flow into any device for which the product of the voltage and current yields a positive, non-zero value. For the transistor shown in Fig. 13.8, the power flow is $v_{CE} i_C$. As energy is dissipated, the temperature of the transistor will rise and, in practice, there is a maximum power rating which will ensure that the rise is not beyond safe limits. As may be expected, the power rating will depend upon the operating environment; for example, whether the transistor is enclosed within a confined space or whether it is placed in a stream of cooling air. **Heat sinks** are used for high-power applications. These are high thermal-conductivity metal blocks having large radiating surfaces, possibly employing a fin-type construction such as may be seen on air-cooled motorcycle engines.

Transistor temperature rises are quantified by junction-ambient thermal resistance Θ_{JA}. This is defined by the relationship

$$T_J - T_A = \Theta_{JA} P_D,$$

where T_J is the collector-junction temperature, T_A is the ambient temperature and P_D is the power dissipation. The value of Θ_{JA} depends on the environment and the transistor, typically ranging from $1\,°C/W$ to $500\,°C/W$; the higher values apply for low-power devices used without heat sinks. For example, if a direct current of $10\,mA$ flows in a bipolar transistor and the collector-emitter voltage is $5\,V$, a thermal resistance of $100\,°C/W$ would result in a junction-ambient temperature difference of $\Theta_{JA} P_D = 100 \times 10 \times 10^{-3} \times 5 = 5\,°C$. Alternatively, if the ambient temperature is $80\,°C$ and the maximum junction temperature is specified as $150\,°C$, the maximum allowable power dissipation would be $(T_J - T_A)/\Theta_{JA} = 70/100 = 0.7\,W$.

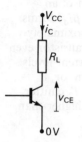

Fig. 13.9 Power relationships

When, as in the example quoted above, a direct voltage is maintained across the transistor and the collector (or source) current is also direct, the power dissipation is simply given by the product of the two values. Furthermore, if an alternating current is superimposed on the direct component (but the voltage remains constant), the power will be unchanged because the product of the alternating component of current and the direct voltage contributes nothing to the mean-power dissipation, the integral of the product of a sinusoid and a constant over a period being zero. However, for the arrangement shown in Fig. 13.9 the presence of R_L will cause v_{CE} to vary as i_C varies. Furthermore, the situation differs from that in which two resistors are connected in series in that the variation in v_{CE} is in the opposite sense to that of the current, i.e. v_{CE} decreases as i_C increases. As a result, the mean power dissipation in the transistor is reduced below the direct value $V_{CE}I_C$ by an amount $V_{ce}I_c$, where V_{ce} and I_c are the r.m.s. values of the variations. Nevertheless, from the argument presented above, the total mean power in resistor and transistor together must remain constant (at $V_{CC}I_C$) and therefore the power dissipation in the transistor decreases by the same amount as the load-power increases.

The transistor power dissipation can therefore never exceed the direct voltage–current product $V_{CE}I_C$ and to ensure that the device can never overheat this power should never exceed the maximum specified value of P_D. A convenient method of implementing this requirement is to plot a maximum-power-dissipation curve given by the equation $v_{CE}i_C = P_{D_{max}}$. The shape is a hyperbola, as shown in Fig. 13.10(a). Provided the quiescent operating point of the transistor lies inside this curve, the transistor will remain at a safe operating temperature. A typical load line and quiescent operating point are shown.

13.2.2 Large-signal operation and power relationships

There are a number of reasons for operating a transistor over a wide range of its characteristics. For example, it may be required to extract the maximum power output. For the typical operating condition shown in Fig. 13.10(a), setting the quiescent value of v_{CE} (V_{CEQ}) at about $\frac{1}{2}V_{CC}$ would permit the largest possible collector-voltage swing without incurring undue distortion. The collector current would then vary between the approximate limits 0 and $2I_{CQ}$. With swings approximately equal to the quiescent values and the quiescent collector voltage at approximately $\frac{1}{2}V_{CC}$, the power resulting from these variations is given by the product of the r.m.s. values which, assuming the variation is sinusoidal, is

$$\frac{V_{CEQ}}{\sqrt{(2)}} \cdot \frac{I_{CQ}}{\sqrt{(2)}} = \frac{V_{CC}}{2\sqrt{(2)}} \cdot \frac{I_{CQ}}{\sqrt{(2)}} = \frac{V_{CC}I_{CQ}}{4}.$$

But, the power supplied to the whole circuit (i.e. transistor and collector-load resistor) is $V_{CC}I_{CQ}$ and hence the ratio of the signal power to the power supplied is

$$\frac{V_{CC}I_{CQ}}{4} \cdot \frac{1}{V_{CC}I_{CQ}} = 0.25.$$

Fig. 13.10 Load-line constructions

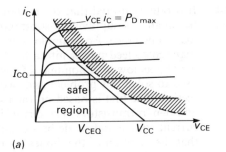

(a)

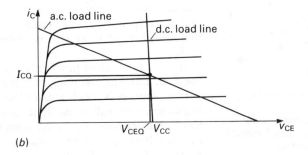

(b)

This figure (25%) is the collector-circuit efficiency for this arrangement.

A power-conversion efficiency of only 25% is not particularly high and there are various methods by which it may be improved. One is to use a load whose resistance to bias currents is relatively small but whose signal resistance is large. As shown in Fig. 13.10(b), two load lines are used to represent this condition. The near-vertical line passing through V_{CC} on the v_{CE} axis represents the low-value bias resistance and is known as the **d.c. load line**. The larger signal-resistance value is represented by the second load line whose slope is determined by the signal-resistance value and which passes through the quiescent operating point Q. It is known as an **a.c. load line**. A device which has been used very effectively in this application is the transformer introduced in Chapter 2; its resistance to bias currents is simply the primary coil resistance whereas its signal resistance is (approximately) $n^2 R_L$, where n is the turns ratio and R_L is the secondary-load resistance. This expression may be briefly justified through Fig. 13.11 and the ideal loss-less relationship, $V_p I_p = V_s I_s$. Because $V_p = n V_s$, $I_p = I_s/n$ and R_{in} $(= V_p/I_p)$ becomes $n^2 V_s/I_s = n^2 R_L$.

The reason for the increase in the efficiency of the transistor circuit can be explained by reference to Fig. 13.10(b). The available collector voltage swing is now almost twice V_{CC}, which with the same current doubles the power output. However, the power supplied stays the same (because the quiescent current stays nominally the same) and hence the ideal efficiency rises by a factor of two to 50%. Even greater efficiency is possible with the complementary-pair output stage described in the next section.

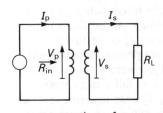

turns ratio, $n : 1$

Fig. 13.11 A transformer

13.2.3 Power output stages

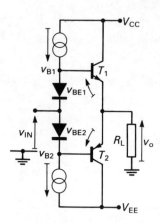

Fig. 13.12 Power-output stage using a complementary pair of transistors

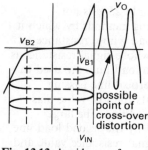

Fig. 13.13 Avoidance of cross-over distortion

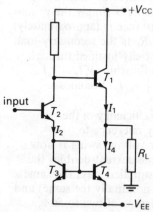

Fig. 13.14 A totem-pole power-output stage

It is often required that the output stage of a circuit should be capable of supplying a substantial power into a specified load impedance. An example is an audio-amplifier stage required to feed power into a loudspeaker whose impedance may be as low as a nominal $4\,\Omega$. Many methods have been used to solve this problem and two are presented in this section. The first is based on the use of complementary n–p–n and p–n–p transistors. The circuit is shown in Fig. 13.12. The current source and diode bias chain set up potentials such that the junction of the diodes is at zero potential with $v_{B_1} = +0.7\,\text{V}$ and $v_{B_2} = -0.7\,\text{V}$. Base currents flow causing the transistors to conduct, raising v_{BE_1} and v_{BE_2} to virtually v_{B_1} and v_{B_2}, respectively, but (assuming the transistors are matched) leaving v_0 at zero potential. Hence, no current flows in R_L.

If v_{IN} is now taken positive, v_{B_1} and v_{B_2} will rise by almost the same amount assuming that the signal resistance of the current sources is much greater than the diode signal (slope) resistance. This will cause T_1 to conduct more heavily and T_2 less so but, because v_{BE_1} must remain substantially constant, v_0 will follow v_{B_1} and hence v_{IN}. A current will then flow in $R_L\ (= v_0/R_L)$, supplied by T_1.

If v_{IN} is taken negative, the procedure is reversed with T_2 supplying current into R_L. In effect, the circuit comprises two emitter followers conducting an opposite-polarity input signals. Provided the diodes and transistors are well matched (and remain so through variations in temperature and current) **cross-over distortion** between positive and negative half-cycles is negligible. This is illustrated for a sinusoidal signal in Fig. 13.13. Assuming that the current in each transistor is a perfect half sinusoid (for a sinusoidal input signal), the mean value of the current is its peak value divided by π. Thus, for an ideal peak output-voltage swing equal to V_{CC} (or V_{EE}) across R_L, the maximum power output is $(V_{CC}/\sqrt{2})^2/R_L = V_{CC}^2/2R_L$ and the input power is the d.c. supply voltage multiplied by the mean value of the half-wave rectified current $V_{CC}/\pi R_L$. The maximum efficiency in this configuration is therefore $V_{CC}^2/2R_L$ divided by $2V_{CC}(V_{CC}/\pi R_L) = \pi/4$ assuming that the magnitudes of V_{CC} and V_{EE} are the same. As a percentage this is $78.5\,\%$.

A second type of output stage is the **totem-pole type** used in both linear and switching applications. An outline circuit is shown in Fig. 13.14. Transistors T_3 and T_4 constitute a current mirror making $I_4 \simeq I_2$. A more positive input-signal voltage on the base of T_2 increases I_2, lowering the base of T_1 and hence I_1. Thus, as $I_4\ (\simeq I_2)$ rises, I_1 falls, and current flows in the load resistor R_L. Taking T_2 base negative reverses the current flow in R_L. In effect, T_2 behaves as a phase splitter for the 'totem-pole' transistors T_1 and T_4. A detailed discussion of a wide range of power-output circuits is given in the references.

13.3 Power supply circuits

13.3.1 A.C. to d.c. conversion: rectification

A simple rectifying circuit was introduced in Section 4.3 of Chapter 12. There, a p–n junction diode was connected in series with a load resistor to produce a half-wave rectified voltage across the resistor. This section describes **full-wave rectification** with the output waveform shown in Fig. 13.15(c).

The circuits shown in (a) and (b) are the **full-wave centre-tapped** and **full-wave bridge** rectifying circuits respectively. In both cases current flows through the load resistor R_L unidirectionally; in (a) this is achieved by D_1 and D_2 alternately conducting on positive and negative half-cycles respectively. The centre-tapped transformer ensures that the two secondary voltages are equal and hence each 'half' of the waveform has the same amplitude. In circuit (b) no transformer is required to split the alternating voltage although, as is often the case, one may be required in any case to step the voltage level down (or up) from what is normally the mains-supply voltage. Conduction on both half-cycles is achieved by virtue of the circuit arrangement in which only one pair of diodes conducts at a time, the other pair being effectively open circuit. Thus, D_2 and D_3 conduct on positive half-cycles and D_1 and D_4 on negative half-cycles.

Fig. 13.15 Centre-tapped and bridge-rectifier circuits with a rectified output waveform

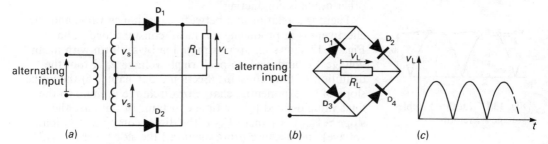

(a) (b) (c)

13.3.2 A.C. to d.c. conversion: smoothing

Although unidirectional, the waveform in Fig. 13.15(c) is still far from constant. To remove the substantial variations (at double the supply frequency) some form of **smoothing** or low-pass filtering is required. A simple and practical arrangement is shown in Fig. 13.16(a) with approximate voltage and current waveforms in Fig. 13.16(b).

Fig. 13.16 Rectifier with capacitor smoothing

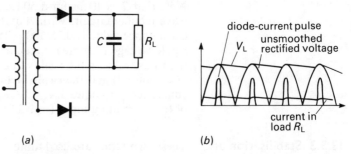

(a) (b)

To explain the operation it is assumed that the capacitor is initially charged almost to the peak value of the rectified voltage. Not until the transformer secondary voltage instantaneously rises above this value does the diode conduct and current flow take place. However, the capacitor is chosen to ensure that the time constant CR_L is long (of the order of 1 s for a 50 Hz supply), and as the diode input voltage falls, the capacitor voltage remains approximately constant, discharging only slowly through R_L. As soon as the diode input voltage falls below the capacitor voltage the diode current flow ceases.

The diode current flows in short pulses. However, the current flow in R_L will be substantially constant being the resistor (or capacitor) voltage divided by R_L, and because all the charge must be transferred during the pulse period, the mean value of the current pulses must equal the almost constant load current. Thus, if the diode current flowed for only one-twentieth of the available time, an (assumed rectangular) pulse would have a height equal to twenty times the value of the load current. A very large capacitor, whilst improving the smoothing properties of the circuit, shortens the charging period and thereby increases the peak current flow for a given mean current; this peak current may exceed the rating of the available diodes. When considering diode ratings, the **peak inverse voltage** (PIV) should also be considered: for the centre-tapped circuit, twice the peak input voltage appears across the reverse-biased diode whilst the other diode is conducting.

There is a relationship between capacitance value and the effectiveness in producing an 'ideal' constant load voltage. Fig. 13.17 shows an approximate load waveform with mean voltage V_{DC} and peak-to-peak **ripple voltage** V_R. From the definition of time constant (Section 2.5, Chapter 6) the initial slope of an exponential charge or discharge is equal to the final value divided by the time constant. In this case the slope $\simeq V_{DC}/CR$ (where V_{DC} is the direct component of load voltage) and because (from diagram) the slope is also V_R/T,

$$V_R/T = V_{DC}/CR \quad \text{or} \quad V_R = \frac{T}{CR} V_{DC}.$$

For example, for a circuit required to supply 50 mA at 5 V with a peak-to-peak ripple of 200 mV, the effective load resistance would be $5/50 \times 10^{-3} = 100\ \Omega$ and, with $V_R = 200 \times 10^{-3}$, $CR = 5(10 \times 10^{-3})/(200 \times 10^{-3}) = 0.25$ s. Note that T is 10 ms for a 50 Hz mains supply and a full-wave rectifier circuit. With R at $100\ \Omega$, the required capacitance value is $0.25/100 = 2500\ \mu\text{F}$. Frequently the r.m.s. ripple voltage is quoted; because the waveform is triangular, the r.m.s. value is the peak value divided by $\sqrt{(3)}$ (Section 1.3 of Chapter 4) and the **ripple factor** ($=$ r.m.s. ripple/direct component) becomes $1/4\sqrt{(3)}CRf$, where f is the frequency of the alternating input ($= 1/2T$).

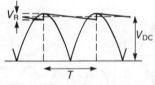

Fig. 13.17 Idealised ripple-voltage waveform

13.3.3 Stabilisation and regulation

These two terms are used almost interchangeably to describe the process of holding the load voltage approximately constant (at a selected value) in spite of variations in load resistance and supply voltage. In doing so, the ripple voltage

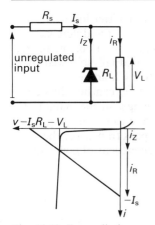

Fig. 13.18 Zener-diode regulator circuit with a load-line construction

is also reduced by a significant amount as compared with the simple capacitor smoothing case. In that case, consideration of Fig. 13.16(*b*) shows how, as the load resistance falls, the time constant falls and the capacitor discharges by a larger amount between peaks: this leads to increased ripple and a reduced direct component.

A simple regulator based on the Zener diode described in Section 4.6 of Chapter 12 is shown in Fig. 13.18. Also shown is the Zener-diode circuit symbol and a typical breakdown characteristic. Because the load resistor R_L and the diode are connected in parallel, the load-line construction is the dual of that shown in Fig. 12.7 for the series circuit. In this case, the sum of the two currents i_Z and i_R is the supply current I_s which must exceed the breakdown voltage divided by R_L. Provided that this condition is satisfied, the breakdown voltage will be substantially constant, independent of variations in the supply current or load resistance. That this is the case may be appreciated from the diagram by visualising changes in load-line position along the current axis (for changes in I_s) or in slope (for changes in R_L). The diode characteristic does have a slight slope, resulting in some variation in the load-resistor voltage as the operating point varies.

Notwithstanding improvements in circuit performance, the regulator in Fig. 13.18 has disadvantages; power is wasted in the Zener diode and the output voltage is necessarily fixed at whatever breakdown voltage the particular diode happens to have. The latter is not so restricting as may appear because, at the initial design stage, a range of voltage values is selectable. The value of the series resistor R_s is determined by the difference between the nominal unregulated and Zener voltages and by the range of load currents expected. For example, with an unregulated supply of 10 V, a Zener voltage of 6 V and an anticipated load current variation from 0 to 60 mA (corresponding to load resistance values down to 100 Ω), R_s would need to be approximately $(10 - 6)/70 \times 10^{-3}$ or, say, 56 Ω in order that, even with the full 60 mA flowing in the load, some current would still flow in the Zener (see Fig. 13.19(*c*)). Effectively, the Zener behaves as a current by-pass valve as R_L is varied. Fig. 13.19(*b*) shows the limiting case in which the full 70 mA flows in the Zener.

Fig. 13.19 Maximum and minimum diode currents

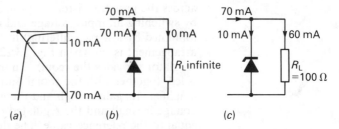

(*a*)   (*b*)   (*c*)

A better (although more costly) approach is to use the Zener circuit simply as a reference source. In Fig. 13.20, a difference amplifier is fed from a Zener reference and from a signal derived from the output voltage v_o. Its output feeds what is known as the **pass transistor**, an emitter-follower circuit whose output voltage (i.e. v_o) follows the difference-amplifier output. Thus if, for example, due to a change in R_L, v_o started to rise, the amplifier input would fall, followed by its output and the emitter of T_1, effectively holding v_o substantially constant. The magnitude of v_o can be adjusted by adjusting the ratio of R_1 to R_2. Changes in the magnitude of the unregulated input voltage (e.g. due to mains-supply variations) would be absorbed by the pass transistor, the emitter voltage being substantially independent of collector voltage.

Fig. 13.20 A transistorised voltage regulator

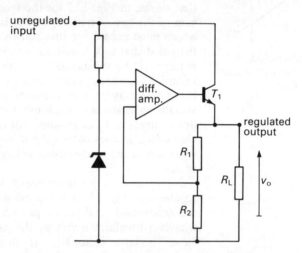

Voltage-regulator circuits lend themselves to circuit integration, an example of which is the 7800 series of three-terminal fixed-voltage regulators. As shown in Fig. 13.21, the regulator is complete apart from capacitors C_1 and C_2, C_1 being necessary if the regulator is an appreciable distance from the power-supply filter and C_2 providing improved transient response. A range of output voltages is available from 5 V to 24 V and additional circuitry enables a variable output voltage to be obtained.

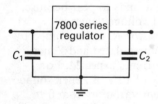

Fig. 13.21 An integrated-circuit voltage regulator

13.3.4 Switching regulators

Greater flexibility is provided by the **switching regulator** as compared with the series-pass regulator. Furthermore, greater efficiency results in cases where a large voltage is dropped across the pass transistor. In principle, regulation is effected by switching an input voltage and using the average value (obtained by low-pass filtering) to form the output. An arrangement is shown in Fig. 13.22. The low-power reference regulator provides the required nominal output voltage which is fed, together with the actual output voltage, into an error amplifier. Its gain is high and therefore the differential input voltage is small and the regulated output is approximately equal to the reference value. The difference in amplitude between the unregulated input and the regulated output is then achieved by switching the input on and off and filtering the waveform to obtain the average value. If the difference in amplitude is large the switch conducts in relatively short pulses: if the difference is small, the switch conducts most of the time. Thus, the voltage level is reduced without the drop across a series element and the consequent power loss which occurs with the pass regulator.

Fig. 13.22 Switching regulator block diagram

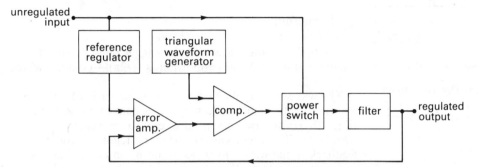

Fig. 13.23(*a*) shows how the switch conduction period would vary with variation in the unregulated input, maintaining the mean output nominally constant. The switch conduction time is controlled through the error amplifier, the comparator and the sawtooth-waveform generator. Thus, any tendency for the output voltage to rise in sympathy with an unregulated-input rise causes the error-amplifier output to rise. As shown in Fig. 13.23(*b*), this causes the comparator to switch over later in the sawtooth-waveform period thus reducing the pulse width and so regulating the output back towards its nominal value. A reference regulator is still required in this circuit but its power consumption is relatively low. Furthermore, all the low-power components may be integrated onto a single chip. The filter must generate an output proportional to the mean value of its input rather than the peak value as in the case of the smoothing circuit described in Section 13.3.2.

Fig. 13.23 Switching regulator waveforms

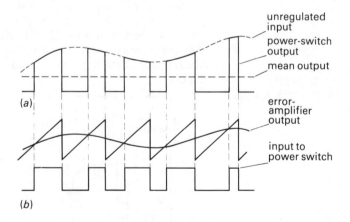

13.3.5 Thyristors

The improved power efficiency of the switching regulator also applies to the **thyristor**-based circuit. The thyristor is a four-layer semiconductor device in which the conduction period of the rectifier element itself is varied in order to control the mean output level. Fig. 13.24 shows the output from a half-wave circuit for two positions of the thyristor triggering pulse.

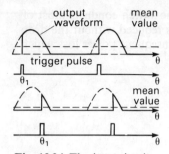

Fig. 13.24 Thyristor-circuit output waveforms showing two positions of the trigger pulse

As the pulse is delayed, so the mean (d.c.) value of the output is reduced.

The mean value (as a proportion of the peak value) is readily calculated using the expression

$$\frac{1}{2\pi} \int_{\theta_1}^{\pi} \sin\theta \, d\theta,$$

where θ_1 is the angle at which the trigger pulse occurs. For example, if $\theta_1 = 60°$ the proportion is $(1/2\pi)(-\cos\theta)_{\pi/3}^{\pi}$ whose value is 0.238.

The waveform conduction angle may be varied from 0 to 180° and, with such a wide range, it is convenient to think of the thyristor-based circuit as a 'controller' rather than a 'regulator'. Thus, whereas the switching regulator compared a feedback signal with a reference input in order to obtain a constant output, the thyristor could be considered to be an open-loop controller with a variable output.

13.4 Integrated-circuit technologies

This section is intended to provide a brief survey of some of the more commonly-encountered integrated-circuit families using bipolar and MOS technologies.

13.4.1 Transistor–transistor logic (TTL)

This is a bipolar technology first introduced in 1964 which has since become well established and has a number of derivatives. The prefix 74 is used for device type numbers with a temperature range 0–70 °C with 54 indicating a 55 °C extension in both directions.

The basic circuit for a 2-input NAND gate (described in Section 3.5 of Chapter 16) is shown in Fig. 13.25. The T_3, T_4 power output stage is a totem-pole configuration (similar to that described in Section 13.2.3) driven by a phase splitter T_2. The input transistor T_1 has a multiple-emitter configuration, the number of emitters corresponding to the number of inputs.

Fig. 13.25 A TTL NAND gate

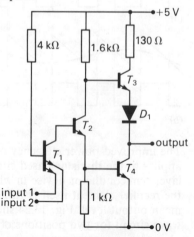

In principle, the operation is as follows. With any one input line low (say 0.2 V), T_1 base-emitter junction is forward biased, a large base current flows and the transistor saturates with its collector about half a volt above earth. Because the sum of T_2 and T_4 base-emitter voltages is then only about half a volt, T_2 is cut off, driving T_4 base low and cutting T_4 off. T_3 base is driven high by T_2 cutting off and T_3 remains at the threshold giving an output voltage of V_{CC} less the voltage drops across the diode and T_3 base-emitter junction, i.e. with $V_{CC} = 5$ V, the output is approximately 4 V. This is the output-high condition.

If all inputs to T_1 are now taken high, T_1 emitter-base junctions are reverse biased, and with the collector held negative with respect to base, T_1 collector-base junction acts as a forward-biased diode with the transistor in reverse-active mode. In effect, there is a current path through the forward biased T_1 base-collector and T_2 base-emitter junctions which then saturates T_2. Raising T_2 emitter saturates T_4 taking the output down to about 0.2 V. T_3 is cut off because, with T_2 and T_4 saturated, and with D_1 acting as a voltage level shifting device, T_3 base-emitter voltage is too small to support conduction.

For a more detailed explanation, including consideration of the effect of circuit capacitance on the switching action, references such as Millman, for example, may be consulted.

13.4.2 Operating aspects of TTL logic

In the explanation of the circuit behaviour, certain voltage levels were used to represent the logic 1 state and others to represent logic 0 (see Chapter 16); the input and output levels were not necessarily the same. Clearly, the levels depend on the nature of the circuit, the supply voltage ($+5$ V for TTL) and on external connections to the circuit. Fig. 13.26 summarises the specification limits for TTL logic. All voltages are positive with the logic 1 condition represented by a more positive voltage than logic 0; this is known as **positive logic**. **Negative logic** is the reverse.

In the circuit description, output voltage levels were discussed without reference to an external 'load'. Frequently the gates will be driving other gates and it is necessary to consider the effect of such connections. As explained, with the output high and with no following gates, the output settles at about 4 V. Although very little current flows into an input-high gate, the output voltage does fall and the significance of the information in Fig. 13.26 is that, with the maximum specified number of gates connected, the voltage will not drop below 2.4 V. With the driving-gate output low, the open-circuit operating condition has been described as T_3 cut-off and T_4 saturated with an output voltage at less than about 0.2 V. When 'driving' other gates the situation differs from that in which passive circuits are driven because there is a current flow back into the driving gate and the output voltage rises. The driving gate is said to 'sink' the current. According to Fig. 13.26, the output voltage will not rise above 0.4 V when the specified maximum number of gates is connected.

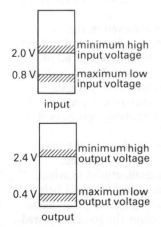

2.0 V — minimum high input voltage

0.8 V — maximum low input voltage

input

2.4 V — minimum high output voltage

0.4 V — maximum low output voltage

output

Fig. 13.26 Specification logic levels

The maximum number of driven gates is governed by the **fan-out** of the driving gate. The value of the fan-out is dependent on the current flow into or out of each device; the total current must not exceed that amount which will cause the gate voltage to lie outside the given performance limits. In this context, **the unit TTL load** (UL) current may be used. The UL value is 40 μA for the high output value and 1.6 mA for the low value.

There is a gap between the maximum output voltage in the low state (0.4 V) and that which must exist at an input in order to be recognised as low (0.8 V). This gives a margin for error known as the **noise margin**. Thus, $0.8 - 0.4 = 0.4$ V is allowed for noise voltages which may be superimposed on the output-low level. This is a guaranteed level; in practice a greater margin (about 1 V) may be achieved. Similarly, there is a guaranteed 0.4 V between the 2.4 V high-output level and the minimum required high-input level.

Another important parameter in gate interconnection is the **propagation delay**. The existence of circuit capacitances was mentioned above and these place a limit on the speed at which the output state changes in response to an input state change. TTL gates are designed to minimise the delay and times of the order of 10 ns are obtained with standard TTL. However, smaller delays are obtainable using **Schottky TTL** in which **Schottky transistors** (Fig. 13.27) are used. These have a diode fabricated between collector and base which prevents the transistor from saturating heavily by establishing a conducting path between collector and base as the collector voltage falls (for the n–p–n transistor). The metal-semiconductor **Schottky diode** has a forward voltage drop of about 0.4 V and this is sufficient to hold the transistor approximately on the edge of saturation.

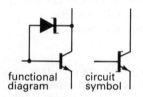

functional   circuit
diagram   symbol

Fig. 13.27 Schottky transistor

Saturation increases the switching time because there is an increase in the charge storage in the base. It is, of course, necessary that the diode itself does not exhibit a charge-storage effect but this is effectively achieved in the metal-semiconductor device. The references investigate the effect in greater depth.

Delays of the order of 3 ns may be achieved in the Schottky device (suffixed S); with a power dissipation per gate of about 20 mW, this gives a **delay-power product** of 60 pJ. Low-power Schottky (suffix LS) with large resistance values decreases the power dissipation to about 2 mW per gate which, with a delay of 10 ns, gives a delay-power product of 20 pJ. With an advanced form of construction, figures of 4 ns and 1 mW per gate may be obtained.

The circuit described above is self-contained in the sense that no additional (external) components are required. However, **open-collector** devices are manufactured in which T_3 and D_1 in Fig. 13.25 are omitted, the output terminal being the collector of T_4. Such devices require an external collector load or **pull-up resistor** but they do permit the so-called **wired-AND** connection to be made. In this connection, an AND function is achieved by connecting several outputs together with a common pull-up resistor. Such a connection is not possible with the gates previously described.

It is shown in Fig. 13.28 that two open-collector NOR gates (for example) with their outputs connected to a common pull-up resistor perform the logic function $\overline{A+B}\cdot\overline{C+D}$ which would otherwise require three gates. In effect, connecting the two outputs together means that the output will only go high if (as if with separate pull-up resistors) both NOR-gate outputs go high, i.e. if either NOR-gate output transistor is conducting, the combined output will be low. This is effectively the AND function and the connection is therefore known as the wired-AND connection. The symbol at the node in Fig. 13.28 is used to imply this function. In the context of an active-low system the arrangement effectively provides a wired-OR facility, the output going low if either (or both) inputs are low.

Fig. 13.28 Wired-AND connection

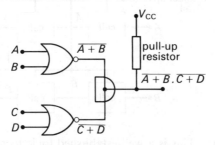

13.4.3 Integrated injection logic (I^2L)

This is a multiple-collector bipolar technology, without resistors, used in large-scale integration and occupying a much smaller chip area than the TTL gate. A delay-power product of better than 1 pJ may be obtained. The structure of a basic I^2L cell is shown with its logic function in Fig. 13.29. T_1 is a p–n–p transistor functioning as a current source, the current being externally controlled by the potential on the injection-voltage connection. Depending on whether the input is low or high, the current either flows back to the source through the input terminal or to the base of T_2 respectively.

Fig. 13.29 Basic I^2L cell

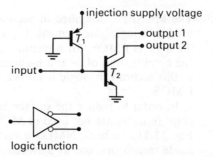

Thus, a low input level will cut T_2 off, giving a high output in each collector. A high input will saturate T_2 giving a low voltage on each collector and the circuit behaves as a multiple-output inverter. Integrated-circuit fabrication is such that the collector of the p–n–p transistor is merged with the base of the n–p–n type. The injection supply voltage is obtained via a single external resistor linking V_{CC} to all the injection supply terminals via an injection rail. The current supplied (and the cell operating speed) may be varied by varying the rail supply voltage.

The cell will be seen to be essentially open collector and, if required, the output may be wire-ANDed. In other situations, the collector outputs will drive other cells to build up a more complex logic function. For example, a self-contained NAND gate could be assembled from five cells and a wired-AND connection. This is shown in Fig. 13.30. The wired-AND connection can only be made from collector outputs; if A and B were available at collectors (from a previous stage), the first two pairs of cells would not be required.

Fig. 13.30 I^2L cell interconnection

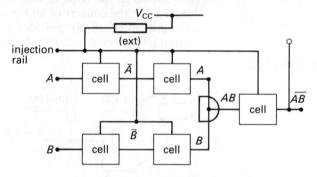

13.4.4 Emitter coupled logic (ECL)

This is a well-established logic technology (also known as **current-mode logic** (CML)) offering very low propagation delays. Thus, such gates will be found in applications where high speed is essential. With delays of less than 1 ns, the delay-power product is between 10 and 100 pJ.

The gate is based on the differential-amplifier stage shown in Fig. 13.5 but with one of the bases held at a fixed reference potential. The input is at the other base; multiple inputs for the basic OR and NOR logic function are provided by paralleling input transistors and feeding individual bases. The transistors do not saturate and ECL is known as non-saturating logic.

13.4.5 MOS logic

The MOSFET described in Section 8.4 of Chapter 12 may be used as a logic-gate element. If p-channel devices are used, the logic is PMOS, for n-channel devices it is NMOS and for the combination of p- and n-channel devices (also described in this section) the logic is known as complementary MOS or CMOS.

In order to reduce the surface area of the integrated-circuit chip, resistors are not used in MOS logic. As shown in Fig. 13.31(a) a basic NMOS inverter uses two enhancement-mode transistors, one as a switching element (T_2) and the other as an active load (T_1). The nature of the voltage/current relationship for the load transistor T_1 may be deduced from the set of typical characteristics shown in Fig. 13.31(b). Because T_1 drain and gate are common, the load characteristic must satisfy the relationship $v_{GS} = v_{DS}$; points where this applies are joined by the dashed line.

Fig. 13.31 An NMOS
inverter and its
characteristics

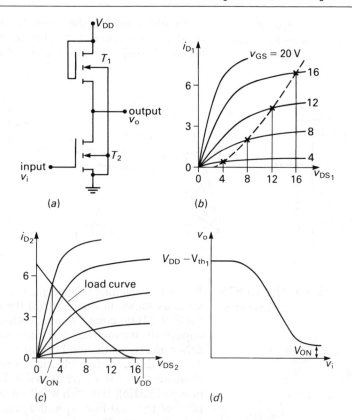

(a)

(b)

(c)

(d)

Operation of the switching element T_2 is now governed by
the load 'curve' shown in Fig. 13.31(c) after the manner of the
load line shown, for example, in Fig. 12.22. When $v_i = 0$ V, T_2
is cut off and v_o is approximately equal to the supply voltage
less T_1 threshold. When v_i is raised to a value approximately
equal to the supply voltage (the logic 1 condition), v_o falls to
a low value, V_{on}. The basic circuit therefore operates as an
inverter. Fig. 13.31(d) is a transfer of characters showing
variation of v_o ($= v_{DS_2}$) with v_i ($= v_{GS_2}$).

To implement a NAND gate, two or more switching
transistors may be connected in series to a common active
load. Then, only when all inputs are high (i.e. all transistors
conducting) will the output go low. A NOR function can be
realised by connecting the switching transistors in parallel.

An alternative arrangement uses an NMOS depletion-mode
load with an NMOS enhancement-mode driver. Fig. 13.32(a)
shows the arrangement. With v_{GS_1} equal to zero the
voltage–current characteristic for the load is the $v_{GS} = 0$
characteristic in Fig. 12.34(c), and superimposing this on the
output characteristics for the driver (T_2) gives the result in
Fig. 13.32(b); the load line curves in the opposite direction to
that for the enhancement load in Fig. 13.31(c). The transfer
characteristic is shown in Fig. 13.32(c) from which it will be
seen that, in the input-low state, the output reaches the full
V_{DD} value whereas with the enhancement load it is reduced by
the factor V_{th}.

Fig. 13.32 An NMOS inverter with depletion and enhancement transistors

An additional transfer characteristic is shown for a device in which the channel width/length ratio for the driver is increased compared with that for the load.

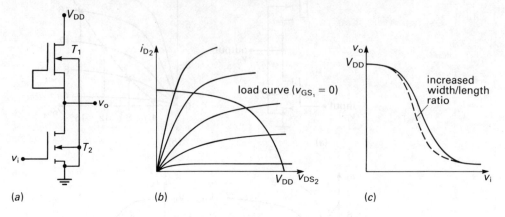

(a)　　　　　(b)　　　　　(c)

13.4.6 The CMOS inverter

If p- and n-channel enhancement devices are connected in series as shown in Fig. 13.33(a) the basic complementary MOS (CMOS) circuit results. Although the arrangement is apparently symmetrical it is convenient to regard T_2 as the driver and T_1 as the load (as for the NMOS circuits above). To establish a transfer characteristic for the circuit the output characteristics for T_2 are drawn in Fig. 13.33(b) (as they were in Fig. 13.31(b)) but with a full set of characteristics for T_1 in place of the load line. T_1 and T_2 characteristics are assumed to be the same. The gate-source voltages for the two devices must add up to V_{DD} so that, for example, with $V_{DD} = +20$ V and with $v_{GS_2} = +4$ V, v_{GS_1} will be -16 V and the operating point as shown at point B. As v_{GS_2} is taken from 0 up to $+20$ V and v_{GS_1} correspondingly changes, a locus A to G (shown dotted) is traced out. Since v_{GS_2} is v_i and v_{DS_2} is v_o the transfer characteristic is shown in Fig. 13.33(c).

Normal operating points are A and G for $v_i = 0$ and $v_i = V_{DD}$ respectively. In each case only a very small current flows (of the order of 1 nA) in the quiescent condition and the static power consumption is of the order of 10 nW. A current flows during the switching operation and the active power

Fig. 13.33 A CMOS inverter

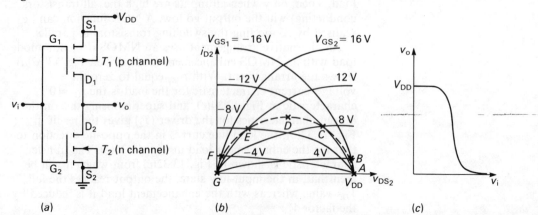

(a)　　　　　(b)　　　　　(c)

consumption then depends on the switching rate. Typically, power consumption is 0.5 mW at 1 MHz which, with propagation delays of the order of 20 ns, results in a power-delay product of 10 pJ. The device behaves as an inverter because with $v_i = 0$, T_2 is off and has a much higher drain-source resistance than T_1. Thus V_{DD} appears across T_2 and v_o is high. As v_i swings high, T_1 has the high resistance and v_{DD} is dropped across it, taking v_o low.

The essential advantages of CMOS will be seen to be low power consumption, a non-critical supply voltage (typically, 5–15 V), a high input impedance (leading to high fan out), and a threshold level halfway between 0 and V_{DD} giving a noise margin of about $0.4V_{DD}$. Disadvantages are the dangers of charge build up on the insulated input gates which can destroy the circuit. To prevent this happening, input gates should always be connected to a specific circuit potential (e.g. unused NAND-gate inputs should be connected to V_{DD}). To reduce the chances of accidental damage diode protection circuits are provided on the input gates but care must still be exercised when handling and operating MOS devices.

It will be appreciated from the discussion above that the output impedance is relatively high. This does not present a particular problem when feeding other CMOS circuits with their very high input impedances, but when feeding TTL or similar circuits there can be difficulties and an interface circuit may be required.

As for the TTL families, a number of CMOS derivatives exist. The original 4000 series of logic devices is now complemented by the 4000B buffered types. Also available is the 74HC family with an improved performance, comparable with the 74LS logic.

13.4.7 Other CMOS circuits

The form of a 2-input CMOS NAND gate is shown in Fig. 13.34. The T_3 and T_4 transistors are connected in a 'series' form (as for the NMOS NAND gate) so that a low output will only be obtained if both inputs are high. The complementary transistors effectively form a parallel grouping. The CMOS NOR gate reverses this grouping.

Fig. 13.34 A CMOS NAND gate

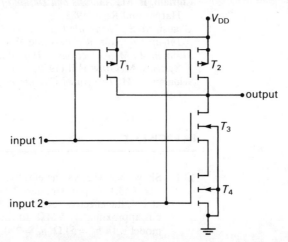

MOS devices are also used in linear circuits. For example, the operational amplifiers discussed in Chapter 14 traditionally used only bipolar technology but are now available in forms which combine bipolar and FET circuits as well as CMOS devices.

Key points to remember

- a transistor current source has a high resistance to small-signal variations; the current-mirror circuit can be used for biasing;
- the differential amplifier provides high gain to the difference between the input voltages at two terminals;
- the direct (bias) component of a signal may be shifted without substantially altering the time-varying component;
- transistor instantaneous-power dissipation can be calculated as the product of voltage and current but due allowance must be made for polarities;
- power output stages aim to give maximum efficiency with minimum distortion;
- full-wave rectification can be effected by bridge and centre-tapped circuits, capacitor smoothing can be applied to either;
- a Zener diode can be used as a simple voltage regulator, other regulator types include pass-transistor and switching types; controlled rectification is also possible;
- a number of logic families exist, including TTL, I^2L, ECL, MOS and CMOS; each has particular advantages.

Further reading

Chirlain, P. M., *Analysis and Design of Integrated Electronic Circuits.* Harper and Row (1982).

Ghausi, M. S., *Electronic Devices and Circuits: Discrete and Integrated.* Holt, Rinehart and Winston (1985).

Millman, J., *Microelectronics: Digital and Analog Circuits and Systems.* McGraw-Hill (1979).

Seidman, A. H., *Integrated Circuits Applications Handbook.* J. Wiley (1983).

EXERCISES 13

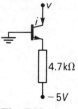

Fig. E13.1

13.1   Show that whereas the effective resistance v/i of the circuit in Fig. E13.1 is approximately $2.1\,\text{k}\Omega$ when v remains constant at 2 V, the effective resistance when there are small changes in v is approximately $5\,\text{M}\Omega$. In the latter case use a small-signal model with $h_{ie} = 5\,\text{k}\Omega$, $h_{fe} = 200$, $h_{oe} = 20\,\mu\text{S}$ and $h_{re} = 0$.

13.2 In the current mirror in Fig. 13.2, the currents flowing in T_1 and T_2 are almost the same. If a resistor R_3 is introduced between T_2 emitter and earth, its base-emitter voltage will be less than that of T_1 by the magnitude of the voltage drop across R_3, permitting independent control of I_2 (with I_2 always less than I_1) by choice of R_3. Calculate the value of R_3 required to set $I_2 = 0.1 I_1 = 0.1$ mA at 290 K.

Note: it is necessary to utilise the exponential relationship between emitter current and base-emitter voltage in Section 5.4 of Chapter 12.

13.3 The circuit in Fig. 13.3 is designed to minimise the effect of changes in β, perhaps arising from the use of different transistors. Another factor which might cause collector-current changes is a change of base-emitter voltage with temperature: base-emitter voltage decreases with temperature at approximately 2 mV/°C. Using the data from Example 13.1 determine the effect on the collector current of a change in V_{BE} due to a temperature rise of 40 °C, assuming that β is nominally constant at

(i) 100, and
(ii) 200,

as was the case in Example 13.1.

13.4 The differential-amplifier stage shown in Fig. E13.2 uses identical transistors.

Fig. E13.2

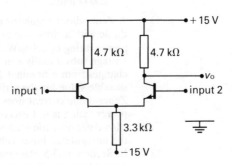

(a) Determine the currents in each branch of the circuit and the output voltage v_0 when both bases are at earth potential. Assume matched transistors with $V_{BE} = 0.65$ V.
(b) Using the small-signal model in Fig. 13.5, determine v_0 when

(i) a sinusoidal voltage of 10 mV amplitude is applied to input 1, and
(ii) a sinusoidal voltage (in phase with that applied to input 1) of amplitude 15 mV is applied to input 2 at the same time.

(Assume a temperature of 290 K when determining g_m.)
(c) With input 1 held at earth potential, determine v_0 when input 2 is raised to a (constant) value of 100 mV.

13.5 In the level-shifting circuit shown in Fig. E13.3, calculate approximate values for v_0 when

(i) $v_i = 0$ V, and
(ii) $v_i = 10$ V,

for three settings of R_1, zero, 5 kΩ and 10 kΩ (i.e. six calculations in all) and hence sketch input/output characteristics for the three settings of R_1.

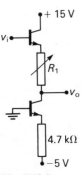

Fig. E13.3

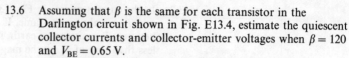

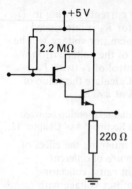

Fig. E13.4

13.6 Assuming that β is the same for each transistor in the Darlington circuit shown in Fig. E13.4, estimate the quiescent collector currents and collector-emitter voltages when $\beta = 120$ and $V_{BE} = 0.65\,V$.

13.7 (a) Explain why the power dissipated in the transistor in a simple resistance-loaded common-emitter amplifier reduces as the r.m.s. collector-current increases.

(b) A common-emitter amplifier with a collector load resistance of $100\,\Omega$ is operated with a $20\,V$ supply. Calculate the quiescent collector current and collector-emitter voltage which will allow maximum load power (avoiding distortion). Determine the maximum power and the minimum power rating of the transistor to ensure safety under no-signal conditions.

(c) What would be the maximum output power into a transformer coupled load assuming the same transistor and the same supply voltage.

13.8 A full-wave centre-tapped rectifier circuit with capacitor smoothing is required to provide a constant output voltage of approximately $15\,V$ from a $240\,V$ sinusoidal mains supply. Determine

(i) the transformer turns ratio required; and
(ii) the value of shunt capacitance required to ensure that the r.m.s. ripple does not exceed $100\,mV$ when feeding a $200\,\Omega$ load.

13.9 A Zener-diode regulator circuit (as in Fig. 13.18) uses a $6.3\,V$ diode with a slope conductance of $0.8\,S$ and a maximum power rating of $300\,mW$. It is required to hold the $600\,\Omega$ load voltage substantially constant as the circuit input voltage changes from a nominal $10\,V$ to a nominal $20\,V$. Calculate a suitable value for the series resistance R_s to ensure that the Zener-diode current does not fall below $5\,mA$ and that its power rating is not exceeded.
Also determine the load-voltage ripple if the ripple voltage on the unregulated input voltage is $200\,mV$.

13.10 In Section 13.3.5, the mean value of the output waveform is shown to be 0.238 of the peak value. What would be the r.m.s. value in the same circumstances? If the thyristor were used to control the heat output from an oven, which figure would have the greater significance?

13.11 A simple bipolar inverter gate is shown in Fig. E13.5. If $V_{CE(sat)} = 0.2\,V$ and $V_{BE(on)} = 0.6\,V$ and $\beta = 150$ deduce the shape of the transfer characteristic of v_o plotted against v_i. What are the inverter noise margins when operating with other gates of the same type?

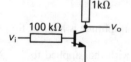

Fig. E13.5

14 Feedback and operational amplifiers

The principal learning objectives of this chapter are to:

	Section	Exercise
• state the properties of feedback systems;	1.1	
• describe the block-diagram representation of systems;	1.2	14.1
• analyse feedback systems with respect to:		
gain sensitivity;	2.2	14.2
non-linear distortion;	2.3	14.3
amplitude and phase distortion;	2.4	14.4
• state the properties of the ideal operational amplifier;	3.1, 3.2	
• apply the operational amplifier to simple amplifying and arithmetic circuits;	3.3	14.5
• determine the behaviour of a simple integrating circuit;	3.4	14.6
• understand the limitations and imperfection of operational amplifiers;	4.1	
• analyse operational-amplifier circuits to determine their frequency response;	5.1–5.3	14.7
• explain slew rate;	5.4	14.8
• apply the Nyquist criterion to determine the stability of feedback circuits;	6.1, 6.2	14.9
• determine relative stability using Bode diagrams;	6.3	14.10
• analyse a range of active-filter circuits;	7.1–7.5	14.11
• describe a number of applications of operational amplifiers.	8.1–8.4	

14.1 The basic feedback system

14.1.1 Some properties of feedback systems

Feedback is the process by which a signal derived from one point in a processing or controlling system (often the output) is returned to an earlier point in the system. It is used in a wide range of applications. In controlling applications it is used in a 'corrective' way. For example, a car driver continually feeds information on speed and road conditions back, through his eyes and brain, to his hand and foot muscles. This is a very complex process; in electromechanical systems only one factor may be monitored and, normally, this is also the controlled quantity. For example, a voltage regulator may feed back a signal proportional to its output voltage so that any tendency for the output to vary is counteracted.

In signal processing applications, feedback is often used to desensitise a system: for example, the operation of a system may be critically affected by a component whose behaviour is erratic. Feedback is capable of reducing the system's dependence upon the properties of this single element. Feedback may also be used regeneratively. This is the desensitising process in reverse in which changes in an output signal are fed back so as to reinforce the change. Often, this is an undesirable effect (occurring unintentionally) but it is deliberately used in, for example, the design of oscillators for waveform generation.

14.1.2 Block diagram representation of feedback systems

When dealing with signal levels, a feedback system may be represented by a **block diagram**. Fig. 14.1 shows two commonly used forms. A variety of symbols for the input and output variables may be encountered, often related to the nature of the controlled quantity. Possibilities are current, voltage, shaft velocity and angular position: the variable v is used here in a representative way. The $G(s)$ and $H(s)$ notation used in Fig. 14.1(a) to represent the block functions emphasises that the transfer function may be a function of the complex variable s and is usually associated with control-systems analysis. In electronic systems, the use of β and A (Fig. 14.1(b)) is more common.

Fig. 14.1 Feedback-system arrangements and symbols

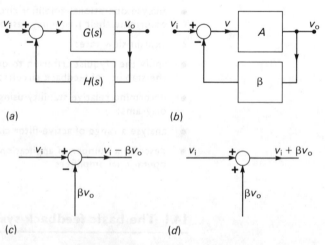

(a)   (b)

(c)   (d)

Fig. 14.1(c) and (d) shows in greater detail alternative forms of a **summing junction** which, in principle, could be used in conjunction with either (a) or (b). In practice, both forms are used, particularly with the β, A model. The junction could be a resistive network or may be one of the operational-amplifier circuits described later in this chapter.

The arrows effectively imply that the signal's path is unidirectional, i.e. the signal moves through the block in the stated direction but not in the other. For blocks and summing junctions containing active devices, almost complete isolation of the input from the output may exist but, by their nature, resistive networks are not unilateral. Nevertheless, even here, signal levels are often such that unilateral conditions effectively exist.

For the single-loop feedback systems shown it is possible to deduce the **closed-loop transfer function** (CLTF) $V_o(s)/V_i(s)$ as follows:

$$V(s) = V_i(s) - H(s)V_o(s),$$

and

$$V_o(s) = G(s)V(s).$$

Combining the two equations,

$$V_o(s)/V_i(s) = \frac{G(s)}{1 + G(s)H(s)}.$$

The corresponding expression for Fig. 14.1(*b*) is

$$\frac{A}{1 + \beta A},$$

and, for the alternative summing junction form in Fig. 14.1(*d*),

$$\frac{A}{1 - \beta A}.$$

The term $G(s)H(s)$ (or βA) is known as the **open-loop transfer function** (OLTF).

Whilst systems may comprise only a single feedback loop, multiple loops may exist; however, these may be reduced to

Fig. 14.2 The effect of system-block transfers

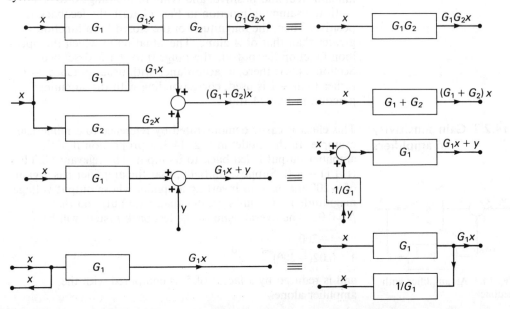

the single-loop form provided that the summing devices and the blocks themselves are linear and there is no loading effect of one upon another. Fig. 14.2 illustrates the basic rules of reduction as well as demonstrating their validity. An application is illustrated in Section 14.5.1.

14.2 Analysis of feedback systems

14.2.1 Introduction

Interpretation of the closed-loop transfer function depends upon the type of system involved. For example, it may be required to check that a proposed control system will be stable and, if so, what its time response to a step change in input is likely to be. In an electronic system it may be required to estimate the effect of a change in the gain of an amplifier due, for example, to changes in temperature. Or it may be to determine the effect on the frequency response or on the input impedance of a network. Representative examples are discussed in the following sections.

In discussing the effects of feedback it is common practice to divide the arrangement into two broad classifications. These are **negative** and **positive feedback**, also known as **degenerative** and **regenerative feedback**, respectively. If, for example, the open-loop transfer function is real and negative (with the summing junction in Fig. 14.1(d)) then the feedback is negative; the feedback is also negative if, with the open-loop transfer function positive, a minus sign is introduced at the junction as in Fig. 14.1(c). In these circumstances the denominator of the closed-loop transfer function is greater than 1 and the magnitude of the whole function is less than the magnitude of A (or $G(s)$) alone. With the open-loop function real and positive, and lying in the range 0 to $+1$ (with the summing junction in Fig. 14.1(d)), the feedback is positive. Then, the magnitude of the closed-loop function is greater than that of A alone. The situation in which the open-loop function lies outside the range 0 to $+1$ is described in Section 14.6.1; there, in accordance with usual practice, -1 rather than $+1$ is used, corresponding with the summing junction in Fig. 14.1(c).

14.2.2 Gain sensitivity in amplifiers

This effect is easily demonstrated by reference to a numerical example. In the model in Fig. 14.3, a proportion β of the amplifier output is fed back to its input. The relevant CLTF is $A/(1 - \beta A)$. Suppose, initially, that the amplifier has a gain of -200 (i.e. it is an inverting amplifier whose output voltage magnitude is 200 times greater than its input) and that $\beta = 0.02$. The overall gain of the feedback system will be

$$\frac{-200}{1 - 0.02(-200)} = -40$$

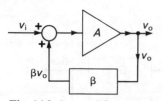

Fig. 14.3 An amplifier with feedback

and is reduced by a factor of 5 as compared with the amplifier alone.

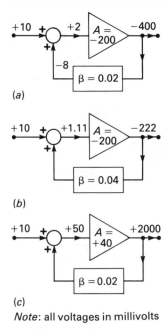

(a)

(b)

(c)

Note: all voltages in millivolts

Fig. 14.4 The effect of different combinations of A and β

The real interest, however, is not centred on the reduction in gain but on the comparative reduction which occurs when, perhaps due to manufacturing tolerances, the amplifier is replaced with one having a gain of only -120, a 40% fall on the -200 figure. The new gain with feedback is $-120/(1 - 0.02(-120)) = -35.3$, a reduction of only 11.8% compared with the amplifier-gain reduction of 40%. It will be seen that the closed-loop system is relatively insensitive to amplifier-gain changes. The overall reduction in gain from 200 to 40 (or 120 to 35.3) is assumed not to be important. The implication is that, in designing such a system, the gain of the component amplifier must be much greater than the required gain of the system. Inspection of the expression will show that as either A or β increases, and $|\beta A|$ becomes large compared with unity, the closed-loop gain tends towards $A/(-\beta A) = -1/\beta$. For example, if A is -2000 (or $+2000$), the closed-loop gain is -48.8 (or -51.3). Both values approach $-1/\beta$ ($= -50$). Fig. 14.4 illustrates three possible feedback situations. Fig. 14.4(a) restates the original calculation above with a closed-loop gain of -40. Fig. 14.4(b) shows the effect of increasing the feedback factor. The feedback is still negative and the output voltage falls; this is because the input to the amplifier has reduced (from 2 mV to 1.11 mV) as a greater voltage is subtracted from the 10 mV input. In Fig. 14.4(c) the amplifier gain is $+40$, giving an open-loop transfer function between 0 and $+1$. The feedback voltage now adds to the input to give an output magnitude in excess of that of the amplifier alone. In this case the circuit is very sensitive to gain changes. For example, if the amplifier gain increases by 1% to 40.4, the new output is 2104 mV, an increase of 5.2%.

14.2.3 Non-linear distortion

Non-linear transfer characteristics and their effects are described in several chapters. In Chapter 13, for example, non-linearity arising in the complementary-pair output stage occurs. In this, as in many instances, the effects are unwanted. For example, the non-linear characteristic shown in Fig. 14.5 implies that the gain of the circuit is a variable dependent upon the magnitude of the input signal v_i. The following numerical analysis shows that the desensitising effect of negative feedback tends to make the gain constant and, hence, the characteristic more linear. The scales used in Fig. 14.5 indicate that the device gains at the input voltages 1, 2, 3 and 4 are 10, 25, 33 and 50 respectively. Applying 10% feedback by means of the circuit shown in Fig. 14.1(b), for which the closed-loop gain is given by $A/(1 + \beta A)$, reduces the gain to the respective values, 5, 7.1, 7.7 and 8.3. To present a fair comparison with the previous values, the closed-loop gain is now linearly increased so that the gain with an input voltage of 4 is the same as without feedback (i.e. increasing by a factor $50/8.3 = 6$). The revised gain values are 30, 42, 46 and 50. Multiplying by the respective input voltages, gives new output voltages of 30, 84, 138 and 200, shown dashed on Fig. 14.5; the linearity will be seen to be significantly improved. Taking the argument to the limit, the

Fig. 14.5 Amplifier linearity, with and without feedback

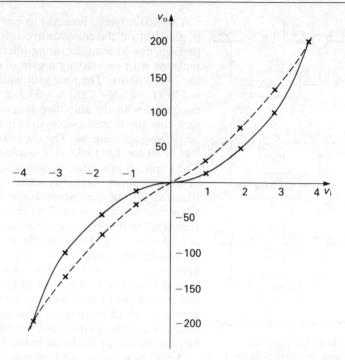

closed-loop gain tends toward $+1/\beta$ and the transfer characteristic is linear with a slope $1/\beta$ or $10 \times 6 = 60$ in this example.

If the additional stage introduced to increase the gain by 6 were itself non-linear the advantage would, of course, be lost. However, in practice, such a preamplifier would be operating at lower output-voltage levels and could reasonably be expected to be much more linear than the main output stage.

14.2.4 Amplitude and phase distortion

As described in Section 5.2 of Chapter 8, these distortions are introduced as a result of non-ideal frequency-response characteristics. Fig. 14.6 shows typical magnitude and phase characteristics (full lines) in the form described in Chapter 7.

Unfortunately it is less easy to generate new graphs than in the previous section because the amplifier gain is now

Fig. 14.6 The effect of feedback on frequency response

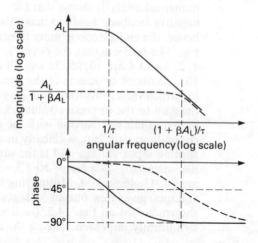

complex, i.e. it has a phase shift as well as magnitude. A general expression for closed-loop-gain is therefore obtained and illustrated in terms of symbols by the dashed lines (Fig. 14.6).

Suppose the gain of the amplifier alone is $A_L/(1 + j\omega\tau)$ where A_L is the low-frequency gain and τ is the time constant. The closed-loop gain is now given by

$$\frac{A_L/(1 + j\omega\tau)}{1 + \beta A_L/(1 + j\omega\tau)} \quad \text{(for the arrangement in Fig. 14.1}(b)\text{)}$$

$$= \frac{A_L}{1 + j\omega\tau + \beta A_L}$$

$$= \frac{A_L/(1 + \beta A_L)}{1 + j\omega\tau/(1 + \beta A_L)} = \frac{A_L'}{1 + j\omega\tau'}.$$

Arranging the closed-loop gain in the form shown indicates a new low-frequency gain $A_L' = A_L/(1 + \beta A_L)$ and a new time constant $\tau' = \tau/(1 + \beta A_L)$. In drawing the graphs it is assumed that βA_L is real and positive so that $1 + \beta A_L$ is positive and greater than unity. The results show that the gain–bandwidth product remains the same with feedback applied: the value is A_L/τ in each case. Thus, as the low-frequency gain is reduced so the bandwidth is increased.

The effective reduction in distortion can be illustrated by reference to Figs. 8.11 and 8.12. In that example, the waveform at the output differs from that at the input as a result of the differential amplitude and phase responses at the two harmonic frequencies. In this present case, the frequency response of the amplifier has the same general response shape as the CR network in Example 8.2 and therefore the same considerations apply. However, with feedback applied the extension of the constant gain and zero-phase-shift conditions (shown by dashed lines in Fig. 14.6) could well mean that both fundamental and second harmonic components are subject to the same amplification, thereby removing most of the waveform distortion.

14.3 The ideal operational amplifier

14.3.1 Introduction

The operational amplifier is the most commonly encountered linear (or analogue) integrated circuit, and is produced in many varying forms by the major linear-circuit manufacturers. In carrying out work on operational circuits, i.e. circuits capable of performing mathematical operations such as addition and integration, it was found that the inclusion of a very high gain amplifier enabled near-ideal conditions to be established. As high-gain direct-coupled differential-input amplifiers became available in integrated form, the name 'operational amplifier' was applied to the amplifying element alone even though applications of the new circuit element extended beyond the operational circuits.

14.3.2 The ideal operational amplifier

The properties of the ideal amplifier are illustrated in Fig. 14.7(a) with the circuit symbol in Fig. 14.7(b). The ideal amplifier has an infinitely high input impedance between each of the differential-input terminals (labelled + and −) and earth as well as between the terminals themselves. The output voltage is A times the differential-input voltage v_i where A is a very large real value. Equal voltages applied to each terminal (i.e. $v_i = 0$) result in zero output voltage and the output impedance is zero. Practical amplifiers fall short of this ideal but such imperfections are not discussed until Section 14.4 following an introduction to a number of basic applications.

Fig. 14.7 The ideal operational amplifier

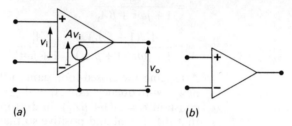

(a)   (b)

14.3.3 Basic amplifying and arithmetic circuits

The operational amplifier is almost always used in a feedback-circuit configuration, examples of which are shown in Fig. 14.8. A logical approach to the analysis of the circuits would seem to be to apply the principles introduced in Section 14.2. This approach is adopted in Section 14.5, but a short cut will be used here, based on the high-gain and high-input impedance properties of the device. It is known as the **virtual-earth** or **virtual-ground** principle by which (in Fig. 14.8(a)) it is argued that because the gain is very large, typically 10^5, v_i must be small for all reasonable values of v_o, and the inverting terminal is virtually at the same potential as the non-inverting terminal, i.e. at earth (ground) potential. For example, if v_o were 6 V, v_i would be $(6/10^5) = 60\ \mu V$. It follows that the potential differences across R_2 and R_1 are fixed at approximately v_o and v_{in}, respectively, with the reference directions shown in the diagram. These in turn fix the currents in R_1 and R_2 at v_{in}/R_1 and v_o/R_2, and because it is assumed that no current flows into the inverting terminal of

Fig. 14.8 Operational-amplifier based amplifying circuits

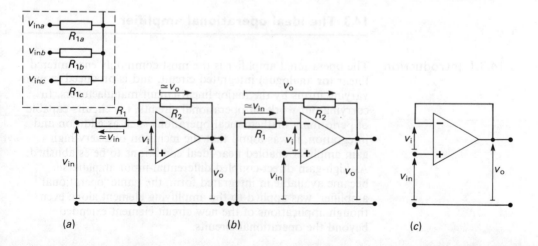

(a)   (b)   (c)

the amplifier, their sum is zero, i.e. $v_{in}/R_1 + v_o/R_2 = 0$. The output-voltage is therefore given by

$$v_o = -\frac{R_2}{R_1} v_{in}.$$

Subject to the assumption that the gain A is very large, the gain of the circuit as a whole is dependent entirely on the values of the externally connected resistance. This is consistent with the general feedback principle by which a high open-loop gain results in a closed-loop gain which is dependent only on the feedback factor β.

A variation on Fig. 14.8(a) (shown in the inset) has a number of resistances (three in this example) feeding the inverting terminal which, in this context, is called the summing junction. The currents through these resistances when added to v_o/R_2 still sum to zero so that

$$(v_{ina}/R_{1a}) + (v_{inb}/R_{1b}) + (v_{inc}/R_{1c}) + (v_o/R_2) = 0$$

and hence

$$v_o = -\left(\frac{R_2}{R_{1a}} v_{ina} + \frac{R_2}{R_{1b}} v_{inb} + \frac{R_2}{R_{1c}} v_{inc}\right).$$

The circuit is thus a summing circuit. For example, if all the resistance values are the same, the output voltage is simply the inverted sum of the three inputs,

$$v_o = -(v_{ina} + v_{inb} + v_{inc}).$$

Inputs may be added in differing proportions by suitable choice of resistance values.

The circuit in Fig. 14.8(a) is an inverting amplifier in which, at low frequencies, the output voltage is always of opposite polarity to the input as well has having its amplitude scaled by the factor R_2/R_1. Fig. 14.8(b) is a non-inverting circuit, for which an approximate analysis may be made using the same principle as for the virtual-earth method in Fig. 14.8(a). With both amplifier-input terminals at substantially the same potential, v_{in} appears across R_1. With v_o appearing across R_1 and R_2 in series, and negligible current into the amplifier terminals, simple proportionality gives

$$\frac{v_o}{v_{in}} = +\frac{R_1 + R_2}{R_1}.$$

A variation on this circuit is to make R_1 infinite, giving a gain of $+1$ independently of R_2. This results in the **unity-gain buffer** or **voltage follower** whose function is to provide a high-input impedance and low-output impedance (without changing the signal amplitude). Typically, it is used to prevent one stage loading a previous stage. The operation of the circuit may alternatively be explained by arguing that if there is negligible voltage difference between inverting and non-inverting terminals, there is negligible difference between input and output potentials. A consequence of this circuit arrangement is that (ideally) no current flows in R_2 and hence its value is not critical. Setting R_2 at zero ensures that there is no voltage drop, even if a small current does flow. The circuit is shown in Fig. 14.8(c).

14.3.4 An integrating circuit

If the resistance R_2 in Fig. 14.8(a) is replaced by a capacitor, the output voltage is proportional to the integral of the input voltage. Fig. 14.9 shows the arrangement. Using the virtual-earth approach, $i_R + i_C = 0$ from which $v_{in}/R_1 + C \, dv_o/dt = 0$ and thus

$$v_o = -\frac{1}{CR_1} \int v_{in} \, dt.$$

Fig. 14.9 An integrator

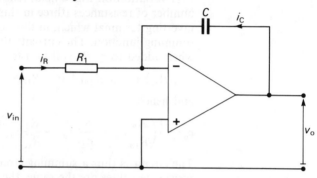

Example 14.1   Determine the output-voltage waveform for the circuit shown in Fig. 14.9 with $C = 0.1\,\mu F$, $R_1 = 10\,k\Omega$ (and a very high amplifier gain) for the input-voltage waveform in Fig. 14.10(a). Assume that v_o is initially zero.

The time constant CR_1 is $10^{-7} \times 10^4 = 10^{-3}$ s. During the first 0.5 ms,

$$v_o = -\frac{1}{10^{-3}} \int 8 \, dt = 8 \times 10^3 t \text{ V}.$$

This is a linear ramp reaching a value of $-8 \times 10^3 \times 0.5 \times 10^{-3} = -4$ V after 0.5 ms. Up to 1 ms,

$$v_o = -\frac{1}{10^{-3}} \int 5 \, dt - 4 = -5t - 4 \text{ V},$$

where t is measured from 0.5 ms. At $t = 1$ ms, $v_o = -6.5$ V. The remainder of the output waveform is determined in a similar way and the result is drawn in Fig. 14.10(b).

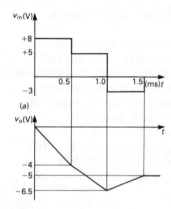

Fig. 14.10 Integrator response

There is further discussion on the integrating circuit in Section 14.5 and further general applications of the operational amplifier in Section 14.8.

14.3.5 Circuit input impedance

For the circuit in Fig. 14.8(a), the right-hand end of R_1 is virtually at earth potential and therefore the input impedance is approximately R_1. Typically, the value is of the order of a few kilohms. For Fig. 14.8(b) and (c) the input impedance is much higher, being that of the non-inverting terminal of the amplifier alone.

An expression of general interest is the input impedance of the circuit shown in Fig. 14.11, in which upper-case symbols

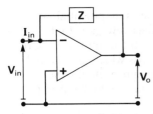

Fig. 14.11 An operational amplifier with a general feedback element

denote the use of an impedance operator. As in previous cases, the current flowing into the amplifier itself is assumed to be negligible and therefore

$$\mathbf{I}_{in} = -(\mathbf{V}_o - \mathbf{V}_{in})/\mathbf{Z}$$

$$= \mathbf{V}_{in}(1 + \mathbf{A})/\mathbf{Z}$$

because $\mathbf{V}_o = -A\mathbf{V}_{in}$ at the inverting terminal. A is, in general, complex. The input impedance is then $\mathbf{V}_{in}/\mathbf{I}_{in} = \mathbf{Z}/(1 + \mathbf{A})$. For a resistive element, R, and assuming that $\mathbf{A}$ is real and large, the input resistance reduces to R/A. For example, if R were $100\,k\Omega$ and A were $+10^5$, R_{in} would be $1\,\Omega$.

If the feedback element is capacitive, $\mathbf{Z} = 1/j\omega C$ at frequency ω and

$$\mathbf{Z}_{in} = 1/j\omega C(1 + \mathbf{A}).$$

Assuming again that $\mathbf{A}$ is real, the circuit behaves at its input terminals as a capacitance of value $C(1 + A)$.

14.3.6 Limitations of the virtual-earth method

The virtual-earth method can hide a number of important factors. For example, the analysis presented would not have been affected if the inverting and the non-inverting terminals were interchanged. This is clearly misleading because the input voltage, although small, must have the polarity appropriate to the circuit connection and the sign of the output voltage. For example, in Fig. 14.8(a), v_i must be positive in order that, being applied to the inverting terminal, the output be negative.

A potentially more serious problem with the virtual-earth method in the form used above is the assumption that because A is large (and real) at low frequencies it remains so at all frequencies. Thus, whilst its absence from the quoted results may well be valid under the stated conditions, the circuit's high-frequency behaviour may be quite different. It is shown in Section 14.5 that a system designed on the assumption of a 'flat' amplifier may well oscillate when amplifier phase shifts are taken into account. Although the virtual-earth technique can be extended to include the effect of a non-zero value for v_i, and hence bring the amplifier gain into the overall gain expression, the feedback-analysis methods developed in Section 14.2 are more suited to a general analysis. This follows a brief discussion on practical-amplifier limitations.

14.4 The practical operational amplifier

Although the internal circuitry of the amplifier is not described, it may be helpful to refer to the description of the differential amplifier in Section 1.3 of Chapter 13. The following definitions are usual but there are some variations:

(i) Small imbalances in the circuit mean that even with

both differential input terminals at the same potential, an output voltage appears. The **input offset voltage** is that differential input voltage which causes the output to be zero: **offset null** pins are often provided across which an external potentiometer may be connected to compensate for the imbalance. Alternatively, external circuitry may be used to provide a bias voltage.

(ii) Although small, currents do flow into the input transistors. These are called the **input bias currents**. For a differential amplifier, input bias current is used to mean the average of the two input currents. They may be different, and the term **input offset current** is used to describe their difference. All the terms are defined at zero output voltage. In order to avoid differing input voltages due to the bias currents, it is common practice to ensure that the resistance to earth from each input is the same, ensuring that, for equal currents, the voltage drops are the same.

(iii) Although previously assumed to be respectively infinite and zero, the input and output resistances of the practical amplifier do not meet these ideals. Both are defined as the ratio of small changes in input (or output) voltage divided by the corresponding change in current.

(iv) The ideal differential amplifier responds only to the *difference* between the two signals at its terminals. For example, the output resulting from $V_+ = 25\,\mu V$ at the $+$ terminal and $V_- = 15\,\mu V$ at the $-$ terminal should be identical to that resulting from $V_+ = 65\,\mu V$ and $V_- = 55\,\mu V$. However, any differences in the gain of the two 'halves' of the differential circuit will cause this not to be the case. Fig. 14.12(*a*) shows a balanced amplifier, with each 'half' having a gain magnitude of 20, a low value being chosen to illustrate the point. Input signals of $55\,\mu V$ and $65\,\mu V$ are applied. The net output is $200\,\mu V$, consistent with a difference input of $10\,\mu V$ multiplied by a gain of 20.

Fig. 14.12 How an input signal can be resolved into a common-mode and a difference signal

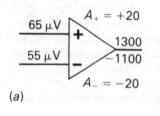

(a)

(b)

Fig. 14.12(*b*) shows an amplifier with an imbalance due to A_- being -21 with A_+ remaining at 20. In this case the input voltage is broken down into a **common-mode signal** (i.e. $60\,\mu V$) given by $(V_+ + V_-)/2$ and a **difference signal** $(V_+ - V_-)$ half of which is added to the common-mode signal to give V_+ and the half taken away to give V_-. The new output, whose total value is $65 \times 20 - 55 \times 21 = 145\,\mu V$, can be regarded as comprising a common-mode output given by

$$(A_+ + A_-)\left(\frac{V_+ + V_-}{2}\right) = -1 \times 60 = -60\,\mu V,$$

together with a difference output given by

$$\left(\frac{A_+ - A_-}{2}\right)(V_+ - V_-) = 20.5 \times 10 = 205 \,\mu\text{V}.$$

The output will be seen to be $A_c \times$ common-mode signal plus $A_d \times$ difference signal, where A_c is the **common-mode gain** $(A_+ + A_-)$ and A_d is the **differential-mode gain**, given by $(A_+ - A_-)/2$. To illustrate these results, suppose the input signals were 85 and 75 μV, with gains as in Fig. 14.12(b). The difference signal remains the same and the new output should only change by the change in the common-mode signal (20 μV) multiplied by A_c $(= -1)$, i.e. $-20\,\mu$V. Direct calculation gives $85 \times 20 - 75 \times 21 = 125 \,\mu$V, a decrease of $20\,\mu$V over the previous output.

The **common-mode rejection ratio** (CMRR) is a measure of the relative magnitude of common-mode and difference gains. In decibel, it is $20\log_{10}(A_d/A_c)$. In the example above, CMRR $= 20\log_{10}(20.5/1) = 26$ dB, but typical operational-amplifier values are of the order of 80 dB.

(v) The output-voltage swing available from an operational amplifier is limited by the supply voltages and may be, typically, ± 12 V across a specified load resistance with ± 15 V d.c. supplies. This means that if the amplifier has a gain of 10^5, a differential input voltage as low as $12/10^5 = 0.12$ mV is sufficient to cause output saturation.

(vi) Although the gain of the amplifier has been denoted simply by A, it is in fact a function of frequency. Indeed, without external feedback components, the gain of an amplifier may start to reduce at frequencies as low as a few hertz.

Frequency response and related topics are discussed in the next section.

14.5 Frequency response of operational amplifier circuits

14.5.1 Block diagram analysis

Pitfalls arising from the non-appearance of the amplifier gain A in overall-circuit gain expressions were mentioned in Section 14.3.6 in which it is suggested that a convenient method of including the gain factor is to use the feedback models. To illustrate how this may be done, the model in Fig. 14.1(b) (or Fig. 14.1(a) if preferred) is used to represent the circuit in Fig. 14.8(b). From the circuit diagram, the voltage fed back to the inverting terminal is, by the potential-divider effect, a proportion $R_1/(R_1 + R_2)$ of the output voltage v_o. The block diagram, Fig. 14.13, follows immediately from this statement as does the closed-loop transfer function,

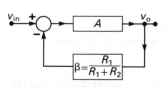

Fig. 14.13 An operational-amplifier circuit represented by a general feedback model

$$\frac{v_o}{v_{in}} = \frac{A}{1 + \beta A} = \frac{A}{1 + (AR_1/(R_1 + R_2))}.$$

The analysis may be extended from this point. Suppose, for example, that the amplifier itself has a single negative real pole at $-1/\tau$ and a low-frequency gain A_L. The frequency response of the amplifier has the form shown in Fig. 14.6 and its transfer function may be written, $A_L/(1+s\tau)$. The new closed-loop transfer function becomes

$$\frac{A_L/(1+s\tau)}{1+\dfrac{A_L R_1/(1+s\tau)}{R_1+R_2}},$$

which rearranged in the form used in Section 14.2.4 gives

$$\frac{A_L/(1+\beta A_L)}{1+s\tau/(1+\beta A_L)}, \quad \text{where } \beta = \frac{R_1}{R_1+R_2},$$

and, using the technique developed in Chapter 7, a new response shape as shown by the dashed lines in Fig. 14.6.

The circuit in Fig. 14.8(a) can be represented by the block diagram in Fig. 14.14(a) in which an inverting amplifier is fed from a summing junction. In this case, the amplifier inversion must be allowed for by taking the gain to be $-A$. Using the superposition principle, one of the summer input signals is derived from the output signal, scaled by a factor $R_1/(R_1+R_2)$, and the other from the circuit-input signal, scaled by a factor $R_2/(R_1+R_2)$. Using the methods of Section 14.1.2, the block diagram reduces to the form shown in Fig. 14.14(b).

Fig. 14.14 Circuit-block transfer to give the general feedback model

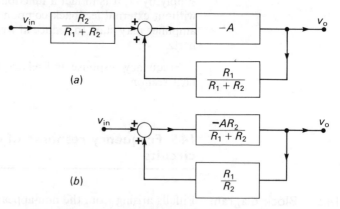

(a)

(b)

The closed-loop transfer function for this circuit is given by

$$\frac{v_o}{v_{in}} = \frac{-AR_2/(R_1+R_2)}{1-\dfrac{R_1}{R_2}(-AR_2/(R_1+R_2))} = \frac{-AR_2}{R_1+R_2+AR_1}.$$

Example 14.2   *Sketch straight-line approximations to the magnitude response of an operational amplifier having a low-frequency gain of 100 dB and a single pole at $-50\,\mathrm{s}^{-1}$,*

(i) alone;
(ii) used in the circuit in Fig. 14.8(a) with $R_1 = 10\,\mathrm{k\Omega}$ and $R_2 = 15\,\mathrm{k\Omega}$.

   (i) The amplifier transfer function is $10^5/(1+0.02s)$ and the sketch may be drawn immediately with the given data (Fig. 14.15).

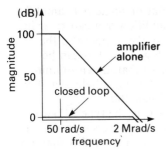

Fig. 14.15 Solution to Example 14.2

(ii) The closed-loop transfer function is given by substituting values into the expression derived above:

$$\frac{V_o(s)}{V_{in}(s)} = \frac{-15 \times 10^3 \times 10^5/(1 + 0.02s)}{(15 + 10) \times 10^3 + 10^5 \times 10^4/(1 + 0.02s)}$$

$$= \frac{-15 \times 10^8}{25 \times 10^3(1 + 0.02s) + 10^9}$$

$$= \frac{-1.5}{1 + 5 \times 10^{-7}s}.$$

The two responses are shown in Fig. 14.15. The closed-loop low-frequency gain is 3.5 dB and the break frequency is 2 Mrad/s. It will be seen that the gain-bandwidth product is slightly less with feedback in this case. Analysis will show the product to be reduced by a factor $R_2/(R_1 + R_2)$. The value is 4.4 dB in this example.

14.5.2 Frequency response of circuits with capacitive feedback

The circuit shown in Fig. 14.9 with the capacitive feedback element can be analysed in the same way as that of Fig. 14.8(*a*) (as in the previous subsection) but with R_2 replaced by $1/sC$. Thus, with a single-pole amplifier with time constant τ and low-frequency gain A_L,

$$\frac{V_o(s)}{V_{in}(s)} = \frac{-A_L/sC(1 + s\tau)}{R_1 + A_L R_1/(1 + s\tau) + 1/sC}.$$

Re-arranging and assuming that $A_L \gg 1$ gives,

$$\frac{V_o(s)}{V_{in}(s)} = \frac{-A_L/CR_1\tau}{s^2 + sA_L/\tau + 1/CR_1\tau}.$$

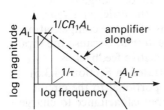

Fig. 14.16 Frequency response of an integrator

With the help of a binomial approximation, the roots of the denominator of the transfer function can be shown to be approximately $-1/CR_1 A_L$ and $-A_L/\tau$. These give the typical two-pole frequency response shown in Fig. 14.16. The circuit behaves as an ideal integrator over a wide frequency range, typically between 0.1 Hz and 1 MHz.

14.5.3 Compensation

The operational-amplifier integrated circuit comprises a number of stages and it may be expected that its transfer function will have a number of poles. Typically, real negative poles may be found at 1 MHz, 5 MHz and 25 MHz. Fig. 14.17 shows a typical frequency response.

It is shown in Section 14.6 that a three-pole amplifier can cause instability in a feedback circuit which is apparently

Fig. 14.17 The effect of compensation on gain

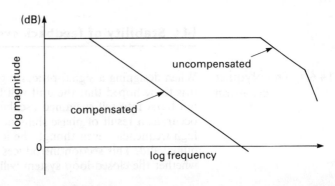

stable when based on an assumed flat or single-pole amplifier response. However, the deliberate addition of a capacitor in the circuit can be sufficient to modify the response so that instability is avoided. As shown in Fig. 14.17 this can be achieved by modifying the response so that, down to unit-gain frequency, it is effectively that of a single-pole amplifier and the phase shift is therefore less than 180°.

Some integrated-circuit amplifiers (e.g. the type 741) are internally compensated and have the response shape similar to that shown in Fig. 14.17. Avoidance of instability may not be the only factor to be considered and other amplifiers may be externally compensated to provide the most appropriate compensation for a particular application.

14.5.4 Slew rate

Considerable attention has been focussed on the frequency response of operational-amplifiers and more is to follow in discussing active filters. This is because the time response to a variety of input-waveforms can be predicted from the frequency response. However, with active devices such as these there is an additional factor which does not exist with passive circuits arising from non-linear effects in the active circuits. The effect is quantified by the **slew rate** of an amplifier, defined as the maximum rate of change of the output voltage. Typical values are of the order of $1\,V/\mu s$.

The primary determining factor is often the compensating component(s), whether internal or external. Because the input impedance of a stage subject to capacitive feedback is substantially capacitive (as demonstrated in Section 14.3.5), feeding the stage with a current proportional to the circuit input voltage causes the effective input capacitance to charge and the output voltage to rise in proportion. This is consistent with the normal circuit behaviour of a large capacitor fed from a resistive source: the initial slope is substantially constant and proportional to the input voltage (Fig. 14.18). However, in the active circuit under discussion, the current supplied from the resistive source has a maximum (saturated) value which will limit the rate of charge to a maximum value. This in turn will limit the maximum rate of change of output voltage. This maximum value is the slew rate. Thus, the rate of change of the output voltage may only be determined from the frequency response and the input-voltage waveform if the slew rate is not a limiting factor.

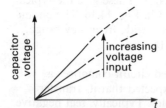

Fig. 14.18 Variation in capacitor voltage for various input voltages

14.6 Stability of feedback systems

14.6.1 The Nyquist criterion

When designing a signal-processing unit such as an amplifier it is to be hoped that the unit will behave as an amplifier and not burst into self-sustained oscillation. Such instability can occur, as a result of phase shifts in the components at high frequencies even though the low-frequency design is quite valid. This section introduces a method for predicting whether the closed-loop system will be unstable by carrying out a frequency-response test on the open-loop system. Essentially, the method looks for the presence of closed-loop poles in the right-hand half of the s plane. Only an outline is given: reference should be made to specialist texts for further details and limitations.

Poles of the closed-loop transfer function $G(s)/(1 + G(s)H(s))$ result from zeros of the denominator $1 + G(s)H(s)$. Also, if a closed contour is drawn on an s plane so as to enclose one or more zeros of $1 + G(s)H(s)$, mapping this contour on to a $1 + G(s)H(s)$ plane will encircle the origin. Thus, the existence of system poles in the right-hand plane, and hence instability, is detected by the mapped contour enclosing the origin on the $1 + G(s)H(s)$ plane or -1 on the $G(s)H(s)$ plane. The latter will be recognised as the open-loop transfer function, signifying that closed-loop stability can be predicted from open-loop characteristics.

As an illustration of the mapping process, suppose a function $1 + G(s)H(s)$ has a value $s^2 - 6s + 13$. This has zeros at $3 + j2$ and $3 - j2$ (Fig. 14.19(a)). Setting s at a series of values so as to follow a contour enclosing the zeros, gives a series of values for $G(s)H(s)$. For example, point B in Fig. 14.19(a), at which $s = +j3$, maps to $(j3)^2 - 6(j3) + 13 - 1 = 3 - j18$ on the $G(s)H(s)$ plane in Fig. 14.19(b). Point A, at which $s = 0$, maps to $12 + j0$, and so on, until the whole of Fig. 14.19(b) is built up.

Fig. 14.19 The encirclement of the point $-1 + j0$

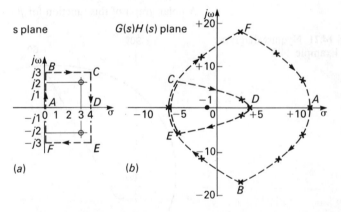

(a)   (b)

The Nyquist technique is to enclose the entire right-hand half of the s plane in order to detect any zeros therein. This can be done by varying s around the semicircular path shown in Fig. 14.20, where the radius R tends to infinity. As shown in Example 14.3, this maps to zero on the $G(s)H(s)$ plane for the low-pass system described. The non-infinite part of the path lies along the imaginary axis (where $s = j\omega$) and may therefore be included by allowing s to vary from $-j\infty$ to $+j\infty$. Thus, sketching the open-loop transfer function $G(j\omega)H(j\omega)$ as frequency is varied from $-\infty$ to $+\infty$, and determining whether the point $-1 + j0$ is encircled, will indicate whether the closed-loop system is stable.

One form of the **Nyquist criterion** may be stated: if the open-loop transfer function itself does not have any poles in the right-hand half-plane, the Nyquist plot of $G(j\omega)H(j\omega)$

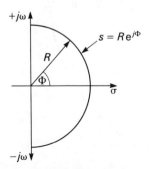

Fig. 14.20 Enclosure of the right-hand half plane

must not encircle the point $-1 + j0$, for the closed-loop
system to be stable.

Example 14.3   *Sketch a Nyquist diagram to show that the three-pole amplifier
described by*

$$G(s) = \frac{7200}{(s+2)(s+3)(s+12)}$$

*is stable when 10% of the output is fed back (as in Fig. 14.1(a)) but is
unstable when the feedback is increased to 20%.*

$$G(s)H(s) = \frac{7200\beta}{(s+2)(s+3)(s+12)}.$$

For the large-radius semicircle on the s plane

$$G(s)H(s) \rightarrow \frac{7200\beta}{(R\,e^{j\phi})^3} \quad \text{as } R \rightarrow \infty.$$

This is a vanishingly-small-radius rotation from $-270°$, at
$\phi = +90°$, to $270°$ at $\phi = -90°$. This result applies for both values
of β.
   For $s = j\omega$ (with ω ranging from $-\infty$ to $+\infty$),

$$G(j\omega)H(j\omega) = \frac{7200\beta}{(j\omega+2)(j\omega+3)(j\omega+12)}$$

$$= \frac{7200\beta}{(72 - 17\omega^2) + j(66\omega - \omega^3)}.$$

A polar graph of this function for $\beta = 0.1$ is shown in Fig. 14.21. It

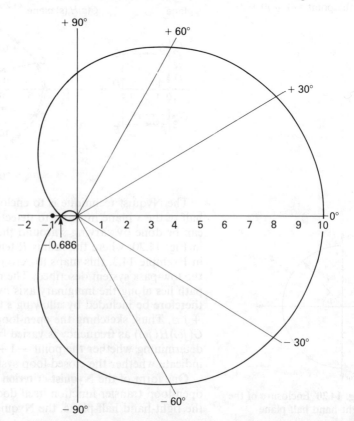

Fig. 14.21 Nyquist diagram
for Example 14.3

is evident from the diagram that with $\beta = 0.1$ the point $-1 + j0$ is not encircled. However, if β is set at 0.2, each magnitude value is doubled and the point is enclosed twice. The system is then unstable.

14.6.2 Relative stability and Bode diagrams

The Nyquist diagram is a polar plot of a function having magnitude and angle. As described in Chapter 7, such information can also be shown on Bode diagrams and it follows that the stability condition can also be related to the Bode diagram. Furthermore, it is relatively easy to estimate how far from an unstable condition a system may be although, as shown in Fig. 14.22, this can also be shown on the Nyquist diagram. The straight-line approximations and an estimate of the actual response shapes are shown in Fig. 14.22 for $\beta = 0.1$. The frequency range is from approximately $\omega = 0.2$ rad/s to $\omega = 50$ rad/s and the Nyquist plot corresponding to the positive-frequency range of approximately 5 rad/s upward is shown in the inset.

Fig. 14.22 Relative stability on Bode and Nyquist diagrams

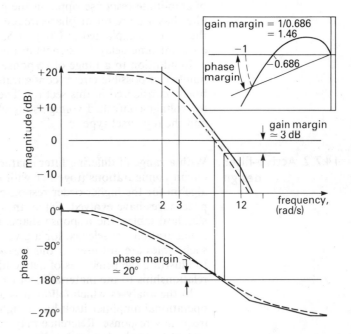

Reference lines at 0 dB magnitude and 180° phase angle have been drawn on the Bode diagram and these correspond to the point $-1 + j0$ on the Nyquist diagram. Related to this critical point are the **gain margin** and the **phase margin**. The former is that magnitude increase which would raise the magnitude ratio to unity (i.e. 0 dB) when the phase shift is 180° and the latter is the change in phase angle which would make the phase shift 180° when the magnitude ratio is unity. In Fig. 14.22 gain and phase margins are approximately 3 dB and 20° respectively.

14.7 Active filters

14.7.1 Introduction

In the past, inductance–capacitance filters were used extensively and circuits of the form described in Chapter 5 (and derivatives thereof) were the norm. However, the resistance–capacitance, operational-amplifier configuration has now replaced the inductance in this application. Thus, the study of active filters is concerned with the determination of the operational-amplifier circuit configurations and components required to produce frequency responses of a given shape. The **Butterworth response** described in Section 3.4 of Chapter 7 is an example of such a shape.

The Butterworth response is a commonly used magnitude characteristic, being flat in the pass band, but other filter characteristics are used, the Chebyshev and Bessel responses being examples. The former has a sharper roll-off around the break frequency, achieved at the expense of a certain amount of amplitude-response ripple in the pass band. The Bessel filter has a more linear phase/frequency characteristic and therefore, as explained in Chapter 8, introduces a nominally constant time delay for signals in the pass band.

In addition to a range of response shapes, there are a number of possible circuit configurations three of which are briefly considered in this section. They are the Sallen and Key (or voltage-controlled voltage-source) type, the Biquad type and the universal type.

14.7.2 Active-filter design

With a range of differing filter characteristics and differing circuit configurations (together with some quite involved algebra for the higher-order responses) a number of design procedures have evolved. Often, these are based on the use of standard tables; the response shape, the order and the circuit configuration are selected for a given application. However, such tables are not used in this treatment which is intended to illustrate the principles of active filters and their relationships to the material in other chapters.

In the analyses which follow it is assumed that the operational amplifier itself has a high gain and has a flat frequency response. Reference may be made to Sections 14.5 and 14.6 of this chapter for discussion on the implications of this assumption.

14.7.3 Butterworth and Chebyshev responses with a Sallen and Key circuit

A second-order unity-gain circuit is shown in Fig. 14.23. In this example, the transfer function $V_o(s)/V_i(s)$ is readily obtained by means of the nodal-analysis method (Chapter 3). Applying the same principle as used in the virtual-earth method, the inverting and non-inverting terminals are at substantially the same potential v_0. Then, at node P,

$$V_i(s)/R_1 = (1/R_1 + 1/R_2 + sC_1)V_P(s) - (1/R_2 + sC_1)V_Q(s),$$

and at node Q,

$$0 = -(1/R_2)V_P(s) + (1/R_2 + sC_2)V_Q(s).$$

Fig. 14.23 A VCVS (Sallen and Key) active-filter circuit

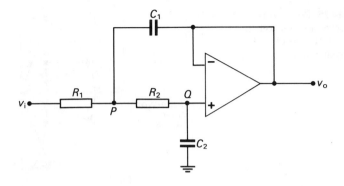

Setting $V_Q(s) = V_o(s)$ and rearranging,

$$\frac{V_o(s)}{V_i(s)} = \frac{1}{s^2 C_1 C_2 R_1 R_2 + s C_2(R_1 + R_2) + 1}.$$

The denominator will be seen to be a second-order expression which, if equated to zero, is of the form $s^2 + 2\xi\omega_0 s + \omega_0^2 = 0$ (see Section 3.3 of Chapter 7), where the undamped natural frequency is given by $\omega_0 = 1/\sqrt{(R_1 R_2 C_1 C_2)}$ and the damping ratio by $\xi = ((R_1 + R_2)/2\sqrt{(R_1 R_2)})\sqrt{(C_2/C_1)}$. Response shapes are shown in Fig. 7.21 for various values of ξ.

Without restriction on the C and R values, the network function has a pair of poles somewhere on the left-hand side of the s plane as shown in Fig. 7.19. A Butterworth response may be obtained by further restricting the values in order to place the poles at 45° to the axes (Fig. 14.24). As explained in Section 3.4 of Chapter 7, this is the required position for the poles for a second-order Butterworth response. In this case, α and ω_d are numerically equal (or $\xi = 1/\sqrt{(2)}$) and hence

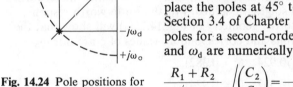

Fig. 14.24 Pole positions for a Butterworth response

$$\frac{R_1 + R_2}{2\sqrt{(R_1 R_2)}} \sqrt{\left(\frac{C_2}{C_1}\right)} = \frac{1}{\sqrt{(2)}}.$$

Example 14.4

Determine values for $R_1 = R_2$ ($= R$), C_1 and C_2 for a second-order Butterworth Sallen and Key circuit having unity gain and a cut-off frequency of 10 kHz.

For $R_1 = R_2 = R$ the design formulae became $\omega_0 = 1/R\sqrt{(C_1 C_2)}$ and $\xi = \sqrt{(C_2/C_1)}$. With $\xi = 1/\sqrt{(2)}$ for the second-order filter and $\omega_0 = 2\pi \times 10^4$ rad/s, the formulae become $C_2/C_1 = 0.5$ and $R^2 C_1 C_2 = 1/(2\pi \times 10^4)^2$. Setting, $C_1 = 0.01\,\mu\text{F}$ makes $C_2 = 0.005\,\mu\text{F}$ (or 5 nF) and $R = 2.25\,\text{k}\Omega$.

A number of stages may be cascaded to obtain a higher-order filter. For example, the fourth-order Butterworth response whose poles are shown in Fig. 14.25(*a*) could be realised by cascading two stages, each of which contributes one pair of conjugate poles.

If the disposition of the poles is changed so that they lie on an ellipse rather than a circle, the **Chebyshev response** results. This is also illustrated in Fig. 14.25(*a*). As previously mentioned, the effect of the changed pole positions is to give a sharper roll-off at the expense of some magnitude ripple in

Fig. 14.25 Pole positions
and responses for fourth-
order Butterworth and
Chebyshev filters

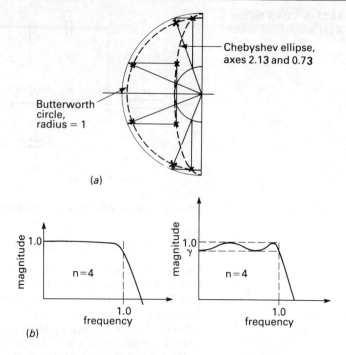

Chebyshev ellipse,
axes 2.13 and 0.73

Butterworth
circle,
radius = 1

(a)

(b)

the pass band. To illustrate how the response is affected,
response shapes for both Butterworth and Chebyshev types
are shown in Fig. 14.25(b) and (c). These may be formed by
the method demonstrated in Fig. 7.25 in which the responses
of the two stages are added. For the Butterworth response,
reference to the geometry of Fig. 14.25(a) will show that the
pole positions and corresponding values of ξ are (for $\omega_0 = 1$),

$$-0.382 \pm j0.924 \quad (\xi = 0.382),$$

$$-0.924 \pm j0.382 \quad (\xi = 0.924).$$

For the Chebyshev response the procedure is more
complex, the magnitude of the allowable pass-band ripple
entering into the calculation of the shape of the ellipse. The
amount of ripple, as quantified by γ in Fig. 14.25(c), enables a
factor e to be calculated in accordance with $\gamma = 1/\sqrt{(1 + e^2)}$.
Thus for $\gamma = 1\,\mathrm{dB}$ for example, e is 0.509. The major and
minor axes of the ellipse are then given by (see Kuo 1966)

$$2\omega_0 \cosh\left(\frac{1}{n} \sinh^{-1}\left(\frac{1}{e}\right)\right) \quad \text{and} \quad 2\omega_0 \sinh\left(\frac{1}{n} \sinh^{-1}\left(\frac{1}{e}\right)\right).$$

For $\omega_0 = 1$, $n = 4$ and $e = 0.509$ the axis magnitudes are 2.13
and 0.73. Scaling approximate values from Fig. 14.25(a), there
are poles at

$$-0.14 \pm j0.98 \quad \text{(corresponding to } \xi \simeq 0.14$$
$$\text{at a cut-off frequency of 0.99),}$$

and

$$-0.34 \pm j0.41 \quad \text{(corresponding to } \xi \simeq 0.64$$
$$\text{at a cut-off frequency of 0.53),}$$

leading to the response shape shown in Fig. 14.25(c).

14.7.4 The biquad filter

This circuit (shown in Fig. 14.26) comprises three stages. The operational amplifier (A_1) is effectively a summing circuit (accepting the signals v_i and v'') but with the feedback components R_2 and C_2 rather than simply R_2 as in the previously described summing circuit. Using the virtual-earth approximation, the output from the A_1 stage is given by

$$V'(s) = -\frac{Z_2(s)}{R_1} V_i(s) - \frac{Z_2(s)}{R_4} V''(s),$$

where

$$Z_2(s) = 1/(1/R_2 + sC_2) \quad \text{or} \quad R_2/(1 + sC_2R_2).$$

Fig. 14.26 A Biquad filter

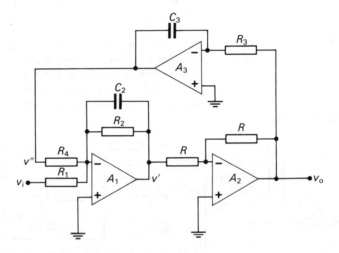

The second amplifier stage (A_2) is a unity-gain inverting amplifier giving an output

$$V_o(s) = -V'(s) = \frac{R_2}{R_1(1 + sC_2R_2)} V_i(s) + \frac{R_2}{R_4(1 + sC_2R_2)} V''(s).$$

The third stage (A_3) is an integrator and therefore, ideally,

$$V''(s) = -V_o(s)/sC_3R_3.$$

Substituting for $V''(s)$ gives

$$V_o(s) = \frac{R_2}{R_1(1 + sC_2R_2)} V_i(s) - \frac{R_2}{sC_3R_3R_4(1 + sC_2R_2)} V_o(s),$$

which, rearranged, gives

$$\frac{V_o(s)}{V_i(s)} = \frac{s/C_2R_1}{s^2 + s/C_2R_2 + 1/C_2C_3R_3R_4}.$$

In this derivation it is assumed that each stage does not load the previous stage.

Comparing the denominator with the standard expression $s^2 + 2\xi\omega_0 s + \omega_0^2$ gives

$$\omega_0 = \frac{1}{\sqrt{(C_2C_3R_3R_4)}} \quad \text{and} \quad \xi = \frac{1}{2}\sqrt{\left(\frac{C_3R_3R_4}{C_2R_2^2}\right)}.$$

The frequency response for a typical value of ξ is shown in Fig. 7.22.

Alternatively, the transfer function may be compared with the resonant-circuit admittance expression in Section 3.2 of Chapter 7, i.e. $(s/L)/(s^2 + sR/L + 1/LC)$. The output-voltage response will then have the same form as the current in that case, but with $C_2 R_1$ replacing L, R_1/R_2 replacing R and $C_3 R_3 R_4/R_1$ replacing C. For example, if in a given design $R_2 = 200\,\text{k}\Omega$, $C_2 = 0.1\,\mu\text{F}$, $R_3 = 5\,\text{k}\Omega$, $C_3 = 0.1\,\mu\text{F}$ and $R_4 = 5\,\text{k}\Omega$, the value of ω_0 would be 2000 rad/s ($f_o = 318$ Hz) and $\xi = 0.0125$ ($Q = 1/2\xi = 40$). The equivalent series-circuit values are $L = 1\,\text{mH}$, $C = 250\,\mu\text{F}$ and $R = 0.05\,\Omega$. Cross-checking the ω_0 and Q values, $\omega_0 = 1/\sqrt{(LC)} = 2000$ rad/s and $Q = \omega_0 L/R = 40$.

14.7.5 The universal filter

This filter comprises three stages and (at different terminals) provides low-pass, high-pass and band-pass outputs, The arrangement is shown in Fig. 14.27. Transfer functions for the low-, band- and high-pass outputs may be determined using standard circuit-analysis methods.

Fig. 14.27 A universal filter

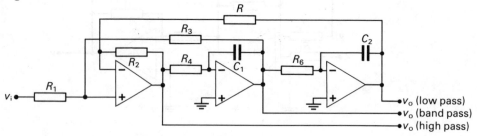

14.8 Other operational-amplifier applications

There are a great number of applications for the operational amplifier, and the previous sections have described some of the standard arrangements. This section contains a representative selection of additional applications; specialist texts list many more. The selected circuits are an instrumentation amplifier, an oscillator, a voltage comparator and a precision rectifier.

14.8.1 An instrumentation amplifier

When measuring the often small signals such as may appear at the output of a transducer used for measuring physical quantities such as pressure, temperature, etc., it is helpful to have an amplifier which will,

(i)   respond to a change in differential output level;
(ii) ignore changes which affect equally both transducer output terminals;
(iii) not load the transducer or earth either terminal; and
(iv) have a reasonably high gain.

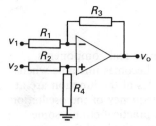

Fig. 14.28 An instrumentation amplifier

The circuit in Fig. 14.28 meets these needs except that for high input impedance; depending on the application, additional input buffer stages may be required. The operation of the circuit is as follows.

With $v_2 = 0$ (R_2 returned to earth), the circuit reduces to that in Fig. 14.8(a) with an output voltage (assuming an ideal amplifier),

$$v_o' = \frac{-R_3}{R_1} v_1.$$

With $v_1 = 0$ (R_1 returned to earth), the circuit reduces to that in Fig. 14.8(b) but with the input voltage attenuated by a factor $R_4/(R_2 + R_4)$. Using the result from Section 14.3.3 the output voltage is therefore:

$$v_o'' = \frac{R_4}{R_2 + R_4} \cdot \frac{R_1 + R_3}{R_1} v_2,$$

which, on setting $R_2/R_4 = R_1/R_3$, reduces to $(R_3/R_1)v_2$. Thus the total output voltage with v_1 and v_2 present is

$$v_o = v_o' + v_o'' = \frac{R_3}{R_1} (v_2 - v_1).$$

This represents an ideal differential amplifier whose gain is determinable through the ratio of two resistors. As mentioned above, instrumentation amplifiers typically employ additional stages.

14.8.2 The Wein-bridge oscillator

A commonly used oscillator known as the **Wien-bridge** type is shown in Fig. 14.29(a). There are two feedback paths. One is through R_1 and R_2 to the inverting input giving a basic non-inverting amplifier in the form of Fig. 14.8(b). The other is through the CR network to the non-inverting input which, as shown below, can result in the circuit becoming intentionally unstable and providing a sinusoidal output.

Following the techniques developed in Section 14.5.1 the circuit can be represented by the block diagram in Fig. 14.29(b). The gain of the non-inverting amplifier is A (which is assumed to be positive and real in all circumstances) and the feedback-network transfer function $H(s)$ is given (by potential-divider) as

$$H(s) = \frac{R/(1 + sCR)}{R/(1 + sCR) + R + 1/sC},$$

the impedance of the parallel CR network being given by $R/(1 + sCR)$. Rearranged, this becomes

$$H(s) = \frac{s}{s^2 CR + 3s + 1/CR}.$$

The closed-loop transfer function is $G(s)/(1 - G(s)H(s))$ whose poles are given by equating the denominator to zero:

$$1 - \frac{As}{s^2 CR + 3s + 1/CR} = 0,$$

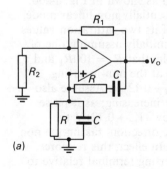

(a)

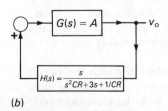

(b)

Fig. 14.29 A Wien-bridge oscillator and its block diagram

or

$$s^2CR + (3 - A)s + 1/CR = 0.$$

It is evident that the roots have positive real components when $A > 3$ and therefore the circuit becomes unstable when the gain just exceeds 3. Then, the poles of the function are at approximately $s = \pm j/CR$ and the frequency of the oscillation is therefore given by $\omega = 1/CR$. In a practical circuit some means will be provided to hold the amplitude of the oscillation constant.

14.8.3 A voltage comparator

The analogue-to-digital converter circuits described in Chapter 15 make extensive use of voltage-level comparators. These are but one example of a range of comparator applications.

An operational amplifier can be used in the open-loop mode as a comparator. If one terminal is held at a reference potential, and assuming a gain of 10^5 with a maximum output-voltage swing of ± 12 V, a small input change of $12/10^5 = 120\,\mu\text{V}$ either side of the reference voltage is sufficient to take the output to one or other of the saturated-output values. No problem should occur if, as may well be the case, the input voltage is ramping steadily downward (or upward); as it passes through the $\pm 120\,\mu\text{V}$ window around V_{ref}, the comparator output will switch over. However, if the input dwells near V_{ref} for some reason, the inevitable noise voltages superimposed upon the signal may cause large and erratic swings in the output voltage.

To avoid this problem, circuit instability through the use of positive feedback may be harnessed as shown in Fig. 14.30. With the circuit operating in an essentially non-linear mode, having the output voltage at one of its two saturation values, the operation can be described by initially assuming one of the two states. Suppose, for example, that $R_2 = 100R_1$ and v_o is initially at $+12$ V. The potential at the non-inverting terminal will be approximately $(V_{\text{ref}} + 0.12)$ V. Assume also that v_{in} is initially less than V_{ref}, but increasing; as it passes through a voltage level $120\,\mu\text{V}$ below $(V_{\text{ref}} + 0.12)$ V the output starts to swing in a negative direction, taking the non-inverting terminal negative with it. In effect, this reinforces the net positive voltage on the inverting terminal relative to that on the non-inverting terminal, driving the output to its negative saturation value of -12 V. An unstable situation exists momentarily at the switch-over point but the circuit becomes stable as the non-inverting terminal is taken to approximately $(V_{\text{ref}} - 0.12)$ V.

Inevitably, there is a hysteresis effect in which the switch over takes place at a different point with a decreasing input (i.e. at $(V_{\text{ref}} - 0.12)$ V) as compared with the increasing one. Hysteresis is reduced by reducing the ratio R_1/R_2 but, as R_2 becomes large, the circuit tends towards the open-loop condition.

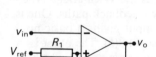

Fig. 14.30 A voltage comparator

14.8.4 A precision rectifier

As discussed in Section 4.3 of Chapter 12, the p–n-junction diode is a non-linear circuit element which, when used as a rectifier of signals whose amplitude is comparable with the threshold voltage ($\simeq -0.6\,\text{V}$ for silicon), introduces considerable distortion. The circuit shown in Fig. 14.31(a) effectively overcomes the threshold problem, having an output characteristic of the form shown in Fig. 14.31(b).

A negative input voltage reverse biases the diode and results in zero output voltage. A positive input voltage causes the amplifier output to go positive, forward biasing the diode and establishing a conducting path through R to earth. This raises the potential of the output terminal and, with it, the inverting input to the amplifier which rises to a potential only slightly less than the input on the non-inverting terminal. Thus the output will effectively follow the input only for positive inputs giving a forward transfer characteristic of unit slope. The threshold effect is negligible, an input voltage of only (V_{thres}/A) being required to establish linear operation.

Fig. 14.31 A precision rectifier

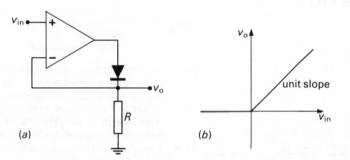

(a)   (b)

Key points to remember

- feedback systems may be represented in block diagram form giving a general closed-loop transfer function $G(S)/(1 + H(S)\,G(S))$;

- feedback has an effect on gain, gain sensitivity and distortion;

- the operational amplifier can be used as the basis of summing and integrating circuits;

- operational amplifier circuits can be analysed by the virtual-earth or block-diagram methods, the later providing a more comprehensive method;

- slew rate defines the maximum rate of change of output voltage;

- the Nyquist stability criterion enables closed-loop stability to be predicted from open-loop frequency response;

- operational amplifiers can be used with resistors and capacitors (not requiring inductors) to generate a variety of filter characteristics such as the Butterworth response;

- operational-amplifier based circuit may be used in a very wide range of applications.

Further reading

Clayton, G. B., *Operational Amplifiers*. Macmillan (1979).
Irvine, R. G., *Operational Amplifiers: Characteristics and Applications*. Prentice-Hall (1981).
Kuo, B. C., *Automatic Control Systems* (5th edn). Prentice-Hall (1987).
Roberge, J. K., *Operational Amplifiers*. J. Wiley (1975).
Van Valkenburg, M. E., *Analogue Filter Design*. CBS College Publishing (1982).
Williams, B. A., *Filter Design Handbook*. McGraw-Hill (1981).

EXERCISES 14

14.1   Reduce the block diagram shown in Fig. E14.1 to the basic form in Fig. 14.1.

Fig. E14.1

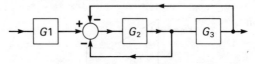

14.2   A power amplifier exhibits a temperature-dependent voltage gain, varying between the limits 50 and 80 as it warms up. Sketch a feedback arrangement which would reduce the gain variation to not more than 10% of its lowest value.
Also determine the gain of a preamplifier (assumed ideal) required to compensate for the loss of gain.

14.3   Explain how the results of Exercise 14.2 could relate to the reduction of amplitude non-linearity in a power amplifier.

14.4   In the arrangement shown in Fig. E14.2, $G(s)$ represents a single-pole amplifier with a low-frequency gain of 100 and a time constant of $1\,\mu s$. $H(s)$ is a resistive feedback network feeding 20% of the output back to the input. By sketching the output pulse with and without feedback when a 50 mV, $2\,\mu s$ period square wave is applied to the input, show that distortion is significantly reduced.

Fig. E14.2

14.5   Sketch the output voltage v_o for the circuit shown in Fig. E14.3, assuming that the operational amplifier is ideal.

Fig. E14.3

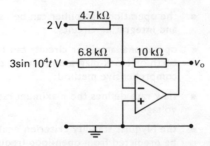

14.6   Sketch the steady-state input and output voltage waveforms for the integrator circuit shown in Fig. 14.9 if $C = 50\,nF$, $R = 10\,k\Omega$ and the input voltage is $3 \sin 10^3 t$ V.

14.7   Using the same general technique as in Example 14.2 (Section 14.5.1), draw straight-line approximations to the Bode magnitude diagrams for v_o/v_i for the circuit shown in

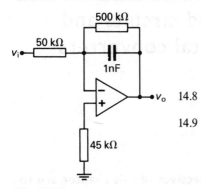

Fig. E14.4

Fig. E14.4 when

(i) the amplifier frequency response is flat with a gain of 10^5;

(ii) the amplifier transfer function is $5 \times 10^6/s$; and

(iii) amplifier transfer function is $10^5/(1 + 0.02s)$.

14.8 Calculate the maximum rate at which v_o can change in Fig. E14.5 assuming I is constant at $10\,\mu A$.

14.9 Show, by sketching the open-loop transfer function in polar form, that the feedback system in Fig. E14.6 is stable. To what value should $G(s)$ be raised in order to cause the system to become unstable?

Note: for this form of the block diagram, encirclement of the point $+1 + j0$ should be looked for.

14.10 By drawing Bode magnitude and phase diagrams for the open-loop transfer function in Fig. E14.6 determine the gain margin.

14.11 Repeat the design procedure in Example 14.4 (Section 14.7.3), but for a Chebyshev response with a 2 dB pass-band ripple. Adjust the gain so that its maximum value is 0 dB.

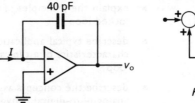

Fig. E14.5

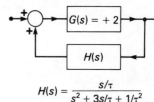

$$H(s) = \frac{s/\tau}{s^2 + 3s/\tau + 1/\tau^2}$$

Fig. E14.6

15 Linear integrated circuits and analogue-to-digital converters

The principal learning objectives of this chapter are to:

	Section	Exercise
● explain the operation and applications of the balanced modulator;	1.1	15.1
● describe a typical integrated-circuit voltage-controlled oscillator;	1.2	15.2
● explain the principles of the phase-locked loop;	1.3	
● describe typical applications and the characteristics of a typical phase-locked loop;	1.4	15.3
● describe the concepts associated with analogue-to-digital conversion;	2	15.4
● discuss digital-to-analogue conversion techniques;	3.1–3.3	15.5
● state the terminology associated with digital-to-analogue conversion;	3.4	
● describe the analogue-to-digital converter types:		
digital-ramp	4.2	15.6
successive-approximation;	4.3	15.7
dual slope;	4.4	15.8
charge-balancing;	4.5	
parallel converter.	4.6	

15.1 Linear integrated circuits

Whilst the operational amplifier described in Chapter 14 is the most important and widely applicable linear integrated circuit, there are a number of other types of circuits which are extensively used in particular applications. Nevertheless, the functions they perform are in general not highly specialised and a brief study of their characteristics is of interest at an introductory level.

15.1.1 The analogue multiplier and balanced modulator

These two terms are sometimes used interchangeably and the initial description is general in this sense. The device is known as a multiplier because the output contains a signal proportional to the product of the two input signals; the modulator description is used because, as shown in Chapter 23, a multiplicative process lies at the heart of amplitude and frequency-modulation techniques.

Multiplication can in fact be achieved very simply by means of a non-linear device and Section 4.4 of Chapter 12 shows how this occurs. An extreme form of non-linearity is shown in Fig. 15.1 in which one analogue input signal is switched by a second although, in principle, it does not matter which does the switching and which is the switched.

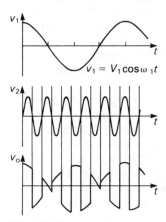

The link between switching and multiplication may be explained by reference to two sinusoidal waveforms shown in Fig. 15.1. Signal v_2 is shown at much higher frequency than v_1 although this assumption is only made to clarify the explanation; it is not a necessary operating condition. The output waveform v_o is proportional to v_1 but with its instantaneous polarity reversed (i.e. switched) in accordance with the polarity of v_2. The output signal may therefore be regarded as a signal proportional to v_1 but multiplied by a bipolar unit-amplitude square wave at the frequency of v_2.

Fig. 15.1 Input and output waveforms for a switching modulator

The Fourier expansion for the square wave may be derived from the result quoted at the end of Section 2.1 of Chapter 8 by omitting the a_0 component, setting $V = 2$, and writing ω_2 in place of ω_0. Thus,

$$v_2(t) = \frac{4}{\pi} \sin \omega_2 t + \frac{4}{3\pi} \sin 3\omega_2 t + \cdots.$$

Multiplying by $KV_1 \cos \omega_1 t$ gives,

$$v_o = \frac{4KV_1}{\pi} \sin \omega_2 t \cos \omega_1 t + \frac{4KV_1}{\pi} \sin 3\omega_2 t \cos \omega_1 t + \cdots.$$

The first term is proportional to the product of v_1 and v_2.

Although the analysis yields other product terms, $\sin 3\omega_2 t \cos \omega_1 t$, etc., these may be filtered out if necessary. Alternatively, the circuit design may generate the non-limited waveform shown in Fig. 15.2: this does not contain the higher-frequency components. Fig. 15.2 is characteristic of the waveform of two signals close in frequency and added together. In some contexts, it is known as a **beat note** between two sinusoidal tones. The summation of two sinusoids is quite consistent with a trigonometric analysis of the output waveform, where the expanded first term gives $(2KV_1/\pi)(\sin(\omega_2 - \omega_1)t + \sin(\omega_2 + \omega)t)$, indicating two sinusoidal components at frequencies $(f_2 - f_1)$ and $(f_2 + f_1)$. However, the point is not that the waveform consists of the sum of two sinusoids (this could be produced by a resistive summing network) but that two sinusoidal components at new frequencies have been generated.

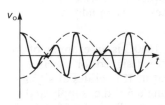

Fig. 15.2 Balanced-modulator output waveform

The distinction between the analogue multiplier and the balanced modulator lies in the input coupling. The former is direct coupled whereas the latter is not. Thus, the analogue-multiplier output may be controlled by a d.c. level on one of the inputs whereas the balanced modulator will only operate with signals above a specified minimum frequency.

Typical applications of the devices include the following.

(i) **A frequency changer:** there are situations, particularly in radio-reception circuits, where it is required to translate a signal up or down in the frequency spectrum. This may be done by feeding the signal into one of the input terminals and a locally-generated sinusoidal signal into the other. The output will contain the original signal translated up and down the frequency spectrum by the magnitude of the frequency of the sinusoid. One of the two output signals is then selected for further processing. For example, an incoming radio signal may contain components in the frequency range 1.234–1.244 MHz. Frequency changing, or **mixing** as it is sometimes called, using a sinusoid at 1.704 MHz, would generate signals in the range 2.938–2.948 MHz (sum components) and 460–470 kHz (difference components). In this example the difference-frequency components would be accepted and the sum components rejected.

(ii) **Phase detector:** if the input signals are at the same frequency but differ in phase, the output contains a direct component proportional to the cosine of the phase difference between them. Thus, for inputs $V_1 \sin \omega t$ and $V_2 \sin(\omega t + \phi)$, the output contains a term proportional to $\sin \omega t \sin(\omega t + \phi) = \cos \phi - \cos(2\omega t + \phi)$; in practice, the component at frequency 2ω can be filtered out.

(iii) **A frequency doubler:** following the same argument as for the phase detector, applying the same signal at frequency ω to each input terminal will generate a double-frequency component at the output.

(iv) **Modulators and demodulators:** reference to the use of balanced modulator is made in Chapter 10 in which it is explained that the modulation process is essentially a multiplicative one.

The Plessey Semiconductors' SL 1640C is an example of an integrated-circuit balanced modulator designed for use as a mixer, phase comparator or modulator. It operates at signal frequencies up to 75 MHz from a single 6 V d.c. supply and requires no external biasing components. Typical performance figures include a conversion gain of 0 dB, a noise figure of 10 dB, input impedances of the order of 1 kΩ and intermodulation products 45 dB down.

15.1.2 The voltage controlled oscillator

It is often convenient to be able to control the frequency of an oscillator by means of a variable bias (or control) voltage. Such a device is known as a **voltage-controlled oscillator** (VCO). A VCO may be used as part of a wider system (such as the phase locked loop described in the next section). However, this section is concerned with the integrated circuit whose primary purpose is to generate a voltage-dependent frequency. In such circuits the voltage-control facility may be combined with the generation of differing waveforms (e.g. sinusoidal, triangular, etc.) and the term **function generator** is then used. With no bias, the oscillator frequency is known as the **free-running frequency** and is selected by means of an externally connected capacitor or resistor–capacitor combination. Instructions on how this should be done are provided with the circuit data as are the required bias voltage magnitudes for a given frequency deviation.

The type XR-2206 (Fig. 15.3) is an integrated-circuit function generator. The following data is extracted from the Exar data sheet.

> The XR-2206 is a monolithic function generator capable of producing high quality sine, square, triangle, ramp and pulse waveforms of high stability and accuracy. The output waveforms can be both amplitude and frequency modulated by external voltages. Frequency of operation can be selected externally over a range of 0.01 Hz to 1 MHz. It has a typical drift specification of 20 ppm/°C and the oscillator can be linearly swept over a 2000:1 frequency range by the external control voltage with very little effect on distortion.

A functional block diagram is shown in Fig. 15.3.

Fig. 15.3 Diagram of function generator (with acknowledgement to Exar I.C. Design Ltd.)

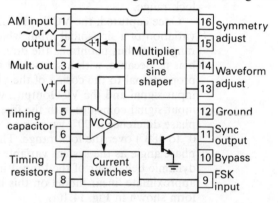

15.1.3 The phase locked loop

The phase locked loop (PLL) is an electronic control system which uses three of the previously described circuits arranged in a feedback loop. The block diagram is shown in Fig. 15.4. It is a multifunction circuit and an output may be taken from the filter or the VCO, depending upon the use to which the circuit is to be put.

Fig. 15.4 Block diagram of a phase-locked loop

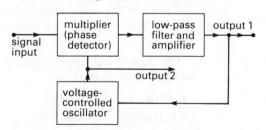

With no input to the phase detector, the VCO free-runs at a frequency determined by an external capacitor or resistor; in the context of PLL operation, this free-running frequency is known as the centre frequency f_0. When an input signal, whose frequency is close to f_0, is applied to the phase detector, the VCO is pulled into lock such that its frequency is identical to that of the input signal f_i, i.e. $f_{osc} = f_i$. The detailed process of locking is not described. However, once locked, the phase detector generates sum- and difference-frequency components at $2f_i$ and zero frequency. It is this zero-frequency component which provides just that bias which the VCO requires to pull its frequency from f_0 to f_i, and it is implicit that the input and VCO signals must differ in phase by an amount consistent with this bias voltage.

Once locked, the circuit remains in lock over a frequency range either side of the centre frequency and this is known as the **lock range**. When initially out of lock, f_i and f_0 are normally different and the phase detector generates sum- and difference-frequency components at $f_0 + f_i$ and $f_0 - f_i$; the difference-frequency component is fed back to the VCO through the filter and the maximum value of the difference frequency at which the loop will pull into lock is therefore a function of the filter time constant. The **capture range** is that range of frequencies in which the loop will pull into lock if not already locked. The capture range is always less than the lock range.

Once captured, the VCO will follow any frequency variation of a sinusoidal input which lies within the lock range and thus maintains the direct component required to bias it. Because, with a sinusoidal input, this component is proportional to the cosine of the phase difference between the input signal and the VCOoutput, when the frequency of the input signal coincides with the free-running frequency, the phase difference is 90°, varying an additional ±90° (i.e. from 0° to 180°) over the lock range. Thus, it is convenient to use phase angle as the system variable in the analysis of the dynamic behaviour of the loop. Fig. 15.5 shows an approximate linear model on this basis drawn in the general form shown in Fig. 14.1(a).

Fig. 15.5 Linear model of a phase-locked loop

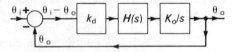

k_d is the phase-detector constant (V/rad);
$H(s)$ is the filter transfer function;
k_o/s is the VCO transfer function: because the device is a voltage-to-frequency converter, it behaves as a phase-angle integrator.

The closed-loop transfer function of the system is (using Section 1.2 of Chapter 14),

$$\frac{k_d H(s) k_o/s}{1 + k_d H(s) k_o/s} = \frac{k_d k_o H(s)}{s + k_d k_o H(s)}.$$

Without the low-pass filter in circuit (i.e. $H(s) = 1$ or a constant) the loop has a first-order response and is known as a **first-order loop**. If the filter itself has a first-order response, the loop has a second-order response and is known as a **second-order loop**. The frequency and time responses are characteristic of such systems, as illustrated in Exercise 15.3.

Two applications illustrate differing approaches to the use of the phase-locked loop.

(i) **Frequency synthesiser:** by inserting a programmable counter (operating as a frequency divider) into the feedback loop between the VCO and the phase detector, the loop will lock such that the counter-output frequency is (exactly) equal to a reference-frequency input signal. The VCO output frequency will then be exactly nf_{ref} where n is the divider ratio and f_{ref} is the reference frequency. By programming the counter to give differing values of n, a step-variable frequency output may be obtained. This will have the stability and accuracy of the reference signal. A signal generator based on the generation of multiple-frequency outputs from a limited number of sources is known as a **frequency synthesiser**.

(ii) **A frequency-modulation demodulator:** in this case the loop is used in the form shown in Fig. 15.4 with the output taken from the filter output, i.e. output 1. Frequency modulation (f.m.) is a process by which the instantaneous frequency of a high-frequency sinusoid is varied in accordance with information to be transmitted and is described in Chapter 10. The PLL behaves as a demodulator by virtue of the fact that the VCO follows the input frequency-modulated signal and, as such, behaves as a sympathetic modulator. Provided that it is linear, the VCO input signal (the filter output) will reproduce the original modulated signal and thus provides a demodulated output at this point in the circuit.

Fig. 15.6 shows the pin connections for the Signetics NE 565F designed to operate at VCO frequencies up to 500 kHz.

Fig. 15.6 Diagram of type 565 PLL (with acknowledgement to Mullard Ltd.)

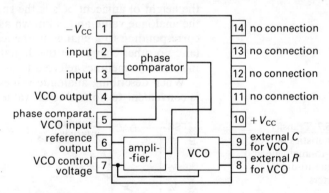

An extract from the electrical characteristics, highlighting a few key figures related to the above description, is given below. These apply under certain specified operating conditions.

d.c. supply voltage V_{CC}	± 6 V to ± 12 V;
phase comparator input impedance	10 kΩ;
input sensitivity at 10 kHz	10 mV r.m.s.;
maximum VCO frequency	500 kHz;

VCO sensitivity $\qquad \pm 0.1f_0$ per 300 mV p-p;

lock range round VCO $\qquad f_L \simeq \pm 0.7f_0$ (at $V_{CC} = \pm 6$ V);
centre frequency f_0

capture range $\qquad f_C \simeq \pm \dfrac{1}{2\pi} \sqrt{\left(\dfrac{2\pi f_L}{\tau}\right)};$

where τ is a time constant determined by externally connected filtering components.

15.2 Analogue/digital conversion

The study of the devices for implementing digital-to-analogue (DAC) and analogue-to-digital conversion (ADC) processes starts by considering the operational requirements and some of the commonly used terminology. The function of the DAC is to produce a (quantised) analogue output corresponding to a particular binary-digital input code and the function of the ADC is to reverse the procedure, although the analogue signal is not normally quantised before encoding; the converter necessarily quantises the signal in the conversion operation. Transfer characteristics for ideal 3-bit converters are shown in Fig. 15.7(a) and (b) for the DAC and the ADC respectively. In (a), each digital code corresponds to a specific analogue-output value as indicated by an × on the graph. Only the eight analogue values shown (including zero) can exist; no intermediate values are possible. The difference in the height of adjacent ×'s is the smallest possible change in the analogue value and is known as a **quantisation interval**, corresponding to a change in the least-significant bit (LSB) (and no other change) of the digital code; the quantisation interval is sometimes referred to as 1 *LSB*.

When describing analogue values associated with a DAC it is convenient to normalise all values to a **full-scale range**

Fig. 15.7 Transfer characteristics of 3-bit digital-to-analogue and analogue-to-digital converters

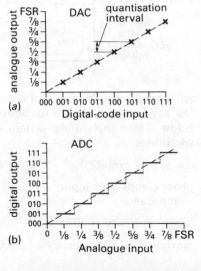

(FSR) as shown on the vertical axis of the graph. The FSR is given by the quantisation interval multiplied by 2^n (n is the number of bits) so that the maximum analogue output then becomes $(2^n - 1)FSR/2^n$; for the 3-bit system shown, the maximum output is $\frac{7}{8}FSR$, corresponding to the maximum 3-bit digital input 111. Once the FSR is defined, the weight of the least-significant bit is given by $FSR/2^n$ and the weight of the most-significant bit is $FSR/2$. The quantisation interval (or $1\,LSB$) is also given by $FSR/2^n$. Table 15.1 gives quantisation intervals for commonly used numbers of bits.

Table 15.1. *Quantisation intervals*

Number of bits	Quantisation interval		
	fractional	*decimal*	*dB scale*
4	1/16	0.0625	−24
8	1/256	0.003 91	−48
10	1/1024	0.000 977	−60
12	1/4096	0.000 244	−72
16	1/65 536	0.000 015 3	−96

In Fig. 15.7(*b*) the analogue-input signal range is shown on the ADC input axis. Because this continuous range must be quantised into (in this case) 8 discrete digital-code values, a section of the analogue range is allocated to each code; in other words, any analogue-signal value within each section of the range will convert into its corresponding discrete code value. Comparing the diagrams in (*a*) and (*b*), it will be seen that the discrete analogue output of the DAC corresponds to the centre value of each of the sections shown in (*b*) and, as a result of the quantisation process, an error of up to $\pm\frac{1}{2}$ quantisation interval (or $\pm\frac{1}{2}LSB$) will be introduced in the analogue-to-digital-conversion process. This error is known as **quantisation error** or **uncertainty**. Increasing the number of bits in the code reduces the magnitude of the quantisation intervals and, hence, the quantisation error: both are halved for each bit added to the code length.

15.3 Digital-to-analogue converters

15.3.1 Weighted-resistor and ladder principles

Because each bit in the binary code has a weight, generating and adding weighted voltages (or currents) corresponding to each bit set at 1 will give the analogue equivalent of the digital input. Fig. 15.8 shows an arrangement which would perform these functions. Assuming that the operational-amplifier input is virtually at earth potential (see Section 3.3 of Chapter 14), applying a standard voltage to any input terminal for which the bit value is 1 will cause a current proportional to the weighting of the bits to flow into the common junction.

Fig. 15.8 Weighted-resistor digital-to-analogue converter

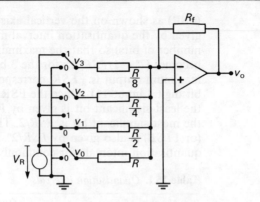

The circuit is essentially the summing circuit discussed in Chapter 14 with its input resistors weighted in the ratios 1:2:4:8. Following the analysis given in that chapter, the output voltage will be:

$$v_o = -\left(\frac{R_f}{R}v_0 + \frac{R_f}{R/2}v_1 + \frac{R_f}{R/4}v_2 + \frac{R_f}{R/8}v_3\right)$$

$$= -\frac{R_f}{R}(v_0 + 2v_1 + 4v_2 + 8v_3).$$

Setting v_0–v_3 in accordance with a binary input signal so that, with a binary input of 1101 for example, $v_0 = -V_R$, $v_1 = 0$, $v_2 = -V_R$ and $v_3 = -V_R$, the output voltage will be:

$$v_o = \frac{R_f}{R}V_R(8 + 4 + 0 + 1) = 13\frac{R_f}{R}V_R,$$

and the output amplitude will be seen to be proportional to the value of the binary number at the input. For a general binary input, $b_3b_2b_1b_0$, the output voltage will be:

$$v_o = V_R\frac{R_F}{R}(8b_3 + 4b_2 + 2b_1 + b_0).$$

Because of problems associated with the wide range of input-resistor values required (a range of 256:1 for an 8-bit converter), a preferable alternative is the **R–2R ladder network**. In this case, only two resistor values are required. The circuit shown in Fig. 15.9 is referred to as a current-switching circuit in which the 2R resistors are returned either to earth or to the operational-amplifier input terminal (which

Fig. 15.9 R–2R ladder digital-to-analogue converter

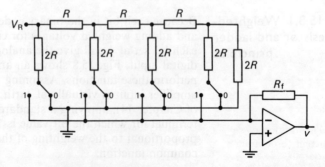

is virtually at earth potential). Thus, the current is effectively diverted either to earth or the operational-amplifier input according to whether the corresponding bit is 0 or 1. In principle, the circuit operates as follows: in Fig. 15.10 each 2R resistor is effectively returned to earth potential and the circuit-current pattern is as shown. Working from the right-hand side, the resistance looking towards the right at the indicated sections is always 2R. Thus, the current in the series branch splits into two halves, one half flowing in the 2R resistor and the other into the next series branch. In this way, an appropriately weighted current flows into the operational-amplifier input when the relevant switch is closed. The operational-amplifier output voltage is proportional to the current flow into the input and hence to the magnitude of the binary number at the converter input.

Fig. 15.10 The R–$2R$ ladder principle

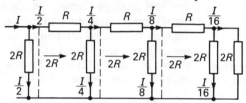

15.3.2 Bipolar digital-to-analogue converters

In the previous section it is assumed that the digital input signal is a natural-binary coded signal and that the converter produces an output signal of a single polarity; such converters are known as **unipolar converters**. The need may arise for a converter which can provide positive and negative outputs in response to signed-binary inputs, possibly in one of the three forms discussed in Section 2.4 of Chapter 16, sign plus magnitude, offset binary and 2's complement.

Table 15.2. *Offset binary numbers*

Decimal	Binary
3	111
2	110
1	101
0	100
−1	011
−2	010
−3	001
−4	000

Table 15.2 shows the offset-binary form. In order to obtain a bipolar output from a DAC designed to accept this input, it is necessary to arrange that the output voltage (or current) is zero when the binary input is 100, this being zero in offset-binary form. One way to achieve this is to add a bias or offset to the converter, as shown in Fig. 15.11: an offset current, $-I/2$, is injected into the summing junction. In this case, a binary input of 100 results in a current $+I/2$ flowing in the left-hand shunt 2R resistor, resulting in a net zero current flowing into the summing junction and, hence, zero output.

Fig. 15.11 Addition of an offset current to obtain a bipolar output

15.3.3 Multiplying DACs

Reference to the output voltage expression in Section 15.3.1 shows it to be proportional to the reference voltage, V_R, as well as to the binary input. A device capable of accepting a variable reference voltage is known as a **multiplying digital-to-analogue converter** (MDAC), since the output is proportional to the product of the (variable) analogue reference voltage and the analogue equivalent of the digital input. Fig. 15.12(a) shows a schematic representation of the MDAC. If the device accepts analogue and digital inputs which are both unipolar, the device is known as a one-quadrant multiplier; if one or the other is bipolar, the device is a two-quadrant multiplier and, finally, if both inputs are bipolar, a four-quadrant multiplier results.

There are a number of applications for such devices. The output may be regarded as a scaled version of the reference-terminal analogue input, the scaling factor controlled by the digital input. Such an arrangement could form the basis of a digitally controlled attenuator or amplifier. Another possibility is to connect an ADC and a MDAC together, as shown in Fig. 15.12(b), to form a high-precision analogue multiplier (see Section 15.1.1).

Fig. 15.12 Block diagram of a multiplying DAC and a precision multiplier

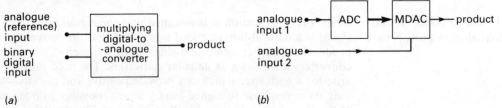

(a)   (b)

15.3.4 Specification terminology used for digital-to-analogue converters

There is some variation in the meaning of the terms used by manufacturers to specify the performance of DAC's but the following are commonly used.

Fig. 15.7(a) showed the ideal transfer characteristic of the DAC; Fig. 15.13(a), (b) and (c) show, respectively, a non-ideal converter in which there is an **offset error**, resulting in an analogue output with zero digital input, a **gain error** (or **scale-factor error**), given by the difference between the actual and the ideal full-scale values, assuming zero offset, and a **linearity error**, expressed as the greatest deviation of the transfer characteristic from the ideal, with zero gain and offset errors. Additionally, the **differential-linearity error** describes the greatest deviation from the ideal analogue-output change (i.e. $1\,LSB$) in response to an increment in the digital input.

Fig. 15.13 Errors in digital-to-analogue converters

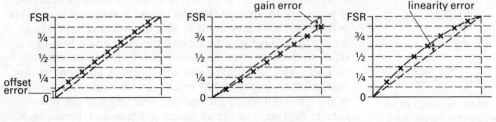

(a)   (b)   (c)

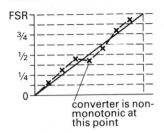

Fig. 15.14 Non-monotonicity

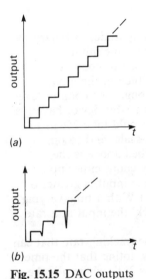

Fig. 15.15 DAC outputs

With a differential-linearity error of $\pm\frac{1}{4}LSB$, the actual analogue-output change in response to a 1-bit increment in the input would lie between $\frac{3}{4}$ and $1\frac{1}{4}LSB$. Another term associated with incremental changes is **monotonicity**; a converter is monotonic if its output amplitude does not decrease (increase) with upward (downward) increments in the digital input. Fig. 15.14 shows the characteristic of a converter which is non-monotonic.

The specification terms discussed above have been associated with **static** errors, i.e. errors which exist when the input and output have settled to a steady state. However, there are also errors which result when the input changes state. If the output of a natural-binary converter is observed on an oscilloscope as the binary input is incremented upward, the output waveform will (ideally) be as shown in Fig. 15.15(*a*). However, changes in the digital input result in one or more switches operating and, particularly when a large number of switches operate 'together' (e.g. if the binary input changes from 011 to 100, in a 3-bit converter), small differences in switch-on and switch-off times can result in a transient condition. For example, with certain switches opening before others close, the output could fall to zero for a short period of time. Such transients, illustrated in Fig. 15.15(*b*), are sometimes called 'glitches' and their appearance is also affected by the response of the output amplifier. The time taken for the output to 'settle' to within specified limits of its final value, is known as the converter **settling time**. When specifying settling times it is not sufficient just to consider incremental changes in the binary input since such changes will not result in worst-case figures. Accordingly, the settling time would normally be specified for a zero to full-scale transition.

15.4 Analogue-to-digital converters

15.4.1 Introduction

There is a variety of ADC types having a wide range of operating principles. The following sections cover five representative types; reference may be made to more specialised literature for a fuller discussion.

15.4.2 The digital ramp converter

This is a feedback-type converter whose block diagram is shown in Fig. 15.16. The circuit operation is as follows. On receipt of a 'convert-start' signal, the counter is reset and then follows a natural-binary counting sequence. As it does so, the digital-to-analogue converter output increases steadily (as shown in Fig. 15.15(*a*)), gradually approaching the analogue-input signal amplitude, which at this stage is assumed to be constant. As soon as the DAC output just exceeds the analogue-input amplitude, the comparator sends a signal to the control unit which stops the counter and issues a 'convert-complete' signal. Because the output of the DAC is

Fig. 15.16 A digital-ramp digital-to-analogue converter

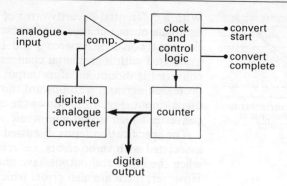

(almost) equal to the analogue-input amplitude, its binary input is the digital equivalent of the analogue input.

The conversion time (from convert-start to convert-complete signals) varies with the amplitude of the input signal: the greater the amplitude, the longer the counter takes to reach its final value. For example, an 8-bit device having a 1 MHz clock (i.e. a 1 μs clock period) would take 256 μs to reach full-scale reading, 128 μs for half-scale, and so on.

A variation on the ramp type described above is the **tracking type** in which the counter may count either up or down according to whether the analogue input is greater or less (respectively) than the DAC output With a time-varying input, the output would follow or 'track' the input at a rate determined by the clock frequency.

There is an inherent limitation to the tracking rate that can be achieved. This may be quantified by noting that the time taken to count from zero to full scale is $2^n T_c$, where n is the number of bits and T_c is the clock period; if the analogue input were changing at just this rate (i.e. zero to full scale in a time $2^n T_c$), the digital output could exactly represent the analogue input at every instant in time, subject of course to the quantisation error. Because the digital output cannot change more rapidly than this, analogue variations in excess of this rate will not be tracked correctly.

The maximum tracking rate may be related to a sinusoidal input of frequency f_{max} and amplitude V_m: its maximum rate of change (as it crosses zero) is $2\pi f_{max} V_m$, so that making V_m equal to half the full-scale range and equating the two expressions for maximum rate of change, gives $2\pi f_{max} V_m = 2V_m/2^n T_c$ and, hence, $f_{max} = f_c/\pi 2^n$. For example, with $f_c = 1$ MHz and $n = 8$, the maximum frequency would be 1.24 kHz.

An alternative type uses an analogue-ramp generator, a comparator and a natural-binary counter. The digital output is generated by starting the counter at the same time as the ramp and stopping it when the ramp reaches the input voltage, this condition being signalled by the comparator. Fig. 15.17 illustrates the action. This type may be described as an **analogue-ramp** device as compared with the digital-ramp type described above.

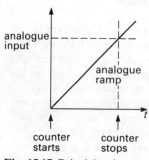

Fig. 15.17 Principle of an analogue-ramp converter

15.4.3 The successive-approximation converter

Whereas the tracking converter starts from its existing value and counts one bit at a time to its new value, the successive-approximation type employs an *n*-bit register, each bit location being loaded sequentially (working from the MSB to the LSB) with a 1. Each 1 is tested and either retained or reset until the register contains the binary equivalent of the analogue input. The conversion time (in clock periods) is equal to the number of bits plus one, e.g. 9 periods for an 8-bit system. Fig. 15.18 shows a block diagram.

Fig. 15.18 A successive-approximation digital-to-analogue converter

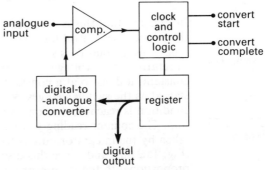

In greater detail, the operation of the successive-approximation type is as follows: at the start of a conversion, the most-significant bit (MSB) in the register is set at 1 with all other bits at 0; this sets the DAC output at $\frac{1}{2}$-full-scale range. The DAC output is now compared with the analogue input, and if the input is larger, the MSB is held at 1. If it is smaller (i.e. if the analogue input is less than $\frac{1}{2}$-full-scale) the MSB is reset to 0. The next bit is now set at 1 resulting in a DAC output of either $\frac{3}{4}$-full scale if the MSB was retained at 1 or $\frac{1}{4}$-full scale if the MSB had been reset to 0. This output is now compared with the analogue input and the bit either retained at 1 or reset to 0 according to whether the input is greater or smaller than the DAC output. The procedure is repeated for each bit in the register, its contents become a closer and closer approximation to the correct binary representation of the analogue input. Fig. 15.19 contrasts the DAC outputs after successive clock cycles for 4-bit ramp and successive-approximation types for an analogue input just in excess of $\frac{9}{16}FSR$ with an assumed clock period of $1\,\mu s$. For the successive-approximation type, the DAC output is that existing *before* the bit is either set or reset following the test.

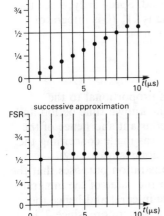

Fig. 15.19 Ramp and successive-approximation converters

15.4.4 Dual-slope type

In contrast with the previous examples (which incorporate feedback) the dual-slope type is an **integrating** converter, working on what is sometimes known as the **charge-balancing** principle.

The outline block diagram is shown in Fig. 15.20 and the operating principle is as follows: assuming, initially, that the integrator output is zero and that the control logic places the switch in the 'analogue-input' position for a known period of time *T*, the integrator output will reach a value

$$k \int_0^T v_i \, dt \quad (k \text{ is a constant}).$$

Fig. 15.20 A dual-slope analogue-to-digital converter

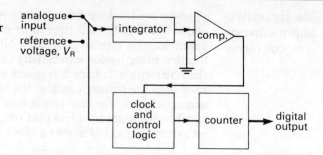

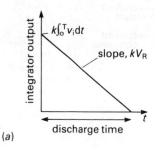

(a)

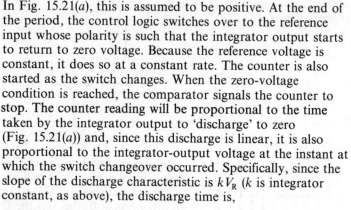

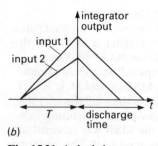

(b)

Fig. 15.21 A dual-slope analogue-to-digital converter

In Fig. 15.21(*a*), this is assumed to be positive. At the end of the period, the control logic switches over to the reference input whose polarity is such that the integrator output starts to return to zero voltage. Because the reference voltage is constant, it does so at a constant rate. The counter is also started as the switch changes. When the zero-voltage condition is reached, the comparator signals the counter to stop. The counter reading will be proportional to the time taken by the integrator output to 'discharge' to zero (Fig. 15.21(*a*)) and, since this discharge is linear, it is also proportional to the integrator-output voltage at the instant at which the switch changeover occurred. Specifically, since the slope of the discharge characteristic is $k V_R$ (k is integrator constant, as above), the discharge time is,

$$\frac{k \int_0^T v_i \, dt}{\text{slope}} = \frac{\int_0^T v_i \, dt}{V_R}.$$

In other words, the binary count is proportional to the integral of the input voltage over the known time period and is independent of the value of the constant and hence of the component values. No assumption was made concerning the nature of the input waveform (and none is necessary). However, if it is assumed for demonstration purposes that the input is a constant voltage, V_i, then the value of the integral will be $V_i T$, and since T is fixed, the integral and hence the binary count is proportional to V_i. Furthermore, since T is determined by the same clock as is used to generate the binary count in the discharge period, the magnitude of the count is independent of the clock frequency, unless there are any short-term variations, a relatively unlikely occurrence. The device's operation with a constant input, resulting as it does in a linear increase in the integrator output (as well as the decrease) accounts for the name 'dual slope'. Fig. 15.21(*b*) illustrates the waveforms in this circumstance for two specimen input values; the diagram also emphasises the nature of the operation with its constant charge time but with a discharge time directly proportional to the magnitude of the input.

Although potentially a very accurate converter (given an accurate reference), it is slow in operation; indeed, the period, T, may be deliberately made quite large (e.g. 20 ms) in order to minimise the effect of noise on the input signal and this inevitably results in slow operation. For example, if measuring a constant voltage to which mains interference is

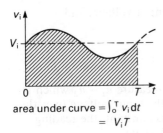

area under curve $= \int_0^T v_i \, dt$

$\quad\quad\quad\quad = V_i T$

Fig. 15.22 How the effect of an interfering signal can be zero

15.4.5 The charge-balancing converter

added, the charge period can be designed to be 20 ms (the period of the mains supply) in order that when integrated over this period the alternating component will be zero but the direct component unaffected. Fig. 15.22 shows how this would occur. In fact, any superimposed signal whose period is an exact submultiple of the fixed timing period would be eliminated in this way.

For high-frequency interference signals, the cancellation effect is progressively more effective even though there may not be an exact integral relationship between the noise-signal period and the charging period T. Consideration of a diagram, similar to Fig. 15.22 but having many cycles in the period T, would show how this occurs.

This type may be considered to be a development of the dual-slope type, one form of which is shown in Fig. 15.23. In principle, the operation is as follows.

Fig. 15.23 A charge-balancing digital-to-analogue converter

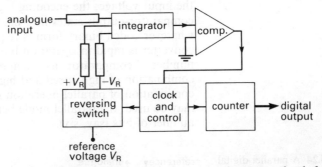

reference
voltage V_R

The analogue input and reference voltages are both fed into an integrator (Chapter 14), the polarity of the reference voltage being reversible according to the state of the comparator output. The polarity is determined by the polarity of the integrator output at the incidence of each clock pulse. The sense of the reference voltage is such that the integrator output voltage is always driven towards zero.

Because the integrator output is virtually zero after a large number of clock pulses, the output voltage due to the analogue input $k \int_0^T v_i \, dt$ is equal to the integration of the reference voltage over the same period. This is itself made up of two components

$$k \int_0^{n_1 T_c} V_R \, dt + k \int_0^{n_2 T_c} (-V_R) \, dt,$$

where n_1 is the number of clock pulses for which $+ V_R$ is connected, n_2 is the number of pulses for which $- V_R$ is connected and T_c is the clock-pulse period. Assuming that the integrator constants are the same,

$$\int_0^T v_i \, dt = V_R T_c (n_1 - n_2).$$

Also, because $T = (n_1 + n_2) T_c$,

$$\int_0^T v_i \, dt = (n_1 + n_2) T_c V_{in},$$

where V_{in} is the mean value of the input voltage, and therefore,

$$\frac{V_{in}}{V_R} = \frac{n_1 - n_2}{n_1 + n_2}.$$

The display counter is arranged to measure $n_1 - n_2$ which is proportional to the mean value of the input voltage over the timing period. If the input voltage is constant, the reading will be proportional to the constant value.

15.4.6 The parallel or 'flash' converter

In this type, one comparator is used for each quantisation interval so that, for an n-bit converter, $2^n - 1$ comparators are needed. Each comparator is biased (i.e. the decision level is set) by a resistive potential-divider chain supplied from a voltage-reference source (Fig. 15.24). Then, application of the analogue-input voltage will change the state of all those comparators which have a bias voltage of lower value than the input voltage; the encoding logic then translates the comparator-output states into natural-binary form or whatever coded binary form is required. The parallel converter is rapid in operation but does require a very large number of comparators as the number of bits increases. If the combination of high speed and high resolution is needed, a combination of parallel-operation mode and some other form may be used, the parallel mode being used for a limited number of bits (say, six).

Fig. 15.24 A parallel digital-to-analogue converter

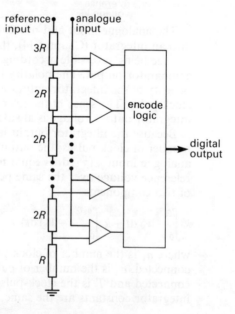

reference input   analogue input

3R

2R

2R   encode logic

                    digital output

2R

R

15.4.7 Specification terminology used with analogue-to-digital converters

The following brief summary builds on the introductory work in Section 15.2.

Conversion time: this is the time required to complete a conversion, i.e. between the 'convert-start' and 'convert-complete' signals.

Resolution and quantisation interval: these terms are described in Section 15.2. The **offset**, **gain** and **linearity** errors associated with the DAC have their counterparts in the ADC, Fig. 15.25(*a*), (*b*) and (*c*), respectively, showing these effects.

Fig. 15.25 Errors in analogue-to-digital converters

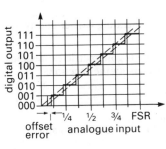

(*a*)

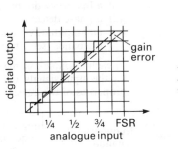

(*b*)

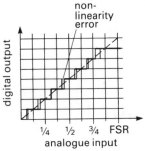

(*c*)

Key points to remember

- the balanced modulator is a multiplicative device generating sum- and difference-frequency components; it has many applications;

- the voltage-controlled oscillator can provide a bias-controlled frequency variation over a wide range;

- the internal oscillator of a phase-locked loop runs in synchronism with an external input, the device can be used in a range of applications;

- analogue-to-digital conversion implies sampling and encoding (usually into binary form) a continuous-time signal;

- digital-to-analogue conversion can be effected by weighted resistors or ladder networks;

- multiplying digital-to-analogue converters accept variable reference voltages;

- there is a range of analogue-to-digital converters operating on a variety of different principles; commonly used types are successive-approximation and dual-slope types.

Further reading

Clayton, G. B., *Data Converters.* Macmillan (1982).

Clayton, G. B., *Linear Integrated Circuit Applications.* Macmillan (1975).

Gray, P. R. and Meyer, R. G., *Analysis and Design of Analog Integrated Circuits* (2nd edn). J. Wiley (1984).

Sheingold, D. A., *Analogue-to-Digital Conversion Notes.* Analog Devices (1977).

EXERCISES 15

15.1 (a) Draw arrangements by which an ideal analogue multiplier could be used as

    (i) a frequency doubler;
    (ii) a phase detector;
    (iii) an amplitude modulator, generating carrier and two sidebands (see Chapter 10).

In each example assume suitable trigonometric expressions for the input signals and hence justify the functional properties of the device.

Fig. E15.1

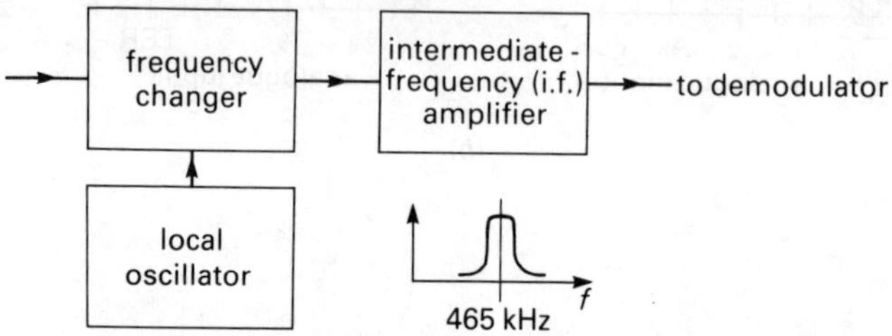

```
          ┌──────────┐      ┌────────────────┐
 ────────→│ frequency│─────→│  intermediate- │──────→ to demodulator
          │ changer  │      │ frequency (i.f.)│
          └──────────┘      │   amplifier    │
                ↑           └────────────────┘
          ┌──────────┐
          │  local   │              ╱╲
          │oscillator│             ╱  ╲        f
          └──────────┘        ────┘    └──────→
                             465 kHz
```

(b) Fig. E15.1 shows part of a radio receiver of the **superheterodyne** type. It employs a frequency changer and a local oscillator to generate a signal which will be amplified by the fixed-frequency intermediate-frequency amplifier which then provides the main gain and selectivity of the receiver. Tuning is provided by varying the oscillator frequency. Assuming the intermediate frequency is 465 kHz and the receiver is tuned to receive a signal centred on 1.2 mHz, what other station (if it exists) might be picked up?
Suggest a method of preventing the second signal being picked up.

15.2 An automatic-frequency-control (AFC) system uses a voltage-controlled oscillator and a frequency-to-voltage converter as shown in Fig. E15.2. If the VCO constant is 50 kHz/V and the f to v converter constant is 0.03 V/kHz (and both are linear) to what value would an open-loop oscillator frequency error of 10 kHz be reduced on closing the loop? Assume that the f to v converter has a bipolar output producing zero feedback voltage when the VCO is running at its nominal frequency.

Fig. E15.2

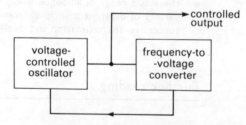

15.3 A phase-locked loop is to be used as a frequency-to-voltage converter. Using the block diagram in Fig. 15.4, deduce a closed-loop transfer function relating the *frequency* of an input signal (rather than the phase as in Fig. 15.5) to the voltage appearing between the filter and the voltage-controlled oscillator. Assume that the filter is a simple low-pass CR network.

If, in the terminology of Fig. 15.5, $k_d = 0.68$ V/rad and
$k_o = 6.6$ kHz/V, and assuming a filter time constant of
0.5×10^{-4} s, determine the voltage response to a step-
frequency input.

15.4 A 4-bit digital-to-analogue converter has a full-scale range of
± 2.5 V and is designed to accept offset-binary coded data.
Sketch one complete cycle of the output waveform which
would appear on an oscilloscope if the converter were driven
by a continuously repeated natural-binary sequence. Show
amplitude and time scales (with exact amplitudes at key levels)
assuming the binary-sequence generator has a 1 MHz clock.

15.5 Fig. E15.3 shows a possible voltage-switching digital-to-
analogue converter circuit. Explain how an analogue output is
obtained in response to operation of the logic-controlled
switches.

Fig. E15.3

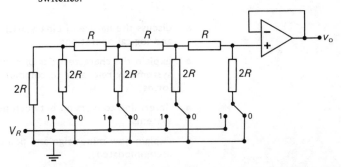

15.6 Calculate the clock rate required to ensure that the restriction
imposed by the sampling theorem (Chapter 9) is met when
converting a signal having a maximum frequency component
of 3 kHz and using an 8-bit digital-ramp converter.
What would be the maximum frequency of a sinusoid which
could be accurately tracked (using a tracking converter) at this
clock rate?

15.7 How many tests would be required to establish the integer
value of a number in the range 0–255 if the response to each
test simply indicated whether the number was in the lower half
of the range under consideration?

15.8 An 8-bit dual-slope converter is to be used in an environment
where a significant amount of mains-supply interference (at
50 Hz) is added to the signal; the converter is therefore
designed to operate with a 20 ms charging period.
If the peak amplitude of the interference signal were 15% of
FSR what would be the maximum percentage output error
due to a timing-period error of 1 ms, assuming that the
converter is otherwise ideal.

16 Arithmetic and logical operations

The principal learning objectives of this chapter are to:

		Section	Exercise
•	discuss the nature of binary arithmetic and logical operations;	1.1, 1.2	16.1
•	explain the characteristics of number systems by reference to commonly used forms;	2.1, 2.2	16.1
•	determine conversion between number systems;	2.3	16.3
•	explain how minus sign and point can be accommodated;	2.4	16.4
•	discuss the nature of a logical problem and express it as a truth table;	3.1, 3.2	16.5
•	define the logical operations AND, OR and NOT;	3.3	16.6
•	explain the meaning of three-state logic and active-low signals;	3.4	16.7
•	define the logical operations NAND and NOR;	3.5	16.8
•	discuss the significance of minterms and maxterms;	3.6	16.9
•	apply the laws of Boolean algebra to logic-system analysis;	4.1, 4.2	16.10
•	relate logic diagrams to Boolean expressions;	4.3, 4.4	16.11
•	deduce logical expressions for binary addition;	5.2	16.12
•	show how subtraction can be implemented using the 2's complement method;	5.3, 5.4	16.13
•	describe the compare operation;	5.5	
•	explain methods of binary multiplication and division;	5.6, 5.7	16.14
•	state the principal functions of an arithmetic logic unit (ALU);	5.8	
•	state the meaning of rotate and shift operations;	6	

16.1 Introduction

16.1.1 The nature of digital operations

Most digital systems are designed with the primary objective of executing logical or arithmetic operations with the input data in a two-value or binary form. There is a fundamental difference between digital and analogue systems in the sense that whereas the data in the analogue system is continuous in both time and amplitude, in the digital system it is discrete in both respects. This is an aspect discussed more fully in Section 3 of Chapter 9.

A **logical operation** is one which results in one or more outputs (each of which may take on one of two values, true or false, high or low, 1 or 0, etc.) in response to a set of binary input conditions. For example, I decide to travel if the weather is fine (yes/no), if the bus is running (yes/no) and if I feel well enough (yes/no). The decision is the output and the conditions are the inputs.

The **arithmetic operations** are the familiar operations of addition, subtraction, multiplication and division. In the systems to be discussed these operations are implemented in the binary number system where they effectively become a series of two-level logical decisions. Thus, allied to the flexibility of circuitry which may be used for either logical or arithmetic functions is the ease with which two-level data can be handled with a low probability of error: digital subsystems may consist of thousands of interconnected circuit elements, but by ensuring that each is only required to take up an unambiguous 'on' or 'off' state, a virtually error-free system may be implemented.

16.1.2 Combinational and sequential systems

Digital logic systems may be categorised as combinational or sequential. In the **combinational system**, the outputs are functions of the present input only whereas, in the **sequential system**, the outputs are determined by the present-state inputs and by the existing state of the circuits, the latter depending on past inputs and, in the general case, the initial state of the circuit. These systems have respective parallels in analogue systems in which the output from a resistive circuit depends only on the existing inputs, whereas the output from a circuit containing energy-storage elements (inductance or capacitance) depends on the present input as well as the existing state of the energy-storage elements. Because the outputs of both energy-storage analogue circuits and sequential-logic digital circuits depend partially on past inputs, each may be regarded as having a 'memory'. The ways in which the analogue-circuit output depends upon past inputs are discussed in Chapter 2 and the digital-memory elements are considered in Chapters 17 and 18. However, one significant difference may be noted: whereas the digital-memory elements can be constructed from the basic non-storage logic elements (using feedback), capacitors and inductors cannot be formed from the non-storage (resistive) elements. That the digital-memory element can be formed from non-storage elements is a direct consequence of the discrete-time nature of the digital system.

The use of binary numbers is central to the discussion of both arithmetic and logical operations and the chapter therefore starts with a brief discussion on number systems.

16.2 Number systems

16.2.1 Base, positional value and point

The **base** or **radix** of a number system is the number of symbols used in its presentation. The decimal system, for example, has the ten symbols $0, 1, \ldots, 9$ and the binary system has two symbols, 0 and 1.

The value of the symbol (which becomes a **digit** when written as part of a number) depends on its position in the number. When written on the immediate left of a **point**, it has a value given by the value of the symbol multiplied by the base raised to the power 0. Moving farther to the left of the point raises the power in integer steps. Digits to the right of the point have positional values given by the value of the symbol multiplied by increasingly negative powers of the base. As an example the decimal number 453.26 can be analysed as follows.

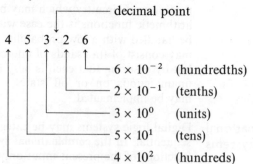

6×10^{-2}	(hundredths)
2×10^{-1}	(tenths)
3×10^0	(units)
5×10^1	(tens)
4×10^2	(hundreds)

A second example analyses a binary number:

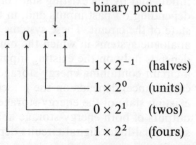

1×2^{-1}	(halves)
1×2^0	(units)
0×2^1	(twos)
1×2^2	(fours)

This example illustrates a four-digit number, normally abbreviated to 4-bit number, **bit** being the recognised abbreviation for binary digit. The digit on the far right is known as the **least-significant bit** (LSB) and that on the far left is the **most-significant bit** (MSB). A group of bits is known as a **byte**, the term normally implying a group of eight bits.

The positional analysis of the number enables the decimal equivalent to be determined. Thus, in the binary example above, the decimal value is

$$1 \times 2^2 + 1 \times 2^0 + 1 \times 2^{-1} = 4 + 1 + 0.5 = 5.5.$$

16.2.2 Hexadecimal and octal numbers

Numbers to any base can be expressed in the general form described in the previous section. In practice, one other base is commonly used: this is the base 16 or **hexadecimal** form. Occasionally, the base 8 or **octal** system is also used. Table 16.1 shows the complete set of hexadecimal symbols from 0 through 9 to F. Also shown are the decimal and binary equivalents so that the table may also be used as a conversion chart. For example, the hexadecimal number 3AD is equivalent to decimal 941:

Table 16.1. *Hexadecimal, decimal and binary equivalents*

Hexadecimal	Decimal	Binary
0	0	0000
1	1	0001
2	2	0010
3	3	0011
4	4	0100
5	5	0101
6	6	0110
7	7	0111
8	8	1000
9	9	1001
A	10	1010
B	11	1011
C	12	1100
D	13	1101
E	14	1110
F	15	1111

3   A   D

$$D \times 16^0$$
$$A \times 16^1$$
$$3 \times 16^2$$

i.e.

$$3 \times 256 + 10 \times 16 + 13 \times 1 = 941.$$

The octal system uses the first eight symbols from the decimal code, i.e. 0–7.

When writing numbers there is a need to differentiate between the different bases used. Conventionally, a small suffix is added: for example, 46_{10} (decimal), 101110_2 (binary), $2E_{16}$ (hexadecimal) and 56_8 (octal). To avoid what can become a rather tedious notation, the following convention is used in the remainder of this book: hexadecimal numbers have H written immediately following the digits, e.g. 3ADH. Decimal and binary numbers can be distinguished by the form of the number or by the context in which it is used. There is little further reference to octal numbers.

16.2.3 Number conversions

In illustrating the structure of numbers, a method for converting from binary or hexadecimal to decimal has been demonstrated. Conversion in the other direction can be performed in a number of ways:

(i) For small numbers, decomposition into powers of 2 or 16 can be performed by inspection. For example, 22 can be expressed as $16 + 4 + 2$ or $2^4 + 2^2 + 2^1$ which is 10110 in binary. In hexadecimal form 22 is $16 + 6$ or $1 \times 16^1 + 6 \times 16^0$, i.e. 16H.

(ii) For numbers up to about 256, a conversion chart can be used with reasonable convenience.

(iii) For larger numbers and those involving a decimal point the following formal method may be used: initially, take the digits to the left of the decimal point, and successively divide by two (for binary), recording the remainders until the quotient is zero. These remainders constitute the binary number. For example, given decimal 46:

$46 \div 2 = 23$ rem 0   least significant bit

$23 \div 2 = 11$ rem 1

$11 \div 2 = 5$ rem 1

$5 \div 2 = 2$ rem 1

$2 \div 2 = 1$ rem 0

$1 \div 2 = 0$ rem 1   most significant bit.

The binary number is 101110. A similar procedure is followed for digits to the right of the decimal point except that the number is multiplied by 2 and the carries are used to provide the binary number. For example, given decimal 0.8125,

$0.8125 \times 2 = 0.625$ carry 1   most significant bit

$0.625 \times 2 = 0.25$ carry 1

$0.25 \times 2 = 0.5$ carry 0

$0.5 \times 2 = 0$ carry 1   least significant bit.

The binary number is 0.1101. Combining the two figures, 46.8125 is 10110.1101 in binary. Conversions from decimal to hexadecimal can follow the same method. For example, given decimal 46

$46 \div 16 = 2$ rem 14 (EH)   least significant digit,

$2 \div 16 = 0$ rem   2   (2H)   most significant digit.

The hexadecimal number is 2EH.

As mentioned above, Table 16.1 can be used as a conversion chart between hexadecimal and binary numbers up to FH. The virtue of the hexadecimal system lies in the property that conversion from multiples of groups of four bits can be achieved by converting each group independently. The groups are always taken from the binary point. For example, taking groups of four bits and using Table 16.1

$01001101.1011 \leftrightarrow 4\text{D.BH}$

and

$110110.10 \leftrightarrow 36.8\text{H}.$

The octal system shares this advantage (although the bits are in groups of 3 in this case) but is less widely used because machines normally use data in four-bit multiples.

(iv) Electronic calculators performing hexadecimal, decimal, octal and binary number conversions and arithmetic are now widely available.

16.2.4 Machine-handling of numbers

It has been argued that the most convenient number system for electronic-circuit implementation is the binary system. However, the use of only two symbols does leave the problem of representing the binary point and the minus sign. This section shows how both can effectively be represented by the two symbols, starting with methods of representing negative numbers: three are given.

(i) **Sign plus magnitude:** in this case the most significant bit (MSB) of the number is used as a **sign bit**, 0 for plus and 1 for minus, natural binary being used for the magnitude. Table 16.2(*a*) shows the codes for the three-bit binary numbers and their decimal equivalents.

(ii) **Offset binary:** this code shown in Table 16.2(*b*) follows the normal binary counting sequence except that, as the name suggests, it is offset such that the lowest code 000 represents the most negative number in the system and 100 represents zero. The MSB is again a sign bit, this time 1 for plus and 0 for minus.

(iii) **Two's complement:** this is the same as offset binary but with the sign bit reversed, i.e. 0 for plus and 1 for minus. This means that the positive numbers follow the natural binary counting sequence and are the same as for the sign plus magnitude form. Table 16.2(*c*) shows the format for a three-bit binary number.

There is further discussion of the two's complement notation, including methods for its determination, in Section 16.5.3.

The binary point can be handled using the **floating-point** notation. Here, the point is understood to be immediately to the left of the most-significant non-zero digit and its true position is indicated by means of an exponent. For example, in decimal notation, 323.6 would be expressed as 0.3236×10^3 or $0.3236E + 3$ and the binary number 110010.01 would be

Table 16.2. *Negative number representation*

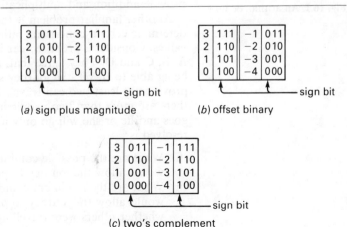

3	011	−3	111
2	010	−2	110
1	001	−1	101
0	000	0	100

sign bit

(*a*) sign plus magnitude

3	111	−1	011
2	110	−2	010
1	101	−3	001
0	100	−4	000

sign bit

(*b*) offset binary

3	011	−1	111
2	010	−2	110
1	001	−3	101
0	000	−4	100

sign bit

(*c*) two's complement

expressed as $.11001001 \times 2^{110}$ or $.11001001E110$. Thus, to represent a number in floating-point notation it is necessary to state the number itself, the exponent and the signs of both the number and the exponent, all arranged in a predetermined format.

16.3 Logical operations

16.3.1 The nature of the problem

The type of problem in which it is required to calculate a man's age is no doubt familiar. A typical example is: 'A man's age is twice that of his son's and their combined age is 66. What are their ages?'

Without the use of algebra the solution would be a matter of trial and error. However, by representing the unknown quantities by algebraic symbols, say M and S for the man's and son's age, respectively, the solution can proceed along the following lines:

If their total ages are T,

$$M + S = T.$$

If the ratio of their ages is R,

$$R = M/S \quad \text{or} \quad M = SR.$$

Therefore,

$$SR + S = T,$$

and hence,

$$S = T/(R + 1) \quad \text{and} \quad M = RT/(R + 1).$$

Substituting the numerical data $R = 2$ and $T = 66$ gives $S = 22$ and $M = 44$.

Fig. 16.1 introduces the notion of an arithmetic device which could be used to perform these operations. Although not shown, the internal circuits or the program would have to provide addition and multiplication facilities.

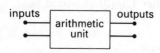

Fig. 16.1 An arithmetic unit

Another familiar problem is that in which it is required to determine certain conditions rather than certain numerical values. Consider a proposed car journey for four people, A, B, C and D. They agree that, in the event of everyone not being able to travel, the journey should still go ahead provided at least two can travel. However, A will go only if there are more than two people in the car, C will go only if B goes and he or she will go only if D goes. The problem to be resolved is:

(i)   What are the possible combinations of people which would allow the journey to proceed?
(ii) What are the minimum combination(s) which, if satisfied, would allow the journey to proceed irrespective of whether others were travelling?

In order to obtain a solution (and, perhaps, ultimately to

design a circuit or program to solve the problem) it is necessary to formalise the problem as an algebraic statement. Initially, therefore, the 'input' and 'output' must be expressed in terms of variables just as in the arithmetic case. Suitable names for the input variables are A, B, C and D, and, in the context of the problem, the output variable is called J (for journey). Because any device which may be used to solve this problem will operate with two-digit (binary) variables, the data is put into this form. The notation $A = 1$ is used to indicate that A is travelling (and $A = 0$ to indicate that he or she is not). Similarly, $J = 1$ means that the journey will take place and $J = 0$ that it will not, etc. It is emphasised that 1 and 0 do not have arithmetic significance but simply indicate logic values: possible alternatives are true and false, high and low, etc.

16.3.2 Truth tables

For the arithmetic problem the next stage was to express the written statement in algebraic form and this will be done for the logical problem; initially, however, the **truth table** is introduced. This shows all possible combinations of the input values and the corresponding output values. It is possible to do this for the logic problem because of the two-value nature of the variables; it would not be practicable to do the same thing for the arithmetic example because each input may take on one of an infinite range of values. This is not because it is arithmetic rather than logical but because the data is continuously variable (i.e. analogue) as opposed to taking on the limited number of discrete values characteristic of a digital system.

Table 16.3. *Truth table for the journey problem*

Row label	A	B	C	D	J
0	0	0	0	0	0
1	0	0	0	1	0
2	0	0	1	0	0
3	0	0	1	1	0
4	0	1	0	0	0
5	0	1	0	1	1
6	0	1	1	0	0
7	0	1	1	1	1
8	1	0	0	0	0
9	1	0	0	1	0
10	1	0	1	0	0
11	1	0	1	1	0
12	1	1	0	0	0
13	1	1	0	1	1
14	1	1	1	0	0
15	1	1	1	1	1

Table 16.3 shows the truth table with the 16 possible combinations of the four two-value input variables tabulated on the left-hand side. As a matter of convenience, they are normally listed in natural binary-counting sequence although they do not have arithmetic significance. The right-hand column gives the condition of the output variable. Its value is determined by studying each row of the table and deciding whether, in this case, the journey will take place or not. In practice, it is often possible to deal with a group of rows at a time. Thus, for rows 1, 2, 4 and 8, J is 0 because there is only a single 1 in the input and it is known that at least two must travel. Similarly, $J = 0$ for rows 9, 10 and 12 because A will only travel with at least three present. The remaining rows can be dealt with individually: row 3 gives $J = 0$ since C will not go without B, and so on, until all the output conditions are specified and the table completed.

Having established the table, an algebraic statement of the problem may be formulated. Sometimes, the situation is the reverse of this. For example, if two algebraic statements exist, the truth table may be used to determine whether they are equivalent. Proof of an identity, by showing that equality exists for all possible values of the variables is known as proof by **perfect induction** (see Example 16.4 in Section 16.4.2).

16.3.3 The basic logical operations

The algebra used to describe arithmetic problems involves the four arithmetic operations, add, subtract, multiply and divide. The logical problem on the other hand is not concerned with sums, and differences, products and quotients, but with propositions such as whether *A and B* are travelling together or whether *C or D* are travelling. Accordingly, the basic logical operations are AND, OR and NOT, for which the symbols are, respectively, a dot, a plus sign and a bar over the variable. The circuits used to implement these logical functions are known as **gates**. Thus, there are the **AND gate**, the **OR gate** and the **NOT gate**, also known as an **inverter**.

The three logical operations are formally defined as follows. Although stated in terms of two variables *A* and *B*, the results apply in general to more than two variables.

(i) **AND:** *A* AND *B* (written $A . B$) is 1 only when both *A* and *B* are 1; in all other cases $A . B = 0$;

(ii) **OR:** *A* OR *B* (written $A + B$) is 1 when either *A* or *B* (or both) is 1; in the other case $A + B = 0$.

A variation on the basic OR gate is the exclusive OR operation, *A* XOR *B* (written $A \oplus B$). In this case, the result is 1 when either *A* or *B* (but not both) is 1; in the other two cases $A \oplus B = 0$.

(iii) **NOT:** NOT *A* (written $\bar{A}$) is 0 when $A = 1$; $\bar{A} = 1$ when $A = 0$.

The four operations are illustrated in Fig. 16.2(*a*), (*b*), (*c*) and (*d*) respectively. In each case the truth table summarises the operation, the circuit symbol is shown and a typical integrated-circuit packaging arrangement is given. The symbols used are the American standard symbols, conforming with usual practice. The gate circuits are described in Chapter 13. It is emphasised that the operational symbols '.' and '+' do not represent multiplication and addition in the arithmetic sense. However, the terms **logical multiplication** and **logical addition**, respectively, are used and expressions involving them are known as **products** and **sums**. The special meaning should be clear from the context of statements.

16.3.4 Three-state logic and active-low signals

Notwithstanding the essentially two-level nature of the logic, devices are available for the implementation of what is known as **three-state logic** (also known by the trade name **Tristate**™†). This is a modification to standard logic which permits the output to be put into a high-impedance (high-Z) state, i.e. the gate output is effectively isolated from the rest of the circuit. In effect, the logic-gate output has three values, 1, 0 and high-Z. The three-state control line is normally shown entering the side of the gate as illustrated in Fig. 16.3(*a*). The diagram shows a three-state inverter gate and the **three-state buffer** (Fig. 16.3(*b*)). The buffer itself is not a logic gate and has no logical effect in the normal sense but is extensively used in situations where, for example, the current required by a driven device exceeds that which the driving device can

---

† Tristate is a registered trade mark of the National Semiconductor Corporation.

Fig. 16.2 AND, OR, XOR
and NOT gates and typical
integrated-circuit packages

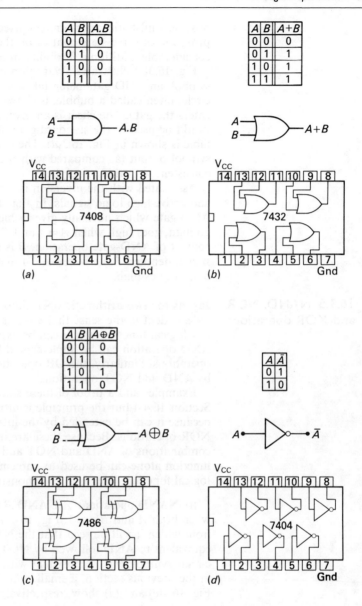

Fig. 16.3 Three-state logic
and inversion symbols

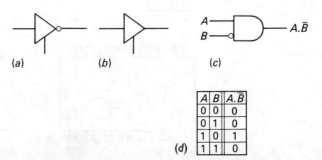

provide whilst still maintaining correct operation. The provision of three-state control on the buffer makes for considerable additional flexibility in its use.

Fig. 16.3(*c*) illustrates a variation on the normal logic gate symbol, an AND gate being taken as an example. A small circle, often called a bubble, is shown where the *B* input enters the gate. The effect is an inversion so that wherever *B* would be used in the standard gate, $\bar{B}$ is used here. The truth table is shown in Fig. 16.3(*d*). The circle on the inverter-symbol output (as compared with the buffer symbol) is consistent with this principle.

Associated with the inversion is the concept of **active-low** and **active-high** logic signals. In Fig. 16.3(*c*) for example, the AND gate which normally gives a high output when *A* and *B* go high, goes high when $A = 1$ and $B = 0$ in this case. In the context of AND-gate operation, *B* is then an **active-low** input signal, denoted $\bar{B}$, i.e. when $A = 1$ and $\bar{B} = 1$ the AND-gate output goes high.

16.3.5 NAND, NOR and XOR operations

Just as the two arithmetic operations × and ÷ are not independent in the sense that $a \div b$ is the same as $a \times (1/b)$, any logical function which can be expressed in terms of the AND operation can be implemented by OR and NOT operations. Similarly, the OR operation can be implemented by AND and NOT operations.

Examples and a proof of these statements are given in Section 16.4.4 but the principle is introduced at this stage because it can be extended by the introduction of NAND and NOR operations. Because these are, respectively, combinations of AND and NOT and OR and NOT, either function alone can be used to implement any combinational logical function. This is also demonstrated in Section 16.4.4.

(i) **NAND operation:** *A* NAND *B* (written $\overline{A \cdot B}$) is 0 only when both *A* and *B* are 1. Fig. 16.4(*a*) shows the truth table from which it will be seen that the NAND operation is equivalent to AND followed by NOT. Fig. 16.4(*b*) shows the circuit symbol: this is consistent with the notation introduced in the previous section, a small circle indicating inversion. Fig. 16.4(*c*) and (*d*) show, respectively, the triple 3-input and

Fig. 16.4 A NAND gate and typical integrated-circuit packages

A	B	A.B
0	0	1
0	1	1
1	0	1
1	1	0

(*a*)

(*b*)

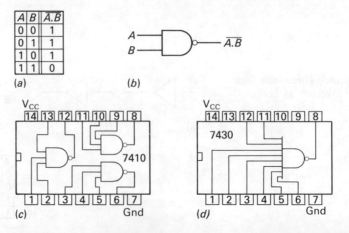

(*c*)

(*d*)

the single 8-input NAND-gate integrated circuits types 7410 and 7430. Quad 2-input and dual 4-input types are also available as the types 7400 and 7420, respectively.

(ii) **NOR operation:** A NOR B (written $\overline{A+B}$) is 0 when either A or B (or both) is 1. Fig. 16.5(*a*) shows the truth table from which it will be seen that the NOR operation is equivalent to OR followed by NOT. Fig. 16.5(*b*) shows the circuit symbol. A quad 2-input NOR-gate integrated circuit, type 7402, is shown in Fig. 16.5(*c*).

Fig. 16.5 A NOR gate and typical integrated-circuit packages

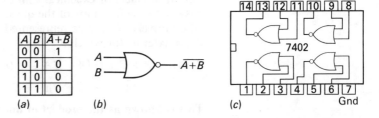

A	B	$\overline{A+B}$
0	0	1
0	1	0
1	0	0
1	1	0

(*a*)   (*b*)   (*c*)

16.3.6 An algebraic statement; minterms and maxterms

Inspection of the truth table relating to the journey problem (Table 16.3) shows that there is a total of four input conditions which will allow the journey to proceed ($J = 1$). The first of these, for example, is $A = 0$, $B = 1$, $C = 0$ and $D = 1$ and, in this condition, the logical product $\bar{A}B\bar{C}D$ is 1 (because $\bar{A} = 1$, $B = 1$, $\bar{C} = 1$ and $D = 1$). For all other values of the input variables and their complements this logical-product term (AND function) will be 0 and for this reason $\bar{A}B\bar{C}D$ is called a **minterm**. Table 16.4 shows the 16 minterms, each of which will be 1 for one, and only one, combination of input values.

Also shown in the table is a list of **maxterms**. Each of these logical-sum terms (OR functions) will be 1 for all

Table 16.4. *Maxterms and minterms*

Minterms	Maxterms
$\bar{A}\bar{B}\bar{C}\bar{D}$	$A + B + C + D$
$\bar{A}\bar{B}\bar{C}D$	$A + B + C + \bar{D}$
$\bar{A}\bar{B}C\bar{D}$	$A + B + \bar{C} + D$
$\bar{A}\bar{B}CD$	$A + B + \bar{C} + \bar{D}$
$\bar{A}B\bar{C}\bar{D}$	$A + \bar{B} + C + D$
$\bar{A}B\bar{C}D$	$A + \bar{B} + C + \bar{D}$
$\bar{A}BC\bar{D}$	$A + \bar{B} + \bar{C} + D$
$\bar{A}BCD$	$A + \bar{B} + \bar{C} + \bar{D}$
$A\bar{B}\bar{C}\bar{D}$	$\bar{A} + B + C + D$
$A\bar{B}\bar{C}D$	$\bar{A} + B + C + \bar{D}$
$A\bar{B}C\bar{D}$	$\bar{A} + B + \bar{C} + D$
$A\bar{B}CD$	$\bar{A} + B + \bar{C} + \bar{D}$
$AB\bar{C}\bar{D}$	$\bar{A} + \bar{B} + C + D$
$AB\bar{C}D$	$\bar{A} + \bar{B} + C + \bar{D}$
$ABC\bar{D}$	$\bar{A} + \bar{B} + \bar{C} + D$
$ABCD$	$\bar{A} + \bar{B} + \bar{C} + \bar{D}$

Note: the dot, used in AND and NAND operations is often omitted, its presence being implied in expressions such as AB or $\overline{AB}$ in the same way as for the arithmetic multiplication sign.

Table 16.5. *Minterms and maxterms against $J = 1$ and $J = 0$*

A	B	C	D	J	Minterms	Maxterms
0	0	0	0	0		$A + B + C + D$
0	0	0	1	0		$A + B + C + \bar{D}$
0	0	1	0	0		$A + B + \bar{C} + D$
0	0	1	1	0		$A + B + \bar{C} + \bar{D}$
0	1	0	0	0		$A + \bar{B} + C + D$
0	1	0	1	1	$\bar{A}B\bar{C}D$	
0	1	1	0	0		$A + \bar{B} + \bar{C} + D$
0	1	1	1	1	$\bar{A}BCD$	
1	0	0	0	0		$\bar{A} + B + C + D$
1	0	0	1	0		$\bar{A} + B + C + \bar{D}$
1	0	1	0	0		$\bar{A} + B + \bar{C} + D$
1	0	1	1	0		$\bar{A} + B + \bar{C} + \bar{D}$
1	1	0	0	0		$\bar{A} + \bar{B} + C + D$
1	1	0	1	1	$AB\bar{C}D$	
1	1	1	0	0		$\bar{A} + \bar{B} + \bar{C} + D$
1	1	1	1	1	$ABCD$	

combinations of input values except one. For example, $\bar{A} + B + C + \bar{D}$ will be 1 for all combinations except $A = 1$, $B = 0$, $C = 0$ and $D = 1$, for which it will be 0.

Table 16.5 shows the minterms and maxterms against each $J = 1$ and $J = 0$ condition respectively. J may then be represented by a logical sum of the minterms for which $J = 1$, i.e.

$$J = \bar{A}B\bar{C}D + \bar{A}BCD + AB\bar{C}D + ABCD \quad \text{in this case.}$$

This expression is known as the **sum of minterms**, **standard sum of products** or **canonical sum of products**: this is the answer to the first part of the question in Section 16.3.1. Alternatively, J may be represented by the logical product of the maxterms for which $J = 0$, i.e.

$$J = (A + B + C + D)(A + B + C + \bar{D}) \cdots$$

$$(\bar{A} + \bar{B} + C + D)(\bar{A} + \bar{B} + \bar{C} + D) \quad \text{(12 terms in all).}$$

This is known as the **product of maxterms**, **standard product of sums** or **canonical product of sums**.

16.4 Boolean algebra and the use of logic gates

16.4.1 Laws of the algebra

The previous section established a logical algebraic statement in both the standard sum-of-products and product-of-sums forms. This section is concerned with an investigation into the possibility of simplifying these expressions.

The algebraic relationships, involving two-value variables and a number of theorems associated with the relationships, constitute a **switching algebra** derived from an algebraic treatment of logical problems proposed by G. Boole (1815–64) and generally known as **Boolean algebra**. The postulates of the algebra are:

(i) a variable has two exclusive values, designated 0 and 1;
(ii) a NOT operation such that $\bar{0} = 1$ and $\bar{1} = 0$;
(iii) an AND operation such that $\quad 0.0 = 0$
$\qquad\qquad\qquad\qquad\qquad\qquad 0.1 = 0$
$\qquad\qquad\qquad\qquad\qquad\qquad 1.0 = 0$
$\qquad\qquad\qquad\qquad\qquad\qquad 1.1 = 1;$
(iv) An OR operation such that $\quad 0 + 0 = 0$
$\qquad\qquad\qquad\qquad\qquad\qquad 0 + 1 = 1$
$\qquad\qquad\qquad\qquad\qquad\qquad 1 + 0 = 1$
$\qquad\qquad\qquad\qquad\qquad\qquad 1 + 1 = 1.$

From these postulates it is possible to establish a number of theorems which are listed below in **dual** pairs. Duality exists between these relationships in the same way as between the voltage/current relationships in Chapter 2, i.e. a valid relationship in one form translates into a valid relationship in the dual form. The dual statements are not, however, equivalent to each other. In this case, the dual is formed by

(*a*) interchanging AND and OR operations, and
(*b*) interchanging 0's and 1's.

The theorems are as follows:

(i) $A \cdot 0 = 0$		$A + 1 = 1$
(ii) $A \cdot 1 = A$		$A + 0 = A$
(iii) $A \cdot A = A$		$A + A = A$
(iv) $A \cdot \bar{A} = 0$		$A + \bar{A} = 1$
(v)	$\bar{\bar{A}} = A$	
(vi) $A \cdot B = B \cdot A$		$A + B = B + A$

$\qquad\qquad\qquad\qquad\qquad\qquad\qquad$ (The Commutative Laws)

(vii) $A \cdot (B \cdot C) = (A \cdot B) \cdot C \qquad A + (B + C) = (A + B) + C$

$\qquad\qquad\qquad\qquad\qquad\qquad\qquad$ (The Associative Laws)

(viii) $A \cdot (B + C) \qquad\qquad\qquad A + (B \cdot C)$
$\qquad = (A \cdot B) + (A \cdot C) \qquad\qquad = (A + B) \cdot (A + C)$

$\qquad\qquad\qquad\qquad\qquad\qquad\qquad$ (The Distributive Laws)

(ix) $A \cdot (A + B) = A \qquad\qquad A + (A \cdot B) = A$

$\qquad\qquad\qquad\qquad\qquad\qquad\qquad$ (The Absorption Laws)

(x) $\overline{A \cdot B} = \bar{A} + \bar{B} \qquad\qquad \overline{A + B} = \bar{A} \cdot \bar{B}$

$\qquad\qquad\qquad\qquad\qquad\qquad\qquad$ (DeMorgan's Theorems)

Notes:
(i) Each theorem may be proved by perfect induction, using a truth table.
(ii) The variables A, B and C may themselves represent a function of other variables. For example, from theorem (iv), $XYZ + \overline{XYZ} = 1$.

The final set of Laws, attributed to **DeMorgan**, illustrates the process of **complementing** or **inversion** of Boolean functions. Two expressions are complements if, for a given set of values for the variables, the first expression is equal to 1 when the second is equal to 0 or vice-versa. The complement may be found by a process similar to that used to determine the dual but, in addition, each variable is complemented. For example, $A + \bar{B}C$ is the complement of $\bar{A}(B + \bar{C})$ as may be proved by drawing up a truth table for the two functions.

Before proceeding with the applications, proofs for two representative theorems are given in the following examples.

Example 16.1   *Prove that (i) $A + (BC) = (A + B)(A + C)$ and (ii) $A + AB = A$ using truth tables.*

(i) The truth table (Table 16.6(*a*)) may be built up in stages; first BC, then $A + B$ and $A + C$ are determined. The relevant terms are then combined to give the required results which are shown in the two right-hand columns. These will be seen to be identical.

(ii) In Table 16.6(*b*), the left- and right-hand columns are identical.

16.4.2 Minimisation of the algebraic statement

The statement to be considered is the sum of products derived in Section 16.3.6:

$$J = \bar{A}B\bar{C}D + \bar{A}BCD + AB\bar{C}D + ABCD.$$

Table 16.6. *Truth tables for Example 16.1*

A B C	BC	A + B	A + C	A + BC	(A + B)(A + C)
0 0 0	0	0	0	0	0
0 0 1	0	0	1	0	0
0 1 0	0	1	0	0	0
0 1 1	1	1	1	1	1
1 0 0	0	1	1	1	1
1 0 1	0	1	1	1	1
1 1 0	0	1	1	1	1
1 1 1	1	1	1	1	1

A B	AB	A + AB
0 0	0	0
0 1	0	0
1 0	0	1
1 1	1	1

(b)　　　　　　　　　　(b)

Applying the distributive law to the first and second and to the third and fourth terms gives

$$J = \bar{A}BD(\bar{C} + C) + ABD(\bar{C} + C)$$

$$= \bar{A}BD + ABD \qquad \text{(because } \bar{C} + C = 1\text{)}$$

$$= BD(\bar{A} + A)$$

$$= BD \qquad \text{(because } \bar{A} + A = 1\text{)}.$$

In effect, the result states that to satisfy the conditions, the journey may proceed when travellers B and D only are present; it is immaterial whether they are joined by A and C and this is the answer to the second part of the problem posed in Section 16.3.1.

The process of reducing the number of terms (and in this case the number of variables upon which the output is dependent) is known as simplification or **minimisation** of the standard form and plays an important part in the design of logical systems. It is unlikely that a circuit would be designed to make the once-only decision on who would travel on a particular journey. However, in a typical process-control situation a circuit or program may well be needed which would continuously monitor several inputs looking for a change in status which may affect the running of a plant or machine. In these circumstances use of the minimal form as a basis for the design has obvious advantages, although the possibility of hazards may need to be taken into account. These are discussed in the next chapter.

Three further examples illustrate the minimisation process:

Example 16.2　Show that $A(\bar{A} + B) = AB$.

Using the distributive law $A(\bar{A} + B) = A\bar{A} + AB$. But, $A\bar{A} = 0$. Therefore $A(\bar{A} + B) = AB$.

Example 16.3　Show that $A + \bar{A}B = A + B$.

Using the dual form of the distributive law $A + \bar{A}B = (A + \bar{A})(A + B)$. But, $A + \bar{A} = 1$. Therefore $A + \bar{A}B = A + B$.

Example 16.4　Show that $\overline{AB}(A + B) = A \oplus B$ (*the exclusive OR operation*) using Boolean algebra and by perfect induction.

Using DeMorgan's theorem,

$$\overline{AB}(A + B) = (\bar{A} + \bar{B})(A + B)$$
$$= A\bar{A} + A\bar{B} + \bar{A}B + \bar{B}B$$
$$= A\bar{B} + \bar{A}B = A \oplus B.$$

A truth table for the function $\overline{AB}(A + B)$ is shown in Table 16.7. Comparison of the right-hand column with the truth table in Fig. 16.2(c) shows them to be identical, proving the relationship.

Table 16.7. *Truth table for Example 16.4*

A B	$\overline{AB}$	$(A + B)$	$\overline{AB}(A + B)$
0 0	1	0	0
0 1	1	1	1
1 0	1	1	1
1 1	0	1	0

16.4.3 Logic circuit diagrams

These are circuit diagrams consisting of interconnected gates drawn to represent logical expressions. Each logical operation, AND, OR and NOT, etc., is represented by the appropriate logic symbol with its relevant inputs. For example, to implement $(AB) + (BC)$ requires three gates, as shown in Fig. 16.6(a). Alternatively, expressing the function in the form $B(A + C)$ using the distributive law, gives the two-gate diagram shown in Fig. 16.6(b). The reverse procedure of deriving a logical expression from the logic diagram can be effected by writing down the appropriate output from each gate, as shown in the diagram.

Fig. 16.6 Logic diagrams

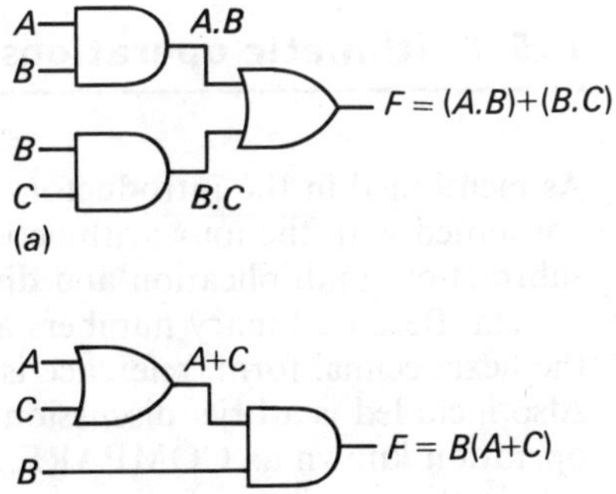

(a)

(b)

16.4.4 Using specified gates

The principle of representing given logical functions by different logic circuits is demonstrated in Fig. 16.6. Also, it was noted in Section 16.3.5 that AND and NOT may be used to implement OR and that OR and NOT can implement AND. It was further noted that either NAND or NOR can implement all three functions and, for this reason, NAND and NOR are said to be **universal** gates. Some of these statements are illustrated in Example 16.5.

Example 16.5   *Show that the OR function $A + B$ can be implemented using (i) AND gates and inverters and (ii) NAND gates only.*

Using DeMorgan's theorem

$$A + B = \overline{\overline{A + B}} = \overline{\overline{A} \cdot \overline{B}}.$$

Logic diagrams implementing the function $\overline{\overline{A} \cdot \overline{B}}$ are shown in Fig. 16.7(a) (using AND gates and inverters) and Fig. 16.7(b) (using NAND gates).

Fig. 16.7 Solutions to Example 16.5

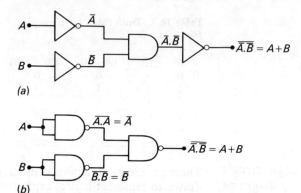

(a)

(b)

The minimisation of logical functions and their implementation is dealt with in greater detail in the next chapter. This includes a discussion on minimisation by Karnaugh maps as well as the implementation of combinational-logic circuits with the help of read-only memory, multiplexers and the programmable logic array (PLA).

16.5 Arithmetic operations

16.5.1 Introduction

As mentioned in the introductory remarks, this chapter is concerned with the four arithmetic operations of addition, subtraction, multiplication and division in the binary-number system. Because binary numbers are frequently expressed in the hexadecimal form, reference is also made to this system. Also included is a brief discussion of the pseudo-subtractive operation known as COMPARE. This plays a very significant role in the execution of programs in microprocessor and computer-based systems.

16.5.2 Addition

The addition process is essentially the same in all the number systems. For example,

in the decimal system,

$5 + 8 = 13$ i.e. 3 and carry 1,

in the hexadecimal system,

$5H + 8H = DH$ (no carry),

and

$9H + AH = 13H$ i.e. 3H and carry 1H,

in the binary system,

$0 + 1 = 1$ (no carry),

and

$1101 + 0101 = 10010.$

Integrated circuits are available which provide **half-adding** and **full-adding** facilities. The **half-adder** simply adds two bits together to give sum and carry outputs, as shown in Table 16.8(*a*) for all combinations of the two inputs *A* and *B*. The Boolean expression for sum and carry outputs of the half-adder are, by inspection of the truth table,

$$\text{sum} = \bar{A}B + A\bar{B},$$

and

$$\text{carry} = AB.$$

The sum output will be seen to be the exclusive-OR function of the inputs.

Table 16.8. *Adder truth tables*

Inputs		Half-adder output	
A	*B*	*Sum*	*Carry*
0	0	0	0
0	1	1	0
1	0	1	0
1	1	0	1

(*a*)

Inputs			Full-adder output	
Carry in, C	*A*	*B*	*Sum*	*Carry out*
0	0	0	0	0
0	0	1	1	0
0	1	0	1	0
0	1	1	0	1
1	0	0	1	0
1	0	1	0	1
1	1	0	0	1
1	1	1	1	1

(*b*)

The truth table for the **full-adder**, which allows for a carry input as well as *A* and *B* inputs, is shown in Table 16.8(*b*). The full-adder outputs may be derived from the truth table as follows:

$$\text{sum} = \bar{A}\bar{B}C + \bar{A}B\bar{C} + A\bar{B}\bar{C} + ABC,$$

and

$$carry = \bar{A}BC + A\bar{B}C + AB\bar{C} + ABC,$$

which reduces to

$$AB + AC + BC.$$

16.5.3 Subtraction

If the sign of one number is changed and it is then added to another number, the result is the difference between the two. Thus, subtraction may be performed by expressing the number to be subtracted as a negative quantity and adding. The two's complement representation of negative numbers (Section 16.2.4) is suitable for this operation as may be demonstrated by adding the signed forms of decimal 3:

$$
\begin{array}{ll}
011 & (3) \\
+ 101 & (-3) \\
\hline
1\ 000 & \\
\end{array}
$$

↑

carry

The result is zero if only three digits are considered.

The complement itself may be formed by an addition process so that the whole subtraction procedure may be implemented by means of adding circuits; this is illustrated as follows. Suppose that it is required to subtract decimal 79 from decimal 103. Initially, the complement of the binary equivalent of 79 is formed by complementing each bit (giving what is known as the **one's complement**) and then adding 1. 79 in binary is 01001111 and its two's complement is therefore $10110000 + 1 = 10110001$; this binary number now represents -79. Adding it to the binary equivalent of 103 (01100111) gives a result (neglecting the carry) of $01100111 + 10110001 = 00011000$, the binary equivalent of decimal 24. It is necessary that the binary equivalents of 79 and 103 both have 0 as a most-significant bit in order to ensure that they are treated as positive numbers in the complement notation, i.e. eight bits are required.

The procedure also works when subtracting larger numbers from smaller ones: the complement of the binary equivalent of 103 is $10011000 + 1 = 10011001$. Adding to the binary equivalent of 79 gives $10011001 + 01001111 = 11101000$, which should be (and is) $79 - 103 = -24$ in the complement notation. That this is the case may be checked by complementing the binary result; thus, the complement of 11101000 is $00010111 + 1 = 00011000$, which is the equivalent of decimal $+24$.

An alternative method of forming the two's complement of a binary number involves repeating each digit, working from right to left, up to and including the first 1, after which each digit is complemented. For example, the complement of 00011000 (decimal 24) is 11101000 (decimal -24).

The complement method of representing signed numbers may be used for number systems to any base. For example, the complement of a decimal number is given by complementing each digit individually (giving the so-called **nine's complement**) and then adding one to the result; this gives the **ten's complement**. Thus, the ten's complement of 37 is formed by subtracting each digit from 9 and then adding one, i.e. $62 + 1 = 63$. Now, adding 37 and 63 gives 00, neglecting the carry into the hundreds column. In effect, 63 represents -37 in the two-digit signed-number system.

Complementing in the two-digit decimal system means that, in effect, the numbers, 0 to 49, represent themselves whilst the numbers, 50 to 99, are codes for the negative numbers, -50 to -1, respectively; in the example above, 63 is the code for -37. Although complementing in the decimal system is of limited value (being included here principally to illustrate the coding method), the sixteen's complement used in the hexadecimal-number system can be useful when dealing with microprocessor machine code, which is normally written in hexadecimal form. For example, decimal 24 (binary 00011000) is 18H in hexadecimal; complementing each digit by subtracting from FFH and adding one to the result gives E8H. Converting E8H back to binary form gives 11101000 which is the two's complement representation of -24.

16.5.4 Two's complement overflow conditions

The use of complement notation can create problems. For example, consider the addition,

$$
\begin{array}{ll}
01010110 & \text{(86 decimal)} \\
+01110011 & \text{(115 decimal)} \\
\hline
11001001 & (-55 \text{ decimal in complement notation).}
\end{array}
$$

Adding the two positive numbers (for which the most-significant bit is 0) results in a negative number in complement notation as indicated by the most-significant bit being 1; the result is clearly incorrect. There is always a real possibility that situations such as this can occur and, in general, it is desirable to identify them. An **overflow** condition is said to exist when, as a result of adding two signed binary numbers (i.e. number in complement form), the sign of the result differs from the sign of each component (when they are the same). If the components are of different sign, an overflow condition cannot occur.

The overflow condition may be stated in Boolean algebraic terms as,

$$V = A_M B_M \bar{S}_M + \bar{A}_M \bar{B}_M S_M,$$

where A_M, B_M and S_M are the most-significant bits (the sign bits) of the two numbers to be added and their sum, respectively.

It should be appreciated that an addition, such as in the example above, will be perfectly valid for unsigned numbers, i.e. in this case binary $11001001 =$ decimal 201; if set, the overflow indicator only states that the result is invalid when the numbers are interpreted in their signed (complement) form.

16.5.5 Compare operation

When executing microprocessor or computer programs it is frequently necessary to compare one piece of data with another as the basis of a decision. Often, the comparison results in a 'greater than', 'less than' or 'equal to' statement reached through an essentially subtractive process. Thus, if data B is subtracted from data A (i.e. result is $A - B$), a positive result means that B is less than A, a negative result means that B is greater than A and a zero result that B is equal to A. In this way, testing the sign bit or checking for a zero result, allows the inequality or equality condition to be determined.

16.5.6 Multiplication

In the decimal system, two methods of multiplication are used. For example,

(i) 23×16 can be obtained by multiplying 23 by 6 to give the 'units' (with a carry) and then 23×1, shifting the result one place to the left before adding to the partial product already obtained, i.e.

```
23    multiplicand
16    multiplier
```

$\left. \begin{array}{l} 138 \\ 23 \end{array} \right\}$ partial products

```
368   product
```

(ii) 23×16 can also be obtained by adding 16 to itself 23 times.

The first method is by far the more usual and is also an attractive method in the binary system. This is because multiplication by 0 gives zero and multiplication by 1 simply repeats the multiplicand. The process is therefore one of shifting and adding.

Example 16.6   *Multiply 10010 by 101.*

```
    10010
      101

    10010
    00000
   10010

  1011010
```

Of course, the 00000 partial product need not be included but the multiplicand must still be shifted to the left by the appropriate amount.

Hexadecimal multiplication can be obtained by the same general method.

Example 16.7   *Multiply B6H by 52H.*

B6H
52H

16CH
38E0H

3A4CH

The second method (i.e. adding the multiplicand several times over) would be very tedious in normal use but can be implemented easily on a machine. However, it may take a long time to carry out all the additions bearing in mind that machines normally only add two numbers at a time.

In contrast with the usual manual decimal-addition procedure, a 'running total' is kept in what may be known as an **accumulator**. Thus, using the shift-and-add method, the following *algorithm* can be used. An algorithm is essentially a sequence of operations and is considered again in Section 16.7.1.

(1) Set partial product at zero.
(2) Test the least-significant bit of the multiplier:

   if it is 1, add the multiplicand and go to 3,
   if it is 0, go directly to 3.

(3) Shift multiplicand one place to the left.
(4) Test next bit (to the left) of multiplier:

   if it is 1, add the shifted multiplicand and go to 3,
   if it is 0, go directly to 3.

The sequence is repeated until all the bits are tested. To illustrate the algorithm, the solution to Example 16.6 (multiplication of 10010 by 101) is now written out in accordance with the sequence:

Step	Operation	Accumulator contents	Test condition
1	Set partial product to zero	00000	
2	Test LSB of multiplier		LSB $= 1$
	Add multiplicand	10010	
3	Shift multiplicand		
4	Test next bit of multiplier		next bit $= 0$
3	Shift multiplicand		
4	Test next bit of multiplier		next bit $= 1$
	Add shifted multiplicand	1011010	

The algorithm used above does not give the correct answer when using the two's-complement notation but can be adapted to do so.

16.5.7 Division

Long division can be carried out in the binary system just as in the decimal system. For example, the division of decimal 22 by decimal 7 in both forms as:

```
       3.14 ···                    11.0010 ···
     _____                    _____
  7 ) 22                    111 ) 10110
     21                           111
     ___                          ___
     10                           1000
      7                            111
     ___                          ____
     30                             10
     28                            100
     ___                          1000
      2, etc.                      111
                                  ____
                                    10, etc.
```

Whilst the amount of work needed to perform division of binary numbers is greater than that for decimal, it is simpler inasmuch as it is not required to decide how many times 7 will 'go into' 22 as in the decimal case; the quotient is either a 0 or 1 at each stage. Effectively, a simple subtraction of the divisor from the appropriate digits of the dividend is all that is required. The process continues with the 'bringing down' of the remaining digits, further testing by trial subtractions and the insertion of the binary point in the appropriate place.

16.5.8 An arithmetic logic unit (ALU)

Type 74181 integrated circuit is an example of a device capable of carrying out a range of arithmetic and logical operations. The range is illustrated in Fig. 16.8. A single device can handle two four-bit word inputs but the number of bits can be increased by linking more than one circuit. Where appropriate, they can be used in conjunction with a type 74182 Look-Ahead Carry Generator permitting 16-bit addition in a typical time of 30 ns.

Fig. 16.8 Functions of an ALU

Selection				M = H logic functions	Active high data		
					M = L; Arithmetic operations		
S3	S2	S1	S0		C_n = H (no carry)	C_n = L (with carry)	
L	L	L	L	$F = \bar{A}$	$F = A$	$F = A$ plus 1	
L	L	L	H	$F = \overline{A + B}$	$F = A + B$	$F = (A + B)$ plus 1	
L	L	H	L	$F = \bar{A}B$	$F = A + \bar{B}$	$F = (A + \bar{B})$ plus 1	
L	L	H	H	$F = 0$	$F = $ Minus 1 (2's compl)	$F = $ Zero	
L	H	L	L	$F = \overline{AB}$	$F = A$ plus $A\bar{B}$	$F = A$ plus $A\bar{B}$ plus 1	
L	H	L	H	$F = \bar{B}$	$F = (A + B)$ plus $A\bar{B}$	$F = (A + B)$ plus $A\bar{B}$ plus 1	
L	H	H	L	$F = A \oplus B$	$F = A$ minus B minus 1	$F = A$ minus B	
L	H	H	H	$F = A\bar{B}$	$F = A\bar{B}$ minus 1	$F = A\bar{B}$	
H	L	L	L	$F = \bar{A} + B$	$F = A$ plus AB	$F = A$ plus AB plus 1	
H	L	L	H	$F = \overline{A \oplus B}$	$F = A$ plus B	$F = A$ plus B plus 1	
H	L	H	L	$F = B$	$F = (A + \bar{B})$ plus AB	$F = (A + \bar{B})$ plus AB plus 1	
H	L	H	H	$F = AB$	$F = AB$ minus 1	$F = AB$	
H	H	L	L	$F = 1$	$F = A$ plus A^*	$F = A$ plus A plus 1	
H	H	L	H	$F = A + \bar{B}$	$F = (A + B)$ plus A	$F = (A + B)$ plus A plus 1	
H	H	H	L	$F = A + B$	$F = (A + \bar{B})$ plus A	$F = (A + \bar{B})$ plus A plus 1	
H	H	H	H	$F = A$	$F = A$ minus 1	$F = A$	

*Each bit is shifted to the next more significant position.

16.6 Shift and rotate operations

One of the stages in the multiplication algorithms in Section 16.5.6 was a shift instruction. There is, in fact, a range of special terms used to define particular forms of shift, some or all of which may be available on an arithmetic device such as a microprocessor. These are illustrated in Fig. 16.9 in which an 8-bit number (with provision for a carry) is assumed. As a consequence of the positional property of binary numbers, the arithmetic shift divides or multiplies the numbers by two, according to whether the shift is to the right or to the left, respectively. It will be seen that the bits are labelled 0–7 in these diagrams. This is common practice in digital systems and applies when items are being *labelled* rather than counted. Thus, whilst eight items would be counted 1–8, it is more convenient to label them 0–7.

Fig. 16.9 Shift and rotate operations

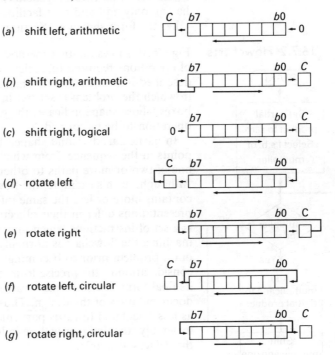

(a) shift left, arithmetic

(b) shift right, arithmetic

(c) shift right, logical

(d) rotate left

(e) rotate right

(f) rotate left, circular

(g) rotate right, circular

16.7 Algorithms and flowcharts

16.7.1 Algorithms

These are sets of operational steps which specify each stage in a process in such a way that it may be implemented in a routine manner, usually by means of a machine. The sets of rules for multiplication listed in Section 16.5.6 are examples of algorithms. The degree of detail required in an algorithm depends on the type of operation the machine can perform in one step. To take an example from the logical operations, an algorithm resulting in an exclusive-OR output F requires only the single step,

$$F = A \oplus B$$

if an exclusive-OR gate is available. If, however, only AND, OR and NOT operations are available, either in the form of gates or, possibly, as three operating steps on a microprocessor, the algorithm becomes

$$F_1 = \bar{A} \qquad \text{(NOT operation)},$$
$$F_2 = \bar{B} \qquad \text{(NOT operation)},$$
$$F_3 = \bar{A} . B \qquad \text{(AND operation)},$$
$$F_4 = A . \bar{B} \qquad \text{(AND operation)},$$
$$F_5 = \bar{A} . B + A . \bar{B} \quad \text{(OR operation)}.$$

As an example of an arithmetic operation, the algorithm for multiplication is simply $F = A \times B$ if a multiplying device is available. If, however, a general-purpose microprocessor having only add and shift facilities is used, then the algorithm takes the form shown on Section 16.5.6.

16.7.2 Flowcharts

Fig. 16.10 shows another method of describing the sequence of operations required to achieve the multiplication process described in Section 16.5.6. This is an example of a **flowchart** in which the problem is set out in the form of a set of linked boxes whose shape indicates the general nature of the operation to be performed.

In particular, diamond-shaped boxes indicate decision points in the sequence, from which the operation may follow one of two or more paths to other points in the sequence. Although, in this example, the flowchart and the algorithm contains more or less the same information, the two presentations differ in their objectives: whereas the algorithm is a set of instructions which may be followed by man or machine, the flowchart is normally used as a means of setting out a problem prior to becoming involved in detailed consideration of the precise form of the algorithm; as such, in its final form, it also forms a valuable part of the documentation of the design. Thus, the flowchart may be seen as less orientated towards particular devices although, inevitably, the designer will be influenced by his knowledge of the devices available.

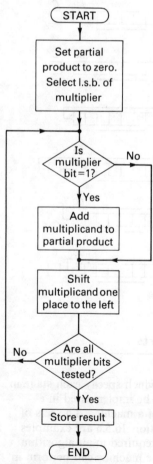

Fig. 16.10 A flowchart for the multiplication process

16.8 Codes and coding

16.8.1 Introduction

Coding is a large topic on which it is only possible to describe a limited number of examples; those selected are intended to illustrate some of the different aspects of coding. All the codes discussed are binary and the number of **code words** which can be constructed depends on the number of digits, e.g. for an 8-bit code, 256 ($= 2^8$) different words are possible.

It is common practice to refer to numbers expressed in binary or hexadecimal form as codes but, strictly speaking, there is no fundamental reason why the representation of a number in a non-decimal system should be regarded as a code any more than its decimal representation. However, the term is widely used and this is accepted subject to the use of the prefix **natural** binary coding to indicate a normal counting sequence. Without this qualification, the term **binary coding** is assumed to describe a process by which a special set of combinations of binary digits is devised to represent a number, an alphanumeric symbol, or any other piece of quantised data, in such a way that it offers some advantage over the natural-binary sequence representation. A typical advantage might be the ease with which coding or transmission errors could be detected. The following sections describe representative examples of some of the more common forms of code.

16.8.2 Binary-coded decimal

Whilst, in most engineering systems, analogue-signal levels may be converted directly into binary form, this process will, in general, incur errors known as quantisation errors. These are discussed in Chapters 9 and 15. Other systems, such as those dealing with money, require that a given decimal quantity should be converted *exactly* into binary form. In such cases, it is necessary to convert each decimal digit individually into binary form, resulting in what is known as the **binary-coded decimal** (BCD) form.

Because there are ten digits in the decimal system, ten binary-code words are required and, therefore, four binary digits must be used. Typically, the natural binary values of the decimal digits 0–9 may be used so that, for example, 379 in the natural BCD format would be 0011 0111 1001. The six binary codes 1010 to 1111 are not used although, as discussed in Section 16.8.5, this facility could be used as part of an error-detecting process. Also related to these unused codes is the need for decimal adjustment as described in Section 16.8.4.

The combinations of binary symbols used to represent the decimal digits are quite arbitrary, the only necessary requirement being that the encoder and the decoder are compatible. However, the term 'coding' does imply an ordered way of making the conversion and it is clearly preferable to use a coding method which is convenient to use, common to a number of systems and, possibly, has some other virtue. An example of the latter might be to ensure that only one bit at a time changes when counting through the decimal equivalents in normal counting sequence.

A **weighting** technique may be used in the coding process by which each bit in the 4-bit code word is assigned a decimal weight. Weighting is in fact a more general form of positional value in which the digit in a specific position may take on a range of values rather than being limited to powers of the base (i.e. powers of two in the natural-binary case). Although weighting in ascending powers of two is commonly used in BCD systems some of the other possible forms are as follows: by reference to Table 16.9, the decimal number 1984 would be coded as follows:

(i) 8–4–2–1	(natural) BCD:	0001	1001	1000	0100
(ii) 7–4–2–1	BCD:	0001	1010	1001	0100
(iii) 4–3–1–1	BCD:	0001	1111	1110	1000

(the spaces between the groups of four digits are shown to clarify the structure of the code).

Table 16.9 shows examples of BCD codes. In each case, the value of the decimal digit is the sum of the weighted values for which there is a 1 in the code word, e.g., for 4–3–1–1 code, code word 1011 represents decimal $4 + 1 + 1 = 6$.

Although a large number are not in common use, certain codes have special properties. For example, in the 4311 code, the complement of 0100 (representing decimal 3) is 1011, which represents decimal 6, the 9's complement.

Table 16.9. *BCD codes*

Decimal number	Code:	Natural BCD	4–3–1–1 BCD	7–4–2–1 BCD
	Weight:	8421	4311	7421
0		0000	0000	0000
1		0001	0001	0001
2		0010	0011	0010
3		0011	0100	0011
4		0100	1000	0100
5		0101	0111	0101
6		0110	1011	0110
7		0111	1100	1000
8		1000	1110	1001
9		1001	1111	1010

16.8.3 Gray and excess-3 codes

In applications such as the binary encoding of the position of a rotating shaft the probability of error is reduced if successive code words differ by only one bit. The **Gray code** meets these requirements (Table 16.10). Because the primary function of the code is to detect position, it is not necessary for it to have arithmetic properties. The Gray code is not weighted but this is not important since Gray-to-binary-code converters are easy to implement.

Table 16.10 shows the Gray-codewords for the first 19 values starting from zero. The code will be seen to be a

Table 16.10. *A reflected code*

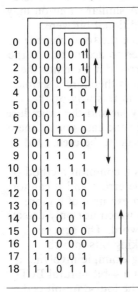

0	0	0	0	0	0
1	0	0	0	0	1
2	0	0	0	1	1
3	0	0	0	1	0
4	0	0	1	1	0
5	0	0	1	1	1
6	0	0	1	0	1
7	0	0	1	0	0
8	0	1	1	0	0
9	0	1	1	0	1
10	0	1	1	1	1
11	0	1	1	1	0
12	0	1	0	1	0
13	0	1	0	1	1
14	0	1	0	0	1
15	0	1	0	0	0
16	1	1	0	0	0
17	1	1	0	0	1
18	1	1	0	1	1

reflected code in the sense that all the columns except the most significant are mirror images about the midpoint of any group of two, three, four, etc., digits. Such groups are boxed in the table.

In a reflected number system, only one digit changes as the value of the number progresses sequentially; for example, counting in the reflected decimal system would follow the sequence: 1 2 3 4 5 6 7 8 9 19 18 17 16 15 14 13 12 11 10 20 21. Furthermore, there is only a 1-bit change between 'first' and 'last' values in a given sequence, e.g. between 0 and 7 or between 0 and 15.

The **excess-3 code** is another unweighted code. In this case, the decimal number is represented by the 4-bit natural-binary number corresponding to the decimal number plus 3. For example, the excess-3 representation of decimal 5 is the natural binary equivalent of $5 + 3$, i.e. 1000. The code has the properties of always having at least one 1 in the codeword, and complementing the codeword gives the equivalent of the 9's complement, e.g. the complement of 1000 is 0111 which is equivalent to decimal $7 - 3 = 4$, which is the 9's complement of decimal five.

6.8.4 Decimal adjustment

It was noted in the previous section that six combinations of the 4-bit code are redundant in the BCD representation. An encoder should not generate the unused codes but, during arithmetic processing, an illegal code is bound to appear sooner or later. For example, in natural BCD, the addition,

$$\begin{array}{ll} 0101 & \text{(decimal 5)} \\ +0111 & \text{(decimal 7)} \end{array}$$

gives 1100, which is an illegal code.

The correct result may be obtained by adding six to a result greater than nine (which effectively 'skips' over the six unused codewords) and, of course, a 1 must be carried across to the next most significant codeword. Thus, the additions,

$$\begin{array}{ll} 0101 & \text{(decimal 5)} \\ +0111 & \text{(decimal 7)} \\ \hline 1100 & \\ +0110 & \text{(decimal 6)} \\ \hline 0001 \quad 0010 & \text{(decimal 12)} \end{array}$$

carry

The answer is decimal 12, which is correct. The microprocessors described in Chapter 19 have special instructions for handling BCD arithmetic.

16.8.5 Error detecting and correcting codes

The possibility of an error-correcting code may seem a little unlikely but examples of error correction in everyday life are quite common. For example, if a chair is seen to have only three legs, this would be recognised as an error because, normally, chairs have four legs; furthermore, not only would the absence of one leg be recognised as an error, but it could be corrected by adding the fourth leg. A similar situation may exist with codes. If, for example, an additional bit were included in each codeword so as to make the total number of 1's in the word even, a receiver, designed to accept this as the normal condition, would indicate an error if it were not the case. The inclusion of the additional bit is therefore a simple method of error detection. A bit added in this way by the transmitting device is known as a **parity bit** and the procedure is known as **parity checking**; when, as in the case above, there is an even number of 1's, the parity is said to be **even**. Odd parity may also be used.

Whilst the inclusion of a parity bit is a common method of error detection, it cannot detect multiple errors and it cannot correct errors. The **Hamming code** is an example of a more sophisticated system of parity checking which not only detects but can also correct an error in a codeword. The general technique is to insert a number of checking bits into the codeword as illustrated by the following example involving a code which can correct a single error in a 4-bit natural BCD code. Three check bits are included in the four-data-bit code, arranged as follows:

$$C_1 \quad C_2 \quad 8 \quad C_3 \quad 4 \quad 2 \quad 1,$$

where C_1, C_2 and C_3 are the check bits and 8, 4, 2 and 1 are the weighted data bits. The check bits are associated with groups of data bits thus:

$$C_1 841, \quad C_2 821 \quad \text{and} \quad C_3 421,$$

each check bit being set on transmission such that even parity exists within its own group of four bits. Taking decimal 5 as an example, the natural BCD code is 0101, so that the 7-bit Hamming code will have the form, $C_1 C_2 0 C_3 101$. C_1, C_2 and C_3 will be determined in accordance with the groupings shown above, i.e.

$C_1 011$ makes $C_1 = 0$ for even parity,

$C_2 001$ makes $C_2 = 1$ for even parity,

and

$C_3 101$ makes $C_3 = 0$ for even parity.

The codeword is therefore 0100101 (i.e. $C_1 C_2 8 C_3 421$). Now, to effect an error correction, if one exists, the groups are parity checked, success being indicated by a 0 and failure by a 1. The 0's and 1's generated by the check are then used to form a binary number whose value indicates the position of the error in the 7-bit codeword working from *left to right*. In forming the number, the result of the 'C_3' check is the most-significant bit and the 'C_1' check the least. To take an example, suppose that an error occurs on transmission so that the received codeword is 0110101, instead of 0100101. The receiver parity checks on the groups will yield:

1 for the group, $C_1 841$ which is received as 0111 (failure);

1 for the group, $C_2 821$ which is received as 1101 (failure);

0 for the group, C_3421 which is received as 0101 (success).

The resulting binary number, 011 (decimal 3) indicates that the error is in the third character from the left. This is in fact the case.

Although the ratio of three check bits to four data bits is rather expensive, the check bits need appear only in the first, second, fourth, eighth, etc., positions in the code word (working from left to right). Thus, for example, a 16-bit word would contain only five check bits, leaving 11 data bits. Even so, error-correcting codes are only used in situations where the possibility of error would have serious consequences.

A code having more bits than necessary to represent the data is said to contain redundancy. Redundancy is necessary if error checking or detection is to be carried out but some codes have redundancy because of their construction; the BCD code is an example, six of the possible code combinations not being used.

Table 16.11. *The ASCII code*

Character	Hex. code	Character	Hex. code	Character	Hex. code	Character	Hex. code
NUL	00	!	21	A	41	a	61
SOH	01	"	22	B	42	b	62
STX	02	#	23	C	43	c	63
ETX	03	$	24	D	44	d	64
EOT	04	%	25	E	45	e	65
ENQ	05	&	26	F	46	f	66
ACK	06	'	27	G	47	g	67
BEL	07	(	28	H	48	h	68
BS	08	)	29	I	49	i	69
HT	09	*	2A	J	4A	j	6A
LF	0A	+	2B	K	4B	k	6B
VT	0B	,	2C	L	4C	l	6C
FF	0C	−	2D	M	4D	m	6D
CR	0D	.	2E	N	4E	n	6E
SO	0E	/	2F	O	4F	o	6F
SI	0F	0	30	P	50	p	70
DLE	10	1	31	Q	51	q	71
DC1	11	2	32	R	52	r	72
DC2	12	3	33	S	53	s	73
DC3	13	4	34	T	54	t	74
DC4	14	5	35	U	55	u	75
NAK	15	6	36	V	56	v	76
SYN	16	7	37	W	57	w	77
ETB	17	8	38	X	58	x	78
CAN	18	9	39	Y	59	y	79
EM	19	:	3A	Z	5A	z	7A
SUB	1A	;	3B	[	5B	{	7B
ESC	1B	<	3C	\	5C			7C
FS	1C	=	3D	]	5D	}	7D
GS	1D	>	3E	Λ	5E	~	7E
RS	1E	?	3F	−	5F	DEL	7F
US	1F	@	40	`	60		
SP	20						

16.8.6 Alphanumeric codes

If it is required to transmit or store data containing letters, numbers and punctuation marks, it is basically only necessary to ensure that enough bits are used to represent the range of symbols required by the system and (arbitrarily) allocate a unique combination of bits to each symbol, ensuring that the transmitting/receiving or storing/retrieving equipments are compatible. If each manufacturer follows this procedure independently problems are bound to arise when attempting to interconnect different equipments and, to avoid such difficulties, the American Standard Code for Information Interchange (ASCII) has been developed (although other codes, such as EBCDIC, are in use). A version of this code is shown in Table 16.11.

The 7-bit code allows for up to $2^7 = 128$ different characters. Since the code is often used in conjunction with 8-bit devices (such as the 8-bit microprocessors) it could then be regarded as an 8-bit code for which the most-significant bit is 0; alternatively, the MSB may be used as a parity bit. Machine-control instructions are also included in the code, being the first 33 characters (00H to 20H, inclusive).

Key points to remember

- numbers in common use are binary, decimal and hexadecimal, all use the positional-value principle;

- in machine handling, methods must be provided for dealing with negative numbers and points;

- logical statements may be made in the form of a truth table;

- the basic logical operations are AND, OR and NOT, these may be implemented using the NAND or NOR operations;

- logical statements may be made algebraically as a sum of minterms or product of maxterms;

- Boolean algebra enables logical statements to be manipulated and, where appropriate, simplified (minimised);

- the binary arithmetic operations of add, subtract, multiply and divide can be implemented by logic circuits;

- arithmetic and logical sequences can be presented in the form of an algorithm or a flow chart;

- binary coding is used for many different purposes, including error detection and correction, minimising possibility of error, useful arithmetic properties and accurate representation of alphanumeric and financial statements, etc.

Further reading

Floyd, T. L., *Digital Fundamentals*. Bell and Howell (1986).
Mano, M. M., *Digital Design*. Prentice-Hall (1984).
Roth, C. H., *Fundamentals of Logic Design*. West Publishing (1985).

EXERCISES 16

16.1 Refer to Chapter 9 (Section 3) and then briefly explain in your own words the difference between analogue and digital signals.

16.2 (a) The Roman number system counts i, ii, iii, iv, v, x, xi, ... for decimal 1, 2, 3, 4, 5, 10, 11, ... Is the positional-value principle used in this system?

    (b) List the numbers which would be needed to count up to decimal-20 objects

        (i) if a base of 5 were used; and
        (ii) if a base of 20 were used.

        With five fingers (including thumb) per hand, base-five might seem more logical than base ten. State a possible reason for the common use of ten rather than five.

16.3 Carry out the following number conversions:

    (i) decimal 57 to binary;
    (ii) hexadecimal 57H to binary;
    (iii) octal 57 to binary;
    (iv) decimal 57 to hexadecimal;
    (v) binary 101101 to decimal;
    (vi) binary 101101 to hexadecimal.

16.4 Write down decimal -13 in binary

    (i) sign-plus-magnitude form;
    (ii) offset form; and
    (iii) 2's-complement form.

    By writing down the natural-binary equivalent of decimal $+13$ determine the result (as a 5-bit number) of adding the binary equivalents of -13 to $+13$ in all three systems.

16.5 Draw up a truth table showing the output from a 4-input logical industrial process controller operating as follows:

    (i) output is high when at least one of the four inputs A, B, C and D are high; but
    (ii) output is low when either A and C or A and D are high together.

16.6 Devise an arrangement of switches which would perform

    (i) the AND function;
    (ii) the OR function; and
    (iii) the XOR function.

    Assume that there are two input variables which determine whether individual switches are either on or off.

16.7 Explain the operation of that part of Fig. 17.35 comprising the two AND gates and two sets of four three-state buffers.

    All four combinations of conditions of $\overline{CS}$ and $\overline{WE}$ should be considered.

16.8 (a) Draw switch arrangements (as in Exercise 16.6) which perform two-input NAND and NOR operations.

    (b) Draw up a truth table to show that a two-input NAND operation results if both variables are inverted and fed through an OR gate.

16.9 Identify the minterms and maxterms in Exercise 16.5.

16.10 Write down a Boolean expression for the output of the controller described in Exercise 16.5 (using the result of Exercise 16.9) in logical sum-of-product and product-of-sum forms. Obtain minimal forms using the Boolean-algebra relationship in Sections 16.4.1 and 16.4.2 and, finally, use a truth table to show that the minimal forms are the same as the original table derived in Exercise 16.5.

16.11 (*a*) Draw logic diagrams using AND and OR gates (and inverters as required) to implement the expressions derived in Exercise 16.10.

(*b*) Apply the DeMorgan relationship,

$$\overline{x + y + z} = \bar{x}, \bar{y}, \bar{z}$$

to deduce a NAND-gate implementation of the minimised sum-of-product expression derived in Exercise 16.10.

16.12 (*a*) Add the following numbers:

binary 0110110 and 001010,
hexadecimal 3C4H and BA7H.

(*b*) Draw a logic diagram for a 2-input full-adder circuit using only NAND gates.

16.13 Subtract decimal 27 from 43 by converting each to two's complement binary form, carrying out the subtraction and converting back to decimal form. Repeat, but subtract 43 from 27.

16.14 (i) Use the shift-and-add method to multiply the binary equivalents of decimal 473 and 14. Convert back to decimal form and check the calculation using decimal multiplication.

(ii) Divide decimal 24 by 5 by expressing both numbers in binary form and performing binary division. Check with a decimal division.

16.15 Draw up a flow chart for the following segment of a microprocessor program. Three numbers are added and the result tested to determine whether it is positive, zero or negative. If positive, the result is sent to store A; if zero, a fixed number is added and the result sent to store B; if negative, the two's complement is formed and the result sent to store A.

16.16 Add the two decimal numbers 86.15 and 27.68 using natural-binary-coded-decimal arithmetic. Check the answer by converting back into decimal form.

16.17 Draw up a table showing the excess-3 binary-coded-decimal equivalents of the decimal digits 0 to 9. What are the invalid codes? Show that in each case the one's complement of the binary form yields the nine's complement of the decimal digit.

16.18 (*a*) Explain what is meant by a parity bit. Write down the hexadecimal form of the ASCII codes for *A* and *T* with an even-parity bit added.

(*b*) Form a Hamming code word for the 4-bit data word 1100. Assuming an error is made in one of the bits of the codeword, use the checking procedure explained in Section 16.8.5 to determine the position of the assumed error.

17 Combinational logic and semiconductor memory

The principal learning objectives of this chapter are to:

	Section	Exercise
• discuss the general properties of combinational-logic systems;	1	
• describe the principle of the Karnaugh map;	2.1	17.1
• apply the K map to minimise logical expressions;	2.2–2.5	17.1–17.3
• determine the effect of incompletely specified functions;	2.6	17.4
• show how to prevent static hazards;	2.7	17.5
• describe the properties of encoders and decoders;	3.1, 3.2	17.6
• apply a decoder–encoder structure to the implementation of combinational systems;	3.3	17.7
• describe the principles of the read-only memory (ROM) and programmable logic array (PLA);	3.4, 3.5	17.8
• apply the multiplexer to the implementation of combinational systems;	3.6–3.8	17.9
• describe the organisation, pin connections and structure of semiconductor memory;	4.1, 4.3	17.10
• explain how memory systems can be expanded;	4.4	17.11
• state the principal memory timing considerations;	4.5	
• describe various forms of read-only memory;	5.1	
• describe the principles of static (SRAM) and dynamic (DRAM) random-access memory.	5.2	

17.1 Introduction

A combinational-logic system was described in Chapter 16 as one whose output code is a function of the present input. This was illustrated by an example in which a single output (whether a journey should take place or not) was determined for sixteen possible combinations of four inputs (whether individuals were travelling or not). During the development of this example, the basic logical operations, AND, OR and NOT were introduced, together with an algebra which enabled logic statements to be manipulated. It was also shown that, by using this algebra, the minimal form of the output (as a function of the inputs) could be obtained. The universal operations NAND and NOR were introduced and, finally, it was shown how relatively simple logic functions could be implemented by means of specified gates.

The purpose of this chapter is to investigate a wider range of combinational-logic problems. The discussions will include the use of the Karnaugh map (K map) as a more convenient method for the expression of logical functions in their minimal forms. The implementation of combinational-logic systems by means of read-only memory, programmable logic arrays and digital multiplexers is also described.

Before proceeding with these objectives, Table 17.1 lists the sixteen logical output functions which can be generated by a two-input combinational unit. Included amongst these are the operations described in the previous chapter: F_8 is the AND operation; F_{14} is OR; F_7 is NAND; F_1 is NOR; F_6 is XOR and F_9 is XNOR. In general, for a circuit having N binary input variables there are 2^{2^N} possible output functions.

Table 17.1

Input states		Output functions															
A	B	F_0	F_1	F_2	F_3	F_4	F_5	F_6	F_7	F_8	F_9	F_{10}	F_{11}	F_{12}	F_{13}	F_{14}	F_{15}
0	0	0	1	0	1	0	1	0	1	0	1	0	1	0	1	0	1
0	1	0	0	1	1	0	0	1	1	0	0	1	1	0	0	1	1
1	0	0	0	0	0	1	1	1	1	0	0	0	0	1	1	1	1
1	1	0	0	0	0	0	0	0	0	1	1	1	1	1	1	1	1

17.2 The Karnaugh map (K map)

17.2.1 The form of the map

The information contained in the truth tables shown in the previous chapter may also be presented on a **K map**. To illustrate the basic form of the map a simple truth table (which conforms with F_5 in Table 17.1) is shown in Fig. 17.1(a), together with the corresponding map in Fig. 17.1(b). To form the map, the variable A is 'plotted' horizontally and B vertically, the possible values of the two variables being shown across the top and along the left-hand

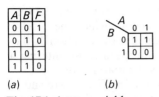

(a)   (b)

Fig. 17.1 A two-variable Karnaugh map

A	B	F
0	0	1
0	1	0
1	0	1
1	1	0

side of the map respectively. Within the cells so created is entered the value of the output variable F corresponding to the co-ordinate of A and B. For example, in the cell corresponding to $A = 0$ and $B = 1$ (lower left-hand cell), $F = 0$.

Maps may be drawn for three and four input variables quite conveniently. Beyond four, the method starts to become rather cumbersome and alternative methods may be preferred. Fig. 17.2(b) and (c) illustrates three and four-variable maps, (b) corresponding to the truth table in Fig. 17.2(a) whilst (c) corresponds to the truth table for the journey problem in Table 16.3 in the last chapter. The general principle of plotting the input-variable values across the top and left-hand side of the map is followed in both cases, four combinations being shown for the two variables. The values are not plotted in natural 'binary counting' sequence. This is an important aspect and is done deliberately to ensure that the input variables differ by no more than one digit in adjacent cells. In turn, this permits the map to be used for logic-function simplification by the methods to be described.

Fig. 17.2 Three- and four-variable Karnaugh maps

A	B	C	F
0	0	0	1
0	0	1	0
0	1	0	0
0	1	1	0
1	0	0	1
1	0	1	1
1	1	0	0
1	1	1	0

(a)

(b)

C \ AB	00	01	11	10
0	1	0	0	1
1	0	0	0	1

(c)

CD \ AB	00	01	11	10
00	0	0	0	0
01	0	1	1	0
11	0	1	1	0
10	0	0	0	0

17.2.2 Minimisation of logical expressions using the K map

As explained in Chapter 16, simplification by means of Boolean algebra is possible in an example such as that shown in Fig. 17.1(a) in which the output F is the sum of minterms $\bar{A}\bar{B}$ and $A\bar{B}$. In this example the expression reduces to $(\bar{A} + A)\bar{B} = \bar{B}$. The simplification is quite straightforward but there are situations when this is not so and the map method is more convenient.

To illustrate the map method, reference is made to Fig. 17.1(b) in which there are two cells containing 1's in the top row of the map. If these two 1's are considered *as a group* it will be seen that, for the group, $B = 0$ but A may be either 0 or 1. Thus, the two 1's may be represented by the statement $F = \bar{B}$, independent of A. This is the same result as that obtained by the Boolean-algebraic method.

A second example is provided by the map in Fig. 17.2(b). Here there are two groups of two 1's which, in accordance with the principle established above, are labelled $A\bar{B}$ (independent of C) and $\bar{B}\bar{C}$ (independent of A). Fig. 17.3 shows these groupings: for the $\bar{B}\bar{C}$ group, cells at either end of the row are grouped. This is possible because these cells, like other adjacent cells, differ by only one variable. The formal rules of grouping are detailed in the next section.

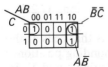

Fig. 17.3 Cell grouping

17.2.3 Formal minimisation procedure using the K map: minterm groupings

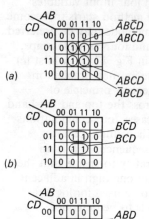

(a)

(b)

(c)

Fig. 17.4 Cell grouping

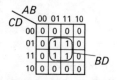

Fig. 17.5 Karnaugh map for the journey problem

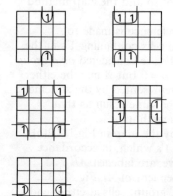

Fig. 17.6 Grouping cells at the map edges

For a given problem, the minterms representing the function are specified by entering a 1 in each cell for which the particular combination of variables makes the function 1; the maxterms representing the function are specified by entering a 0 in all the other cells. Fig. 17.4(a) is the map for the travelling problem discussed in Chapter 16. The 1's are shown encircled and labelled with the minterm which they represent. The two upper terms $\bar{A}B\bar{C}D$ and $AB\bar{C}D$ will be seen to differ by only one variable, A in this case, and their sum is: $\bar{A}B\bar{C}D + AB\bar{C}D = B\bar{C}D(\bar{A} + A) = B\bar{C}D$. Thus, it is possible to write down an expression for a group of two 1's. As a further example, the two lower 1's may be grouped to give BCD (Fig. 17.4(b)). Each expression contains only three variables and, as a general rule, any group of two 1's (or 0's) is independent of one variable. In this case, the expressions are independent of A because, for both groups, the variable A may be either 0 or 1. Alternative groupings are shown in Fig. 17.4(c): these are independent of C.

As two 1's may be grouped so two groups of two 1's may be further grouped into a set of four adjacent 1's. As a group, this will be independent of two variables: in general, a group of 2^n 1's or 0's will be independent of n variables. Fig. 17.5 shows a group of four 1's for which the $J = 1$ condition is independent of A and C, i.e. A and C may be either 0 or 1; furthermore for the group as a whole, B and D are always 1 and the group may therefore be represented by the expression BD: this is the same result for the journey problem as was obtained in Chapter 16.

A general procedure may be outlined as follows:

(i) Place a 1 in each cell in accordance with data obtained from a truth table or from a sum-of-product expression for the function.

(ii) Loop together the cells containing 1's in accordance with the following rules:

(a) Each group (containing $2, 4, 8, \ldots$ adjacent 1's) must be as large as possible and form a square or rectangular shape such that, with 2^n cells in a group, each cell always has n cells adjacent to it.

(b) The number of groups must be the smallest possible consistent with including every 1. Any 1 may be included more than once if this is necessary to satisfy these requirements.

(iii) The minimal form is deduced from the map, each group resulting in one product term in a sum-of-products expression.

Variants on this procedure are described in Sections 17.2.4 and 17.2.5 below.

A further point, exemplified in Fig. 17.3, is that cells at the edges of the map differ from cells in corresponding positions on other edges (see Fig. 17.6) by only one variable and 1's in these positions may therefore be grouped. Indeed, if the minimal form is to be obtained, the possibility of making such loops, and thus forming larger groups, must not be overlooked. Fig. 17.6 shows a number of examples of alternative methods of grouping.

In general, there may be more than one minimal expression and the grouping should be done in two stages: initially, the groups which can only be formed in one way are considered. These are the **essential groups** and must form part of any minimal expression. Then the groups which can be formed in more than one way are tackled. The procedure is illustrated in Example 17.1.

Example 17.1 *Determine the minimal form of the function,*

$$F = \bar{A}\bar{B}\bar{C}D + \bar{A}BCD + \bar{A}BC\bar{D} + \bar{A}BC\bar{D} + A\bar{B}\bar{C}\bar{D}$$

$$+ A\bar{B}\bar{C}D + A\bar{B}C\bar{D} + A\bar{B}CD + ABC\bar{D}.$$

After having drawn the map and marked the 1's on it (Fig. 17.7), the largest essential groups of cells containing 1's are looked for. There are no groups of eight, but there are two groups of four. Fig. 17.7(a) shows the two groups of four and the expressions by which they are represented. Three 1's remain which cannot be included in a group of four: of the three, the essential group of two is looped as shown in Fig. 17.7(b) and the remaining single 1 is grouped as in Fig. 17.7(c), in which alternative forms are shown. From Fig. 17.7(a) and (b) the essential components of the expression are

$$\bar{B}D + A\bar{B} + \bar{A}B\bar{D}.$$

The complete minimal expression will contain additionally either $BC\bar{D}$ or $AC\bar{D}$ (Fig. 17.7(c)). Truth tables will show that the two forms are equivalent.

Fig. 17.7 Karnaugh maps for Example 17.1

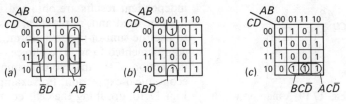

17.2.4 Minimisation on the K map: maxterm groupings

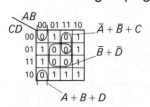

Fig. 17.8 Maxterm groupings

In Example 17.1 minterm grouping is used and this tends to be the most commonly used form. However, there are cases where the 0's are so disposed that a maxterm grouping is more advantageous. Fig. 17.8 repeats the table for the example above but with the cells containing 0's looped and labelled in accordance with Table 4 in Chapter 16 and the general rules established above. From Fig. 17.8, the minimal form of the function will be seen to be,

$$F = (A + B + D)(\bar{A} + \bar{B} + C)(\bar{B} + \bar{D}).$$

Again, a check on a truth table will confirm that this is a valid expression.

17.2.5 Use of complementary function in K-map minimisation

In addition to the minterm and maxterm-grouping methods it is also possible to group 0's in a sum-of-products form and 1's in a product-of-sums form. Thus, there are four ways in which a minimal expression can be determined from the map.

Because complementing an expression reverses the roles of the 1 and the 0, it is possible to write down the complement

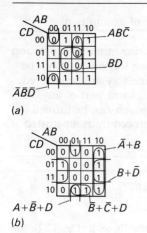

(a)

(b)

Fig. 17.9 Complementary minterm and maxterm groupings

Fig. 17.10 A map on which an alternative grouping may be made

of a minimal expression by looping cells containing 0's. For example, the 0's in the map in Fig. 17.9(a) (the same as Fig. 17.8) may be looped to give the complemented function

$$\bar{F} = AB\bar{C} + \bar{A}\bar{B}\bar{D} + BD.$$

$$\therefore \quad F = \overline{AB\bar{C} + \bar{A}\bar{B}\bar{D} + BD}.$$

A truth table may be used to show that the expression for F is the same as those previously obtained in Sections 17.2.3 and 17.2.4. Alternatively, DeMorgan's theorem may be used:

$$F = \overline{AB\bar{C} + \bar{A}\bar{B}\bar{D} + BD}$$

$$= \overline{AB\bar{C}} \cdot \overline{\bar{A}\bar{B}\bar{D}} \cdot \overline{BD}$$

$$= (\bar{A} + \bar{B} + C)(A + B + D)(\bar{B} + \bar{D}).$$

This is the same as that obtained using the product-of-sums method (Fig. 17.8).

The fourth possibility is to loop the cells containing 1's to give a complementary function in product-of-sum form. In Fig. 17.9(b), the 1's are grouped (as the 0's were in Fig. 17.8) to give,

$$\bar{F} = (A + \bar{B} + D)(\bar{B} + \bar{C} + D)(B + \bar{D})(\bar{A} + B).$$

Again, application of DeMorgan's theorems will show this to be the same as one of the expressions obtained by grouping the 1's to give a sum-of-products form.

Although four methods have been listed, only two independent results are obtained. Thus, only two methods need be used and, in practice, it is generally more convenient to use the sum-of-products form, either directly or in the complemented form. The choice of these may then rest with inspection of the map to determine which results in the most economical expression. For example, in the map shown in Fig. 17.10, grouping the cells containing 1's would yield a three-term sum-of-product form whereas grouping the cells containing 0's would yield a two-term sum-of-product complemented form.

17.2.6 Incompletely specified functions

In a given application there may be input combinations which are of no consequence and it is immaterial whether the output is 0 or 1. In such cases the output may be shown as a X (or d) indicating the so-called 'don't care' condition. The function is said to be **incompletely specified**.

If these conditions exist, they may be included on the map and may be treated either as a 0 or as a 1 according to whichever is the more convenient from the point of view of obtaining a minimal expression. For example, introducing two don't-care conditions into the map used for Example 17.1 allows new groupings of 1's and 0's as shown in Fig. 17.11(a) and (b) respectively. The resulting minimal expressions contain fewer variables than those obtained previously and therefore may be implemented using fewer gates and interconnections.

Fig. 17.11 Maps containing incompletely specified terms

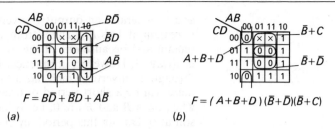

$$F = B\bar{D} + \bar{B}D + A\bar{B}$$

(a)

$$F = (A+B+D)(\bar{B}+\bar{D})(\bar{B}+C)$$

(b)

Example 17.2   *Design a minimal logic network which will convert a natural binary-coded decimal-word, $B_3B_2B_1B_0$, into an excess-3, Gray-code word, $G_3G_2G_1G_0$. The corresponding codes are shown in Table 17.2, the Gray-code words being obtained from Table 10 in Chapter 16 by looking up the codes for the relevant decimal-state plus three.*

Table 17.2

Decimal value	B_3	B_2	B_1	B_0	G_3	G_2	G_1	G_0	
0	0	0	0	0	0	0	1	0	
1	0	0	0	1	0	1	1	0	
2	0	0	1	0	0	1	1	1	
3	0	0	1	1	0	1	0	1	
4	0	1	0	0	0	1	0	0	
5	0	1	0	1	1	1	0	0	
6	0	1	1	0	1	1	0	1	
7	0	1	1	1	1	1	1	1	
8	1	0	0	0	1	1	1	0	
9	1	0	0	1	1	0	1	0	
	1	0	1	0	×	×	×	×	
	1	0	1	1	×	×	×	×	
	1	1	0	0	×	×	×	×	unspecified
	1	1	0	1	×	×	×	×	values
	1	1	1	0	×	×	×	×	
	1	1	1	1	×	×	×	×	

Maps for each of the Gray-code word digits are shown in Fig. 17.12.

Fig. 17.12 Maps for Example 17.2

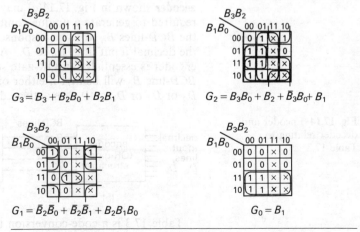

$$G_3 = B_3 + B_2B_0 + B_2B_1$$

$$G_2 = B_3B_0 + B_2 + \bar{B}_3B_0 + B_1$$

$$G_1 = \bar{B}_2\bar{B}_0 + \bar{B}_2\bar{B}_1 + B_2B_1B_0$$

$$G_0 = B_1$$

17.2.7 Static hazards   A circuit is said to contain a **static hazard** if a change in a single independent variable causes a temporary change in a dependent variable when no such change is intended.

Suppose, for example, that a circuit having inputs A, B, $\bar{B}$

and $\bar{C}$ generates an output F given by $F = B\bar{C} + A\bar{B}$. If A and $\bar{C}$ remain at 1 as B changes from 1 to 0 then, ideally, F will remain at 1 because one of the two components $B\bar{C}$ and $A\bar{B}$ is always 1. However, in practice, $\bar{B}$ may be derived from B through an inverter which has a finite propagation delay and there will be a short period of time (order of nanoseconds) when both B and $\bar{B}$ are 0, i.e. B has changed to 0 and $\bar{B}$ is still at 0. During this period, even with A and C remaining at 1, both components of F are 0 and the output level momentarily changes. Although short, the period may be long enough for any following circuit to be triggered. The momentary output change is sometimes called a **glitch** and the circuit contains a static hazard.

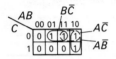

Fig. 17.13 A hazard condition

The hazard condition may be recognised on a K map. In the example above, for which the map is drawn in Fig. 17.13, the touching but non-intersecting cell groupings labelled $A\bar{B}$ and $B\bar{C}$ indicate that a hazard may occur. Furthermore, the hazard may be prevented by linking the two groups with a third link (shown dotted in Fig. 17.13) labelled $A\bar{C}$. Evidently, with A and $\bar{C}$ at 1, $A\bar{C} = 1$ and the output will be held at 1 whatever the state of B. It will be seen from the map that, although the output is now expressed as

$$F = A\bar{B} + B\bar{C} + A\bar{C},$$

it is basically unchanged, $A\bar{C}$ being a 'redundant' term introduced to avoid the hazard condition.

17.3 Encoders, decoders, read-only memories, programmable logic arrays and multiplexers

17.3.1 Encoders

To generate a *BCD* code output from a decimal input, the **encoder** shown in Fig. 17.14(a) may be used. The device is required to generate a unique combination of logic states on the *BCD*-lines B_0 to B_3 in response to an input on any one of the decimal-input lines D_0 to D_9. As Table 17.3 shows, the encoder is essentially an OR-gate structure. For example, *BCD*-line B_2 will be at 1 if either of the decimal lines D_1 or D_2 or D_3 or D_4 or D_9 are activated.

Fig. 17.14 Encoder and decoder relating to Table 17.3

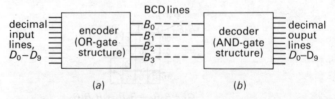

(a)   (b)

Table 17.3 is a code-conversion table for a natural-decimal to excess-3 natural-binary-coded-decimal (XS3 NBCD) converter in which the encode function may be obtained from the table as (for example) $B_2 = D_1 + D_2 + D_3 + D_4 + D_9$. Similar expressions can be obtained for B_0, B_1 and B_3. It is implicit that only one input line of the encoder be active at

Table 17.3

	Natural decimal	B_3	B_2	B_1	B_0	
	D_0	0	0	1	1	
	D_1	0	1	0	0	
	D_2	0	1	0	1	
	D_3	0	1	1	0	
	D_4	0	1	1	1	*Decode*
	D_5	1	0	0	0	*(AND function)*
	D_6	1	0	0	1	
	D_7	1	0	1	0	
	D_8	1	0	1	1	
	D_9	1	1	0	0	

Encode (OR function) ↓ above columns *XS3 NBCD*

inputs	coded outputs $O_3 O_2 O_1 O_0$
I_0	1 0 0 1
I_1	1 0 1 0
I_2	0 1 0 0

(a)

I_2 I_1 I_0	$O_3 O_2 O_1 O_0$
0 0 0	0 0 0 0
0 0 1	1 0 0 1
0 1 0	1 0 1 0
0 1 1	1 0 0 1
1 0 0	0 1 0 0
1 0 1	1 0 0 1
1 1 0	0 0 0 0
1 1 1	0 0 0 0

(b)

Fig. 17.15 Non-priority and priority decoder tables

$$O_2 = I_2 \bar{I}_1 \bar{I}_0$$

Fig. 17.16 Map for one output of a priority decoder

any given time. For example, if D_3 and D_7 were active simultaneously, *BCD*-lines B_3, B_2 and B_1 would all go to 1, giving an erroneous output. It is because this restriction exists that the abbreviated, single-column input notation can be used for the truth table in Table 17.3.

Nevertheless, there may be situations in which two inputs may be active at the same time. Such situations may be accidental (for example, as a result of pressing two input keys at once) or deliberate, requiring for example that a particular key overrides all the others. It may be required that, in an emergency, code 1001 is generated and that the emergency condition would have to activate input line D_6. In this circumstance the device would be known as a **priority encoder**, requiring the addition of an AND-logic stage before the OR-circuitry to effect the input-line priorities.

Fig. 17.15(a) shows the truth table for a simple (non-priority) encoding circuit drawn in the style of Table 17.3; the output codes are arbitrarily chosen. As in the previous example (Table 17.3), it is evident that in this case $O_0 = I_0$, $O_1 = I_1$, $O_2 = I_2$ and $O_3 = I_0 + I_1$. It is now assumed that the encoder is to be converted into a priority encoder such that, if I_0 is activated, code 1001 is generated irrespective of the condition of the other lines. A more comprehensive table is drawn up in Fig. 17.15(b) showing not only the original information but also the priority condition. The two remaining input conditions, $I_2 I_1 I_0 = 000$ and $I_2 I_1 I_0 = 110$, are arranged to provide an output value 000.

The K map for output O_2 is shown in Fig. 17.16; it is given by $O_2 = I_2 \bar{I}_1 \bar{I}_0$ as compared with I_2 for the simpler encoder. An AND gate is required to implement this function.

17.3.2 Decoders   If it were required to convert back from the *BCD* code to the decimal form, the **decoder** shown in Fig. 17.14(b) may be used. Table 17.3 can be applied in reverse in the sense that the device has to recognise *BCD*-code combinations and generate the decimal output corresponding to each combination. Thus, the decoder is essentially an AND-gate

Fig. 17.17 Integrated-circuit
decoder and decoder/driver

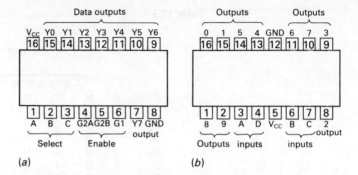

(a)

(b)

structure. For example, decimal output line D_3 will be
activated when $B_3 = 0$, $B_2 = 1$, $B_1 = 1$ and $B_0 = 0$,
i.e. $D_3 = \bar{B}_3 B_2 B_1 \bar{B}_0$. Integrated-circuit decoders are available.
Fig. 17.17(a) and (b) shows two examples, the type 74138 3-
to-8 line (or 1-from-8) decoder and type 74141 *BCD*-decimal
decoder/driver respectively.

**17.3.3 Decoder–encoder
structures**

Although the discussion in the previous section referred to
encoding and decoding, in that order, a more generally useful
arrangement is a decoder followed by an encoder. These
would appear to be exactly the requirements of a code
converter and, indeed, implementation of a *BCD*-to-XS3
BCD code converter is described in the next section. For the
present, the code converter is shown schematically in
Fig. 17.18. The 4-line *BCD* input is decoded into a 10-line
signal (i.e. one line for each *BCD* state) and this is then
'recoded' into the new format, which, in this example, also
requires a 4-line output. The combinational-logic function
described by the truth table in Fig. 17.19(a), for example,

Fig. 17.18 A
decoder–encoder
arrangement

Fig. 17.19 A
decoder–encoder gate
structure

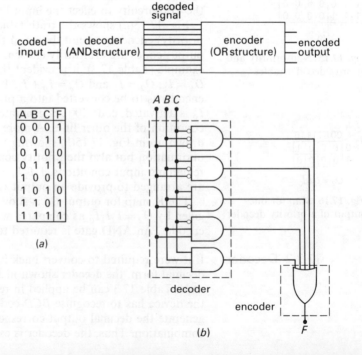

A	B	C	F
0	0	0	1
0	0	1	1
0	1	0	0
0	1	1	1
1	0	0	0
1	0	1	0
1	1	0	1
1	1	1	1

(a)

(b)

could be implemented by the single-output AND–OR, decoder–encoder structure in Fig. 17.19(*b*). At the other extreme, the 2-input, 16-output function illustrated in Table 17.1 could be implemented with the AND–OR structure in Fig. 17.20.

Fig. 17.20 A decoder–encoder arrangement to implement Table 17.1

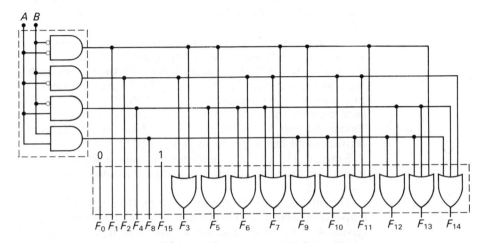

A B

$F_0 F_1 F_2 F_4 F_8 F_{15}$ F_3 F_5 F_6 F_7 F_9 F_{10} F_{11} F_{12} F_{13} F_{14}

17.3.4 Read-only memory (ROM)

The previous section has shown how an AND–OR, decoder–encoder structure can implement not only code-conversion functions but any multi-input/output combinational function. It is now shown that, rather than using separate decoders and encoders, it is possible to use **read-only memory** (ROM) integrated-circuits chips to implement these functions.

The basic ROM structure is just that shown in Fig. 17.18 redrawn in Fig. 17.21 with the input, output and internal lines suitably relabelled.

Fig. 17.21 Read-only memory principle

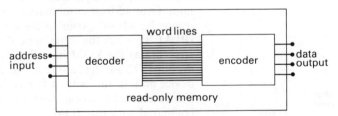

word lines

address input — decoder — encoder — data output

read-only memory

The decoder inputs are now called **address-inputs lines**, the internal lines carrying the decoded information are the **word lines** and the encoder outputs become the ROM **data-output lines**. Unlike Fig. 17.18, the number of word lines is specifically related to the number of address lines, there being 2^N word lines for N address lines.

In principle, application of a particular address input activates a specific word line (through the decoder) and this active word line determines the unique data output (through the encoder) corresponding to that address input. Typically data-output lines are provided singly, in groups of four or in groups of eight. Further detail is given in Sections 17.4 and 17.5.

Table 17.4

ROM address	ROM data
$A_3\ A_2\ A_1\ A_0$	$D_3\ D_2\ D_1\ D_0$
0 0 0 0	0 0 1 1
0 0 0 1	0 1 0 0
0 0 1 0	0 1 0 1
0 0 1 1	0 1 1 0
0 1 0 0	0 1 1 1
0 1 0 1	1 0 0 0
0 1 1 0	1 0 0 1
0 1 1 1	1 0 1 0
1 0 0 0	1 0 1 1
1 0 0 1	1 1 0 0

Very large read-only memories are manufactured but these are primarily intended for use as microcomputer storage media. For the more modest requirements of a small combinational-logic system, a 32×8 ROM for example (having five address pins) may be more suitable. Alternatively, as described in the next section, a programmable logic array may be used where every address combination is not required.

The implementation of a combinational system using a ROM is quite straightforward. The design is executed by programming the ROM in accordance with the system truth table which may then be known as a **ROM program table**. For example, the program table for a *NBCD*-to-XS3 *NBCD* code converter would have the form shown in Table 17.4. Taking the first row as an example, address input 0000 would activate word line 0, producing output 0011.

Example 17.2 could be implemented using a ROM, in which case the program table would be that shown in Table 17.2.

The minimum ROM size for the *NBCD*-to-XS3 *NBCD* converter (Table 17.4) would be 16×4, i.e. 4 address lines (giving $4^2 = 16$ word lines) and 4 data lines. If, for example, the 32×8 ROM shown in Fig. 17.22 were used, four select (address) pins would be used with the most-significant address pin held low. Also shown in Fig. 17.22 is a chip-select pin; its function is described in Sections 17.4.2 and 17.4.4.

17.3.5 Programmable logic array (PLA)

As mentioned in the previous section, there may be situations in which a relatively large number of address and data pins are required but significantly less than the maximum possible number of address combinations is needed. In such situations it may be advantageous to use a programmable-logic array (PLA). This has the same basic AND–OR, decoder–encoder structure as the ROM but all address combinations are not decoded. Those that are required are programmed into the device and, in this way, it is possible to obtain quite complex combinational functions with greater economy of circuitry compared with the ROM.

The number of AND gates utilised in the decoder section of the PLA is determined by the maximum number of product terms which the logic function specifies. For example, to implement the two output functions,

$$F_0 = \bar{A}_1 A_4 A_6 + \bar{A}_0 A_2 \bar{A}_7 \bar{A}_{10} + A_7 \bar{A}_9,$$

$$F_1 = \bar{A}_3 A_{13} + A_1 \bar{A}_4 A_7,$$

where A_0 to A_{13} are the input variables (previously designated A, B, C, etc.), five AND gates, each with up to 14 inputs, would be required. In practice, a much larger number may be provided (e.g. 96) although this would still be fewer than a ROM having 14 address-input pins would require.

With up to eight outputs (of which only two are shown in

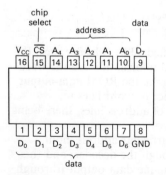

Fig. 17.22 An integrated-circuit read-only memory

the example), eight OR gates would be required, each having as many inputs as there are AND gates, i.e. five in this example but, in practice, typically up to 96.

The AND–OR arrangement for this example is shown in Fig. 17.23.

The PLA may be mask-programmed by the manufacturer or fusible links may be used. These methods are explained in Section 17.5.1.

Fig. 17.23 A programmable logic array

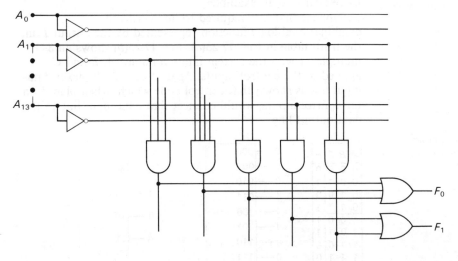

17.3.6 Multiplexers and demultiplexers

In Chapter 9, the analogue multiplexer is described as a device enabling a number of analogue signals to be time-division multiplexed on to a single output line. The essential process is that of connecting each input line to the output line in sequence. This section is concerned with the **digital multiplexer** which, although conceptually similar to the analogue multiplexer, may be more conveniently regarded as a combinational **data selector** having a number of input lines and a single output line. The single data-output line takes up the value (i.e. 0 or 1) of any one of the data-input-line values as determined by a control-input signal. Fig. 17.24(a) shows a 4–1 line multiplexer with 4 data-input pins labelled D_0 to D_3 and a single data-output pin D. Because there are four input lines, two control lines C_0 and C_1 (providing $2^2 = 4$ settings) are needed. Fig. 17.24(b) shows the truth table, indicating the state of D for the 4 combinations of values of C_1 and C_0.

Fig. 17.24 Multiplexer and demultiplexer

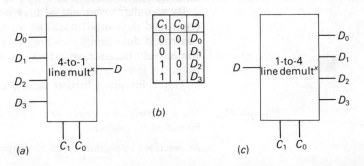

The **demultiplexer** (Fig. 17.24(c)) reverses the process, the value of the single data-input line now appearing on whichever of the four data-output lines is selected by $C_1 C_0$. A **data distributor** would be an apt title.

17.3.7 Implementation of combinational-logic functions using a multiplexer

In addition to the obvious use of a multiplexer/demultiplexer as a data selector/distributor, the multiplexer may be used as a means of implementing other systems. This is demonstrated by reference to an example.

Suppose that it is required to implement the combinational-logic function represented by the output F in the truth table in Fig. 17.25(a). Fig. 17.25(b) shows an 8–1 multiplexer with the system-input variables A, B and C applied to the control inputs. Against each multiplexer data-input line is shown that control code which, when placed on the control inputs, would connect that data-input line to the data-output line.

Fig. 17.25 Truth table implementation using a multiplexer

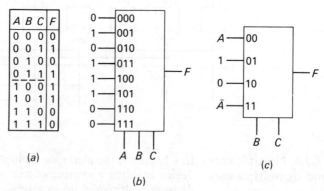

(a)

(b)

(c)

In order to implement the function, the output-function bit pattern (i.e. that shown in column F of the truth table) is placed on the data-input lines. The design is now complete. The operation is quite straightforward: putting $A = B = C = 0$ connects the uppermost data-input line to the data-output line (i.e. to F) and the required 0 state appears at F. A lower pin count results from a process known as **folding**. In this method, a 4–1 instead of an 8–1 multiplexer may be used, as shown in Fig. 17.25(c). A line is drawn across the truth table above which $A = 0$ and below which $A = 1$. Then, in the upper half, when $B = 0$ and $C = 0$, $F = 0 = A$ and, in the lower half, when $B = 0$ and $C = 0$, $F = 1 = A$. Thus whenever $B = C = 0$, $F = A$ and therefore A may be connected to the data-input pins instead of 0 or 1 as in Fig. 17.25(b).

By a similar argument, $\bar{A}$ may be connected to the 11-controlled data-input pin. The inputs to the 01 and 10-controlled data-input pins may be permanently set a 1 and 0 respectively because, with these control inputs, the data output is independent of A.

The technique is further illustrated by Example 17.3.

Example 17.3   *Use a multiplexer to construct a circuit which will generate a 3 data-bit odd-parity character.*

As described in Section 16.8.5 of Chapter 16, odd-parity generation is achieved by setting the parity bit to 1 when the number of 1's in the three data bits is even, i.e. the total number of 1's is then odd. The truth table is shown in Fig. 17.26(a) and the 4–1 multiplexer arrangement required to generate P is shown in Fig. 17.26(b). The data-input line signals are derived from the truth table in accordance with the principles described above.

Fig. 17.26 Truth table and multiplexer for Example 17.3

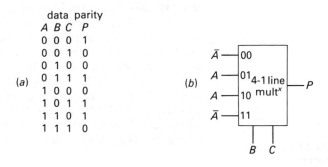

17.3.8 A combined decoder, multiplexer and demultiplexer

Fig. 17.27 shows an AND–OR circuit which may be configured to behave as a 2–4 line decoder, a 1–4 line demultiplexer or a 4–1 line multiplexer. If inputs X and D_0 to D_3 are all held at 1 the circuit behaves as a 2–4 line decoder. The encoded data must be placed on lines C_0 and C_1 and the decoded output then appears at X_0 to X_3. The decoder may be disabled (i.e. all outputs go to zero) simply by taking X to 0.

Fig. 17.27 Multiplexer gate structure

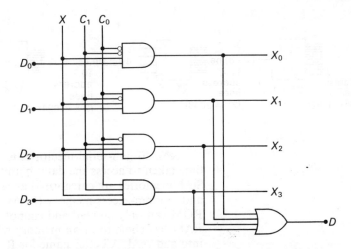

If now D_0 to D_3 are maintained at 1, input data at X is routed to one of four output lines X_0 to X_3 depending on how the control inputs C_0 and C_1 are set. The device behaves as a demultiplexer. For example, if $C_0 = C_1 = 0$, the value of X is transferred to X_0.

Finally, if X is held at 1, the value at what now become the data-input lines D_0 to D_3 is transferred to the single data-output line D in accordance with control inputs C_0 and C_1. The device is now a multiplexer. For example, if $C_0 = 1$ and $C_1 = 0$, the value at D_1 is transferred to D.

17.4 Semiconductor-memory arrangements

17.4.1 Memory organisation

One property shared by all machine memories is the storage of data in binary form and it is convenient, particularly when dealing with semiconductor memory, to think in terms of **memory cells**. Each cell contains data in binary form, high or low, true or false, 1 or 0, etc.; as before, the 1 and 0 notation will be used, it being understood that there is no arithmetic significance in the use of these symbols. The size of memory indicates the number of cells; for example, an 8K × 1 memory contains 8192 cells, K meaning 1024 as is usual in this context. A 1K × 8 memory also contains 8192 cells but arranged in 1024 8-bit groups (bytes). The term 8K memory is also used to mean 8K bytes of memory. Representative arrangements are shown in Fig. 17.28.

Fig. 17.28 Memory-cell arrangements

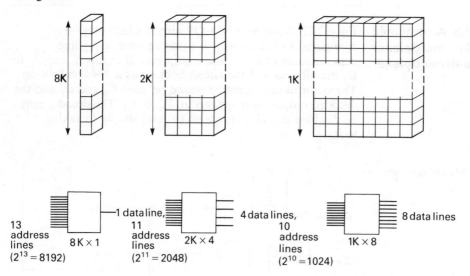

Access to non-serial memories is 'random' in the sense the time taken to access the data in any location is the same. Such memories are categorised as read-only memory (ROM) and random-access memory (RAM). As the name implies, ROM can only be read and cannot be written into whereas RAM has come to mean memory which can both be written into and read. A better name for RAM would be READ/WRITE memory but the use of the former name is now well established. In this context **read** means to transfer data from the memory to another device and **write** means to store data in the memory.

All forms of ROM are **non-volatile**, meaning that the data content of the cells is retained even though the electrical supply is removed. RAM is normally volatile although, by permitting operation in a 'standby' mode in which the power consumption is very low, small batteries may be used to retain the contents over a long period.

17.4.2 Pin connections

In Fig. 17.28 simplified block diagrams were shown with address and data lines. In practice, power supply and chip-control pin connections must also be provided. Typically, chip control is achieved through **chip select** (CS) and **write enable** (WE) pins as shown in the representative integrated-circuit pin designations in Fig. 17.29. The terms **chip enable** and **device select** are also used in place of chip select. The bar over the name indicates that the pin accepts an active-low signal. As indicated in the truth tables, the outputs go into the high-impedance state (Section 3.4 of Chapter 16) when chip select is 1. The function of write enable is also described in the truth table.

Fig. 17.29 Pin connections and operational conditions for two memory chips (with acknowledgement to the Intel Corporation)

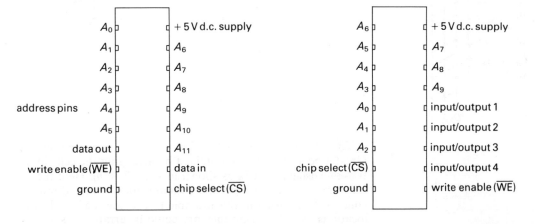

$\overline{CS}$	$\overline{WE}$	mode	output	power
1	×	chip not selected	high Z	standby
0	0	write	data in	active
0	1	read	data out	active

type 2147 4 K × 1 static RAM

(a)

$\overline{CS}$	$\overline{WE}$	mode	output	power
1	×	chip not selected	high Z	standby
0	0	write	data in	active
0	1	read	data out	active

type 2148 1 K × 4 static RAM

(b)

17.4.3 Outline structure

Section 17.3.4 established the concept of a read-only memory (ROM) and introduced the general principle of the AND–OR, decoder–encoder structure. This section considers the structure in greater detail.

The decoder follows the principles previously introduced in which application of a particular address activates the corresponding internal word line in response to which the encoder activates predetermined information on the data lines. The nature of the encoder differs widely with different memory types but a generalised schematic representation for a 16 × 4-bit memory is shown in Fig. 17.30(a).

Each intersection represents a memory cell and the dots are intended to show cells containing 1's. Thus, for example, 0101

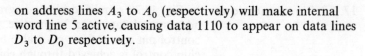

Fig. 17.30 Encoder
arrangements

on address lines A_3 to A_0 (respectively) will make internal
word line 5 active, causing data 1110 to appear on data lines
D_3 to D_0 respectively.

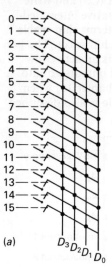

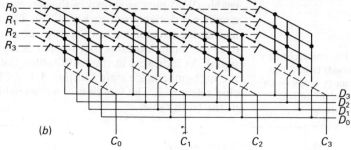

(a)

(b)

The arrangement shown in Fig. 17.30(a) is **one-dimensional**.
Greater economy can be obtained by arranging the cells in a
two-dimensional matrix as shown in Fig. 17.30(b). Here the
cells are arranged in rows and columns, four rows and four
columns being used in this example to provide the 16 address
locations. A 16K × 1-bit memory could be arranged as a
128 × 128 matrix. Thus, in contrast with Fig. 17.30(a) in
which 16 internal address lines are used to access the 16
memory locations, Fig. 17.30(b) shows four **row-address** lines
and four **column-address** lines accessing a 4 × 4 matrix. Each
row-address line accesses all the cells in its row, the required
location in that row then being identified by the column-
address line. For example, to access the location
corresponding to address-line 5 in Fig. 17.30(a), row line R_1
and column line C_1 would be activated.

The row and column format provides a considerable saving
in decoding circuitry, the 16 AND gates required for the 4–16
line decoder in Fig. 17.30(a) being replaced by eight gates
(two 2–4 line decoders) in Fig. 17.30(b). For the larger
memories the saving is greater, reducing from 16 384 gates to
256 for a 16K × 1 memory. Fig. 17.31 gives the arrangement
for the type 2147 RAM whose pin designations were shown in
Fig. 17.29(a). Also illustrated in this diagram are the
read/write control arrangements. Three-state buffers,
controlled by chip-select and write-enable signals, determine
whether the data is fed into the device through D_{IN} (write) or
out through D_{OUT} (read).

An associated principle is that of **address multiplexing** in
which the same address connection pins are used for rows
and columns. In this system, the row address is latched into
the memory by activating a **row-address strobe** (RAS) pin,
followed by latching the column addresses (on the same pins)
in response to a signal on a **column-address strobe** (CAS) pin.

Fig. 17.31 Type 2147 memory (with acknowledgement to the Intel Corporation)

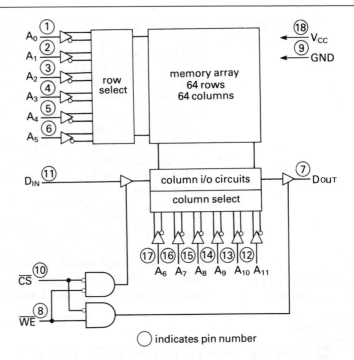

This arrangement is used on the Intel type 2118 memory whose block diagram, pin connections and logic symbol are shown in Fig. 17.32.

This $16K \times 1$ chip is a dynamic RAM to which further reference is made in Section 17.5.2.

Fig. 17.32 Type 2118 memory (with acknowledgement to the Intel Corporation)

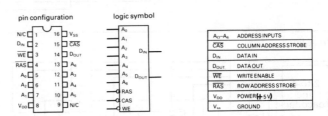

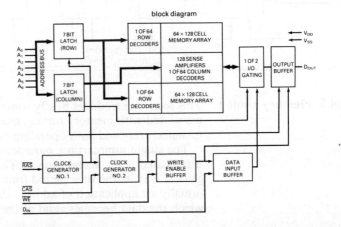

17.4.4 Expanding memory systems

In general, expansion of a given memory system may take the form of expanding the number of addressable locations or the size of the word. To illustrate how both requirements can be met, Fig. 17.33 shows two ways in which a $4K \times 4$ memory could be constructed. In Fig. 17.33(a) four $4K \times 1$ chips are arranged on a common address bus and each data pin is connected to a separate data line. There is a common connection between all $\overline{WE}$ pins and between all $\overline{CS}$ pins. In Fig. 17.33(b), four $1K \times 4$ chips are arranged on a common bidirectional data bus. In this case, the $\overline{CS}$ pins are connected to the output of a 2-to-4 line decoder whose input is the two address lines A_{10} and A_{11}.

If in the arrangement in Fig. 17.33(a), it were required to expand the number of bits (i.e. expand the word size), additional chips could be added in just the same way as the existing four. In the arrangement in Fig. 17.33(b), expanding the number of addressable locations would require additional chips whose $\overline{CS}$ pins would be connected to the output of a larger decoder, e.g. a 3-to-8 line type.

Fig. 17.33 Methods of memory expansion

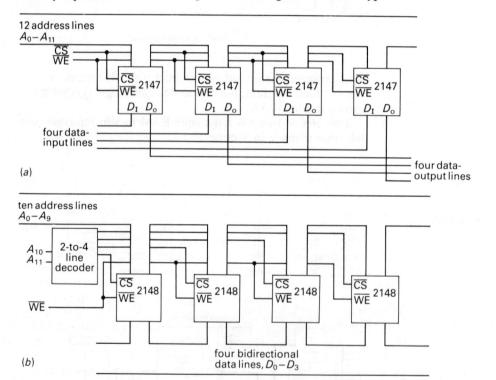

(a)

(b)

four bidirectional data lines, $D_0 - D_3$

17.4.5 Memory timing

This section introduces briefly some of the terminology associated with memory timing; usage may vary with different manufacturers and with operating conditions.

The single summarising parameter by which memory speed is indicated is the **access time** t_A. This may be defined in a general way as the time period from the start of the cycle (usually an application of address information) to the time at which the data becomes valid at the memory output pins.

A more detailed consideration may distinguish between the **address access time** t_{AA} and the **chip-select access time** t_{ACS}, the former being measured from the time the address becomes valid (with the chip-select pin enabled) and the latter from the time the chip is selected with the address already present on the pins.

In the read mode, the read-cycle time t_{RC} is the minimum period between address or chip-select inputs becoming valid and the start of the next address transition following a data read. This period is at least as long as the access time. When used in the write mode, the write-cycle time t_{WC} is the period between the address or chip-select inputs becoming valid and the start of the next address transition. Write-cycle times are typically equal to or slightly less than read-cycle times.

When designing with memories, there are a number of other detailed factors which must be considered. For example, the write-pulse width is the minimum time for which the $\overline{WE}$ pin must be held low when writing into the memory. This and other timing considerations may be obtained from manufacturers' literature.

17.5 Memory types

17.5.1 Read-only memory

The ROM is a combinational device in the sense that, subject to a short time delay (the access time) of the order of 50 ns, data is continuously available at the data pins as long as the address and chip-select pins remain activated.

The matrix form shown in Fig. 17.30(a) could represent the encoder section of a ROM in which the dots represent word-line/data-line connections and no dot means no connection. Thus, placing a 1 on a particular word line would cause the appropriate data to appear on the data lines.

Whilst the dot matrix is a useful concept, it cannot be a practical arrangement because there would be interaction between the word lines if the dots were simple connections. The problem may be avoided using the principle shown in Fig. 17.34(a). The connection at each intersection is made through a diode so that, as shown for a single data line in Fig. 17.34(b), a 'high' positive voltage on the free end of any diode will cause that diode to conduct. Just one conducting diode is sufficient to raise the potential of the diode–resistor junction, producing a 'high' data-out value at this point and reverse-biasing all the other diodes. The circuit is, in effect, an OR circuit, a 1 on any word line resulting in a 1 on those output lines at which there is a connecting diode.

With the diode matrix concept in mind, it is now possible to list three commonly used forms of ROM. In the **mask-programmed ROM** the intersection diodes (or their equivalents) are placed in position during the manufacturing process. As the name implies, a mask is used to identify the positions in accordance with a ROM programming chart

Fig. 17.34 Diode-matrix arrangement for read-only memory

whose form is determined by the system requirements. Several examples of the use of ROM in the design of combinational and sequential circuits are described in this chapter and in Chapter 18.

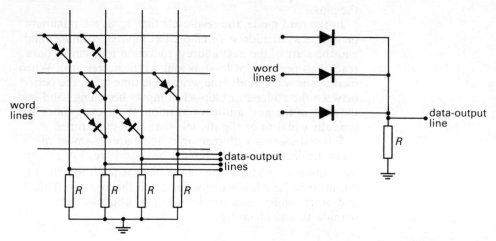

The second type is the **programmable ROM (PROM)** in which diodes are placed at every intersection during manufacture but a small fusible link is provided in series with each one. The memory may now be programmed by the customer. Programming is effected by burning out the links at the intersections where a connection is not required. A typical 2K × 8-bit PROM has an access time of 50 ns and a supply current of 180 mA.

It will be apparent that, once programmed, the data contents of neither the mask-programmed ROM nor the PROM can be changed. This is satisfactory in situations where the program is fully developed and no further changes are required but, during development or if future changes are envisaged, it may be more convenient to use an **erasable programmable ROM (EPROM)**. This device uses a **floating-gate** structure at the intersections. In operation, a charge is induced on the insulated gate of an MOS device by application of a relatively high voltage (e.g. 25 V) between drain and source so as to cause avalanche breakdown. After removal of the high voltage, the charge is trapped and the conducting path between drain and source exists as a result of a reduced threshold voltage (see Chapter 12).

Once programmed in this way, the device may be considered to be effectively programmed for life inasmuch as the charge will remain for periods in excess of ten years. However, by prolonged exposure to ultraviolet light of a specified wavelength (for a period of about $\frac{1}{2}$ hour) the charge can be removed and, hence, the memory erased. After erasure, the device may be reprogrammed. A quartz window in the case of the chip is provided for erasure.

The Intel 2764 is an example, being an 8K × 8 EPROM with an access time of 200 ns and drawing an active current of 150 mA (35 mA in standby). The device normally operates from a single 5 V d.c. supply but requires 12.5 V for programming.

A third type of ROM is the electrically erasable PROM (or E^2PROM). This also uses a floating gate structure but can be erased by applying a reverse polarity voltage. Thus erasure can be carried out 'in circuit' and individual words in the memory can be erased.

17.5.2 Random-access memory

As already mentioned, the term RAM is used to describe memory which may be read from or written into. Two principal types may be identified, the static RAM and the dynamic RAM.

The encoding section of the **static RAM**† is basically an array of elementary bistable elements. Typically, each cell in the memory consists of six MOSFET's, four constituting the bistable element and the other two, row-gating switches. Each column of cells is provided with a column-gating switch and the control logic required to sense the state of the selected bistable (for reading) or, if necessary, to modify the existing state (for writing).

The previously mentioned 2147 and 2148 types are static RAM's. A block diagram for the 2147 was shown in Fig. 17.31 and Fig. 17.35 shows the 2148. Both are housed in an industry-standard 18-pin package and require a single 5 V

Fig. 17.35 Type 2148 memory (with acknowledgement to the Intel Corporation)

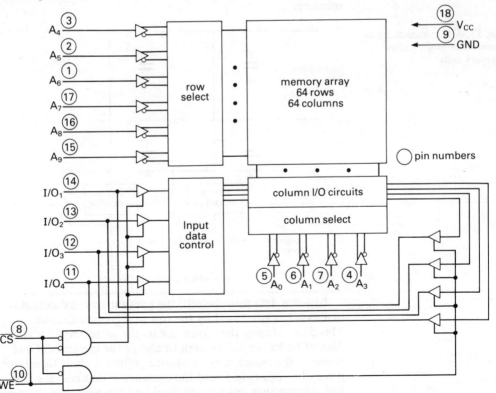

† Notwithstanding its inclusion within a chapter principally concerned with combinational-logic systems, the static RAM cell is essentially a sequential circuit as described in the next chapter.

supply. Access time, read-cycle time and write-cycle time are all quoted at 35 ns (for the 2147H-1) and the access time for the 2148H is given as 55 ns. The circuits consume a reduced standby power under control of $\overline{CS}$; in less than a cycle period after $\overline{CS}$ goes high, the chip is deselected and the power requirement is automatically reduced. It remains in this lower-power standby mode as long as $\overline{CS}$ remains high. In large systems, where the majority of devices will be deselected at any given time, system power savings of up to 85% are thought to be realistic. All signals are TTL compatible and three-state inputs are provided. The data is read non-destructively and has the same polarity as the input data.

The static RAM has the virtue of being simple to use, retaining its data in the bistables as long as the power supply is maintained. However, the six-transistor cell structure is relatively space inefficient and the **dynamic RAM** provides an alternate solution in which each cell consists essentially of a single transistor and capacitor. However, as explained below, it is more demanding in its operation than the static RAM.

The basic storage cell is effectively a MOSFET row-gating switch connected to a small (gate-substrate) capacitance. Fig. 17.36 shows a general schematic form for a dynamic memory.

Fig. 17.36 Representation of dynamic random-access-memory cells

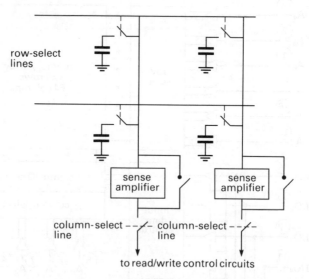

To write data into the cell, the relevant row and column-like switches are closed by the row and column decoders. This done, closing the switch across the sense amplifier allows data to be fed up the column to charge the capacitor. Once charged, the switch may be opened. When, a short time later, it may be required to read the contents of that cell, the row and column switches are activated and the output of the sense amplifier (at its lower end) is passed on to the read line. The function of the sense amplifier is to detect the presence of a charge on the storage capacitor; this may be quite small as a result of leakage and charge sharing with the significant column data-line 'stray' capacitance. The read process itself results in a loss of charge, i.e. it is destructive, and it is therefore necessary to **refresh** the cell immediately after a read process by connecting the output of the sense amplifier back to the cell. Thus, whatever the state of the sense-amplifier output after the read process, this information is fed back to the cell. All the cells in the selected row are refreshed at the same time in this manner.

Although the read cycle refreshes the cells (and the write cycle refreshes all those cells in the selected row except that which is being written into), it is still necessary to initiate a periodic **refresh cycle** so that, whether read or not, each cell will receive a periodic refresh, usually every 2 ms. For example, the Type 2118 16K × 1 dynamic RAM shown in Fig. 17.32 has a 128 row × 128 column matrix and therefore requires 128 refresh cycles every 2 ms.

As discussed in Section 17.4.3, this circuit also uses multiplexed addressing and may be served by devices such as the Type 3242, Address Multiplexer and Refresh Counter, itself a 28-pin package, which deals with both functions.

Key points to remember

- the Karnaugh map is a convenient method for setting out a logical statement and deducing its minimal form;
- minimisation can be effected by minterm or maxterm groupings in both normal or complementary forms;
- incompletely specified functions can result in simpler minimised expressions;
- encoders and decoders (OR and AND structures) can be used in a number of code-conversion configurations, the ROM being essentially a decoder–encoder structure;
- the PLA can be used where only a restricted number of address combinations is required;
- the digital multiplexer (or data selector) can also be used to implement combinational-logic functions;
- semiconductor memory can be broadly grouped as ROM or RAM;
- separate row and column-addressing is used to reduce chip size;
- memory can be expanded by use of multiple chips and suitable decoding arrangements;
- ROM can be subdivided into programmable, erasable programmable and electrical-erasable programmable types;
- RAM can be subdivided in static and dynamic types, the latter requiring refreshing at regular intervals.

Further reading

Floyd, T. L., *Digital Fundamentals.* Bell and Howell (1986).
Mano, M. M., *Digital Design.* Prentice-Hall (1984).
Roth, C. H., *Fundamentals of Logic Design.* West Publishing (1985).

EXERCISES 17

17.1   Use a Karnaugh map to obtain minimal expressions for the logical function in Exercise 16.5. Obtain expressions by minterm and by maxterm groupings.

17.2   Write down sum-of-product and complementary sum-of-product expressions for the cell groups in Fig. 17.10. Draw up a truth table in each case and show that the two expressions are equivalent.

17.3   Use a Karnaugh map to justify the logical relationship

$$\bar{w} + \bar{x} + \bar{y} + \bar{z} = \overline{wxyz}.$$

17.4   Show how both the minterm- and maxterm-group expressions in Exercise 17.1 are simplified if, in the original problem in Exercise 16.5, the eight input conditions for which $A = 1$ have no bearing on the output condition.

17.5   Explain by reference to the Karnaugh map in Exercise 17.1 where a static hazard might occur and how it can be prevented.

17.6   (a) An encoder accepts 4 inputs, generating the codes shown in Fig. E17.6. Draw up a list of OR statements describing each of the five bits of the output code, and draw an OR-structure logic diagram.

input	output
1	00101
2	10110
3	01100
4	11011

Fig. E17.1

(b) Extend the table to show how the system can be modified to indicate when two inputs exist concurrently, by sending the output to 11111. Any other input condition, apart from those listed in Fig. E17.1, is unspecified.

Draw Karnaugh maps for the five output bits and hence determine the additional logic circuitry necessary to implement the modification.

17.7   Draw an AND-gate decoder structure in the style of Fig. 17.19 which will implement the truth table for the journey problem first described in Table 16.3.

17.8   The required output from a combinational-logic unit is given by the following statements in which the four outputs are expressed as functions of the four address inputs A_0 to A_3:

$$F_0 = A_1\bar{A}_2 + A_3,$$

$$F_1 = A_0 A_2 \bar{A}_3,$$

$$F_2 = A_0 A_1 + \bar{A}_1\bar{A}_2 A_3,$$

$$F_3 = A_2 + \bar{A}_0 A_3.$$

Draw up a ROM programming table showing the four address inputs and four data outputs.
Also draw up the PLA logic diagram which would be required to implement this system.

17.9   Implement the logic function

$$F = A\bar{B} + \bar{A}C + AB\bar{C}$$

using a 4-to-1 multiplexer.

17.10 A memory chip has 16 pins: two are used for supply and ground, one each for row and column-address-strobe signals, and one each for a write-enable and chip-select signal. Assuming separate data-in and data-out pins are used, what is the maximum number of addressable locations?

17.11 A 2K × 8 memory chip has three chip-select pins CS_1, $\overline{CS_2}$ and $\overline{CS_3}$. Show how a number of chips can be used to form a memory system providing 16K bytes of memory.

18 Sequential logic

The principal learning objectives of this chapter are to:

	Section	Exercise
• deduce the operation of an S–R bistable circuit;	1.1	18.1
• explain the effect of a clock-input signal;	1.2	
• describe the action of a data latch;	1.3	(see 18.3)
• analyse the operation of the master–slave and edge-triggered J–K bistable;	1.4, 1.5	18.2
• state the operation of a D-type bistable;	1.6	18.3
• discuss the general properties of sequential circuits;	2	18.4–18.6
• analyse a natural-binary counter;	3.1	
• design a synchronous sequential circuit without control inputs;	3.2, 3.3	18.7
• show how ROM may be used as the combinational element in sequential-circuit design;	3.4, 3.5	(see 18.8)
• explain how circuit design can incorporate control inputs;	4	18.8
• describe the construction and two applications of a shift register.	5	18.9

18.1 Introduction

As discussed in the introduction to Chapter 16, a sequential logic circuit may be defined in general as a circuit for which the existing state is dependent on both present and past inputs. In contrast with the combinational circuit described in Chapter 17, the sequential circuit must remember past states and must therefore contain memory devices capable of storing data. The first section of this chapter describes forms of the basic memory element known as the **bistable circuit** or, simply, **bistable**. As the name implies, this is a circuit capable of assuming either one of two stable states.

18.2 Bistable devices

18.2.1 The S–R (set–reset) bistable

An S–R bistable circuit constructed using NAND gates is shown in Fig. 18.1(a). S and R are control inputs and Q and $\bar{Q}$ are the outputs; Fig. 18.1(b) shows the NAND truth table (for reference). If, in Fig. 18.1(a), S = 1 and R = 0, the output of gate 2 will be 1 irrespective of the value of Q because R = 0. Since S = 1 and $\bar{Q}$ = 1, gate 1 will then have 1 applied to both its inputs, thereby ensuring that its output Q = 0. Thus, the circuit state Q = 0 and $\bar{Q}$ = 1 is stable when R = 0 and S = 1. A similar analysis shows that inputs R = 1, S = 0 result in the stable state Q = 1, $\bar{Q}$ = 0.

Suppose now that with Q = 1 and $\bar{Q}$ = 0, R and S are both 1. Because 1 is applied to both inputs of gate 2, $\bar{Q}$ = 0. At gate 1, the input combination S = 1, $\bar{Q}$ = 0 ensures that Q = 1. In short, the outputs Q and $\bar{Q}$ are unaffected by the application of S = R = 1.

Finally, for the case when S = R = 0: since 0 is applied to one input of both gate 1 and gate 2, Q and $\bar{Q}$ will both be 1. Although Q and $\bar{Q}$ are not complementary as the notation suggests, this output condition is permissible and stable. However, if with this output already established, S and R are now both simultaneously set at 1, both NAND-gate outputs will try to go to 0. If these 0 values are fed back to the gate inputs, both gate outputs would try to go to 1 and an apparently unstable condition is reached. In practice, one gate will propagate its signal slightly more quickly than the other allowing the faster-gate output to go to 0 whilst leaving the other at 1. This is a stable condition but it is not possible to predict which gate will take up which state. Simultaneously setting S = R = 1 with the initial state either Q = 1, $\bar{Q}$ = 0 or Q = 0, $\bar{Q}$ = 1 will result in no change in the output.

The operation of the NAND-gate S–R bistable circuit is summarised in the table in Fig. 18.2(a). The information may also be shown in the form of a transition diagram, as shown in Fig. 18.2(c). Each circle on the diagram represents a stable state and the transition from one state to another is indicated by a directed line joining two circles. The value of S and R (i.e. the control input) required to initiate the state transition is shown beside the directed line. Unpredictable transitions are indicated by broken lines. The Q = 0, $\bar{Q}$ = 0 circuit state is not shown since it is not sustainable no matter

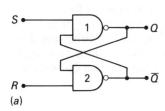

(a)

A	B	A.B
0	0	1
0	1	1
1	0	1
1	1	0

(b)

Fig. 18.1 A NAND-gate S–R bistable circuit with NAND-gate truth table

Fig. 18.2 Operation of the S–R bistable circuit with a transition diagram

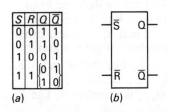

S	R	Q	$\bar{Q}$
0	0	1	1
0	1	1	0
1	0	0	1
1	1	0 1	1 0

(a)

(b)

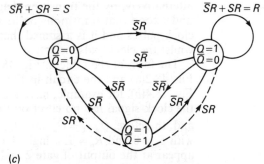

(c)

what the values of the control inputs S and R. As explained above, this state is unstable.

In normal operation (in which the two outputs are to be complementary) the existing state is maintained if S and R are both held at 1. To change the circuit state, R must be set at 0 in order to take Q to 0, and S to 0 in order to take Q to 1. Thus, as far as the circuit as a whole is concerned, the active control-input logic level is 0, as indicated by the notation $\bar{S}$ and $\bar{R}$ on the S–R bistable symbol shown in Fig. 18.2(b).

NOR gates may be employed instead of NAND gates to produce an S–R bistable as shown in Fig. 18.3(a). However, the operation of the NOR-gate implementation differs slightly, as summarised in Fig. 18.3(b). In this case, with both the S and R inputs initially at 0, a 1 applied to either the S or R input causes the circuit to change state, i.e. the active logic level to the control input is 1. The symbol for the NOR-gate S–R bistable is shown in Fig. 18.3(c).

Fig. 18.3 A NOR-gate S–R bistable

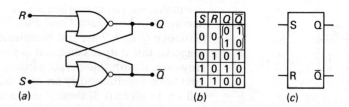

S	R	Q	Q̄
0	0	(0	1)
		(1	0)
0	1	0	1
1	0	1	0
1	1	0	0

(a)　　　　　(b)　　　　　(c)

18.2.2 Clocked S–R bistable

The S–R bistable outputs Q and $\bar{Q}$ react almost immediately to changes in the control inputs S and R. In contrast, the outputs Q and $\bar{Q}$ of the **clocked S–R bistable**, shown in Fig. 18.4(a) respond to the existing value of the control inputs S and R only on the application of a **clock pulse** at the active-high clock pin. The outputs Q and $\bar{Q}$ are therefore constrained to respond to the control inputs S and R synchronously with a train of clock pulses. Since S and R only affect the outputs Q and $\bar{Q}$ at the occurrence of a clock pulse S and R are termed **synchronous control inputs**.

To describe the operation of the circuit, the value of S, R, Q and $\bar{Q}$ prior to the application of the nth clock pulse is denoted by S_n, R_n, Q_n and $\bar{Q}_n$ respectively. The value of Q and $\bar{Q}$ after the nth clock pulse is denoted by Q_{n+1} and $\overline{Q_{n+1}}$ respectively. When the active-low PRESET and CLEAR pins are both held at 1 (i.e. inactive) the operation of the clocked S–R bistable is summarised by the table of Fig. 18.4(b) or, alternatively, by the transition diagram of Fig. 18.4(c). It is understood that transitions occur synchronously with the clock pulses and it is assumed that S and R do not change whilst the clock pulse is active.

The form of the table in Fig. 18.4(b) can be deduced from Fig. 18.2(a) and the circuit in Fig. 18.4(a). For the first line of Fig. 18.4(b), for example, having $S_n = 0$ and $R_n = 0$ means that the clock signal has no effect on the output of gates 1 and 2 and, therefore, $Q_{n+1} = Q_n$ and $\overline{Q_{n+1}} = \bar{Q}_n$. For the second line, with $S_n = 0$ and $R_n = 1$, a high clock signal causes a 0 to appear at the output of gate 2 and Q_{n+1} is therefore 0. The

Fig. 18.4 A clocked *S–R* bistable using NAND gates

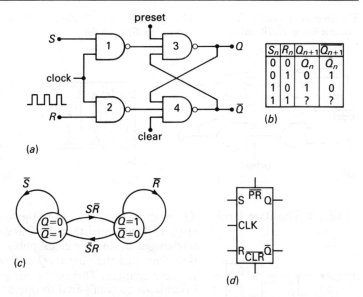

S_n	R_n	Q_{n+1}	$\bar{Q}_{n+1}$
0	0	Q_n	$\bar{Q}_n$
0	1	0	1
1	0	1	0
1	1	?	?

(b)

(a)

(c)

(d)

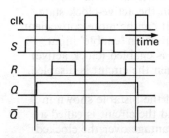

Fig. 18.5 Operation of the *S–R* bistable with a typical input waveform

third line reverses the roles of *S* and *R* and the final line shows the condition which leads to the unpredictable output state.

Fig. 18.5 is an example of a waveform timing diagram illustrating the operation. As shown, *S* and *R* do not change during the period when the clock is active (although this possibility is considered in the next section). When the first clock pulse occurs $S_n = 1$ and $R_n = 0$. Hence the bistable sets, i.e. $Q_{n+1} = 1$. Because the clock is low, the 'pulse' on *R* between first and second clock pulses is ignored.

At the incidence of the second clock pulse S_n and R_n are 0 and therefore (by reference to Fig. 18.4(*b*)) $Q_{n+1} = Q_n$ and the outputs are unchanged. At the third clock pulse, $R_n = 1$ and $S_n = 0$ and the bistable resets to $Q_{n+1} = 0$. In each case, the set and reset operations take place at, or shortly after, the time corresponding to the occurrence of the leading edge of the clock pulse.

It is often necessary to place the output *Q* and $\bar{Q}$ in a desired state prior to the application of a clock pulse, i.e. to initialise the output. This is achieved using the $\overline{\text{PRESET}}$ and $\overline{\text{CLEAR}}$ pins which are held at 1 in the inactive condition. With the clock input inactive (low), application of 0 to the $\overline{\text{PRESET}}$ input will cause the circuit to assume the state $Q = 1$, $\bar{Q} = 0$. Alternatively, the application of 0 to the $\overline{\text{CLEAR}}$ pin will cause the circuit to assume the state $Q = 0$, $\bar{Q} = 1$. The $\overline{\text{PRESET}}$ and $\overline{\text{CLEAR}}$ inputs are termed **asynchronous inputs** because their effects are not synchronised with the clock pulses. The circuit symbol for the clocked *S–R* bistable is shown in Fig. 18.4(*d*).

A clocked *S–R* bistable may be constructed using NOR gates as shown in Fig. 18.6(*a*). The table of 18.6(*b*) summarises its operation. The clock input is active low in this case. Also, the asynchronous PRESET and CLEAR pins are active high but the synchronous inputs are both active low.

Fig. 18.6 A clocked *S–R* bistable using NOR gates.

The symbol for a clocked *S–R* bistable using NOR gates is shown in Fig. 18.6(*c*).

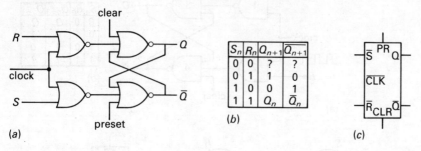

S_n	R_n	Q_{n+1}	$\bar{Q}_{n+1}$
0	0	?	?
0	1	1	0
1	0	0	1
1	1	Q_n	$\bar{Q}_n$

(*b*)

(*a*)

(*c*)

18.2.3 The data latch

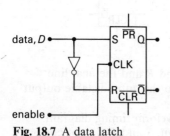

Fig. 18.7 A data latch

The discussion of the NAND-gate clocked *S–R* bistable (Fig. 18.4) assumed that the *S* and *R* control inputs remained unchanged during the clock pulse. However, if such changes do occur then the outputs *Q* and *Q̄* will respond immediately to these changes. This behaviour permits the clocked *S–R* bistable to be configured to operate as a **data latch**, as shown in Fig. 18.7. Here, the inverter ensures that the *S* and *R* are always complementary. Thus, while the clock is active, $Q = D$ since $S = D$ and $R = \bar{D}$. However, when the clock becomes inactive the outputs *Q* and *Q̄* retain the active-clock state despite any further changes in *D*. It can be more convenient to think in terms of the clock input as an 'enable' input. Thus, $Q = D$ as long as the circuit is enabled (clock active) but the existing data is latched when the circuit is disabled.

18.2.4 The master–slave J–K bistable

The synchronous control inputs of the bistable shown in 18.8(*a*) are designated *J* and *K* and the circuit is called a master slave *J–K* bistable. Its advantage over the clocked *S–R* bistable is that its outputs *Q* and *Q̄* are predictable for all four possible combinations of *J* and *K*. This is indicated in the table of Fig. 18.8(*b*).

The master–slave *J–K* bistable comprises two clocked *S–R* bistables in cascade. The cross-coupled feedback permits a

Fig. 18.8 A master–slave *J–K* bistable

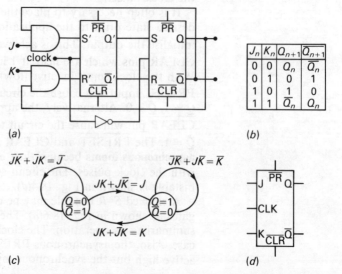

J_n	K_n	Q_{n+1}	$\bar{Q}_{n+1}$
0	0	Q_n	$\bar{Q}_n$
0	1	0	1
1	0	1	0
1	1	$\bar{Q}_n$	Q_n

(*a*)

(*b*)

$$\bar{J}\bar{K} + \bar{J}K = \bar{J} \qquad\qquad JK + J\bar{K} = \bar{K}$$

$$JK + J\bar{K} = J$$

Q=0
Q̄=1

Q=1
Q̄=0

$$J\bar{K} + \bar{J}\bar{K} = K$$

(*c*)

(*d*)

predictable output when $J = K = 1$ and the inverter ensures that complementary clock signals are applied to the master and slave S–R bistables. This arrangement inhibits the feedback which would otherwise cause the outputs to oscillate between 0 and 1 when $J = K = 1$.

The master–slave J–K operates as follows. Q' and $\bar{Q}'$ of the master bistable respond to the inputs $S' (= J\bar{Q})$ and $R' (= KQ)$ when the clock is active high. However, the outputs of the slave bistable Q and $\bar{Q}$ cannot respond to the inputs S and R since the clock input to this bistable is inactive.

When the clock input to the master bistable returns low the master bistable is inhibited but the clock input to the slave bistable becomes active. Q and $\bar{Q}$ of the slave bistable can now respond to the control inputs $S (= Q')$ and $R (= \bar{Q}')$. In effect, the J and K input values are clocked into the master–slave J–K bistable on the rising edge of the clock pulse and the outputs Q and $\bar{Q}$ respond at the next falling edge. Master–slave J–K bistables are also available in which J and K are clocked in on a falling edge and Q and $\bar{Q}$ respond on the next rising edge.

Reference to the table in Fig. 18.8(b) shows that its first three rows are identical to the first three rows of the table for the clocked S–R bistable. However, when $J = K = 1$, $Q_{n+1} = \bar{Q}_n$ and $\overline{Q_{n+1}} = Q_n$; the circuit changes to its complementary state at every clock pulse.

The transition diagram for a J–K bistable is shown in Fig. 18.8(c) assuming that J and K do not change during the period when the clock is active. The symbol for the master–slave J–K bistable is shown in Fig. 18.8(d).

For most applications it is assumed that J and K do not change during the clock pulse. However, the effect of such a change in J or K during a clock pulse is illustrated by Example 18.1

Example 18.1   *Determine the output response of a master–slave J–K bistable, of the form shown in Fig. 18.8(a), for the input waveforms shown in Fig. 18.9(a). Assume that, initially, the output $Q = 0$.*

Fig. 18.9 Waveforms for Example 18.1

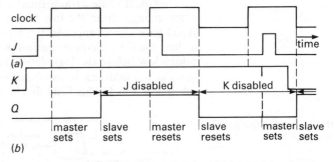

(b)

The output waveform is shown in Fig. 18.9(b). Using subscripts m and s for master and slave, and working from Fig. 18.8(b) and with reference to Fig. 18.9(a):

at the first clock-pulse leading edge: $J = 1$, $K = 1$ and $Q_m = 0$,

∴   master sets at $Q_m = 1$ and $\bar{Q}_m = 0$;

at the first clock-pulse trailing edge: $J_s = 1$, $K_s = 0$,

$\therefore$ slave sets at $Q = 1$ and $\bar{Q} = 0$ (slave follows master).

These outputs are fed back to the master AND gates ensuring that the upper-gate output is 0 (and remaining at 0 until the slave resets) and that the J input is ineffective.

At the second leading edge: $J = 1$, $K = 1$ and $Q_m = 1$ (master still initially set),

$\therefore$ master resets to $Q_m = 0$ and $\bar{Q}_m = 1$.

(The fact that J is ineffective does not alter this operation since $K = 1$ is a sufficient condition for reset.)

At the second trailing edge: $J_s = 0$ and $K_s = 1$,

$\therefore$ slave resets to $Q = 0$ and $\bar{Q} = 1$ (slave follows master).

These outputs are fed back to the master AND gates ensuring that the lower-gate output is 0 (and remaining at 0 until the slave sets) and that the K input is ineffective.

At the next leading edge: $J = 0$ and $K = 1$;

this leaves the master in the reset condition, K being disabled not affecting this result. Now, part way through the clock-pulse period, J goes high and the master sets, again independently of K; however, when, a short time later, J goes low, the fact that K is disabled results in the master remaining set, i.e. $Q_m = 1$ and $\bar{Q}_m = 0$.

Finally, at the third trailing edge: $J_s = 1$ and $K_s = 0$,

$\therefore$ slave sets to $Q = 1$ and $\bar{Q} = 0$, following the master.

Note: even though J was 0 at the start of the third clock pulse, the slave has still set at the end of the pulse. This is because there was a J pulse during the active clock period and this is sufficient to set the master, whose state is subsequently transferred to the slave.

18.2.5 The edge-triggered J–K bistable

Fig. 18.10(a) illustrates a possible arrangement whereby a J–K bistable is implemented using only one clocked S–R bistable. Output oscillations when $J = K = 1$ are prevented by ensuring that the clock input to the S–R bistable becomes inactive before logic-level changes can propagate around the feedback loops. This is achieved by means of the inverter/AND-gate arrangement on the clock input. When the clock changes from the low to the high level the output of the AND gate also changes to the high level. It remains there for a time equal to the propagation delay of the inverter. It will return low before the logic level changes can propagate around the feedback loops. Thus loop oscillation is avoided when $J = K = 1$. This bistable circuit is called an **edge-**

Fig. 18.10 An edge-triggered J–K bistable

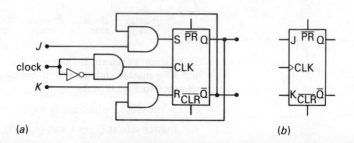

(a)   (b)

triggered *J–K* bistable. The symbol for the circuit is shown in Fig. 18.10(*b*); the triangle on the clock input indicates edge triggering. Falling-edge triggered *J–K* bistables are also available.

18.2.6 The D-type bistable

In the circuit of Fig. 18.11(*a*) the *J* and *K* inputs of the edge triggered bistable are connected through an inverter. Consequently $J = \bar{K}$ and only the second and third rows of the *J–K* bistable table (Fig. 18.8(*b*)) apply. Then, application of a fast rising edge to the clock input causes the state of *D* to be transferred to *Q*, i.e. $Q_{n+1} = D_n$. Thus, a sequential stream of data applied to the *D* input may be 'sampled and held' or **strobed** at any instant by the application of an active edge to the clock input. This circuit is called a *D* or data-type bistable and its symbol is shown in Fig. 18.11(*b*) together with a table in Fig. 18.11(*c*). The data latch (Section 18.2.3) may also be used to strobe data if a short-duration pulse is applied to the ENABLE input.

Fig. 18.11 A *D*-type bistable

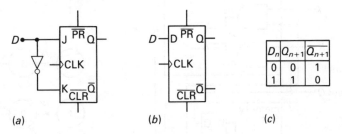

(*a*)   (*b*)   (*c*)

18.3 Introduction to sequential circuits

Fig. 18.12(*a*) illustrates a general schematic form of a sequential circuit. The external input, together with the output from a memory unit, is applied to the input of a combinational unit. The output of the sequential circuit is obtained from the output of the combinational unit. Thus, the sequential-circuit output is a function of both the external input and the memory-unit output which, in turn, depends on its past inputs and, in general, on its initial state.

Fig. 18.12 A general sequential circuit with special cases in (*b*) and (*c*)

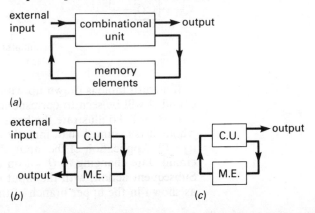

(*a*)

(*b*)   (*c*)

Having introduced the general form of the sequential circuit, it should be noted that there are several, often simpler, variations. Fig. 18.12(*b*) and (*c*) show two examples. In the first, the output is obtained directly from the memory unit without further combinational-logic 'processing'. In the second, there is no external input but the output is subjected to combinational processing after leaving the memory unit.

The bistable devices discussed in Section 18.2 of this chapter may be used as memory devices because data can be clocked into them and retained as long as may be required. The bistable device itself may, in fact, be regarded as an elementary form of sequential circuit and, to illustrate the general principles discussed above, two examples are shown in Figs. 18.13 and 18.14. The first is a *D*-type bistable connected with appropriate combinational logic to form a *J–K*-type.

Fig. 18.13 A *J–K* bistable using a *D*-type bistable as a memory element

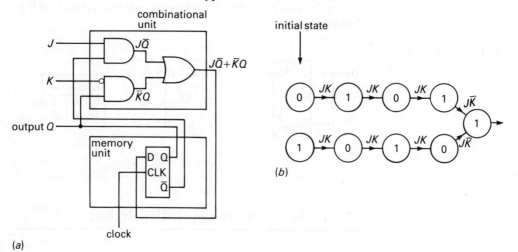

(*a*)

Fig. 18.14 A simple sequential circuit with direct connections from output to input

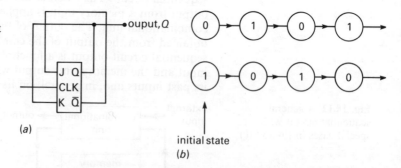

If a truth table is drawn up with $D = J\bar{Q} + \bar{K}Q$, the outputs Q and $\bar{Q}$ will be seen to correspond with the table shown in Fig. 18.8(*b*). To illustrate the behaviour of the circuit as a whole, it is assumed that, initially, the bistable is cleared ($Q = 0$). Application of the input, $J = K = 1$, will result in the circuit state changing to $Q = 1$ on receipt of a clock pulse. Subsequent action, with the input maintained at $J = K = 1$, is as shown in the upper branch of the **state transition diagram**

in Fig. 18.13(*b*). The effect of initially presetting the bistable (i.e. $Q = 1$) results in the lower branch of the transition diagram. In both cases, each state will be seen to depend on the previous state, the circuit inputs and the initial state of the circuit.

The fourth transition (with inputs $J = 1$ and $K = 0$) causes the bistable to set to $Q = 1$ whatever the previous state. The two branches of the diagram merge and the resulting circuit states then depend only on the circuit inputs and the previous states; the initial setting is no longer relevant.

In the second example (Fig. 18.14) the memory unit is a *J–K* bistable and the connection from output to input is direct. There is no external input. The output sequence is shown in Fig. 18.14(*b*) from which it is seen that each state is determined only by the initial bistable condition and the previous circuit state. No input conditions are indicated against the transition lines because there is no external input. The circuit is said to be **autonomous**.

If a single clock source is connected to the clock input of each of a number of bistables forming part of a circuit, then the bistable outputs respond simultaneously, neglecting any variation in propagation delays. Thus, the circuit output is updated in synchronism with the clock; such circuits are known as **synchronous sequential circuits**.

18.4 Synchronous counters

18.4.1 A natural-binary counter

An important application of synchronous sequential circuits is counting pulses. In the example to be described in this section, pulses applied to the clock inputs are counted in a natural binary sequence at the output terminals *A*, *B* and *C*. Up to eight pulses may be counted.

The circuit diagram is shown in Fig. 18.15. The eight possible output states of the three bistables are listed on the left-hand side of a **state-transition table** (Table 18.1) under

Fig. 18.15 A natural-binary counter

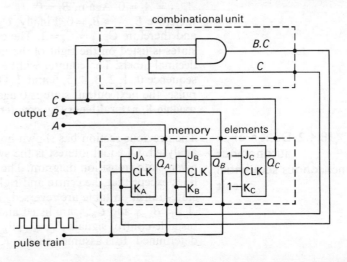

the present-state heading. Decimal labels are indicated against each state. The next output states (which are to be determined) are dependent upon the present output states and the bistable-control inputs J_{A_n}, K_{A_n}, J_{B_n}, K_{B_n}, J_{C_n} and K_{C_n} which, through the combinational unit, are also dependent upon the present-output states. The bistable-control inputs are determined in accordance with the combinational-logic function. Thus, for the first row of the table,

$$J_{A_n} = K_{A_n} = B_n C_n = 0 \quad \text{because } B_n \text{ and } C_n \text{ are 0.}$$

Also,

$$J_{B_n} = K_{B_n} = C_n = 0.$$

Finally,

$$J_{C_n} = K_{C_n} = 1.$$

The complete table is determined in this way and is shown in the centre columns of Table 18.1.

Table 18.1

Present state				Bistable control						Next state			
Label	A_n	B_n	C_n	J_{A_n}	K_{A_n}	J_{B_n}	K_{B_n}	J_{C_n}	K_{C_n}	Label	A_{n+1}	B_{n+1}	C_{n+1}
0	0	0	0	0	0	0	0	1	1	1	0	0	1
1	0	0	1	0	0	1	1	1	1	2	0	1	0
2	0	1	0	0	0	0	0	1	1	3	0	1	1
3	0	1	1	1	1	1	1	1	1	4	1	0	0
4	1	0	0	0	0	0	0	1	1	5	1	0	1
5	1	0	1	0	0	1	1	1	1	6	1	1	0
6	1	1	0	0	0	0	0	1	1	7	1	1	1
7	1	1	1	1	1	1	1	1	1	0	0	0	0

Equipped with the present-output values and the bistable-input control values, the next output state may now be determined from the J–K table in Fig. 18.8(b). For example, in the first row, $A_n = 0$, $J_{A_n} = 0$ and $K_{A_n} = 0$ and therefore $A_{n+1} = A_n = 0$. Again, $B_n = 0$, $J_{B_n} = 0$ and $K_{B_n} = 0$ and therefore $B_{n+1} = B_n = 0$. Finally, $C_n = 0$, $J_{C_n} = 1$ and $K_{C_n} = 1$ and therefore $C_{n+1} = \bar{C}_n = 1$. The complete set of next output states is listed on the right of the table with appropriate decimal labels. The counter will be seen to count through the sequence 0, 1, 2, 3, 4, 5, 6 and 7. On receipt of the eight clock pulse, the next output state is 0 again. The counter is called a **modulo-8, natural-binary up counter.**

18.4.2 Design of an autonomous synchronous sequential circuit

The previous section has shown how a given circuit may be analysed. Of equal interest is the synthesis of a circuit from a given state-transition diagram. The procedure follows similar lines except that the centre and right-hand columns of the state-transition table are reversed. Thus, the required states of A_{n+1}, B_{n+1} and C_{n+1} are listed and, from these, the necessary bistable-control signals J_{A_n}, K_{A_n}, J_{B_n}, K_{B_n}, J_{C_n} and K_{C_n} are determined. It is assumed that J–K bistables are to be used in the design. Finally, these control signals are entered on a Karnaugh map and the minimal form of the combinational unit is thus determined.

In this example, the state sequence is to conform to the transition diagram shown in Fig. 18.16(a). For convenience, the state labels are shown as the decimal equivalent of the binary values. With the largest state value at 7, three bistables are required although only six of the possible eight states are used. The present output states are listed on the left-hand side of the transition table (Fig. 18.16(c)). The two unwanted states, 0 and 5, are included in the list. Working from the state diagram, the centre columns of the table show the required next output states. For example, with the present state of 1, the next state is 4. It is now required to determine the J–K control signals required to produce each individual $n \rightarrow n+1$ transition. In order to do this, it is convenient to use a **bistable-transition table** derived from the transition diagram in Fig. 18.8(c). The transition table is shown in Fig. 18.16(b) and is derived, for the first row for example, by noting that in order to go from a present circuit state of 0 to a next circuit state of 0, the control input J must be 0 but K may be either 1 or 0. Thus, in the table, $J = 0$ and $K = $ X.

Fig. 18.16 Transition diagram and table for the counter design

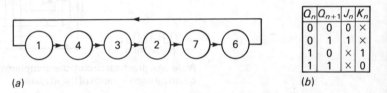

Q_n	Q_{n+1}	J_n	K_n
0	0	0	×
0	1	1	×
1	0	×	1
1	1	×	0

(a)   (b)

present state				next state				bistable control					
label	A_n	B_n	C_n	label	A_{n+1}	B_{n+1}	C_{n+1}	J_{An}	K_{An}	J_{Bn}	K_{Bn}	J_{Cn}	K_{Cn}
0	0	0	0	×	×	×	×	×	×	×	×	×	×
1	0	0	1	4	1	0	0	1	×	0	×	×	1
2	0	1	0	7	1	1	1	1	×	×	0	1	×
3	0	1	1	2	0	1	0	0	×	×	0	×	1
4	1	0	0	3	0	1	1	×	1	1	×	1	×
5	1	0	1	×	×	×	×	×	×	×	×	×	×
6	1	1	0	1	0	0	1	×	1	×	1	1	×
7	1	1	1	6	1	1	0	×	0	×	0	×	1

(c)

The system transition table may now be completed: for the second row, for example, $A_n = 0$ and $A_{n+1} = 1$ for which the required control signals are $J_{A_n} = 1$ and $K_{A_n} = $ X. Also, $B_n = 0$

Fig. 18.17 Karnaugh maps for the counter design

$A_n B_n$

C_n \ 00 01 11 10

	00	01	11	10
0	×	1	×	×
1	1	0	×	×

$J_{An} = \bar{B}_n + \bar{C}_n$

$A_n B_n$

C_n \ 00 01 11 10

	00	01	11	10
0	×	×	×	1
1	0	×	×	×

$J_{Bn} = A_n$

$A_n B_n$

C_n \ 00 01 11 10

	00	01	11	10
0	×	1	1	1
1	×	×	×	×

$J_{Cn} = 1$

$A_n B_n$

C_n \ 00 01 11 10

	00	01	11	10
0	×	×	1	1
1	×	×	0	×

$K_{An} = \bar{C}_n$

$A_n B_n$

C_n \ 00 01 11 10

	00	01	11	10
0	×	0	1	×
1	×	0	0	×

$K_{Bn} = A_n \bar{C}_n$

$A_n B_n$

C_n \ 00 01 11 10

	00	01	11	10
0	×	×	×	×
1	1	1	1	×

$K_{Cn} = 1$

and $B_{n+1} = 0$, requiring control signals, $J_{B_n} = 0$ and $K_{B_n} = X$, etc.

Having completed the system table, the combinational-unit function may be determined by drawing up a Karnaugh map for the six control signals. Each map in Fig. 18.17 is derived from the relevant column in the circuit transition table and shows the bistable-control signal as a function of the present circuit states A_n, B_n and C_n. The minimised expressions are then derived using the methods explained in Section 2.3 of Chapter 17. The required circuit is shown in Fig. 18.18.

Fig. 18.18 Final circuit for the counter design

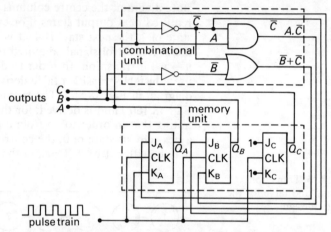

Note: in a practical circuit, the complementary bistable outputs could be used in place of the inverters.

18.4.3 A design using D-type bistables

The same circuit function as in the previous section can be implemented using *D*-type bistables. This is illustrated by the following example.

Example 18.2

Determine the content of the combinational unit required to implement the state-transition diagram in Fig. 18.16(a) using D-type bistables.

From the state table for the *D*-type (Fig. 18.11(c)) the state-transition table becomes as shown in Fig. 18.19(a). Q_{n+1} is independent of Q_n in this case, being determined only by D_n. Thus the bistable-control signal D_n is always a copy of the required next output state. Fig. 18.19(b) shows the required control signals, this table being a copy of the next output-state columns in Fig. 18.16(c).

Fig. 18.19 Tables for Example 18.2

Q_n	Q_{n+1}	D_n
0	0	0
0	1	1
1	0	0
1	1	1

(a)

next-state label	bistable control		
	D_{An}	D_{Bn}	D_{Cn}
×	×	×	×
4	1	0	0
7	1	1	1
2	0	1	0
3	0	1	1
×	×	×	×
1	0	0	1
6	1	1	0

(b)

The Karnaugh maps are shown in Fig. 18.20. It will be seen that the combinational logic function is more complex than when using J–K bistables. In effect, the lesser flexibility of the D-type is compensated by increased complexity in the combinational unit.

Fig. 18.20 Maps for Example 18.2

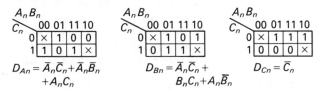

$$D_{An} = \bar{A}_n\bar{C}_n + \bar{A}_n\bar{B}_n + A_nC_n$$

$$D_{Bn} = \bar{A}_n\bar{C}_n + B_nC_n + A_n\bar{B}_n$$

$$D_{Cn} = \bar{C}_n$$

18.4.4 The use of ROM as a combinational feedback element

An alternative method of implementing the combinational section is to use read-only memory (ROM). In this case, the relative complexity of the combinational function when using D-type bistables (Example 18.2) is not a problem and, indeed, the ROM size is actually less than it would be with the J–K type. This is because the D type requires only three ROM output lines (in this example) whereas four would be needed for the J–K type; in general, six lines may be required for three J–K bistables. Furthermore, the ROM program table is simply a copy of the present-state/next-state values, which may be copied directly from the state-transition diagram.

The programming table for the ROM and circuit implementation are shown in Fig. 18.21. In general, the use of a ROM to implement the combinational logic significantly reduces both the chip and pin count of the resulting circuit relative to that using small-scale integrated-circuit logic gates. For example, an 8-bit sequential circuit would require only a single 256×8 ROM integrated-circuit package. Alternatively, integrated circuits are available which combine the combinational and sequential-circuit elements.

Fig. 18.21 A counter design using read-only memory

ROM address			ROM data		
A	B	C	D_A	D_B	C_C
0	0	0	×	×	×
0	0	1	1	0	0
0	1	0	1	1	1
0	1	1	0	1	0
1	0	0	0	1	1
1	0	1	×	×	×
1	1	0	0	0	1
1	1	1	1	1	0

(a)

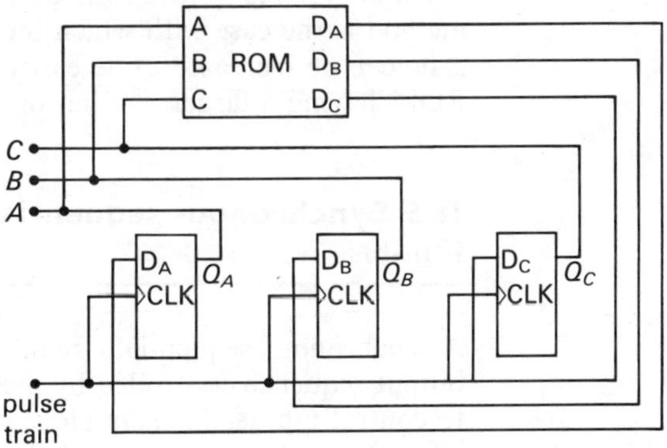

(b)

18.4.5 Use of ROM as combinational output element

The general form of the circuits described in previous sections have followed the form of Fig. 18.12(b) but without the external inputs. An alternative arrangement is shown in Fig. 18.12(c) in which the output is taken through the combinational unit and it is an example of this form which is described in this section.

The circuit is shown in Fig. 18.22. Here the counter generates a natural-binary sequence which becomes the address input to the ROM. The output sequence then appears at the ROM-data pins. In order to implement a circuit having the transition diagram shown in Fig. 18.16(a), the ROM program table would be as shown in Fig. 18.22(b). The ROM data corresponding to the six addresses are the six required output codes in the proper order.

Fig. 18.22 A counter using read-only memory and a natural-binary counter

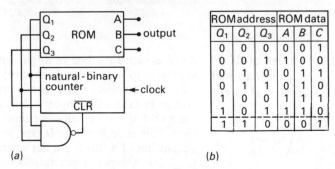

ROM address			ROM data		
Q_1	Q_2	Q_3	A	B	C
0	0	0	0	0	1
0	0	1	1	0	0
0	1	0	0	1	1
0	1	1	0	1	0
1	0	0	1	1	1
1	0	1	1	1	0
1	1	0	0	0	1

(a)   (b)

Because only six codes are to be produced, and hence only six address inputs required, the natural-binary counter must be configured as a modulo-six counter. In this example, this can be done by connecting counter outputs Q_1 and Q_2 to a NAND gate whose output is connected to the CLEAR pin. Thus, generation of a 1 on both lines, as would occur if the counter were generating the binary output states 110 and 111, is inhibited. In effect, the counter follows the 101 output code by 000, as required. The table in Fig. 18.22(b) shows an additional line with address 110 and data 001. This is to ensure that when an output appears momentarily before the counter clears, it is the same as that for the cleared state. Alternatively, a Gray-code counter may be used.

An advantage of using the output-combinational-logic method is the ease with which the number of bits per circuit state can be increased quite easily by, for example, using a ROM having a larger number of data bits per word.

18.5 Synchronous sequential circuits with control inputs

A synchronous sequential circuit may be designed having an output sequence controlled by means of logic signals applied to control inputs. An example is shown in Fig. 18.23(a), where the outputs are Q_1 and Q_2 and the control inputs are A and B. With two output variables, up to four circuit states are possible.

Suppose that the requirement is for the circuit to behave in accordance with the transition diagram shown in Fig. 18.23(b), in which each circle corresponds to an output state Q_1Q_2.

The control input is indicated beside each transition line. For example, at state $Q_1 = Q_2 = 0$ (represented by the top left-hand circle) control inputs $A = 0$ and $B = 0$ will cause the output state to remain unchanged after the next clock pulse. This is indicated by the closed loop carrying the control-signal designation $\bar{A}\bar{B}$. However, if $A = 0$ and $B = 1$ is applied to the control inputs, the output will change to $Q_1 = 0$, $Q_2 = 1$ on the next clock pulse. This is represented by the top right-hand circle, joined to the $Q_1 = 0$, $Q_2 = 0$ circle by the directed line labelled $\bar{A}B$. The whole set of control conditions are given in the transition diagram. Each circle will be seen to have four transition lines joining it and four lines leaving it, corresponding to the four possible values of the control input.

Fig. 18.23 A synchronous circuit with a control input

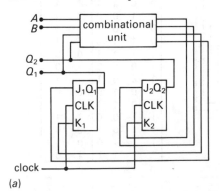

(a)

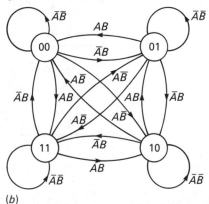

(b)

The first step in designing a synchronous sequential circuit possessing control inputs is to draw the state transition diagram. From this, a transition table may be completed, as shown in Fig. 18.24(a), assuming that J–K bistables are to be used. As with the design of an autonomous circuit, the present value of the bistable inputs J_{1n}, K_{1n}, J_{2n} and K_{2n} necessary to cause the required circuit output-code transitions are determined using the J–K transition table. Finally, the minimised combinational feedback is determined by using a Karnaugh map to plot each of J_{1n}, K_{1n}, J_{2n} and K_{2n} as a

Fig. 18.24 Transition table and map for a synchronous circuit with a control input

present state			control		next state			bistable control			
label	Q_{1n}	Q_{2n}	A_n	B_n	label	$Q_{1(n+1)}$	$Q_{2(n+1)}$	J_{1n}	K_{1n}	J_{2n}	K_{2n}
0	0	0	0	0	0	0	0	0	×	0	0
0	0	0	0	1	1	0	1	0	×	1	×
0	0	0	1	0	2	1	0	1	×	0	×
0	0	0	1	1	3	1	1	1	×	1	×
1	0	1	0	0	1	0	1	0	×	×	×
1	0	1	0	1	2	1	0	1	×	×	0
1	0	1	1	0	3	1	1	1	×	×	1
1	0	1	1	1	0	0	0	0	×	×	0
2	1	0	0	0	2	1	0	×	0	0	1
2	1	0	0	1	3	1	1	×	0	1	×
2	1	0	1	0	0	0	0	×	1	0	×
2	1	0	1	1	1	0	1	×	1	1	×
3	1	1	0	0	3	1	1	×	0	×	0
3	1	1	0	1	0	0	0	×	1	×	1
3	1	1	1	0	1	0	1	×	1	×	0
3	1	1	1	1	2	1	0	×	0	×	1

(a)

Q_1Q_2

AB	00	01	11	10
00	0	0	×	×
01	0	1	×	×
11	1	0	×	×
10	1	1	×	×

(b)

function of Q_{1n}, Q_{2n}, A_n and B_n. The necessary combinational feedback arrangement is $J_1 = K_1 = Q_2\bar{A}B + \bar{Q}_2A + A\bar{B}$ and $J_2 = K_2 = B$. The J_1 map is shown in Fig. 18.24(b) as an example. Alternatively, the circuit can be implemented using a ROM and D-type bistables as shown in Fig. 18.25(a) with the associated ROM program table in Fig. 18.25(b). In this case, the ROM data corresponds with the next-state column in Fig. 18.25(a).

Fig. 18.25 The control input circuit using read-only memory and D-type bistables

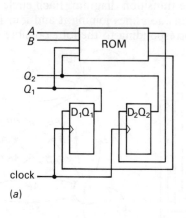

(a)

ROM address				ROM data	
Q_1	Q_2	A	B	D_1	D_2
0	0	0	0	0	0
0	0	0	1	0	1
0	0	1	0	1	0
0	0	1	1	1	1
0	1	0	0	0	1
0	1	0	1	1	0
0	1	1	0	1	1
0	1	1	1	0	0
1	0	0	0	1	0
1	0	0	1	1	1
1	0	1	0	0	0
1	0	1	1	0	1
1	1	0	0	1	1
1	1	0	1	0	0
1	1	1	0	0	1
1	1	1	1	1	0

(b)

18.6 Shift registers

A **shift register** is a particularly important application of a synchronous sequential circuit. It is commonly used as an interface between parallel and serial binary-data transmission systems and to generate and detect serial binary-data patterns. A 3-bit shift register using edge-triggered D-type bistables in which the output from one bistable becomes the input to the next is shown in Fig. 18.26. Thus, a 1 applied at D_C will 'shift' through the system to D_B and thence to D_A as each clock pulse is applied.

Fig. 18.26 A 3-bit shift register

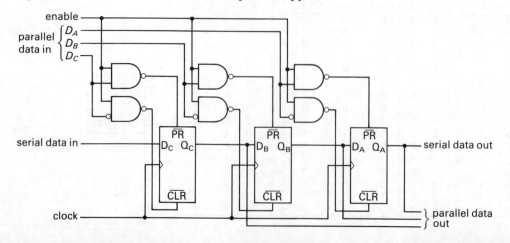

The register shown in Fig. 18.26 may be used as a parallel to serial interface. When the clock is inactive (low) an active-high enable signal will permit the data present at the parallel-data input to be loaded into the shift register through the pins, $\overline{\text{PRESET}}$ and $\overline{\text{CLEAR}}$. For example, parallel data $D_A = 1$, $D_B = 0$ and $D_C = 0$ would result in bistable A presetting and bistables B and C clearing, i.e. $Q_A = 1$ and $Q_B = Q_C = 0$. This result may be justified by considering the function of each NAND gate. Further parallel-data input is disabled by taking the enable input low. Each of three subsequently applied clock pulses will cause the data in the register to move one position toward the right and appear as a 3-bit sequential word on the serial-data-out pin. The serial-output bit rate is determined by the clock frequency.

If a serial-to-parallel interface is required, the enable pin is taken low. The 3-bit serial data word is applied to the serial-data-in pin in synchronism with the clock. After three clock pulses the data word exists at the parallel-data-out pins.

To detect a particular serial-data pattern, a shift register may be used in its serial-to-parallel mode, combinational logic being used to detect the required parallel output. For example, the 2-bit register circuit in Fig. 18.27 will detect the sequences 110 and 101 in a continuous serial-data sequence. To generate a serial-data pattern the shift register is used in its parallel-to-serial mode. The required pattern is loaded in parallel and shifted out in serial form, as explained above.

Fig. 18.27 A shift-register used to detect a pattern of bits

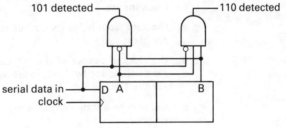

Shift registers are particularly useful for generating **pseudo-random binary sequences** (PRBS), used in the testing of engineering systems. Fig. 18.28(*a*) shows a shift register with exclusive-OR combinational feedback. If each bistable is

Fig. 18.28 A shift-register used to generate a pseudo-random binary sequence

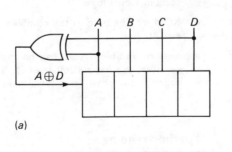

(*a*)

A	B	C	D
1	1	1	1
0	1	1	1
1	0	1	1
0	1	0	1
1	0	1	0
1	1	0	1
0	1	1	0
0	0	1	1
1	0	0	1
0	1	0	0
0	0	1	0
0	0	0	1
1	0	0	0
1	1	0	0
1	1	1	0
1	1	1	1

(*b*)

initially preset, the parallel-output sequence will conform to the sequence table of Fig. 18.28(*b*). Thus, the first row of the table is four 1's. The XOR gate will feed a 0 back to bistable A so that, after the next clock pulse, this will appear at Q_A (and subsequently shift through the register). The input to A after the second clock pulse will be $0 \oplus 1 = 1$, and so on. The serial PRBS may be obtained at any one of the bistable outputs. In this case a 4-bit shift register has generated 15 different parallel output states and a PRBS of 15 bits. In general, an *N*-bit shift register may be used to generate a $(2^N - 1)$-bit PRBS by the application of suitable XOR-logic feedback.

Key points to remember

- a set–reset bistable circuit can be formed by cross coupling two NAND or two NOR gates;

- the behaviour of the bistable circuit depends in general on the existing state of the circuit as well as the input;

- circuits may be constrained to operate in synchronism with a clock input;

- the data latch holds its output at the current input value when disabled;

- the clocked output of the *J–K* bistable circuit is unaffected by $J = K = 0$, is set by $J = 1$, reset by $K = 1$ and toggles when $J = K = 1$;

- the *D*-type bistable copies the input data to the output when clocked;

- a general sequential circuit contains a combinational unit and a memory unit, e.g. AND and OR gates and bistable circuits;

- synchronous sequential circuits can be designed by drawing up a present-state/next-state table and deducing the required combinational logic;

- ROM may be used as the combinational element in a sequential circuit;

- a set of bistable circuits can be configured to behave as a shift register, this has a number of applications in addition to data shifting, one of which is serial/parallel conversion.

Further reading

Floyd, T. L., *Digital Fundamentals*. Bell and Howell (1986).
Mano, M. M., *Digital Design*. Prentice-Hall (1984).
Roth, C. H., *Fundamentals of Logic Design*. West Publishing (1985).

EXERCISES 18

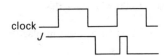

clock

J

Fig. E18.1

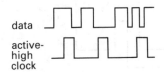

data

active-
high
clock

Fig. E18.2

Fig. E18.3

Fig. E18.4

Fig. E18.5

18.1 Explain the operation of the NOR-gate bistable circuit
(Fig. 18.3) by listing the sequence of events occurring if, with
R and S inputs and Q output initially low, S is taken high and
then returned to the low state, R remaining low throughout.

18.2 The waveforms shown in Fig. E18.1 relate to a master–slave
J–K-bistable circuit. Assuming that K is always high and that
the Q output is initially high, sketch the variation in Q over
the period of the waveform.
Resketch the waveform if the bistable were positive-edge
triggered.

18.3 Distinguish between a D latch and a positive-edge triggered D
bistable by sketching the output waveforms in response to the
input waveform shown in Fig. E18.2.

18.4 (a) The circuit shown in Fig. E18.3 is known as a **ring counter**.
Show that, assuming the Q output of one of the bistables
is 1 and all others are 0 initially, the 1 will circulate
around the ring in response to a clock input.

(b) Changing the connection from Q_0 to $\bar{Q}_0$ on the right-hand
bistable circuit results in the **twisted ring** or **Johnson**
counter. Show that

(i) the waveform at each Q output is at one-sixth of the
clock frequency; and

(ii) starting with output state $Q_2Q_1Q_0 = 000$, successive
clock pulses cause the outputs to cycle through the
sequence 100, 110, 111, 011, 001, 000, and so on.

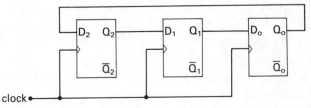

18.5 Fig. E18.4 shows an asynchronous counter known as a **ripple
counter** in which the clock input of a bistable stage is provided
by the data output of the preceding stage. Explain the ripple
action of the counter and show that output *CBA* keeps a
binary count of the number of input pulses assuming negative-
edge triggering.

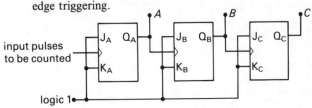

18.6 Analyse the synchronous counter circuit shown in Fig. E18.5.

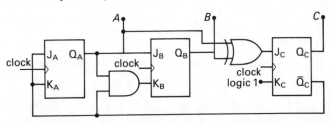

18.7 Design a synchronous sequential counter which counts
      continuously in the sequence of decimal-equivalent values 0, 1,
      2, 3, 7, 6, 5, 4, 0, 1, ... Use *J–K*-bistable circuits.

18.8 Use *D*-type bistable circuits and suitable combinational logic
      to implement a synchronous sequential circuit which
      continuously counts in natural binary sequence from 00 to 11
      when its control input is 1 but resets to 00 whenever the
      control input goes to 0.
      Draw up a programming table for a ROM to be used in place
      of the combinational-logic gates.

18.9 Given that the circuit in Fig. E18.6 is a right-shift register,
      draw a circuit (with suitable logic control) which can shift data
      to the right or to the left.

Fig. E18.6

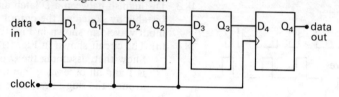

19 Microprocessors

The principal learning objectives of this chapter are to:

		Section
●	discuss the nature of system design using microprocessors;	1
●	explain the relationship between processor and memory;	2.1
●	describe the main features of the architecture of Z80 and M68000 processors;	2.2–2.4
●	explain the function of the processor control unit and program counter;	2.5
●	explain the function of the status (flag) register;	2.7
●	discuss the form of microprocessor instructions by reference to assembly language and machine code;	3.1, 3.2
●	explain the use of addressing modes;	4
●	show how instruction times affect overall program duration;	5
●	explain the operation of data, address and control buses;	6.1, 6.5
●	state techniques for connecting input/ output devices;	7
●	explain the operation and function of a stack;	8
●	discuss the use of subroutines;	9
●	explain the purpose of interrupts.	10

19.1 Introduction

Earlier chapters have discussed systems in which individual logic gates and bistable circuits are interconnected in a particular way to provide a unique logical function. The way in which the circuit elements are combined is determined by the circuit designer and, in this respect, the methods used are those which have been practised by both digital and analogue circuit designers since the inception of electronics. The earliest designs used valves, resistors, capacitors, etc.; as the art progressed the valve was replaced by the transistor and, in time, standard subunits were embodied into single packages and the integrated circuit was born.

Throughout the evolutionary process the essential techniques remained unchanged. The electronic circuit designer was now selecting larger blocks of circuitry and combining these to form a system, but the difference was purely one of scale. More sophisticated systems were possible because of the increased functionality of the individual units, but the essential problem of interconnection remained the same.

The concept of designing with fixed-function units (whether transistors or integrated circuits) may be contrasted with the philosophy of designing with devices such as the microprocessor. In this case the approach is qualitatively different in a fundamental way, as a microprocessor can be made to perform any of a wide range of different functions. The processor is capable of performing a very limited repertoire of arithmetic and logical operations; complex functions are achieved by selecting the sequence in which thousands of these primitive operations are carried out. These operations are usually known as instructions and the sequence of instructions is known as the **program**, and it is for this reason that such devices are said to be programmable. Using this technology it is possible to manufacture a single component which can perform a practically unlimited range of different functions; this combines the advantages of economies of scale in production with flexibility in use.

Since its introduction as a practical electronic component in the early 1970s, the microprocessor has established itself as a powerful and flexible device for the design of complex electronic systems. As a consequence of their widespread use there has been a consistent increase in the proportion of the total circuitry which is available on single devices, and this has resulted in a reduction in the number of devices needed to make up a working system, and has simplified their interconnection. The complexity of processor based systems now lies very largely in the generation of the programs or **software** which enable them to carry out the required functions.

The sequence of instructions is often very long, there being several thousand instructions to be executed to construct the necessary output data. The processor will therefore be slower than an equivalent logic circuit. At the same time it is important that the instructions themselves should be executed very rapidly, so that the time difference is not too serious. For this reason the instructions are stored in memory devices, from which the microprocessor can fetch them at high speed. In effect the architecture of the microprocessor system is identical to that of the stored-program digital computer, and such systems are usually referred to as **microcomputer systems**. As modern microprocessors are comparable with powerful minicomputers of a few years ago, it is increasingly common to drop the prefix micro- and to refer simply to processors.

There are important distinctions between processors belonging to four broad categories, 4-bit, 8-bit, 16-bit and 32-bit. The bulk of the processors currently used in general purpose systems are 8-bit or 16-bit, with the other two having more specialised markets. In practice the distinction between the processors is concerned with capability, the 8-bit being more powerful than the 4-bit, and so on. The distinction is examined in more detail later, but in this chapter the main concern is the operational characteristics of the 8-bit and 16-bit devices, and these will be illustrated by reference to the Zilog Z80, an 8-bit processor, and the Motorola 68000, a 16-bit processor, both of which are widely used. It should be appreciated that these are very sophisticated devices, and it is not possible to provide a comprehensive description in this introductory treatment.

19.2 Operating principles

The essential components of a small processor system are illustrated in Fig. 19.1. In addition to the **central processor unit** (CPU) there is a block of memory, and interface circuits for connection to other equipment. To understand the operation of the processor system it is necessary to appreciate the relationship of the processor and the memory, and the internal structure of the processor. These two aspects are discussed in the following sections.

19.2.1 Relationship of processor and memory

The memory of a processor-based system is a store for numbers. Each memory location can store a single number, usually made up of eight binary digits, or bits, commonly known as a byte. Each location also has an **address**, which uniquely identifies the particular location. The processor is able to carry out either of two operations on the memory. It can read the number stored at any location, and it can write a new number into any location, merely by specifying the address of the location and whether a read operation or a write operation is required. In practice there may also be limitations on the capacity of the processor to write to memory if the physical memory device is read-only memory (see Chapter 17).

The memory can be used to store two distinct types of information, program and data. The instructions that make up the program which controls what the processor does are stored in memory in the form of numerical codes. This makes it possible for the instructions to be read from memory as required. Any data which the program needs to work on can also be stored in memory, and accessed by the processor. In general, data stored in memory will need to be both read and written, whereas the program will only need to be read, and it

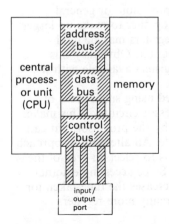

Fig. 19.1 Essential components of a small processor system

is for this reason that most systems have both read-only memory (ROM) and read–write memory (RAM), for program and data respectively.

19.2.2 Internal processor architecture

The internal architecture of a processor is shown in Fig. 19.2. There are four main components, the registers, the arithmetic/logic unit (ALU), the control unit and the bus interfaces. The bus interfaces, being primarily concerned with the interconnection of the processor to other devices, are also discussed in Chapter 20. The **registers** are the working stores used for manipulation and short-term storage of data, and also to keep track of aspects of the internal operation of the processor. These are usually either 8-, 16- or 32-bit stores, and the number of them present will vary from processor to processor. In the architecture of most processors there is a distinction drawn between general-purpose registers and special-purpose registers. The former can be used by the programmer for a wide range of different purposes, while the latter have specific functions allocated to them and they may not be used for any other purpose. While the programmer needs to be concerned with all of the general-purpose registers, and some of the special-purpose registers, there are additional special-purpose registers used for purely internal purposes by the processor. Consideration of these is primarily of interest to the designer of microprocessors, rather than to those who design systems using them, and accordingly they will not be further considered in this book.

Fig. 19.2 Block diagram showing the main processor components

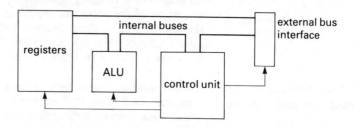

It is common practice to make provision for general-purpose registers to be combined together to make up larger registers. For example, two 8-bit registers may be used together to make a single 16-bit register. Obviously this makes a range of different sized registers available with the minimum amount of circuitry.

Registers are usually implemented using small areas of RAM which form part of the processor circuitry. This makes them available for very fast access by the processor, but can also limit the total number available. An alternative approach used with some processor families is to select an area of the external RAM for use as registers. Since accessing external memory is a slower process this increases the time taken for register operations, but can make many more registers available.

For the purposes of programming, the registers are given identifiable names. These are the names used in assembly language programs (see Section 19.3.1), and are usually

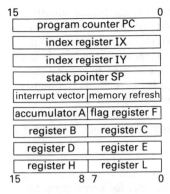

15   0

| program counter PC |
| index register IX |
| index register IY |
| stack pointer SP |

interrupt vector	memory refresh
accumulator A	flag register F
register B	register C
register D	register E
register H	register L

15   8 7   0

Fig. 19.3 A programming model for the Z80 processor (with acknowledgement to Zilog (UK) Ltd.)

presented in a special diagrammatic form known as a **programming model**. This shows the set of registers, and their sizes, and indicates any possible groupings of registers. Fig. 19.3 shows the programming model for the Zilog Z80 processor, and Fig. 19.4 for the Motorola 68000 processor.

Detailed consideration of the register functions is given in the following sections. At this stage it is simply noted that both processors have program-counter and stack-pointer special-purpose registers, the 68000 having two stack pointers. Of the other registers shown, the flag register of the Z80 corresponds to the status byte of the 68000 and contains individual bits which are set or reset as a consequence of the results of certain operations; for example if an arithmetic operation produces a zero result both processors will set the zero flag. The 68000 has no specific register corresponding to the accumulator of the Z80, since any of the eight data registers or the seven address registers can function as accumulators. Similarly there is no need in the 68000 for specific index registers, corresponding to the IX and IY registers in the Z80, as any of the address registers can be used in the same way.

Fig. 19.4 A programming model for the 68000 processor (with acknowledgement to Motorola Inc.)

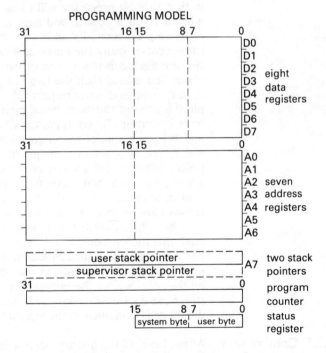

PROGRAMMING MODEL

19.2.3 Arithmetic/logic unit

The manipulation of numbers within the processor is carried out by the **arithmetic/logic unit** (ALU). This can perform a fairly restricted range of arithmetic and logical operations on numbers which will normally be stored in the registers. The arithmetic operations available will always include addition and subtraction, and in the case of 16-bit processors, multiplication and division. The logical functions will include AND, OR and exclusive-OR functions, together with the ability to shift patterns of bits to the left or right, and to test the state of bits. Most of these functions are binary functions, in the sense that there are two inputs to the function, e.g. two numbers to be added or subtracted, etc. Closely associated with the ALU is the concept of an **accumulator**, which is used to hold one of the two input values, and also to receive the result of the function. The earlier, 8-bit processors frequently have only one or two registers that can operate as accumulators, whereas the more modern, 16-bit processors are normally constructed so that any of the general-purpose registers can be used.

19.2.4 Buses and bus interfaces

Communication between the processor and the peripheral units, whether memory devices or devices for connection to outside equipment, is by means of **buses**. There are three buses, known as the **address bus**, the **data bus** and the **control bus**. The address bus is used by the processor to indicate the address of the location with which it wishes to communicate, the data bus is used to actually transfer the data, and the operation is controlled by signals which form part of the control bus. The actual number of bits in each bus is a factor in distinguishing between the various categories of processor, in that an 8-bit processor will usually have an 8-bit data bus, while a 16-bit processor will have a 16-bit data bus.

There are, essentially, only two operations carried out by the processor using the buses; a READ and a WRITE. The two are distinguished by one or two lines in the control bus. If one line is used then the two possible states will be used to indicate read and write respectively. On the 68000 processor pin 9 is used in this way, being high for a read and low for a write operation. By contrast, the Z80 uses separate lines RD and WR, only one of which goes low at any time to indicate which type of operation is required. In a read operation the processor places the address of the target location on the address bus, and then requests the read using the appropriate control lines; after a suitable delay to enable the memory to respond and to place the contents of the read location on the data bus, the data bus is sampled by the processor and the read operation is complete. For a write operation the address bus is controlled in an identical manner, but the processor now controls the data bus; in response to the write request on the control lines the memory samples the data bus and stores the data in the addressed location. The operation of the buses is explained in more detail in Section 19.6.

19.2.5 Control unit

At the heart of the microprocessor is the **control unit** which is responsible for co-ordination of the overall operation of the various component parts of the processor. The stages involved in a single Z80 instruction (see Section 19.3) can be used to illustrate how the various parts of the system are used to perform the required operation. Consider the instruction ADD A, 21 which adds 21 to the contents of the accumulator. The numerically coded machine code (expressed in hexadecimal form) for this instruction is in the form of two consecutive bytes C6H and 21H, of which C6H defines the operation and 21H is the amount to be added. Prior to the start of the execution of the instruction the code for the instruction is stored in memory. The first operation is a read from memory in order to fetch the instruction code C6H. This is then decoded and the control unit recognises the instruction as one which requires that one more byte be fetched from memory. Once this has been read the control unit places it in a temporary register and then instructs the ALU to add it to the contents of the accumulator and place the result in the accumulator again. At the same time the flag bits in the flag register (see Section 19.2.7) are set. In principle, all instructions are executed in this way, with the control unit controlling the bus interfaces to read from and write to memory, the registers to store data and the ALU to perform calculations.

The operation of the control unit is itself controlled by a clock circuit, which produces a signal which changes periodically between logic 0 and logic 1. The simplest type of clock is a square wave but some processors require asymmetric clock waveforms.

The control units of some modern processors use a technique known as **pipelining** to speed up operation. During the time that one instruction is being decoded or the required calculation is being carried out the buses are often inactive. A pipelining processor uses this time to fetch further instructions so that it is looking ahead to instructions that it has not yet reached. When the instruction is reached it is not necessary to read it from memory since the processor has already done so.

The 68020, an advanced version of the 68000, uses an **instruction cache** which provides greater gains in performance than pipelining. Each instruction is stored in a small area of memory within the microprocessor; space is made by deleting instructions that have not been accessed for some time. When an instruction is to be fetched from memory it can frequently be provided from the on-chip cache memory, which saves the time needed to fetch it from main memory. This technique is very effective for running programs containing many small loops, as the code for these loops needs to be read into the processor only once and can then be executed many times. There is further comment on pipelining and caches in Section 8 of Chapter 20.

19.2.6 Program counter

Closely associated with the control unit is the **program counter**, a special-purpose register. As has been noted earlier, the instructions that make up the microprocessor program are stored in memory (usually ROM). Instructions are, with certain exceptions noted below, executed one after the other in the order they are stored in memory; this is made possible by the program counter. At any point in the execution of a program, the program counter holds the memory address of the next instruction to be executed. As the instruction is fetched and decoded the processor can establish how many locations in memory the particular instruction occupies, and the program counter is increased by this amount, so that on completion of the instruction it then contains the address of the next instruction. By constant repetition of this operation the whole program is executed.

All real programs need to deviate from the strict sequential execution of successive instructions in memory. This may arise because certain parts of a program need to be skipped in some circumstances, or because some parts need to be executed repeatedly. The operation of transferring control to an instruction other than that immediately following in memory is known as jumping. A **jump** is an instruction which forms part of the program, and when executed causes a transfer of control to the target of the jump. A jump is achieved very simply by replacing the contents of the program counter with the address of the target instruction. The 68000 has two types of jump, referred to as jumping or branching; the distinction is that a **branch** can only transfer control to a location near to the starting point, whereas the jump operation can reach any part of the address space. The Z80 is similar, except that both types are referred to as jumps; the Z80 equivalent of the branch instruction is known as a Jump Relative.

19.2.7 Status or flag register

Microprocessor programs have frequently to make decisions based on the results of some operations. For example a particular process may be carried out only if a location stores a non-zero value. Special action may be needed if the result of an arithmetic calculation overflows. This type of facility is provided by means of individual bits, called **status bits** or **flags** and collectively referred to as the status register (68000) or the flag register (Z80). Flags are set or reset according to the results of some, but not all, instructions; any instruction which does not set or reset a flag will leave it in its existing condition. For example, the Z80 has a zero flag, which is set to indicate a zero result in an operation; the instruction which adds together the contents of the A and B registers will affect this flag, setting it if the result is zero, resetting it otherwise. However, the instruction to load a number into the A register does not affect the flag at all, so the state of the flag after this load instruction has been executed is determined by the state before the instruction and is quite independent of whether the number loaded was a zero or not. The effect of each instruction on the flags is described in the instruction set summary for the processor.

Flags can be used by instructions which are executed conditionally on the setting of the flag. It is almost invariably true that the conditional instructions are jumps or other transfers of control, so that the type of facility available to the programmer is typically 'jump if the result of a previous operation is zero'.

The flags available on the Z80 processor are as follows:

Sign flag (S)   Set if the result of a two's-complement arithmetic operation is negative.
Zero flag (Z)   Set if the result of an arithmetic or logical operation is zero.

Half-carry flag (H)   Set if there is a carry between bits 3 and 4 in an arithmetic operation.

Parity/overflow flag (P/V)   For LOGICAL operations this is set if the result has odd parity, and for ARITHMETIC operations it is set if there is a two's-complement overflow.

Negative flag (N)   Set whenever a subtraction is performed.

Carry flag (C)   Set when there is a carry out from an addition, or a borrow into a subtraction.

The 68000 has a similar set of flag functions. There are negative, zero, overflow and carry flags as well as an extend flag which serves as an additional carry bit and a number of other bits concerned with the more advanced facilities of the 68000 processor.

19.3 Microprocessor instructions

19.3.1 Mnemonic form

Microprocessor programs are stored in memory in the form of numerical codes which represent the instructions. In discussing the instructions it is more convenient to use **mnemonic form**, in which a short word or an abbreviation is used to provide an easily remembered description of the instruction. Thus the Z80 instruction to add two numbers together is represented by ADD; the 68000 instruction which performs a signed multiply is MULS.

When programs are written in the form of these mnemonics, known as **assembly language**, they are translated into the machine code by a computer program known as an **assembler**. The precise form of the mnemonics is therefore dependent on the particular assembler program being used to translate them. In the following description the forms used for the 68000 are not exactly as proposed by Motorola, but are given in a form which makes them more easily comparable with the Z80 instructions. The reader who wishes actually to write programs should in any case refer to a more detailed text and to the manual for the assembler to be used. There is further discussion of programming languages in Section 20.6.2.

19.3.2 Instruction format

The general form of a microprocessor machine instruction has the following components:

(i) A code which indicates the nature of the operation; this is known as the **operation code**, commonly abbreviated to op-code. Typical operations may be arithmetic or logical functions (such as ADD, OR and MULT), data transfer instructions (MOVE or LOAD), instructions to change the flow of a program (BRANCH, JUMP, CALL and RETURN) and instructions to set the operating mode of the processor (e.g. enable or disable interrupts).

(ii) The addresses of the data (if any) on which the instruction operates, usually known as the instruction operands. In this context the term 'addresses' is used in a general sense to indicate the locations from which the processor fetches its data; such locations may be memory addresses, registers or part of the instruction itself. This point is examined in more detail in Section 19.4.

Instructions can be classified according to the number of data addresses required, and can range from zero-address instructions to three-address instructions. In practice most microprocessors (and most other computer systems) use only zero-, one- and two-address instructions. Each instruction is stored in the memory of the system in the form of a binary number as the **machine code**. For 8-bit processors the machine code will consist of between one and four 8-bit bytes. For 16-bit processors the situation is less clear; some processors have instructions which are coded in single bytes, while for others the instructions are coded in the form of 16-bit words. The 68000 processor adopts this latter approach.

It has already been pointed out that the machine code forms of instructions are binary numbers, and these may be up to 32 bits in length for 8-bit processors or even more for 16-bit processors. It would be difficult and cumbersome to write such instructions out in binary form, and for this reason it is usual practice to use hexadecimal (or occasionally octal) form. As explained in Chapter 16, one hexadecimal digit represents four binary bits, giving a much more compact notation. Note that this is purely a notational convenience, and has nothing to do with the form of the internal storage within the processor and memory.

The following examples may clarify the form of machine code instructions.

The first example is the Z80 instruction ADD A, 6. This is a two-address instruction, specifying the accumulator (register A) and the number 6 as the two operands. The result of the instruction, the sum of the present contents of the accumulator and the number 6, is returned to the accumulator. The machine code for this instruction consists of two bytes. The first is the op-code which defines the instruction, and the second contains the number 6. The two bytes are therefore (in hexadecimal) C6H and 06H.

As an example of a one-address Z80 instruction, consider INC D. This has the effect of adding one to the contents of the register D and returning the result to D. Thus only one address is specified, the D register. The machine code for this is the single byte 0EH (equivalent to 14 decimal). Instructions for the 68000 processor are more complex than the Z80 instructions. A relatively simple example would be the instruction to move data from one register to another. The instruction can specify whether the data is a byte (8 bits), a word (16 bits) or a long word (32 bits); in the case of a word the mnemonic form is MOVE.W D0, D1 which is a two-address instruction, specifying register D_0 as the source of the transfer and D_1 as the destination. The machine code for this instruction is a 16-bit word, 3200H.

Instructions which may affect the status of the microprocessor but do not change any data held in registers or memory are frequently zero-address instructions; for example, the Z80 processor has an enable interrupts instruction EI which allows the processor subsequently to respond to external interrupts.

It should be noted that the machine-code forms of instructions are not normally used in writing programs for microprocessors, either in binary or hexadecimal form. Programs are actually written out using mnemonic forms which are much clearer for a programmer to understand. As explained above, computer programs known as assemblers can read programs written in the form of mnemonics and convert them automatically into machine codes, and it is standard practice to use these for program development. This is also discussed in Chapter 20.

19.4 Addressing modes

The data on which an instruction may operate can be stored in registers or in memory; furthermore there are a number of different ways in which data stored in memory can be located, and therefore ways in which the actual address of the data item is specified. These different forms of **addressing mode** are important in terms of extending the power and flexibility of a processor. Processor manufacturers will often list large numbers of different addressing modes for their products, but in practice there is a relatively small number of fundamentally different addressing modes; most of the large number of modes claimed by manufacturers are merely refinements of the basic types.

Each addressing mode listed below is accompanied by one example drawn from the instruction sets of each of the Z80 and 68000 processors, expressed in both mnemonic form and machine code.

19.4.1 Register addressing

The simplest addressing mode is register addressing, in which the data is held in a register. Many instructions include register addressing for at least one of the operands. The following examples use register addressing for both operands.

(Z80)	CP	B	B8	Compare A and B registers.
(68000)	CMP	D1, D2	B441	Compare D1 and D2 registers.

19.4.2 Immediate addressing

In this mode a number which is referenced by the instruction is included as part of the instruction. This is commonly used for accessing constants.

(Z80)	ADD	A, 2	C6 02	Add 2 to register A.
(68000)	ADD	#2, D0	0640 0002	Add 2 to register D0.

19.4.3 Absolute addressing

In this mode the absolute memory address of the operand is included as part of the instruction.

(Z80)	LD	A, (2A6H)	3A A6 02	Load A from location 2A6H.
(68000)	MOVE	2A6H, D6	3C38 02A6	Load D6 from location 2A6H.

19.4.4 Register indirect addressing

In this mode the absolute memory address of the operand is contained in a register, and the register is specified in the instruction. This type of addressing mode is essential for processing sets of data, and is therefore very extensively used.

(Z80)	LD	E, (HL)	5E	Load register E with the contents of the location whose address is in HL.
(68000)	MOVE	D1, (A0)	3081	Move contents of register D1 to location whose address is in A0.

In the case of the 68000 processor, this type of addressing can be combined with the operations of incrementing or decrementing the address register, A0, in the example given. The increment is performed after the data transfer implied by the MOVE instruction, and is known as a post-increment; the decrement is performed before, and is therefore known as pre-decrement. The mnemonic form for each of these is:

Post-increment   MOVE   D1, (A0)+
Pre-decrement   MOVE   D1, −(A0)

19.4.5 Indexed register indirect addressing

In this mode the absolute memory address of the operand is made up by adding the contents of a register with a fixed value, usually known as an offset. It is therefore an extension of the register indirect mode. For the Z80 processor this mode is available only in conjunction with special index registers, IX and IY, whereas for the 68000 any of the registers can be used.

(Z80)	LD	A, (IX + 18)	DD 7E 12	Load register A from the location 18 bytes beyond the address in register IX.
(68000)	MOVE	18(A0), D1	3228 0012	Move contents of the location 18 bytes beyond the address in A0 into register D1.

Again, the 68000 includes post-increment and pre-decrement operations if required.

19.4.6 Program counter relative addressing

A special case of indexed register indirect addressing arises when the register is the program counter. This mode is not much used in the Z80 processor, occurring only in the relative jump instruction JR , in which the target of a jump is specified as a number of bytes either forward or backward from the jump instruction. The 68000 can use this addressing mode more extensively as it can be used to specify the address of an operand for any of the standard instructions. This mode of addressing is used primarily in order to write **position independent code** (PIC) which can execute unchanged at any point in the memory of the processor; since the addresses of all memory locations are specified relative to the program counter, moving the program to a different set of memory locations moves the data addresses together with the program.

(Z80)	JR	14	18 0E	Jump to location 14 bytes after the address of the next instruction.
(68000)	BRA	860	6000 035C	Jump (branch) 860 bytes forward.

19.5 Instruction timing

Microprocessor instructions take a finite length of time to execute. For simple instructions, such as the load, add, subtract, logical-AND, etc. which make up the instruction set of the Z80, the bulk of the time is taken up with memory accessing; the instructions which take the longest are those which require the greatest number of memory accesses. Thus the instruction to move data from one 8-bit register to another requires only one memory access (to fetch the instruction itself from memory) followed by a relatively simple operation within the processor; this is therefore a very quick instruction, requiring only 4 clock cycles. With a 4 MHz clock this corresponds to an execution time of 1 microsecond. At the other end of the scale for the Z80 are instructions such as loading the 16-bit HL register pair using absolute addressing, LD HL, (02C6H). This instruction requires a total of five memory accesses; one to read the operation code, two to fetch the actual address from the two bytes following the op-code, and two to fetch the 16-bit number from the specified location. This takes a total of four times as long as the simple 8-bit register load.

The greater complexity and power of the 68000 results in a substantial amount of processing being carried out within the processor for some instructions, so that memory accessing is no longer invariably the main factor in determining the instruction execution time. For operations analogous to those which the Z80 can perform, the instructions are quick, but arithmetic operations, such as the multiply and divide, are performed by iterative processes within the processor, and can take considerable lengths of time. Furthermore, the time may not be constant, but can depend on the actual numbers involved in the calculation. The slowest instruction on the 68000 is the signed divide, taking up to 158 clock cycles.

The execution times for individual instructions have some important implications for the speed with which microprocessors operate. For a program of any significance, it is usual to find that a minimum of 100 instructions may be needed to perform the processing which will generate an output from an input. Since each instruction takes a minimum of 1 microsecond to execute, it is reasonable to expect that this conversion process could not be completed in less than 200 microseconds, and that the time required will frequently be much more. This can impose quite severe restrictions on what can be achieved by a microprocessor operating in real-time applications.

19.6 Buses and bus control

19.6.1 Description of buses

The buses form the means of communication between the processor on one hand and the memory and input/output devices on the other. Input/output (I/O) devices are those through which the processor communicates, as described in Section 19.7. There are three distinct buses, address, data and control. The address and data buses are grouped connections used to communicate binary numbers as digital-electronic signals, while the control bus is a collection of control lines used for a variety of purposes, of which one of the most important is the control of the other two buses. Each is considered in more detail in the following subsections.

19.6.2 Data bus

The data bus is a bi-directional bus, and is used to transfer data between the processor and the memory and I/O devices. In a read operation, the data is transferred to the processor, and in a write operation it is transferred from the processor. The Z80 processor has an 8-bit data bus, so that one transfer operation can move an 8-bit number. Larger numbers require more than one operation to effect the transfer.

The 68000 processor, in common with most of the 16-bit processors, has a 16-bit data bus. It is, however, common to find special versions of 16-bit processors which have 8-bit data buses; the 68008 is such a device. This can provide access to all of the processing power of the 16-bit devices with appreciably simpler external circuitry at the price of some loss of speed in bus operations.

19.6.3 Address bus

The address bus is a uni-directional bus, controlled by the processor and used by it to specify a memory (or I/O) address to be accessed by the processor. It consists of a fixed number of lines, each of which carries a single bit. The size of the address bus therefore fixes the largest size of memory that the processor can access. With n address lines the address is an n-bit number; there are a maximum number of 2^n distinguishable n-bit numbers, and this fixes the maximum number of memory locations. For the majority of modern computer systems, each memory location can store one 8-bit number, or byte.

The majority of 8-bit processors have a 16-bit address bus,

giving a maximum addressing capacity of 64K ($= 65\,536$). The 16-bit processors use a range of different configurations, but in general they have larger addressing capabilities than the 8-bit processors. The 68000 effectively has a 24-bit address bus, giving a maximum addressing capability of 16M ($= 16\,777\,216$). The use of a 16-bit data bus introduces additional complexity. The 16-bit data bus can move data simultaneously from two 8-bit bytes; very frequently this method of operation will be required, but it will also sometimes be necessary to access a single byte. This is achieved by ensuring that all bytes with even addresses are connected to the high half of the data bus, and all bytes with odd addresses are connected to the low half. There are two lines which form part of the control bus, upper data strobe (UDS) and lower data strobe (LDS). For any valid address either one or both of these lines must be asserted, giving access to either half of the 16-bit word or to both together. The effect of this is that there is no requirement for the least significant bit A_0 of the address bus since this function is effectively performed by the combination of LDS and UDS. Examination of the pin labels of the 68000 processor will confirm that A_0 is in fact not present. A configuration of this type is normal for 16-bit processors which have 16-bit data buses, although the precise method of implementation varies.

19.6.4 Control bus

The control bus consists of a collection of digital signal paths, some of which are inputs to the processor and some outputs. Collectively they provide the overall control of the way in which the processor interacts with its surrounding devices. The actual lines which make up the control bus will depend on the type of processor to a greater extent than do the address and data buses which are common to all processors. It is possible to group the control bus lines together in broad categories.

A clock input is found on all processors, and provides the main timing of all activity, as detailed in Section 19.5. The clock is usually a constant-frequency square wave input, occasionally with an uneven mark/space ratio. Typical clock frequencies for modern processors are in the range 1 MHz to 10 MHz, and for any processor the manufacturer will quote a maximum clock frequency at which the processor will operate. Both the Z80 and the 68000 are produced in a range of models with different maximum clock frequencies, as shown in Table 19.1. Use of the faster clock rates can clearly increase the amount of processing that can be completed in a given time, but it can also increase the complexity and cost of the circuitry surrounding the microprocessor. For this reason it is frequently easier to use the slower processors for applications in which very high speed is not important.

The bus-control group of lines is used to control the operation of the address and data buses. The functional requirements of this set of control lines can most easily be explained by reference to the two main modes of memory access, synchronous and asynchronous.

Synchronous-mode bus accesses are based on the

Table 19.1. *Microprocessor clock frequency upper limits*

Z80	2.5 MHz
Z80A	4.0 MHz
Z80B	6.0 MHz
Z80H	8.0 MHz
MC68000L4	4.0 MHz
MC68000L6	6.0 MHz
MC68000L8	8.0 MHz
MC68000L10	10.0 MHz

assumption that the memory will respond within a finite and fixed time interval following the initialisation of a data transfer. The processor must initiate the transfer, by indicating that (*a*) there is a valid memory address on the address bus, (*b*) the type of memory transfer required, read or write. For a synchronous read operation the processor must then wait long enough to ensure that the memory device will have placed the contents of the addressed location on the data bus before it can read the number from the bus. Similarly for a write operation it must leave the address and data on the buses for long enough to ensure that the memory device will have copied the data into the addressed location. The 68000 processor can achieve these simple operations using two control lines, address strobe (AS) and read/write (R/W). The Z80 is more complex, because there is an additional requirement to indicate whether the processor is fetching an instruction or data. The lines involved are memory request (MREQ), read (READ), write (WRITE) and memory cycle 1 (M1). One only of READ and WRITE is asserted at any time.†

Synchronous transfers are often inconvenient, because there may be a mixture of different devices in a complex system which can respond in different timescales; it would be inefficient to base all memory accesses on the speed of the slowest peripherals. Both processors can operate in an asynchronous mode, in which the addressed peripheral signals the completion of the transfer, thus allowing the processor to proceed. The Z80 control bus includes a wait input (WAIT); when this is low the processor will enter a waiting mode. In synchronous systems the WAIT line is held in the high state, so that the processor never waits. In asynchronous systems the WAIT line is taken low at the start of the memory access, and the addressed device returns a signal on completion which is used to raise the WAIT line. The equivalent function on the 68000 is provided by the data transfer acknowledge input (DTACK). The processor will wait until DTACK goes low before proceeding.

In practice synchronous transfers are usually used only in small systems, and therefore only with 8-bit processors.

A further group of lines within the control bus is concerned with arbitration between processors in systems which have more than one processor. Since only one processor may control the address and data buses at one time, **multiprocessor systems** must have facilities for deciding which processor is to be in control at any one time. This is done by providing an input to each processor by which the processor is requested to give up control of the buses, and an output by which it signals that it has done so. For the Z80 processor these lines are bus request (BUSRQ) and bus acknowledge

---

† Terms such as MREQ, READ, WRITE, etc. are used here only to describe the function of the control lines. This does not preclude the possibility that the processor may operate with active-low signals; manufacturers' literature provides full details and also see Chapter 20.

(BUSAK), while for the 68000 there is a three-line system comprising bus request (BR), bus grant (BG) and bus grant acknowledge (BGACK).

A final group of control bus lines is concerned with the handling of interrupts; these lines are examined in more detail in Section 19.10.

19.6.5 Multiplexed address and data bus

By consideration of the sequence of operations involved in accessing a peripheral device it can be seen that the address-access procedure (using the address bus) must be completed before any data transfer can take place. This has been used in the design of some processors to reduce the number of pins on the device by using the same set for both address and data. This scheme, known as address/data-bus multiplexing, requires an external latch for the address, and an additional control line to indicate whether the pins are being used for data or for an address; when an address is present it is latched to drive an external address bus, and thereafter the pins can be used as a data bus. This technique is not used by either the Z80 or the 68000, but is found in the Intel 8085 and NSC 800 8-bit processors, and in several 16-bit processors.

19.7 Input and output

There are always two distinct types of peripheral device that a processor must be able to access; these are memory devices and input/output devices. These latter are vital in any practical application since they are the means by which a processor communicates with the outside world; inputs are used to receive instructions, make measurements, etc. and the results are displayed, or external devices are controlled by outputs. Frequently the simplest way of connecting an I/O device to a processor is to connect it as if it were memory. This involves ensuring that there is an address which results in the I/O device being enabled; an input operation is therefore achieved by a memory read from this address, and an output operation is achieved by a memory write. This technique is known as memory mapping (see Section 2.3 in Chapter 20), and is the only method of I/O available on the 68000 processor. Clearly a consequence of this method is that some of the total address space must be used for I/O, with a consequent reduction in the space available for memory; this is not a problem with the 68000 because of the enormous address space available.

The Z80 can have memory mapped I/O, but a separate address space is available and is commonly used instead. This involves control lines, MREQ and IORQ, which are used to request either memory access or I/O access respectively. When MREQ is asserted an address is set using all 16 bits of the address bus; when IORQ is asserted an address is set using only the lowest 8 bits, so that only 256 separate I/O addresses, or ports, are available.† Associated with this technique, known as I/O mapping, are a special set of instructions which are used to perform input and output operations. Section 2.3 in Chapter 20 gives further details.

The connection of input and output devices to microprocessors is a complex topic and is covered in more detail in Chapter 20.

19.8 The stack

An important concept commonly used by microprocessors is that of a **stack**. This is a store for numbers which is organised as a last-in first-out queue. Associated with the stack are the operations of PUSH to place a number onto the stack and POP to remove a number from the stack. These can be used to provide a simple and convenient store for numbers without the need for the programmer to be concerned about their precise location. Most commonly, modern processors place their stacks in an area of the normal memory, although there are processors which have small areas of RAM actually on the processor chip in order to provide the stack. The use of external memory implies that the processor must keep track of the address of the memory being used in this way, and this is done by a register known as the **stack pointer**. In terms of the stack pointer the PUSH operation can be carried out by the following stages:

(1) Decrement the stack pointer.
(2) Store the number to be PUSHed at the location whose address is now in the stack pointer.

The corresponding POP operation is carried out by the sequence:

(1) Recover the number stored in the location addressed by the stack pointer.
(2) Increment the stack pointer.

In practice the Z80 always uses the stack to store 16-bit numbers, and so each of the above sequences is performed twice. On the 68000 the stack is used for holding 32-bit numbers, and again the above sequence is performed twice, since the data bus transfers 16 bits at a time; obviously the stack pointer must be decremented or incremented by 2 in this case.

Stack type operations can be conveniently performed on the 68000 using any of the address registers, together with the facility for post-incrementing or pre-decrementing the register. The instruction MOVE D0, −(A3) has therefore the effect of pushing the contents of register D0 onto a stack maintained by register A3. The equivalent pop operation is MOVE (A3)+, D0. In general, stacks used for temporary

---

† See footnote on page 462 (Section 19.6.4).

data storage are set up in this way, reserving the stack maintained by the stack pointer register for subroutine calls, as detailed in Section 19.9 below.

Prior to using a stack, whether addressed by the stack pointer or another register, the register must be set up to point to the appropriate area. The stack must, of course, be within the RAM area of the system, and since the usual convention is that stacks grow downwards, i.e. towards lower addresses, the most convenient place to locate a stack is often at the top of the available RAM. Instructions are available for loading this initial value into the stack pointer.

19.9 Subroutines

It is impossible to construct programs of significant size without breaking the program down into separate functional blocks called **subroutines**. The overall execution of the program then includes 'calls' to these subroutines; a call implies that control is passed over to the first instruction in the subroutine, the subroutine is executed, and that control then returns back to the instruction which follows the call in the original program. This has three overwhelming advantages. Firstly there may be simple functions, such as summing a set of numbers, which must be done repeatedly, and can therefore be provided in a subroutine which is called more than once; secondly, the structure of the program is easier to understand and describe, since the overall operation is decomposed, not into primitive machine instructions, but into subroutines which may each perform relatively sophisticated functions; and thirdly, subroutines which perform useful functions can be written, thoroughly tested, and then made available for use in any number of programs. Equally important is the ability to use the advantages of subroutine based structure within subroutines themselves; this gives rise to the concept of nested subroutines, where one subroutine may call several other subroutines, any of which may also call further subroutines and so on.

The essential features of a subroutine call facility are that it must provide a means of transferring control from the calling program to the start of the subroutine, and thereafter back from the end of the subroutine to the next instruction of the calling program. The transfer to the subroutine is essentially a jump or branch, but the necessity of a subsequent return implies that there must also be some mechanism for storing the address of the next instruction; most processors, including the Z80 and the 68000 use the stack for this purpose. Thus there are specific instructions which provide all the necessary facilities. For the Z80 processor this is the CALL instruction. For the 68000 it is possible to perform either a branch to subroutine (BSR) or a jump to subroutine (JSR); the distinction is the same as that for the branch or jump instructions (Section 19.2.6).

19.10 Interrupts

Many practical microprocessor circuits, particularly those used in real-time applications, use **interrupts**. An interrupt is a mechanism which allows the processor to suspend normal operations and to execute a particular piece of program in response to a request from outside the processor. This is often necessary when events need a quick response, and it is impractical for the response to be delayed while the processor gets round to looking at the relevant input. An interrupt must be originated by an event which is outside the direct control of the processor. In most cases the source of the interrupt is actually a device which is physically separate from the processor, although advanced processors such as the 68000 may use interrupts as a mechanism to respond to abnormal conditions arising within the processor. There are therefore in the control bus a number of lines concerned with the handling of interrupts. These must include an interrupt-request input line, which is used by the interrupting device to indicate that it wishes to interrupt the processor, and some means for the processor to acknowledge the interrupt. On receipt of the interrupt the processor suspends operation of the program, storing sufficient information to be able to return to the same point later, and then executes a piece of program, known as an **interrupt service routine**, to deal with the interrupt. Interrupt schemes can become quite complicated when there are many possible sources of interrupts in a system, and the processor must be able to determine which interrupt service routine to use; the detailed implementation of such systems is very processor-dependent, and the interested reader should consult the hardware manuals for the particular processor.

There is further discussion of interrupts in Section 4.2 of Chapter 20.

Key points to remember

- system design with microprocessors means that a given set of hardware may be used in a variety of different ways by changing the software;

- a microcomputing system consists, essentially, of a processing unit, memory (to hold program and data) and interface ports, all interconnected by address, data and control buses;

- the processing unit contains registers, an arithmetic-and-logic unit and a control unit together with internal buses and their interfaces;

- the register set normally includes data registers (or accumulators), a program counter and a status (or flag) register;

- microprocessor instructions comprise an operation code and, normally, one or more operands or their address in memory or register;

- the exact form of the operand or its address depends on the addressing mode employed; the control unit must recognise different modes as it recognises different operation codes;

- most processors use a stack as a temporary store into which data and addresses are placed for easy access later in the program;

- although a very simple program could contain a sequential list of instructions (automatically processed in sequence by the program counter), microprocessor instruction sets provide for non-sequential operations through jump, branch and jump-to-subroutine instructions;

- microprocessors are designed to respond to external interruptions via the interface ports.

Further reading

Bacon, J., *The Motorola 68000: An Introduction to Processor Memory and Interfacing*. Prentice-Hall (1986).

Hayes, J. P., *Digital Systems Design and Microprocessors*. McGraw-Hill (1984).

Hutty, R., *Z80 Assembly Language Programming*. Macmillan (1981).

Manufacturers' data (Motorola and Zilog).

Acknowledgements

Reference to Motorola products is made with the permission of the Motorola Company.

Reference to Zilog products is made with permission of Zilog. Zilog Inc., formed in 1975, is a wholly owned subsidiary of Exxon Corporation. The company's Components Division manufactures a complete line of microprocessors and peripheral support circuits, including the Z80® 8 bit CPU, the Z8000® 16-bit CPU, the Z8 8 bit single chip microcomputer, and the Z80000™ 32-bit CPU.

<u>20</u> Microprocessor systems

The principal learning objectives of this chapter are to:

		Section
•	describe the principal components of a microprocessor system;	1
•	state the function of system buses;	2.1
•	explain the principles of address decoding relating them to memory maps;	2.2
•	show how I/O-mapping and memory-mapping systems may be implemented;	2.3
•	explain the implications of bus timing arrangements;	3.1, 3.2
•	discuss methods by which input/output devices may be handled by the processor, including interrupts and polling;	4.1, 4.2
•	explain direct memory access;	4.3
•	relate the principles of input/output transfer to an actual I/O device (Z80 PIO);	5.1
•	describe a counter/timer circuit (Z80 CTC);	5.2
•	discuss aspects of serial-data transmission and explain the operation of a typical UART and a serial I/O device (Z80 SIO);	5.3
•	discuss general aspects of software production with particular reference to structured programming;	6.1
•	distinguish between different high-level languages;	6.2
•	describe aspects of system development and testing;	7
•	discuss future directions in microprocessor technology.	8

20.1 Introduction

The microprocessor itself is the central control component of a microprocessor system, or microcomputer, which also contains a number of other components. This chapter examines these components, and the way in which they and the microprocessor are interconnected to form a working system.

Fig. 20.1 illustrates a small processor system and is virtually a copy of Fig. 19.1. In Chapter 19 the diagram supported a brief discussion on the relationship between processor and memory followed by a detailed description of the processor architecture. In this chapter, it supports a detailed consideration of the processor-to-memory connection as well as input/output. This is followed (in Section 20.5) by details on input/output circuits. The chapter concludes with sections on programming, on system development and testing and on future directions.

Fig. 20.1 Essential components of a small processor system

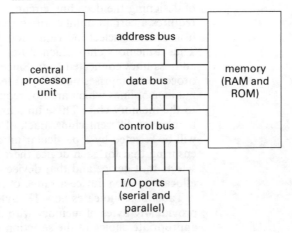

20.2 System interconnection

20.2.1 Microprocessor buses

Section 6 of Chapter 19 describes how the interconnection of the various components of a microprocessor system is achieved by three buses. These are the data bus which moves data between components, the address bus which is used by the processor to specify the source or destination of data transferred, and the control bus which is used to control and synchronise the data transfers and for other special purposes.

The data bus consists of eight lines for an 8-bit processor, and normally 16 lines for a 16-bit processor; some 16-bit processors (e.g. Intel 8088) make do with an 8-bit data bus. These lines are used to transfer data between the processor on one hand and either memories or peripherals on the other. The transfer may go either way, depending on whether the processor wishes to read data or write data, and therefore the data bus is said to be bi-directional.

The address bus consists of at least 16 lines, some 16-bit processors having as many as 24 lines, and is used to specify the location (or address) to or from which the processor wishes to transfer data. The address may specify either memory or peripherals.

The control bus consists of a number of individual logic lines which control the operation of the other buses. The number and designation of these lines depend very much on the processor, but there will in general be lines specifying the direction of data transfer (read and write), a clock line, possibly lines to indicate when the address or data buses are stable and several others. As mentioned, a more detailed consideration of buses is given in Section 19.6.

20.2.2 Address decoding and memory maps

The total memory of a microprocessor system is usually made up of a number of semiconductor memory chips, together with additional logic circuitry to select the device providing memory within a particular address range. The basic problem of designing the decoding circuitry is simple. Each device requires a certain number of address lines to be connected to it in order to select individual locations within the device. Thus a memory chip which stores 1K bytes must have 10 address lines connected to it. Since the address bus of the processor comprises normally at least 16 lines, this leaves a number of lines which are not required for direct connection to the memory chip. These lines are used to select between a number of different chips. Each of a set of memory devices will be selected by a particular unique pattern of bits; by ensuring that for each device there is one pattern which selects that device and that device only, it is possible to allocate to each device a range of addresses.

Table 20.1 indicates how 1K byte devices can be used to provide 4K bytes of memory with address ranges as shown by appropriate choice of the selection logic pattern. Obviously with six selection bits it is possible to generate 64 different selection patterns (and therefore to address 64K bytes of memory). It is rare to find microprocessor systems which actually need that much memory, and therefore it is possible to leave some of the device selection bits unused. Some of the

Table 20.1

Chip no.	Selection pattern (bits A_{15}–A_{10})		
1	000000	START	000000 0000000000 = 0000H
		END	000000 1111111111 = 03FFH
2	000001	START	000001 0000000000 = 0400H
		END	000001 1111111111 = 07FFH
3	000100	START	000100 0000000000 = 1000H
		END	000100 1111111111 = 13FFH
4	001011	START	001011 0000000000 = 2C00H
		END	001011 1111111111 = 2FFFH

address lines are then not actually connected to anything, and therefore the decoding of the devices cannot depend on the state of these address lines. The effect is to reduce the usable address space. For example, if A_{15} has no effect on selection then addresses 000H–7FFFH will have exactly the same effect as addresses 8000H–FFFFH. The usable address space has therefore been halved. For small systems this is not a drawback and it has the advantage of simplifying the selection logic circuitry.

The detailed mechanism of device selection is based on a chip-enable (chip-select) input with which each memory device is provided (see Section 17.4.2). The logic signal at this input must be active if the chip is to respond. Some devices are provided with more than one chip enable, and if so all of them must be satisfied if the chip is to be selected. It is normal for a chip enable to be an active-low input.

There are two broadly recognisable ways of generating the chip-enable inputs, known as **linear addressing** and **decoded addressing**. Linear addressing is most readily applicable to very simple systems and consists of using address lines directly as chip-enable inputs. As an example a system using four 2K byte memory devices requires 11 lines on each device, leaving five available for selection. Since active-low chip enables are required the selection logic patterns in Table 20.2 can be used. The problem with this approach is that an address such as 1010100000000000 ($=$ A800H) will simultaneously select two chips (2 and 4). Bit A_{15} is not connected, and so the selection between devices does not depend on this. Thus there are two immediate consequences of using linear addressing, address ambiguities and reduction of usable address space. Careful programming can avoid the use of addresses which are ambiguous, and as has been pointed out before, the reduction of address space is rarely a problem. Linear addressing can readily be made more flexible by the additional use of a few simple logic gates and inverters. However, powerful MSI integrated circuits are available that permit the various selection logic patterns to be decoded to generate the required chip-enable inputs. These address decoders can easily eliminate the problems of address space reduction and of address ambiguity and so are very commonly used.

Table 20.2

Chip no.	Chip enable			
1	A_{11}	START	11110 00000000000	$=$ F000H
		END	11110 11111111111	$=$ F7FFH
2	A_{12}	START	11101 00000000000	$=$ E800H
		END	11101 11111111111	$=$ EFFFH
3	A_{13}	START	11011 00000000000	$=$ D800H
		END	11011 11111111111	$=$ DFFFH
4	A_{14}	START	10111 00000000000	$=$ B800H
		END	10111 11111111111	$=$ BFFFH

Table 20.3

E	A_0	A_1	O_1	O_2	O_3	O_4
H	X	X	H	H	H	H
L	L	L	L	H	H	H
L	H	L	H	L	H	H
L	L	H	H	H	L	H
L	H	H	H	H	H	L

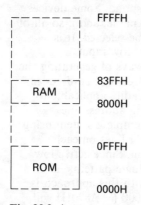

Fig. 20.2 A memory map showing RAM and ROM locations

20.2.3 Single and dual address space systems

The operation of a decoder can be illustrated by considering the truth table of a particular decoder, the 74LS139 device, which is a one-from-four decoder. The inputs to this device are a chip enable, which must be low for the chip to function, and two address inputs (A_0 and A_1). With two address inputs four different binary-number combinations can be applied to the input, and for each of these there is a single output line; each line corresponds to one input binary pattern, and when selected goes low, with all the other lines remaining high. Thus the output lines can be used as chip-enable controls for four memory devices and there will be no ambiguous addresses, and no loss of memory space. The truth table is shown in Table 20.3. In fact the 74LS139 device contains two such decoders on one chip. Another very important decoder is the 74LS138, a one-from-eight decoder. This has three address inputs, and eight outputs, and again only one of the eight outputs is driven low for each of the eight possible input patterns on the three address inputs. This device has also three independent enable inputs. Decoders are also discussed in Chapter 17, the type 74LS138 being shown in Fig. 17.17(a).

Once the circuit design has been completed, it is possible to construct a **memory map**, showing the memory addresses of the various devices in the system. This will normally show the address range to be used for accessing the RAM and ROM, and the individual addresses of any I/O devices. For example, if the address decoders are connected in order to provide 4K of ROM in the address range 0000H–0FFFH, and 1K of RAM in the address range 8000H–83FFH, the memory map will appear as shown in Fig. 20.2. Note that there are large gaps in this memory map where blocks of addresses are unused.

A microprocessor system may have more than one address space. This is analogous to the distinction between two office blocks. Each contains rooms numbered from 1 upwards, but the two rooms numbered 1 are distinguished by being in different blocks. A processor can have different blocks of addresses, containing the same addresses but distinguished by being in different blocks, or address spaces. The most common multiple address space system is a dual address space, where in addition to the memory address space described above there is an address space for input and output devices. This address space will often be smaller than the memory address space, as it would be most unusual to require 64K I/O devices; for example, in the Intel 8085 and Zilog Z80 processors the I/O space contains only 256 addresses. When I/O devices are connected in the I/O address space they are said to be **I/O mapped**, in contrast with **memory mapped** devices.

Obviously the hardware must have a mechanism for distinguishing between the two address spaces, and this can be done by either one or two lines in the control bus. To distinguish between two address spaces only one line is strictly necessary as this can have two states. In practice two are often used, each one going low to enable one or other address space.

The Motorola 8-bit 6800 series and related processors do not have an I/O address space, and therefore all I/O devices have to be connected as memory devices. This avoids the complexity of the additional line or lines needed to distinguish the address spaces but makes it impossible to provide the full 64K of memory. Since only very few systems require 64K of memory this is not a significant disadvantage. One major advantage of single address space systems is that memory access instructions are used to access I/O devices; processors that have dual address spaces are usually provided with more powerful and flexible instructions for accessing memory than for accessing I/O addresses. For small systems it is therefore often better to use memory mapping only, even if I/O mapping is available.

The methods outlined above for the generation of a memory map for a system apply equally well to the

Fig. 20.3 (*a*) I/O mapping (*b*) memory mapping

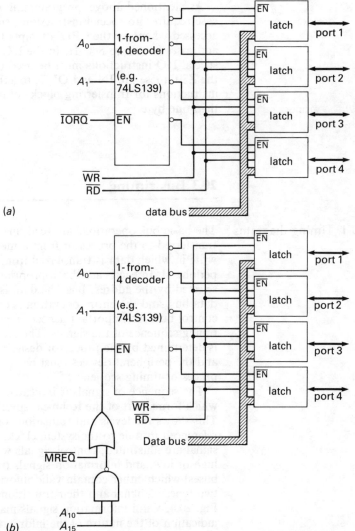

generation of an I/O map for systems which use a dual address space.

The essential difference between I/O mapping and memory mapping is illustrated in Fig. 20.3. In (a), four addresses are generated for the four ports shown. If the processor uses 8-bit I/O addresses (e.g. Z80) then the addresses will be 00H to 03H; for a processor such as the Intel 8086 which has 16-bit I/O addresses the addresses are of course the same, but would normally be written 0000H to 0003H. The ports can only be read from or written to as I/O ports since the one-from-four decoder is only enabled when the $\overline{\text{IORQ}}$ line is active. One of the $\overline{\text{WR}}$ and $\overline{\text{RD}}$ lines is also activated to indicate the direction of the data transfer.

In Fig. 20.3(b), the decoder inputs are changed. In this case the one-from-four decoder is enabled by the $\overline{\text{MREQ}}$ line which is gated with other address lines as shown to place the ports in the address locations 8400H to 8403H, i.e. just above the RAM in Fig. 20.2.

As mentioned above, programming in the memory mapped case requires no special instructions, since the ports will be accessed whenever the CPU attempts to access memory at addresses 8400H to 8403H. In the I/O mapped case the special I/O instructions must be used to access the ports. For the Z80, these are IN and OUT, together with more complex instructions for transferring blocks of data made up of more than one byte.

20.3 Bus timing

20.3.1 Timing diagrams

The basic bus operations are read, in which data is transferred to the processor from a memory or I/O device, or write in which data is transferred from the processor to the peripheral. In each case the appropriate peripheral location is selected by the address bus, the data is transferred on the data bus, and the entire operation is controlled by lines in the control bus. An important aspect of each transfer cycle is the timing sequence of the signals. The sequence for each transfer is determined by the processor design: the external circuitry and the peripheral devices must be chosen to match the processor timing sequence.

The sequence of signals is indicated in a **timing diagram**, which forms part of the technical specification of a processor. This shows the levels and transitions of the relevant signals, referenced in time to the system clock. Two different types of signal are illustrated; control signals which must be either high or low, and information signals (the address and data buses) which either contain valid information or do not. The two types of signal and their transitions are illustrated in Fig. 20.4. Valid information signals may also have some indication of the nature of the information carried.

Fig. 20.4 Control and information signals

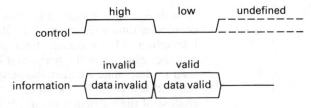

The essential characteristic of a read cycle is that the signals which select the particular device are stable for a period before the processor actually reads the data from the data bus, and that this period is long enough for the peripheral device to respond. Fig. 20.5 illustrates the timing sequence for a **memory read cycle** of the Z80 processor; the memory read condition is signalled by the $\overline{\text{MREQ}}$ and $\overline{\text{RD}}$ lines of the control bus. All events are synchronised to the clock and the length of time that the peripheral device has to respond is therefore about 2 clock cycles (500 ns with a 4 MHz clock) or less if there is a significant amount of gating, buffering or decoding circuitry to introduce additional delays.

Fig. 20.5 Timing diagrams for memory-read and memory-write cycles in a Z80 processor (with acknowledgement to Zilog Ltd.)

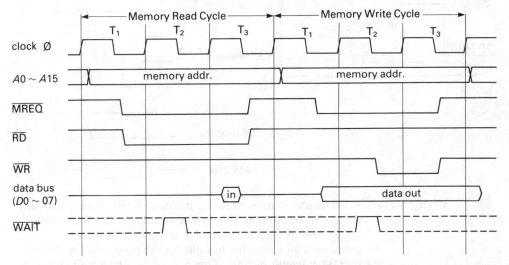

A **memory write cycle** for the Z80 processor has the timing sequence also shown in Fig. 20.5, the control signals in this case being those on the $\overline{\text{MREQ}}$ and $\overline{\text{WR}}$ lines. In this case the data bus is controlled by the processor, and must be stable for long enough to permit the peripheral to read it. The peripheral response time that this requires is similar to that for a read cycle.

These two examples contain the principal characteristics of all read and write cycles respectively, although there are variations between processors, and a processor will normally have a range of different read and write cycles. For example the Z80 processor differentiates between memory-read cycles which fetch instructions and those that fetch data; it also has separate cycles for memory and I/O transfers. In the case of I/O transfers the $\overline{\text{IORQ}}$ line takes over the role of the $\overline{\text{MREQ}}$ line in the above diagrams as well as differences in the detailed timing.

In designing a system, it is often necessary to construct composite timing diagrams (Fig. 20.6). These show the interaction of the processor timings, any additional circuitry and the response of the peripheral being addressed, and are used to determine whether the peripheral will be able to respond fast enough to keep up with the processor in the context of the particular circuit. It is important that in the construction of these diagrams the 'worst case' times must always be taken to allow for tolerance differences between components. A system can only be regarded as adequate if there is a reasonable margin of safety in all timings because they will tend to drift slightly with temperature changes. This could lead to a system which functioned satisfactorily during routine test but which failed when operated for lengthy periods.

Fig. 20.6 A processor with other circuitry and the composite timing diagram

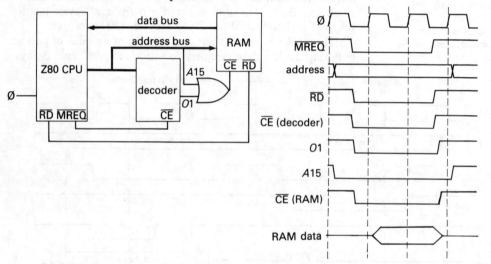

20.3.2 Wait states

It is not uncommon to find a mixture of fast devices and slow devices in one system. When this occurs, the slow devices, which need longer to respond when addressed by the processor, must be able to hold up the processor for the necessary length of time. This is done by using **wait states**. A processor input line is used to signal that the peripheral has not yet completed its part of the data transfer and that the processor must wait, with the address and data lines unchanged. The wait signal may be derived in one of two ways. If it is known that the device will take a fixed period of time to respond, then whenever the address for that device is decoded, a monostable of the appropriate time constant is triggered to provide the delay. Fast devices in the same system do not trigger the monostable, and so there is no corresponding delay. An alternative approach, usually applicable to more sophisticated peripherals is to have an output line on the device which indicates that the process is complete; this is particularly valuable when the required delay is not predictable. For example, a microprocessor system can incorporate a special arithmetic processor to speed up calculations, but the length of time that is required will depend on the complexity of the calculation being performed.

20.4 Input/output techniques

There are two distinct types of data which may form inputs to a microprocessor system; these are either continuous or discrete data. Continuous data would include measurement of temperature, monitoring the state of circuits in an intruder alarm system and other similar applications. Discrete data would include keyboard input, characters arriving on a serial line from another computer, real-time clock pulses and so on. The distinction is often less clear than may at first sight appear; for example, temperature input data is converted from analogue to digital form by an A/D converter, which must repeatedly perform the conversion, and in so doing converts the continuous data into discrete data. From the point of view of the processor itself, all data must necessarily be discrete, though this is not necessarily the case when viewed from the standpoint of the whole system.

There are two ways in which a processor system communicates with devices external to the device. These are by **polling** and by **interrupts**. The fundamental difference can be illustrated by an analogy with the way in which a clerk might work. Many tasks can be carried out within a sequence of operations; for example, if one of the clerk's duties is filing, then after filing one paper he will check his in-tray to see if any further papers have arrived. This is equivalent to the concept of polling; inputs are handled within the normal sequence of events. By contrast, when the phone rings, the clerk will stop whatever he is doing, and answer it, probably after making a quick note of what he was doing so that he can return to it after dealing with the phone call. This is equivalent to an interrupt. The input is dealt with when it arises, rather than within a pre-determined sequence of operations. In designing microprocessor systems a decision that has frequently to be made is between the use of polling and interrupts for handling inputs from a given source. The decision is often complex, but can often come down to how much of a delay is permissible in dealing with the input. Returning to the analogy of the clerk, a paper can usually wait for some time before it needs to be filed whereas a telephone call needs prompt attention. Allowing for a timescale of microseconds rather than minutes the same consideration applies in microprocessor systems; interrupts will usually receive more prompt attention than polled inputs. The two techniques will now be examined in more detail.

20.4.1 Polling

Polling is the most convenient method of input in that some of the complexities of interrupts are avoided and the sequence of events in the system are determined solely by the program. It is therefore to be preferred unless it is not fast enough, or there is a requirement to synchronise with external events. A good example of a device for which polling is convenient is a keyboard. The best typists cannot type characters faster than about 10 characters per second, and this leaves about 100 ms between key depressions. Relative to the frequency with which

processors execute instructions, key depressions occur very
rarely; the software need only look at the state of the
keyboard at about 50 ms intervals to ensure that no key
depressions are missed. Between dealing with key depressions
the processor can do many other things. Input devices which
are to be polled can be connected either as memory devices
with specific memory addresses, or in systems with separate
I/O addressing as I/O devices with specific I/O addresses.
For continuous data inputs, the input will almost invariably
be connected to a single addressable location. To establish the
current value of the input it is only necessary to read the
location, the resulting value being the sampled value at the
time of the read. For discrete data there is a different problem
to be solved. There must be some indication to the system
that there is data to be read. This can be detected in one of
two ways. In the first there are two addressable locations, one
of which is used to present status information; for example a
1 in a particular position can indicate that data is available.
The sequence of operations needed to poll such a device is:

(1) read the status register;
(2) if data is available, then read the data value.

Special-purpose I/O devices designed for use with
microprocessors very commonly support this type of
operation. The second approach is to use a single location
only, but where there is a particular input value which
indicates that no data is available. Thus a keyboard could be
connected to a processor in such a way that eight zeros are
returned if no key has been depressed. The software is then
responsible for taking action only if a key has been pressed.

20.4.2 Interrupts

Interrupts are intrinsically more complex than polled inputs.
However, as discussed above, they are an essential part of
many systems, because they provide a mechanism for dealing
with external events as they occur, giving both fast reaction
and synchronisation with the outside world. The essence of
an interrupt is that the device having data to send (said to
require service) is permitted to signal the processor, which
then stops whatever it is doing and executes a piece of
software, known as an **interrupt service routine**, to deal with
the data.

Processors have the capacity to ignore interrupts by
disabling the relevant input. When interrupts are disabled
there is no reaction to an interrupt, and this situation will
remain until interrupts are enabled under software control.
Without this facility it would be difficult to ensure that
unpredictable circumstances did not arise due to interrupt
conditions being raised while the processor was not able to
react properly. When a processor is reset, interrupts are
disabled.

Interrupts are handled differently within different systems,
but the essential problems are:

(i) How does the processor recognise which device is
interrupting?

(ii) How does the processor respond to the interrupt? and
(iii) What happens if more than one device requires interrupt service at the same time.

Considering initially a system with a single source of interrupts, in which the situation is relatively simple. Microprocessors are provided with input pins which are used to signal interrupts. Frequently there is only one such pin, and a single interrupting device is connected directly to this one pin. When the input is activated the processor must carry out the following actions.

(1) Complete the machine instruction currently being executed. This is essential as the state of the machine is not fully determined by the registers alone during the execution of an instruction.
(2) Disable further interrupts.
(3) Store the current value of the program counter, which is the address of the instruction to be executed immediately after the interrupt has been processed.
(4) Store all working registers that may be used in servicing the interrupt.
(5) Jump to the start of the interrupt service routine.

At the end of the interrupt service routine the processor must restore all registers to their original values, and restore the program counter to the address of the instruction that was to have been executed next in the sequence if the interrupt had not occurred. At some point in the interrupt service routine, interrupts must be re-enabled. The appropriate point for this will depend on the system.

It is clear that some aspects of the interrupt response sequence may be implemented in either hardware or software. The saving and restoring of working registers is an example, as this can be done automatically by the hardware or as a part of the interrupt service routine. Processors differ in the way they do this. For example, the Zilog Z80 assumes it will be provided in the software.

In more complex systems there may be more than one source of interrupts. There are a range of techniques used for recognition of the source of interrupts. The simplest approach from the user's point of view is to provide the microprocessor with more than one interrupt-request input, but this can be difficult within the confines of the standard 40-pin integrated-circuit package. The Intel 8085 does have several interrupt-request inputs, and this offers substantial simplification for small systems. More typically only one or two interrupt-request pins are available, and the methods by which the processor can identify the source of the interrupt become correspondingly more complicated. There are two different ways of solving the problem. The first and more common is to design the microprocessor so that it is able to acknowledge the interrupt request, and in response to this interrupt-acknowledge signal the interrupting device sends some identifying information. The alternative is for the processor to examine status registers in each of the devices which could have raised the interrupt, to find out which one actually has done so. This latter scheme is known as **interrupt polling**. The appropriate form of implementation will depend on the particular system. Different processors offer different facilities and often the families of support chips designed for use with a particular processor will include an interrupt controller. All the interrupting devices are connected to this, enabling it to supply the processor with identification information so that the correct interrupt service routine can be executed.

The other main problem is that of deciding what to do when several devices request an interrupt at the same time; a more realistic coincidence arises when a second device attempts to interrupt during the execution of an interrupt service routine. In these situations it is necessary to allocate priorities to the devices, so that a low priority device can be interrupted by a higher priority device, but not vice versa. Again, the techniques for prioritising interrupts vary between families of processors; the allocation of priorities is also handled by interrupt-controller chips.

20.4.3 Direct memory access

A technique sometimes used when data has to be fed in to or out of a microprocessor system either rapidly, or in large quantities, is **direct memory access** (DMA). A special device, known as a DMA controller, takes over control of the buses and uses them to transfer bytes successively from one location within the memory or I/O address space or a set of such locations to another. A typical application is reading from or writing to a magnetic disk. As the disk rotates the data needs to be transferred to or from memory at high speed; the DMA controller is given instructions by the processor defining the source and destination of the data, and the number of bytes to be transferred, and is then given control of the buses in order to effect the transfer. On completion, control is returned to the processor.

In some specialist applications, the processor must not be permitted to cease operation during the DMA transfer, and the DMA controller is allowed to perform transfers using the buses during that period of each processor instruction cycle in which the processor is decoding the instruction. This technique is known as **cycle-stealing**, and is only rarely used with microprocessors, being more common in larger computer systems.

Zilog manufacture a DMA controller, a 40-pin programmable chip providing both data transfer and search facilities. For transfers, the device takes control of the data and address buses and data is transferred from source to destination byte by byte. For searches, the source data is read and compared with a match byte (or part thereof) held in an internal register. Both operations may be combined to give a simultaneous search and transfer facility.

The controller may be programmed to deal with data either one byte at a time (with buses released after each byte), in bursts (whose duration is controlled by a signal to the DMA ready line) or continuously, in which case the transfer/search process continues until the program block is completed. In the latter case a RDY line signal causes the transfer to pause, resuming when RDY is not active.

20.5 Parallel and serial input/output devices

20.5.1 Parallel input/output devices

Whenever a system is to be connected to digital signals, either as part of a digital logic circuit or more directly to switches, indicators or relays, a **parallel I/O** device is used. In input mode this allows the processor to examine the state (logic 0 or logic 1) of a range of input lines, usually grouped in sets of 8. Typical applications are sensing the output of an analogue-to-digital converter (ADC), sensing position-indicating microswitches and detecting depressions of keys on a keyboard. In output mode, it allows the processor to send an output to a digital-to-analogue converter (DAC), or to control relays (through relay driver circuits to give the required current amplification) or to control LED indicators.

With many modern devices the parallel I/O function is combined with other functions; for example it is possible to buy ADC's which combine the conversion process with the necessary circuitry to permit immediate connection to a microprocessor.

Parallel I/O devices are most widely used for interfacing microprocessors to the outside world, since they act as the immediate interface for a wide variety of other types of device. The Zilog Parallel I/O controller (PIO) is an example whose block diagram is shown in Fig. 20.7. In common with other large scale integrated-circuit chips described in this chapter, the circuit is very complex and the operational description has been simplified in order to provide only a general impression of the behaviour of the device.

Fig. 20.7 Input and output connections to the Zilog Z80 PIO circuit

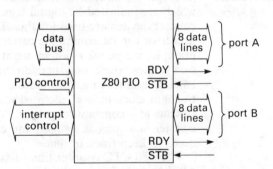

It is a 40-pin programmable component offering, on the peripheral side, two 8-bit ports each with a pair of handshake-control lines and, on the CPU side, a data-bus connection, control lines and a set of interrupt-control lines.

Port A can be programmed (via the control register) to operate in one of four modes, 0, 1, 2 and 3. Port B can operate in modes 0, 1 and 3. Mode 0 is a data-output mode in which the CPU can, at any time, write data to the port registers after which the handshake control line RDY is set. On accepting the data, the peripheral device signals its acceptance with an active STB signal which generates a CPU interrupt, if enabled.

Mode 1 is the corresponding data-input mode. Data from the peripheral device is latched into the port registers with an active $\overline{STB}$ signal which also resets RDY and, if enabled, sends an interrupt request to the CPU. When the latched data is read by the CPU, the RDY line is set. Mode 2 uses port A only, (port B must be made inoperative) together with both sets of handshake control lines. It is a bidirectional mode similar to either mode 0 or mode 1 but with the A handshake control lines used for output control and the B lines used for input control.

In mode 3 individual port lines can be programmed as inputs or outputs, the handshake control lines not being used. The CPU can write to those bits designated as outputs and read those lines designated as inputs. The mode is intended for control use rather than data transfer, there being, in effect, 16 control lines available, any one of which can be made an input or an output line. An interrupt is generated if one or all of the inputs change as specified by an interrupt control word.

The PIO is designed to operate with the CPU in what is known as interrupt mode 2 in which the peripheral effectively specifies the starting address of the interrupt service routine (see Section 20.4.2) via the data bus. This information is known as a **vector**. The operating mode of the PIO is then selected by writing a mode-selector word and the interrupt vector into it from the CPU; additionally, for mode 3 only, three more words are then required to completely specify the operating conditions.

20.5.2 Counter/timer devices

Microprocessor systems frequently need to count events which are indicated by digital logic signals. Special purpose counter devices are used for this. These count events and the processor can determine the current count at any time. For example, a processor system might control the admission of cars to a car park, and therefore have to count cars both entering and leaving. Another use of **counter/timer circuits** is to count clock pulses generated within microprocessor systems at a constant frequency. When this is done the counter functions as a timer, and can be used if the system needs to keep track of time.

The Z80 CTC counter/timer has four channels each of which may be independently programmed with a control word and a time-constant word in the range 1–256. In the counter mode the channel counts down from the time-constant value (and in synchronism with the system clock) in response to input pulses until the count is zero. In the timer mode, timing pulses are generated at multiples of the system-clock period, the multiple being selected by the control word.

Three of the four channels each have an output line indicating zero count (counter mode) or timeout (timer mode). However, any of the four channels may drive the CTC's interrupt-request line at zero count or timeout. Following a CPU response to the request, the CTC places a vector on the data bus.

20.5.3 Serial input/output devices

A more specific form of I/O device in common use is the **serial I/O** device. Serial data transfer occurs when a sequence of bits are transferred on a single line one after the other; this contrasts with parallel data transfer where the bits are all transferred simultaneously on a group of lines, one to each line. Serial data transmission is a common mode of data transmission between microcomputers and similar equipment over substantial distances (typically greater than 1–2 m).

Serial I/O has two forms, synchronous and asynchronous. In **synchronous transmission** a clock line is used to synchronise the transmitter and the receiver and one bit of data is transmitted in each clock pulse period. This is used to achieve high speed transmission of large amounts of data. **Asynchronous transmission** has no synchronising clock; when data is sent the receiver expects the bits to be separated by a prearranged time interval and will only interpret them correctly if this is the case. Because small differences between the timing in the receiver and in the transmitter are inevitable only a few bits can be transferred at a time. Usually each transfer on an asynchronous serial line totals no more than 12 bits. Where high speed is not required the simplicity of eliminating the clock makes asynchronous transmission the best choice.

There are many situations in which the continuous transmission of fully synchronised data is not practical. An example is the data generated by a manually operated keyboard; even if the typing speed appears to be quite fast and regular it will not be synchronous with the system clock, and typing at a rate of 70 five-character words per minute only generates $70 \times 5 \times 8/60 = 47$ bit/s, assuming 8 bit/s per character. In this case asynchronous transmission is used. Each small group of bits (usually 8) is assigned its own synchronising information. Fig. 20.8 shows such a group, the data being the seven bits required to represent ASCII coded S

Fig. 20.8 ASCII coded S with start, parity and stop bits added

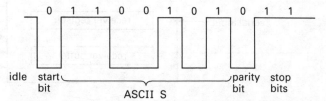

Note: the least significant bit of the ASCII character is transmitted first and the parity bit is the most significant bit of the 8-bit word

together with an even parity bit (see Chapter 16). The receiver is alerted by the falling edge of the start bit after which it senses the signal level at the centre of the following 10 time slots, the whole sequence occupying 11 time slots. With at least 11 bits per character, a transmission rate of 200 bit/s would mean that about 18 characters per second would be transmitted.

The rate of data transfer is normally specified in terms of the signalling speed whose unit is the **baud**. The **baud rate** as it is often called is the number of signalling states per second which, in the binary system, is equal to the bit rate per second, each bit representing one signalling state. In a four-amplitude level system (which permits two bits to be represented by each signalling state) the baud rate would be half the bit rate. In an eight-level (three bits per signalling state) the baud rate would be one-third of the bit rate. Because many systems are binary, baud rate and bit rate are often taken to be the same but this is not generally true.

In order to transmit serial data, a **universal asynchronous receiver transmitter** or **UART** may be used as a parallel–serial and serial–parallel converter. The process of parallel/serial conversion is not intrinsically complex but the typical 40-pin integrated-circuit UART provides more comprehensive facilities. An outline block diagram is shown in Fig. 20.9. Serial input and output pins provide asynchronous formats of the form described, with control over the word length (5, 6, 7 or 8 bits), odd or even parity and choice of the number of stop bits. The 13 transmitter-section pins comprise a serial-output pin, eight parallel-input pins, a buffer-load instruction pin, a transmit-clock pin and two flag pins, one to signify

Fig. 20.9 Outline block diagram of a UART circuit

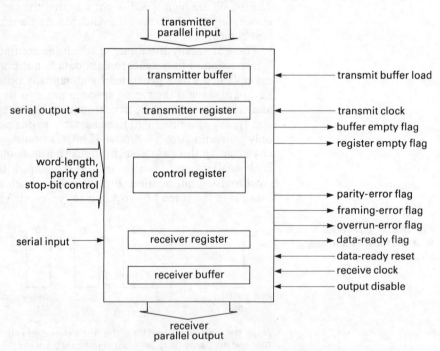

that the buffer is empty and the other that the main register is empty, i.e. all bits have been passed to the serial output.

The 16 receiver-section pins comprise the serial-input pin, eight parallel-output pins, an output disable pin, a data-ready reset pin and the receive-clock pin together with four flag pins; these indicate that the data is ready (waiting in receiver buffer) and the existence of parity, framing and overrun errors. A framing error indicates invalid or absent stop bits and an overrun error indicates that the data-ready flag is not reset before the present data was transferred to the receiver buffer.

In addition to the UART there are a number of serial-data circuits manufactured especially for use with particular microprocessors, of which the Zilog SIO is an example. Fig. 20.10 shows a general arrangement of the SIO chip, a 40-pin programmable device. The CPU side has data bus, control and interrupt line connections similar in principle to

Fig. 20.10 Input and output connections to the Zilog Z80 SIO circuit

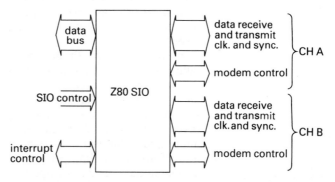

the PIO but differing in detail; it may be operated in polling or in interrupt modes (see Section 20.4).

On the peripheral side the SIO has two independent duplex (two-way transmission) serial-data channels (synchronous or asynchronous) with modem control. Each channel comprises receive and transmit-data lines RXD and TXD, clock-input lines $\overline{\text{RXC}}$ and $\overline{\text{TXC}}$ (data rates may be programmed at $1, \frac{1}{16}$, $\frac{1}{32}$ or $\frac{1}{64}$ of the clock frequency), a synchronising signal $\overline{\text{SYNC}}$ and a wait/ready signal, $\overline{\text{W/RDY}}$, programmed either as a ready line for a DMA controller or as a wait line to synchronise the CPU to the SIO data. The modem control lines provide request-to-send, $\overline{\text{RTS}}$, and data-terminal-ready, $\overline{\text{DTR}}$, lines from the SIO to the peripheral device together with clear-to-send, $\overline{\text{CTS}}$, and data-carrier-detect, $\overline{\text{DCD}}$, lines from the peripheral to the SIO.

20.6 Programming

The generation of the software which converts a microprocessor circuit into a working system is frequently the most important and most costly part of the overall system development. It is therefore necessary to apply proper design and test procedures to programming as much as to hardware design. The aims of good programming differ in some respects from the aims of good hardware design because of the special nature of software. Software has effectively no associated production costs once the development is completed, so there is no way in which design of software can be directed to minimisation of product cost. Similarly software does not wear out, or fail in the sense that hardware does. It is worth examining the characteristics of 'good' software in order to determine the way in which software design should be organised.

Ultimately the aim of any design procedure is the minimisation of cost. For a microprocessor system design this implies minimisation of cost throughout the life of the system, which therefore includes the initial development and debugging, maintenance debugging as faults are discovered during service, and modifications needed to keep systems up to date or to enhance the facilities available. Cost minimisation is achieved by pursuing the aims of productivity, reliability and maintainability. As might be expected, each of these has a particular significance in the context of software. **Productivity** is concerned with the number of man-hours of programming effort needed to produce the software; it is therefore the productivity of the design process. **Reliability** is a measure of the confidence that the software performs the functions for which it was designed. Even a relatively simple microprocessor program may contain more than a thousand instructions. These are executed at a rate of up to a million per second, with continuously changing data. Thus, the operation of software is intrinsically highly complex and errors can emerge long after the software has been tested and approved, as a result of a particularly rare coincidence of circumstances. **Maintainability** is concerned with the ease with which programmers can make changes to the program, and therefore depends heavily on the program being easy to read and understand. Maintainability may also depend on the **portability** of software, the extent to which it can be moved from one processor to another, since this protects the software investment against the obsolescence of the original processor.

20.6.1 Structured programming

The fundamental discipline of program design is frequently referred to as **structured programming**. Though this term has occasionally been used to describe a very restrictive approach to programming, and has therefore attracted some criticism, it more properly refers to a set of techniques for building into the software an overall structure which can be readily grasped and understood. Working within such a framework will greatly assist the development of software, and the extra work needed in the initial planning stages of the development is amply repaid in terms of the increased productivity achieved throughout the rest of the project. A full description of structured programming techniques is outside the scope of this book, but it is worth considering in outline the methods involved.

Outside the realm of software, the design of complex systems follows well established methods which illustrate the basic ideas of structured programming; the overall functioning of a system is understood by breaking it down into smaller units, each with a clearly defined task, and with clearly defined interfaces with other units. The overall function is visible in terms of the concerted operation of these units. Each unit can be similarly broken down in order that its functioning can become clear until the design is implemented in basic components. The idea can be illustrated by considering the design of a car. At the first level the overall vehicle can be understood as made up of engine, gearbox, differential, bodywork, suspension, steering and electrical system. Any one of these can be then further analysed, the engine for example including the cylinder block, cylinder head, carburettors and manifolds, etc. Any description of a car which is to be comprehensible must proceed in this way, rather than by explaining the operation and interactions of all the individual components. Software systems are very much the same, except that software is so easy to generate that there is an ever present temptation to ignore the work needed to formulate the overall structure; when this occurs, the long term result is invariably higher cost and a less reliable system.

The formal name given to this type of decomposition of a complex software system into smaller subsystems is **modular programming**, and the individual units are referred to as modules. Modules are easily implemented using subroutines or procedures and good programming makes extensive use of these. An important part of software design is the choice of how to partition the system into modules; as a rule of thumb, it should be possible to describe the function of a module in a single simple sentence. Since each module carries out some calculation or processing, it will in general have some input variables, and some output variables. The set of input variables consists of all those values which are used in the calculation and therefore affect the outcome. The set of output variables consists of all those variables whose value is affected by the calculation. Variables may be in both sets. It is important that these variables are clearly identified both to assist with the formulation of the modules, and also to enable the individual modules to be tested in isolation. If the purpose of the module is clearly understood, it is usually relatively simple to write a test program which generates values for the input variables and then uses the module to generate the output variables. In this way the overall program is built up of individually tested modules, in much the same way as a car manufacturer will test the engine, the gearbox and the differential individually before assembling them into the complete vehicle. An important part of the way in which an overall software system is broken down into modules is known as **top-down design**. This reflects the natural hierarchy of functional descriptions. At the top 'level' the description of the software covers the overall purpose of the system. At the next level down this is broken down into a small number of subsystems, and then each of these is further broken down until the individual modules become simple enough to be written out as program code without further analysis.

Fig. 20.11 illustrates this idea in a simple data logging system.

Fig. 20.11 Top-down design

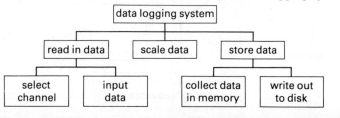

Programs can be kept simple and therefore clear, by restricting the possible types of program flow. Programs which include large numbers of jumps, or GO TO's, become very complex and obscure, and are therefore unreliable and difficult to debug and maintain. The possible forms of program flow are known as **control structures** and it has been established that any program can be written using no more than three basic control structures. These are a sequence, a conditional sequence and an iteration. A **sequence** is a set of operations, which can be merely calculations but may also include the other structures. A **conditional sequence** is a sequence which is carried out only if a particular condition is true. An **iteration**, often known as a loop, is a sequence which is carried out repeatedly until some condition is satisfied. The flow patterns of each of these is indicated in Fig. 20.12. This primitive set of control structures is sufficient for all programming purposes, but is rather limited. Three additional structures are widely used and enhance the clarity of programs. One is the IF...THEN...ELSE structure made up of two sequences, one of which is executed if a condition is true and the other when it is not. The second is the ESCAPE structure, providing for early termination of an iteration if abnormal circumstances should occur. The flow patterns for these structures are as shown in Fig. 20.13. The third is the CASE structure, in which one of a set of sequences is selected depending on the value of a controlling parameter. All of these control structures are said to be well formed in that they have a single entry point and a single exit point. This is an important property, since it permits the replacement of any structure by a single sequence box; the action performed by this box is then a simple description of the function performed by the structure. For example, a loop may be used to set all the entries in a table to zero. The detailed description of the operation of this loop can be replaced by a single sequence box as shown in Fig. 20.14. This technique is essentially a matter of moving to a more abstract description of a program; obviously it need not stop at this level, and in general there will be many such levels of description, from the very abstract level at the top to a detailed description of the implementation at the bottom. A top-down design uses such

Fig. 20.12 Three basic control structures

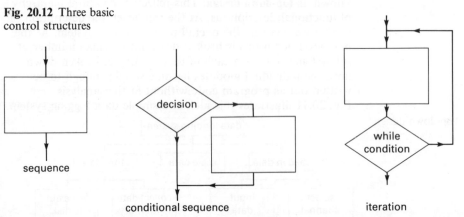

sequence

conditional sequence

iteration

a hierarchy of levels, starting from the high level and progressively filling in the detail.

Some circumstances also can favour a bottom-up design method, in which the implementation details, which may be related to the actual hardware, are used to formulate increasingly abstract descriptions. As an example, the software to receive data from a keyboard must include operations to check whether a key has been pressed, and if so

Fig. 20.13 Three additional control structures

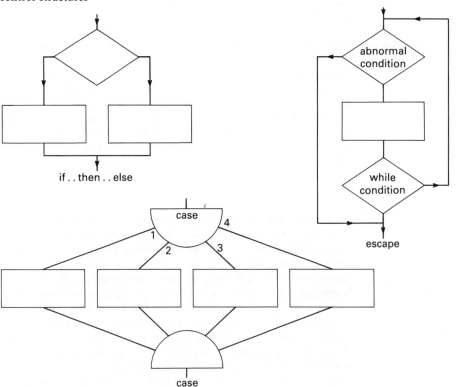

'Fig. 20.14 Replacement of a structure by a single sequence box

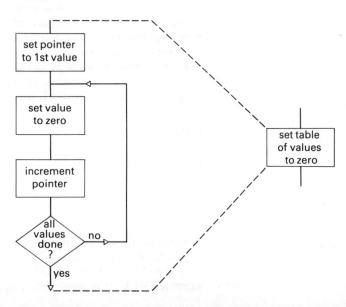

to determine which key, and possibly to convert this into a code; at an early stage in development a piece of software to do all these functions would be written, and this would be called up whenever keyboard input was needed.

Microprocessor software, which is frequently concerned with controlling hardware, will in general require both top-down and bottom-up aspects of design. Top-down design will be used to ensure that the overall task is correctly organised, and bottom-up design will be used to generate convenient interfaces to the hardware.

20.6.2 Choice of language

Software can be written in a number of different **programming languages**. At the lowest level, each processor has a language associated with it which enables the programmer to specify the individual processor instructions to be used. This is known as assembly language (Section 19.3), and in it each machine instruction can be represented by a mnemonic which indicates what the instruction does. For example, the Zilog Z8000 processor has an assembly language in which the instruction to load the contents of one register, R_3, into another register, R_6, is represented by the mnemonic:

LD   R6, R3.

This is much easier to remember than the code for the actual machine instruction which is a 16-bit number (A136 in hexadecimal notation). Because assembly language is used to represent particular processor instructions, assembly languages are all different. Assembly language is a **low-level language**, a description which refers to the close relationship between the language and the basic machine instructions. A program written in assembly language must be converted to machine instructions, a process that is invariably done by computer; the program that does this is known as an assembler, or, if the computer on which the translation process is done is different from that on which the program will be executed, a **cross assembler**.

The alternative to using assembly language is the use of a **high-level language**. A high-level language is totally different from the machine instructions, having instead a close correspondence with the actual calculations or processing to be performed. The following simple example compares a program written in PASCAL with the equivalent in Zilog Z80 assembly language.

PASCAL	Z80 assembly language	
DIFF := SIGNAL − BASE	LD	HL, (BASE)
	EX	DE, HL
	LD	HL, (SIGNAL)
	SUB	HL, DE
	LD	(DIFF), HL

Comparing these, certain points are immediately obvious. The fragment of program calculates the difference between two variables, SIGNAL and BASE, and assigns the result to a variable DIFF. It is immediately apparent that the PASCAL program performs this subtraction operation, while only an experienced Z80 assembly language programmer would be able to see that the assembly language program does. The PASCAL program is also appreciably shorter, which saves time both in programming and in reading the program. However, it must be remembered that the actual processor must, in order to carry out the calculation specified in the PASCAL program, execute a sequence of instructions either the same as or equivalent to the assembly language program. The process of converting a high-level language program into machine instructions is very complex, and is carried out by computers using programs known as **compilers**.

The aims of productivity, reliability and maintainability of software are all achieved more easily with high-level languages than with assembly language since the program source code (the program as actually written out by the programmer) is shorter and clearer. In addition, once a program is written in high-level language it can readily be compiled into machine instructions for any of a range of processors, making it very easy to upgrade systems or to change the processor if this should become necessary through obsolescence. For all these reasons, it is generally better to write microprocessor software in a high-level language.

There are two main drawbacks of high-level languages. Firstly, the machine-instruction programs produced by the compilers are generally less efficient than the programs that could have been produced by an experienced assembly language programmer. This implies that the programs will be larger, occupying more memory space and taking longer to execute, than is strictly necessary. This is not often a serious problem, and can frequently be overcome by using assembly language for those sections of the program where very fast execution is vital. The second problem is that interfacing to particular pieces of peripheral equipment can often be difficult in high-level language; again, use of assembly language for this part of a program will overcome this.

There are a large number of high-level languages available for development of microprocessor systems. Choice of a language will depend on many factors. Very often there will be only one language available in a given development laboratory, and so the choice will be made by default. The languages most widely used for microprocessor system development are:

PASCAL: Language offering good structures, and which is widely known. Compilers are available for most processors.

FORTRAN: Originally developed for scientific programming on large computers, FORTRAN is now available for microprocessors. It is not well structured, but it is very widely known, and offers good control over the resulting machine code.

C: Powerful language for microprocessor programming, usually producing very efficient machine code, particularly on 16-bit processors.

FORTH: An elegantly structured language, again producing efficient code; FORTH naturally imposes a good modular structure.

20.7 System development

20.7.1 Design approach

The development of microprocessor systems can proceed in a number of different ways, depending on a range of factors. One major factor is the number of systems which are likely to be produced; some development techniques reduce development costs at the expense of production costs, and vice versa. For a system of which only a few are to be produced then it is most important to minimise development costs, while for a system which will be produced in very large quantities it is important to minimise production costs. The approach will also depend on any requirement for flexibility of the design, to permit future modifications and upgrades; and on the experience and expertise available in the development team.

For small production runs, it is often convenient to use a **single board computer** (SBC). This is a complete circuit board containing a microprocessor and memory together with supporting logic circuitry and a selection of I/O peripherals. A fairly large range of such boards is available, and one can usually be found with the facilities required for any particular small system. For slightly larger systems, boards can be connected together, with all the address, data and control lines connected between the boards using a standard interconnection bus. This gives considerable scope for design of hardware with the minimum effort, as all the necessary boards can be purchased ready assembled and tested, and they merely need to be plugged into suitable connectors. The buses used for connecting these boards together are now becoming well standardised, the principal ones being MULTIBUS, S-100, EUROBUS, VME bus and STD bus. Using such systems the design is almost entirely concerned with software, and hardware development costs are very low. The production cost may not be so low, since in choosing boards it is often necessary to select those which have more facilities on than are required, and these have to be paid for.

When larger numbers are to be produced, it may well be worth reducing the production cost at the expense of greater development cost by designing the required microprocessor circuit. This will contain only those facilities which are actually needed, and therefore will be cheaper to manufacture provided that a sufficient quantity is produced.

For small systems, it has been possible for chip manufacturers to integrate all the components of microprocessor systems on to single chips, taking only the I/O lines out of the chip connectors. This type of chip, known as a **single-chip microcomputer**, can be cheap to purchase, yet has all the functionality of a small microprocessor system. Provided that the memory and I/O capacity of the chips is adequate for the purpose and that development facilities are available for these devices, they can represent the most cost effective solution to microprocessor system design whether for small or medium production runs.

20.7.2 System integration

There are particular problems associated with the integration of the hardware and the software of microprocessor systems. Faults can occur either in the hardware, or the logic of the software, or in the way the software interfaces with the hardware. It may not be clear whether the fault lies in the hardware or the software. A number of techniques are available for overcoming this problem.

A major advantage of using single board computers is that it is usually possible to assume that the hardware of the board works entirely to specification. Thus faults are either due to design or coding errors in the software, or to a misunderstanding of how to use the facilities of the SBC. The development of SBC-based systems is usually undertaken with a computer comprising the target SBC together with memory and interfaces to disks and to a terminal. The system will include development software tools (editors, compilers, assemblers and debuggers) so that the software can be easily changed and re-loaded into the actual target system. Such a system will also have space for other boards using the same standard interconnection bus to be plugged into the system, so that the interfaces to other items of equipment can be tested within a development environment. Once development is complete and the system is running satisfactorily the software can be committed to ROM and the boards will then function as a stand-alone system. The main difficulty with this sort of development strategy is that the methods for debugging the software will normally be unable to execute the software at full speed; thus errors resulting from timing difficulties will be difficult to debug. This can be solved by the parallel use of logic state analysis.

A **logic state analyser** is commonly used in testing and fault-finding of digital circuits, but in microprocessor system development it is used for monitoring the operation of the actual processor by looking at the address, data and control buses. The actual states of the buses are recorded in fast memory, and can be displayed on the screen in various forms to show exactly what the processor was doing. The bus-state recording can be triggered by a particular combination of events on the buses, so that, for example, the operation of a particular subroutine can be monitored by starting the data capture when the start address of the subroutine is seen on the address bus. Since the processor is running at full speed during the period of data capture, this provides valuable information for locating those difficult bugs which only appear under these circumstances. Another useful facility normally provided by logic state analysers is timing; the time between particular events can be measured with microsecond accuracy, which can be important for ensuring that the processor is able to get through the processing in the time available.

When the SBC is an inappropriate solution, a custom circuit must be designed and built, and therefore tested. A more sophisticated approach to testing is then required and the optimal solution is **in-circuit emulation** (ICE). To use this, the processor itself is removed from the board, and replaced by the pod of an in-circuit emulator which emulates all the microprocessor inputs and outputs, and is connected to a powerful computer system which can control and monitor what the processor lines do. The precise facilities available will depend on the actual ICE unit, but the following list is typical of a well-equipped system.

(1) To develop program source code, and to compile or assemble it for the target processor.
(2) To read from or write to any location in the system, either memory or I/O, under keyboard control. Thus the operation of I/O ports can be tested quite independently of any software in the target system.
(3) To use memory within the ICE system itself in place of that in the target system. This permits the target system to run without ROM or RAM being present.
(4) To execute the program one instruction at a time, so that the exact consequences of each instruction can be seen. This is known as single-stepping.
(5) To stop the execution of the processor when a particular pattern of bits is seen on the address and/or data buses so that single-stepping can be carried on from that point.
(6) Logic state analysis facilities.

ICE is particularly important for the development of systems using single-chip microcomputers, since the address, data and control buses are in general not available outside the chip and an external logic state analyser cannot be used.

Techniques such as in-circuit emulation and logic state analysis are expensive, and in many situations it is possible to complete a system development without them, by use of simpler tools such as resident monitors, ROM emulation, software simulation, etc. It should be appreciated that whilst these approaches result in a saving in the capital investment, they do so at the expense of greater time and therefore cost in the development process.

20.7.3 Documentation

Adequate documentation is a very important part of any engineering development, but the need is particularly severe in dealing with software. Documentation should never be regarded as something to be produced after the system has been completed, but rather it should be produced partly in advance of and partly in parallel with the actual software development. The following represent a minimum requirement.

(1) Requirements specification: this must be written at an early stage in order to define as closely as possible what the system is intended to do. All interfaces with other equipment must be carefully defined.

(2) System specification: this is a description of the way in which the requirements are to be achieved. It includes the definitions of the performance requirements for the hardware, the allocation of functions to either hardware or software, the overall structure of the software and the definitions of the algorithms in the software.

(3) Test specifications: at an early stage, specifications of the tests which will be required to verify the system performance should be written; these may have an impact on the system design, because certain I/O facilities may be required specifically for test purposes.

(4) Software descriptions: the software should be supported by descriptive documentation written at the same time as the software.

(5) Hardware drawings and descriptions: as with any circuit development, the hardware should be supported by full drawings and descriptions.

20.8 Future directions

Microprocessors are a rapidly developing field of engineering. The flexibility which is inherent in programmable systems has opened up an enormous range of possible applications; for some time the practical limits on what was achievable were represented by the limits of software development. As more and more software for microprocessor systems is written in high-level languages, using structured programming methods which permit larger systems to be developed with good reliability, other limitations have become apparent.

The most significant of these is speed. Microprocessor systems carry out complex tasks by execution of complex software, involving many thousands of instructions. Despite many new techniques that have been developed to decrease the instruction execution cycle time, this remains a major limitation, and is likely to remain so, since execution times are limited by a combination of gate switching times and times for signals to propagate across the relatively large areas of silicon which make up these devices. These factors are getting close to the limits imposed by physics rather than by technology. Improvements have been made by partially eliminating the delays involved in accessing memory, either by pipelining or by the use of instruction caches. As explained in Chapter 19, pipelining uses the time when the processor is executing instructions to fetch the next instruction, or few instructions, from memory. It is applicable to processors which include in their instruction sets instructions such as multiplication and division which take a considerable length of time to execute; during this time several instructions can have been fetched from memory. Pipelining fails when program jumps occur, since this involves a change in the sequence in which instructions are executed. Also explained in Chapter 19 is the way in which a small area of memory incorporated within the microprocessor may be used as a cache in which copies of recently executed instruction codes are held. Since programs often execute in small loops, this architecture can lead to entire loops being executed without accessing memory at all. These two techniques are in some ways complementary, in that pipelining works best for long sequences of instructions without jumps or loops, a type of program in which the instruction cache fails completely; conversely small loops make it difficult for pipelining to produce significant gains in speed, while the instruction cache is very effective.

A further important technique is **reduced instruction set computers** (RISC). These have received considerable interest in recent years, and involve processors with small simple instruction sets. This permits the processor to be implemented on a small area of silicon, and by reducing signal propagation delays can operate at higher speeds. It might appear that a small instruction set would offset this advantage by requiring more instructions to perform the same task. However, this is not really the case when the programs are written in high-level language, since compilers (the programs which convert high-level language to machine instructions) usually only use a simple repertoire of instructions; the more complex instructions offered by some processors are too specific in purpose to be of any use except when programs are written in assembly language. As it is now widely accepted that software should be written in high-level languages whenever possible, RISC instruction sets are not in practice a constraint.

None of these techniques for increasing processor speed can provide the increases required for many new applications, particularly in such fields as computer aided design, computer aided manufacture and artificial intelligence. It is estimated that increases of over 1000 times the best currently achievable performance are required. The only solution to this is to split the task to be done between a number of processors – a technique known as **parallel processing**. Unfortunately this is easier said than done. It is often difficult to decide how a task should be partitioned between parallel processors, and it is also necessary to provide a mechanism for the individual processors to communicate with each other. If the partitioning is not done effectively then so much time is spent on communication that there are no significant gains in processing speed. Difficulties also arise in the debugging of parallel processing systems, since errors may arise, not simply as a result of what one processor is doing, but as a result of what several are doing at one particular moment; such a particular combination of circumstances may occur only rarely, giving rise to very infrequent and irreproducible faults which are notoriously difficult to locate.

One important device which incorporates many of the techniques outlined here is the INMOS **transputer**. The TMS T414 is a high performance 32-bit microprocessor with a reduced instruction set. It has 2K bytes of fast static RAM and four high-speed communication links which can be used to communicate with other transputers. This feature is designed to enable the transputers to be used in parallel processing systems, and by using a number of processors, very fast processing has been demonstrated. A special high-level language called OCCAM®,† based on the concepts of concurrency and communication, has been developed to take advantage of the special features of the transputer. Transputers are designed to be programmed in a number of high-level languages including Fortran, C and Pascal.

Key points to remember

- the essential components in a minimum system are a central processor unit, memory and input/output ports, interconnected by buses;

- a memory map may be drawn showing the specified locations for data, program and, where applicable, input/output-port addresses; the map is implemented by suitable address decoding arrangements;

- input/output ports may be I/O mapped (separate I/O addresses) or memory mapped;

- in system design it is important to ensure that the timing diagrams for all the component parts are compatible;

- peripheral devices (such as keyboard, etc.) may gain access to the CPU either by polling or by interrupting via the I/O ports;

- a facility may be provided by which memory can be accessed without reference to the processor;

- special input/output interface chips are available for use between the processor and external devices; both parallel and serial forms are manufactured;

- in structured programming, the overall function is broken down into clearly definable tasks, facilitating correct overall operation and comprehensible documentation;

- programming languages range from machine code (in binary or hexadecimal equivalent) through assembly language (using mnemonic forms for each individual microprocessor instruction) to the high-level languages (which are subsequently compiled into machine code by a separate program).

Further reading

Ferguson, O., *Microprocessor Systems Engineering.* Addison-Wesley (1985).
Craine, J. F. and Martin, G. R., *Microcomputers in Engineering and Science.* Addison-Wesley (1985).
Potton, A., *Microprocessor-Based Systems.* Technician Education Council (1983).

† OCCAM is a trade mark of the INMOS Group of Companies.

Walls, C., *Programming Dedicated Microprocessors*. Macmillan (1986).
Manufacturers' data (Motorola and Zilog).

Acknowledgements   Reference to Zilog products is made with permission of Zilog. Zilog Inc., formed in 1975, is a wholly owned subsidiary of Exxon Corporation. The company's Components Division manufactures a complete line of microprocessors and peripheral support devices, including the Z80® 8-bit CPU, the Z8000® 16-bit CPU, the Z8® 8-bit single-chip microcomputer, and the Z80000™ 32-bit CPU.

Appendix A Reliability

Introduction

Any component or system, whether electronic, electromechanical or purely mechanical, has a finite lifetime. There is a limit to the period for which it will operate within its specification in a given application. **Reliability** is a measure of the probability that a unit will operate within specification for a given time period.

Batches of components or systems are found to exhibit a time/failure-rate characteristic similar to that shown in Fig. A1.1 which, because of its particular shape, is sometimes known as a **bath-tub diagram**. During the first phase, or **burn-in period**, there is a relatively high but decreasing failure rate associated with material imperfections and manufacturing errors. During the **normal-life period**, the failure rate is sensibly constant and the brief analysis in the following section assumes this condition. Finally, the component enters the **wear-out period** and the failure rate starts to rise. It is emphasised that the diagram (and the analysis) refers to statistically predictable failures. It does not imply that every component will individually follow this pattern; however, it does mean that, for example, in a batch of ten thousand units, perhaps five per week may fail to perform within specification and that this figure will remain substantially constant.

Figure A1.1 Failure rate characteristic

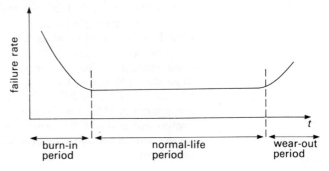

Failure rate and reliability

The failure rate, λ, is the proportion of a total number of units which will fail during a given period. For example, a unit may have a failure rate of 0.1% per 1000 hours. Reliability is then given by,

$$R(t) = e^{-\lambda t}$$

where $R(t)$ is the reliability over time period, t. For example, the reliability of the unit having a failure rate of 0.1% per 1000 hours over a 4000 hour period is $\exp(^-0.1 \times 10^{-2} \times 10^{-3} \times 4000) = 0.996$ or 99.6%. **Unreliability** $Q(t)$ is given by $1 - R(t)$. In the example, the unreliability is $1 - 0.996 = 0.004$ or 0.4%.

For units in series (i.e. where overall correct operation depends on every unit operating correctly) the overall reliability is given by the product of the individual reliabilities. In effect, the failure rates are added together. For example, a system containing three units each with a failure rate of 0.1% per 1000 hours and two units each with a failure rate of 0.04% per 1000 hours would have an overall failure rate of $(3 \times 0.1 + 2 \times 0.04) = 0.38\%$ per 1000 hours. $R(t)$ would then be $\exp(-0.38 \times 10^{-5} \times 8000) = 0.97$ in an 8000 hour period. For units in parallel, where only one need operate correctly in order to maintain correct system operation, the overall reliability is given by the product of the individual reliabilities. The overall unreliability is then one minus the overall reliability.

Mean time between failures

The mean time between failures (m.t.b.f.) is the reciprocal of the failure rate. The term is applied to repairable units or systems but can have relevance to non-repairable units. For a single repairable system, the m.t.b.f. is given by the operating period (or the period of a test run) divided by the number of failures in that period. For example, if there are three failures in a 600 hour test, m.t.b.f. $= 600/4 = 200$ hours and the failure rate for the system is $1/200 = 0.005$ per hour.

For non-repairable batches of components, the operating period can be interpreted as 'survivor hours'. Thus, if during a test on ten components over a period of 200 hours, one component fails after 42 hours, another after 87 hours and a third after 121 hours, the total survivor hours will be $42 + 87 + 121 + (7 \times 200) = 1650$ and the m.t.b.f. for each component is $1650/3 = 550$ hours. The failure rate for each component is then 0.018 per hour. In practice, a larger sample would probably be needed to obtain a statistically valid figure.

Appendix B The decibel

Introduction

The decibel (dB) is a logarithmic measure of the magnitude of voltage or power ratios and is used throughout the text in situations where such a measure has particular advantages. Principally, the advantages are,

(i) that the product of two or more ratios becomes the sum when expressed in logarithmic form. Thus, when in Chapter 7 it was required to obtain an overall Bode magnitude diagram for a network, it was convenient to be able to add the component transfer functions graphically using a logarithmic scale;

(ii) a wide range of values may be conveniently displayed on a logarithmic scale. For example, if it were required to display 2300 and 0.45 on the same scale (either on graph paper or on an instrument), a linear scale showing 2300 would dwarf 0.45. However, $\log_{10} 2300$ $(= 3.36)$ and $\log_{10} 0.45$ $(= -0.35)$ are much more compatible.

Power and voltage ratios

The basic unit is concerned with power ratios. Thus, if the power level in, for example, a resistor changes from P_2 to P_1, the ratio of the new power to the original is $\log_{10}(P_1/P_2)$ bel. The bel is a rather large unit and, normally, the decibel (one-tenth of a bel) is used. The power ratio is then $10 \log_{10}(P_1/P_2)$; a few key values are shown in Table B1.

Although defined in terms of power ratios, the decibel is also used for voltage ratios, in which case the definition is changed to $20 \log_{10}$(voltage ratio). Thus, referring to Table B1, voltage ratios of 100, 10 and 2 become 40, 60 and 6 dB respectively. The reason for the change in definition stems from the need for consistency. Thus, for a given resistance value R, $P_1/P_2 = (V_1^2/R)/(V_2^2/R) = (V_1/V_2)^2$ and $10 \log_{10}(P_1/P_2)$ has the same numerical value as $10 \log_{10}(V_1/V_2)^2$ or $20 \log_{10} V_1/V_2$.

Frequently, the power or voltage ratios will not represent two levels referred to the same resistance (as, for example, they would in the insertion-loss calculation in Section 1.4 of

Table B1

Power ratio	dB
100	20
10	10
2	3

Chapter 5), but might relate device power input to power output. Values for power and voltage gain in this case will only have the same numerical value if input and load resistances are the same. This is often not the case, but does not preclude power and voltage gain being expressed in decibels; they merely do not have the same value. Indeed, it is common practice to disregard any correspondence between voltage and power values, but the factors of 10 and 20 preceding the logarithm remain.

Whether related to voltage or power, it is important to appreciate that the decibel is a measure of relative values. It is meaningless to state, for example, that a power level is 43 dB. A power level of 43 dB above a stated reference level is, however, permissible. In cases where it is convenient to do this, a special notation is used, **dBm** and **dBW** implying absolute power levels above 1 mW and 1 W respectively. Although the decibel is the commonly used unit, Chapter 5 illustrates a situation where, as a result of a formal definition, a quantity is expressed as the *natural* logarithm of a voltage or current ratio. The unit (without any multiplying factor) is the **neper**. Conversion of voltage or current ratios from neper to decibel values is effected by multiplying by $20/2.303 = 8.68$.

Also used are logarithmic measures of frequency. Thus, the **octave** and the **decade** represent frequency ratios of 2:1 and 10:1 respectively. For example, the ratio of two frequencies, 2.3 kHz and 45 Hz is $\log_2 2300/45 = 5.7$ octave or $\log_{10} 2300/45 = 1.71$ decade.

Answers to exercises

Exercises 1. Page 23

1.1 1×10^{-9} C/m^2, 113 V/m; 15.9 fC/m^2; 1.8 mV/m.
1.2   (i) 113 mV, (ii) 0.9 mV.
1.3   0.023 m/s, $0.23 \times 10^3 \cos 10^4 t$ m/s^2.
1.4   4 A/m.
1.5 26.5×10^6 A/Wb, 0.821×10^9 A/Wb, 26.3%, 38.9%.
1.6 2.96×10^6 m/s.
1.8 $(5 + 6 \cos \omega t)$ V, $(-5 + 16 \cos \omega t)$ V; $6 \cos \omega t$ V, $(-10 + 16 \cos \omega t)$ V.
1.9 $22 \cos \omega t$ A.
1.10 2.2 kΩ, 0.455 mS.
1.11 0.72 nJ; 5 V, 0.14 nJ.
1.12 See Appendix 5A.
1.13 $90 \cos 10^3 t$ mV.

Exercises 2. Page 43

2.1 $(1.82 + 2 \sin \omega t)$ mA, $(6.8 - 4.4 \sin \omega t)$ V, $(7.3 + 16 \sin \omega t + 8.8 \sin^2 \omega t)$ mW, 11.7 mW.
2.2 $5.3 \sin 10^4 t$ mA, $v_{R_1} = 14.1 \sin 10^4 t$ V, $v_{R_2} = 14.3 \sin 10^4 t$ V, $v_L = 2.3 \cos 10^4 t$ V, $v_1 = 28.4 \sin 10^4 t$ V, $v_2 = 2.3 \cos 10^4 t + 14.3 \sin 10^4 t$ V.
2.3 $(118 \sin^2 10^4 t + 5.3 \sin 10^4 t \cos 10^4 t)$ mW, 59 mW.
2.6   0.125 mJ.
2.7 $-10.8 \cos \omega t$ A, $170 \sin \omega t$ V; $(5 \sin \omega t - 10.8 \cos \omega t)$ A.
2.8   (i) $V/2R$, (ii) $V/2R$, (iii) 0, (iv) $V/4R$, (v) 0, (vi) $V/4$.

Exercises 3. Page 64

3.1   (a) 6.28 kΩ, (b) 65 pF.
3.2 $v_{oc} = 3.33$ V, $i_{sc} = 1.25$ A.
3.4   (a) 1.89 V, (b) 95 mV.
3.5   (i) +1.06%, (ii) −4.49%.
3.8   0.265 A.
3.9 $(-0.37 + 1.94 \sin \omega t)$ V.
3.10 2.5.
3.11 0.692 A.
3.12 0.692 A.

3.13 $i_{sc} = 0.5v_i$; $v_{th} = 2.5v_i$; $R_{th} = 5\,k\Omega$.
3.14   0.265 A.
3.15   0.265 A.

Exercises 4. Page 89

4.1 $V_m/2$; $V_m/\sqrt{3}$.
4.2   (a) $6.61\underline{/-3.5°}$; (b) $7.77\underline{/110°}$; (c) $24\underline{/20°}$; (d) $0.67\underline{/100°}$.
4.3 $100\,\Omega$.
4.4   (a) $108\underline{/-68°}\,\Omega$; (b) $37.1\underline{/-22°}\,\Omega$.
4.5   (a) $87.2\underline{/-44°}\,\Omega$; (b) $78\underline{/28°}\,mA$; $49.7\underline{/19°}\,mA$.
4.6   (i) 383 mW; (ii) 247 mW; (iii) 136 mW; (iv) 370 var.
4.7 $400\,\Omega$, 66.9 nF; $105\,\Omega$, 90.4 nF.
4.8 $49.7\underline{/19°}\,mA$.
4.9   625 mW.
4.10 $1.76\underline{/0°}\,A$; $1.94\underline{/-117°}\,A$; $1.94\underline{/117°}\,A$.
4.12   (a) $5\,k\Omega$; 0; 200; $20\,\mu S$. (b) -333.

Exercises 5. Page 114

5.1 $118.3\,\Omega$; $33.8\,\Omega$.
5.2 $26\,\Omega$; $35.1\,\Omega$.
5.3   9.2 dB.
5.4   0.531; (i) 0.805 ms; (ii) 37 290 sections per second; (iii) 6.21 sections.
5.5   1.82.
5.6   Termination pulses: 8 V and 4.06 V; source pulses: 5 V and 5.54 V; $21.4\,\Omega$, $142\,\Omega$.
5.7   (b) $-j6.3\,\Omega$; 0.798 V.
5.8   Minima 2.8 and 19.5 cm from termination; $V_{max} = 3.43$ V, $V_{min} = 1.17$ V.
5.9 $56 - j19\,\Omega$, $0.2\underline{/180°}$, 1.5.
5.11 $40\,\Omega$, 10.6 pF.

Exercises 6. Page 146

6.2 $L(di/dt) + iR = E$ for $t > 0$.
6.3 $(E/R)(1 - e^{-Rt/L})$; L/R; 63.2%, 99.3%, 99.995%.
6.4   (b) $R/(1 + s_t CR)$; (i) $-0.762e^{-10^4 t}$, (ii) $0.586\cos(10^4 t - 78°)$.
6.5 $(1 + sCR)/(s^2 LCR + sL + R)$.
6.6 $K = 100$, $z = -10^4$, $p_1, p_2 = -5 \times 10^3 \pm j8.66 \times 10^3$.
6.7 $K = 5$, $p = -15$.
6.9   1.33 V; $2.22e^{-6t}$ V, $1.24\cos(6t - 21.8°)$ V.
6.10 $5(1 - e^{-2s})/s$; $(5 - 3e^{-2s})/(s + 0.255)$;
        $(1 - e^{-2s})/s^2 + (5 - 7e^{-2s})/s$; $7.85(1 + e^{-2s})/(s + 2.47)$.
6.11 $0.01[u(t) - 1.15e^{-5000t}\cos(8660t + 30°)]$ A;
        $115e^{-5000t}\cos(8660t - 30°)$ A.
6.12 $0.01[t - 1.15 \times 10^{-4}e^{-5000t}\sin 8660t]$ A.

Exercises 7. Page 165

7.1 $j\omega CR_2/(1 + j\omega C(R_1 + R_2))$.

7.2 $(1 + j\omega CR_1)/(1 + j\omega C(R_1 + R_2))$.

7.3 $f_0 = 2.52$ kHz; bandwidth is 99.5 Hz; $V_c = 253$ V.
      $f_0 = 2.52$ kHz; bandwidth is 199 Hz; $V_c = 126$ V.

7.6 $z = 0, p = -3330$; $z = -5000, p = -3330$.

7.7 $H(s) = -110(s + 45.5)/(s + 2330)$.

7.8 $z = 0, p_1 = p_2 = -1.58 \times 10^6$; $z = 0$,
      $p_1, p_2 = (-0.791 \pm j1.369) \times 10^6$; $z = 0$,
      $p_1, p_2 = (-0.079 \pm j1.579) \times 10^6$.

7.9   0.924, 0.383.

7.11   2.93 nF; 39.7 μH; 86.2.

Exercises 8. Page 196

8.1   (i) $(8A/\pi^2) \sin \omega_0 t - (8A/9\pi^2) \sin 3\omega_0 t + (8A/25\pi^2) \sin 5\omega_0 t - \cdots$;
      (ii) $(8A/\pi^2) \cos \omega_0 t + (8A/9\pi^2) \cos 3\omega_0 t + (8A/25\pi^2) \cos 5\omega_0 t + \cdots$.

8.2 $15.3 - 10.2 \cos 628t - 2.0 \cos 1257t - 0.9 \cos 1885t - \cdots$ V.

8.5   0.8, 1.53, 1.34, 1.06, 0.72, 0.37, 0.07, −0.17.

8.6 $0.25/\underline{41.6°}, 0.33/\underline{0°}, 0.31/\underline{-19.6°}$.

8.7 $15.3 - 0.81 \cos(628t - 85°) - 0.08 \cos(1257t - 88°)$
      $- 0.02 \cos(1885t - 88°) - \cdots$ V.

8.9   All non-zero frequency components have amplitudes of
      approximately 16 mV.

8.10   (i) $1/(\alpha + j\omega)^2$.

8.11 $Ve^{-t/\tau}u(t) - Ve^{-(t-t_p)/\tau}u(t - \tau)$.

8.13 5.24×10^8 m/s; 1.72×10^8 m/s.

Exercises 9. Page 214

9.1 $125e^{-15t}$ mV.

9.2 $4/(s + 10^4) - 4/(s + 2 \times 10^4)$, $10^{-4}(2 + 2e^{-2 \times 10^4 t} - 4e^{-10^4 t})$ V.

9.8 2.53×10^6 bits/s.

9.10   See Table 9.1.

9.11   0, 2, 6, 12, 20.

9.13   0, 0.33, 0.551, 0.699, 0.798, 0.865, 0.909, 0.939, ...

Exercises 10. Page 236

10.1 $3(1 + 0.2 \sin 1.26 \times 10^4 t) \sin 1.26 \times 10^7 t$ V; 0.2.

10.3   Unmodulated power, 50 W; modulated power, 100 W.

10.5   s.s.b.: 990 Hz or 1010 Hz tone; d.s.b.: modulated 1000 Hz
      tone.

10.7   Two bandwidth figures are 120 kHz and 160 kHz; when
      amplitude is halved these become 70 kHz and 100 kHz.

10.8   Approximately 3%.

10.10 254×10^3 bits/s.

Exercises 11. Page 251

11.1 $6.93\,\mu\text{V}; 2\times 10^{-14}\,\text{W}.$
11.2 0.023.
11.3 63 dB.
11.4 4; 51 dB.
11.5 870 K.
11.6 3 dB; 7 dB.
11.7 2.47 mV.
11.8 1 in 2×10^4.
11.9 62 dB.
11.10 2.5 dB; 22.5 dB.

Exercises 12. Page 289

12.2 $v_D = 0.71\,\text{V}; v_R = 4.29\,\text{V}; i = 5.36\,\text{mA}; 3.81\,\text{mW}.$
12.3 (b) $51.9 \sin \omega t$ mV.
12.4 $1.8\,\mu\text{A}$ (peak).
12.5 $+1.36\% -1.42\%.$
12.6 Between $160\,\Omega$ and $171\,\Omega$.
12.7 0.994; 159.
12.8 Approximate answers: 2 mA; 3 V.
12.9 $R_C = 2.2\,\text{k}\Omega; R_B = 490\,\text{k}\Omega.$
12.10 -156.
12.12 2.26 mA.
12.13 Approximate answers: (b) 2.7 mS; $10\,\text{k}\Omega$; (c) 2.5.

Exercises 13. Page 314

13.2 $576\,\Omega$.
13.3 (i) 3.6% increase; (ii) 3.7% increase.
13.4 (a) 2.17 mA; 4.78 V. (b) 2.04 V; -1.03 V.
13.5 (i) -0.3 V in each case; (ii) 9.3 V, 4.7 V, 0.2 V.
13.6 $83\,\mu\text{A}$, 9.9 mA; 2.17 V, 2.82 V.
13.7 (b) 100 mA, 10 V; 0.5 W, 1 W. (c) 0.5 W.
13.8 (i) 11.3; (ii) $2167\,\mu\text{F}$.
13.9 $237\,\Omega$; approx. 1 mV.
13.10 $0.448V_m$.

Exercises 14. Page 344

14.2 $\beta = 0.0625$; gain = 15.6 dB.
14.5 $-(4.26 + 4.41 \sin 10^4 t)$ V.
14.6 $6\cos 10^3 t$ V.
14.7 Approximate break frequencies: 318 Hz for (i), (ii) and (iii); also, 799 kHz for (ii) and (iii).
14.8 2.5×10^5 V/s.
14.9 3.

14.10 3.5 dB.

14.11 Pole positions: $0.402 \pm j0.813$.

Exercises 15. Page 364

15.1 (b) Carrier frequency of 2.13 MHz.

15.2 4 kHz.

15.3 $k_d H(s)/(s + k_d k_o H(s))$.

15.6 1.536 MHz; 1.91 kHz.

15.7 (a) 8. (b) 5.9 mV; 5 kHz.

15.8 0.7% of FSR.

Exercises 16. Page 397

16.2 (a) No; (b) (i) $1, 2, 3, 4, 10, \ldots$; (ii) $1, 2, 3, \ldots, I, J, 10, \ldots$.

16.3 111001; 1010111; 101111; 39H; 45; 2DH.

16.4 11101; 00011; 10011; 01010; 10000; 00000.

16.10 $\bar{F} = \bar{A}\bar{B}\bar{C}D + \bar{A}BC\bar{D} + \bar{A}BCD + \bar{A}B\bar{C}\bar{D} + \bar{A}B\bar{C}D + \bar{A}BC\bar{D}$
$\qquad + \bar{A}BCD + A\bar{B}\bar{C}\bar{D} + AB\bar{C}\bar{D}$;
$\quad F = (A + B + C + D)(\bar{A} + B + C + \bar{D})(\bar{A} + B + \bar{C} + D) \cdots$.
$\quad$ Minimal form $\quad F = \bar{A}(B + C + D) + A\bar{C}\bar{D}$
$\quad$ or $\qquad\qquad F = (A + B + C + D)(\bar{A} + \bar{D})(\bar{A} + \bar{C})$.

16.12 1000000; F6BH.

16.18 (a) 41H D4H. (b) Correct code word is 3CH.

Exercises 17. Page 424

17.1 See answer for Exercise 16.10.

17.2 $F = \bar{A}\bar{D} + \bar{C}D + AD$; $\bar{F} = A\bar{D} + \bar{A}CD$.

17.4 $F = A + B + C + D$.

17.5 Include term $B\bar{C}\bar{D}$.

17.6 $O_0(\text{LSB}) = 1 + 4$; $O_1 = 2 + 4$; $\ldots$.

17.10 64K.

Exercises 18. Page 445

18.6 Sequence: 0, 4, 3, 2, 7, 6, 0, 4, $\ldots$.

18.7 $J_A = BC$; $K_A = \bar{B}\bar{C}$; $J_B = \bar{A}C$; $K_B = A\bar{C}$; $J_C = \bar{A} + B$;
$\quad K_C = A + B$.

18.8 $D_A = \bar{A}BC + A\bar{B}C$; $D_B = \bar{B}C$ (C is control).

Index